AMBER & DUSK

LYRA SELENE

AMBER & DUSK

LYRA SELENE

Scholastic Press · New York

Library of Congress Cataloging-in-Publication Data available

ISBN 978-1-338-53079-7

10 9 8 7 6 5 4 3 2 1   18 19 20 21 22

Printed in the U.S.A.   23
First printing 2018

Book design by Elizabeth B. Parisi and Mary Claire Cruz

To Mom and Dad,
for encouraging me to dream
of impossible worlds

ONE

The sun had not set on the Amber Empire for a thousand tides. But that didn't mean my world knew nothing of darkness.

Or violence.

The Skyclad platoon bore down on the convoy beneath a sky spackled with blood and charcoal. Bright metal armor glinted red in the twilight. Hoofbeats on packed earth echoed the drum of my heart against my ribs. I reached for the amulet at my neck, letting the familiarity of its skin-warmed planes calm my twisting nerves.

I wasn't the only one who was afraid. Voices of laborers and free travelers rose in panic as the soldats approached. Women drew tight the curtains of their wagons. Men shouted for children scurrying among the mess of tents and cook fires and freight drays. Livestock brayed and squawked.

Only Madame Rina was still. She stood in front of the biggest transport with feet planted wide and dark braids dancing in the hot breeze. She didn't flinch as the platoon drew close enough to see the wild eyes of the mounts and the silvery dristic armor protecting the bodies of the soldats.

"Luca!" I called, although I couldn't drag my eyes away from the approaching platoon. "Luca, where are you?"

"Here, Sylvie." The gentle touch on my shoulder reassured me, but when I turned toward my friend, his normally laughing face was tense and serious. His hazel eyes darted, barely registering his mother's stalwart figure at the front of the camp. "Where's Vesh? Have you seen my brother?"

"He was playing with the other children, last time I saw," I murmured. Vesh was younger than Luca by nearly twelve tides, and rarely strayed far from his older brother's protective eye. "Luca, I'm sure he's fine."

"Fine," Luca agreed. The certainty of the word didn't reach his eyes. "Listen, you stay here. Don't move. Let Maman do the talking. I'm going to find my brother."

"Luca, wait—"

But he was already gone, swallowed up by the permanent twilight. I breathed deeply through my nose and tried to calm the thrumming of my heart. The Sisters of the Scion—the religious sect who raised me—swore my unsanctioned journey to the Amber City would be cursed with misfortune. But I never imagined that menace might come from the Amber Empire's own troops. The Skyclad—the Amber Empress's elite force—were said to be born with a weapon in each hand. Unflinchingly trained. Merciless. Their famed armor was bright and pale as the azure heavens above the distant Meridian Desert.

The platoon thundered to a halt at the front of the camp. The captain dismounted in a flurry of dristic and blue, tossing her reins to a lieutenant and dragging off her helmet. She was a tall woman near Madame Rina's age; grey threads sparked in the brown hair knotted at the nape of her neck. Laugh lines etched her face, but her eyes were forged of hard metal.

"You." The captain glared down her nose at Rina. "This is your convoy?"

"Aye." Rina's voice rang with authority. "Chartered and bonded, these last seven tides."

"Your papers."

Madame Rina thrust a sheaf of parchment into the captain's gloved hand. I hadn't seen the documents since I'd first joined the convoy, but I remembered what they looked like, inked and beribboned.

Madame Rina's bond permits and Charter Writ.

"Everything is in order, I assure you," said Rina. "What quarrel could you possibly have with me or this convoy?"

"No quarrel," the captain grunted, not looking up from her rough perusal of the documents. "We search every convoy with free travelers in this quadrant."

"Since when? My charter grants both bonded laborers and free travelers right of passage along this route."

The captain fixed Madame Rina with a stare. She raised a slow hand toward one of her soldats, and bent a finger.

The soldat broke formation. Shifting patterns of light and shadow danced across the pale metal of his armor. One swift kick sent an iron cook pot lurching off its stand. Boiling water poured across livid embers. Steam billowed to the sky, wafting the stench of seared meat and wet wood across the camp. Somewhere, a child wailed.

I clutched harder at my pendant, biting down my fury. Anything I said would only make this worse. Until I got to the Amber City, my words meant nothing.

Worse than nothing, since I was technically a refugee. The Midnight Dominion—the darkness beyond the reach of our static sun—had been creeping into the Dusklands for tides, sending shadows to swallow light and drive frightened Dusklanders from their homes into the Amber Empire.

But I wasn't running from the darkness at the edge of

nowhere—I was running toward the light at the heart of the empire. I was going to Coeur d'Or, the imperial palais in the Amber City.

But that wouldn't matter to these Skyclad soldats.

"My orders are not your concern, Dusker," the captain said. "But by all means, continue to question them."

Rina's eyes narrowed to slits, but her expression relented.

"Better. Now, tell me—where did this convoy originate?"

"Piana. A village near the edge of the Dusklands."

"Its destination?"

"The Amber City."

"Purpose?"

"It's an ore convoy. Our freight is ambric—a little dristic and kembric too, for trading."

"And who are these folk?"

"My bonded labor, mostly. The rest are free travelers—merchants and herdsman who have paid for our security and company along their passage west."

"Any Dominion refugees?"

Rina hesitated for barely a second before shaking her head no. But the captain saw her hesitation. Everyone did.

The captain swept back her pale cloak and planted her palm on the hilt of her sword.

"Who?"

For one awful moment, I didn't know what Rina would say. The metal clasp of my amulet dug into my palm, but I didn't take my hand away.

Finally, Rina clenched her jaw and shook her head again. "No refugees here, Captain."

A cold smile crept across the captain's face. "We can do it that way too."

The captain raised a gloved fist. Her soldats snapped to attention.

"There are refugees here," she barked. "Find them. Anyone who stands in your way is in defiance of Imperial Law."

Swords rang from scabbards. Helmets snapped down. Booted feet stamped hard-packed earth. The platoon of armored soldats bore down upon the camp.

Panic sprinted ahead of the Skyclad onslaught. Parents rushed for their children. Free travelers reached for meat knives and shovels: anything that could be used to defend themselves. But the soldats were more interested in terror than violence. Laborers were shoved aside to sprawl in the dust. The canvas sides of ore transports tore beneath steel, scattering glowing nuggets. A keening scream splintered the air, then ceased abruptly.

I dived for Rina, who was standing frozen amid the chaos. I grasped her shoulders and yanked her gaze away from the scenes of cruelty and destruction.

"Madame Rina!" I hissed at her. "You have to do something!"

But her gaze was blank and terrible.

"Vesh?" she asked. "And Luca? Are my boys safe?"

"I don't know!" I fought the urge to slap the older woman. "But they're not the only ones who could get hurt if we don't stop this!"

"How?" she asked, and turned away, as though she knew her question had no answer.

I gritted my teeth so hard I thought my jaw might crack. I pushed away from Rina, casting my gaze toward the Skyclad captain. She stood a few strides away with her back to me, arms loosely clasped behind her cloak. Calm. Contained.

I couldn't contain the rage boiling up inside me.

"You!" I shoved all my anger into the word and threw it at the captain, closing the distance between us. "Stop this! Stop it now!"

"I will stop," said the captain. "When someone tells me which of these groveling mongrels was puked up by the Midnight Dominion."

"You're sick." My words rang harsh. "There are no refugees here! Why would you do this to innocent people?"

"I'm doing my duty," she said, turning at last to look at me. "No one is truly innocent. And innocence certainly doesn't pay a soldat's commission."

Fury painted fire along my bones.

The Sisters always swore the Scion would punish me for my sins: my anger, my ambition, my tenacious dreams. But I always thought those features made me stronger.

My secret unfurled gauzy wings inside me.

I caught my lip between my teeth and chewed. Standing up to a Skyclad captain was dangerous. But so was running away from the Sisters, choosing uncertainty over mediocrity and power over poverty. So was traveling halfway across an empire with barely more to live on than crusts of bread and Luca's kind smiles.

There were many kinds of danger. And there were worse things than facing it.

I knew what I had to do.

I squeezed my eyes shut and reached for a single glowing memory: the moment that changed my life.

A dingy, frigid room. Dull, livid light illuminating a sheaf of parchment lined in handwriting so elegant I barely recognized the language. And the Imperial Insignia, ornate and unmistakable—a sunburst bigger than my hand, stamped in amber wax and gilded with kembric. I concentrated on the memory until I could see nothing but the seal, glowering in the bruised dusk.

I forced my eyes open and swallowed down the scorching tang of fear. I stepped toward the Skyclad officer.

"Stay your men, Captain," I snapped, threading my voice with as much command as I could muster. "Your business here is done."

The woman's brows slashed together. Dread kicked my ribs with dristic-toed boots.

"Do you wish to die, girl?" A smile wove the lines of her face into a savage tapestry. "They say it is a great honor to die on a Skyclad's sword."

"And yet, an honor that is beneath me," I snarled, drawing myself up to my full height. I held out an imperious hand, and made the captain see something that wasn't there.

A sheaf of parchment appeared in my hand. An illusion, fashioned from memory and forged in the kaleidoscope crush of my heart. The ink glimmered blood-red and the paper rustled in the breeze, densely woven and fine. And the Imperial Insignia of the Amber Empire glared from the top page, heavy and solid and glittering like a tiny sun.

I held my breath, ignoring the low humming in my ears and the strength sapping from my limbs.

The Skyclad captain took one look at the seal. Her face drained of color. She swept into a bow so low the hem of her silvery cloak stirred up puffs of dust.

"My deepest apologies," she gasped. "I had no idea someone of your station was traveling with this ore convoy. Forgive me!"

She saluted briskly, spun on her heel, and strode forward into the melee.

"Stand down!" she shouted. "Our authority here has been revoked! Return to your mounts at once!"

The order rippled outward through the camp. One by one, soldats lowered their weapons. Free travelers fell back with gasps and cries as the armored men and women turned away to their horses with blank, impassive faces.

I sucked in a deep breath of smoke-smudged air and glanced down at the document in my hand. The edges of my vision curled like flame-eaten parchment as the illusion evaporated, bleeding into wisps of color and form. Within seconds, nothing remained of the Imperial Insignia. Panic burst hot in my veins, but the Skyclad officer kept her gaze diffident and her back angled toward me. She hadn't seen the official seal of the empire melt away into nothing.

I shoved my hands into my pockets, praying to the Scion I'd done enough.

The captain swept me a final salute before mounting her horse. Within moments, the Skyclad platoon was gone, shards of bright metal choked beneath a billow of yellow dust.

Dizziness clutched at me. I forced myself to turn and face the camp.

The damage was bad. Broken glass glittered along the edges of gaping transport windows, mixing with shattered chunks of ambric ore. Tents were nothing more than shredded wisps of canvas. Livestock lay slaughtered and broken, dank blood dampening parched earth. The guttering tongues of scattered cook fires licked at the debris of wagons torn to pieces.

I was so transfixed by the wreckage that it took me a moment to register the heavy press of a hundred eyes. I lifted my gaze, dreading what I knew I would see.

Laborers and free travelers were scattered across the campsite, crouched between overturned transports and cowering in the comfort of one another's arms. And everyone—man, woman, and child—was staring at me. Suspicion gave their eyes sharp edges.

What had they glimpsed, amid the chaos, to make them look at me like that? Had they seen a nameless Dusklander conjure an Imperial Insignia from thin air? Or was it enough that they had watched a penniless orphan singlehandedly banish a platoon of armed Skyclad soldats into the dusk, and walk away unscathed?

Humiliation tinged with old resentment caught in my throat and choked me. Whatever its cause, their palpable suspicion felt all too familiar—I'd spent my life glimpsing it in the grimaces of superstitious Sisters and the sidelong glances of dirt-smudged villagers. Hearing it in the voices of cruel children who couldn't understand where I fit into their narrow worlds.

Freak. Witch. Monster.

A hand fell on my shoulder. I spun, my heart vaulting.

Madame Rina.

"Come, child," she murmured. Her face was unreadable in the dusk. "You've done nothing wrong. We'll find a way to fix this."

I gave a slow nod. But as Rina turned to pick her way through the ruins of her precious convoy, I didn't have the heart to tell her that what the captain had said was true: No one was truly an innocent.

Especially me.

And nobody could fix that.

TWO

The bell for second Nocturne pealed. Though the exhausted camp had mostly cleared away the evidence of the Skyclad attack, the soldats' presence lingered in the air like a bad smell.

I perched on the roof of the biggest ore transport, staring across the plains and trying not to think about what had happened. The sun glared from its spot above the horizon, livid and unmoving. A handful of raindrops splatted into the dusty earth as thunder rumbled behind me, clouds darkening the sky above the Midnight Dominion to a frantic violet.

Dominion. The vast, unexplored land beyond the reaches of our eternal day. A land wreathed in impenetrable shadow and fathomless myth. A land where the darkness had a will of its own, reaching fingers toward the light to snatch away the living.

I grew up in the Dusklands, mere miles from the seething border of Dominion. Abandoned on the steps of their cloister as an infant, I was raised by the Sisters of the Scion, who sheltered me from the shadows of Dominion prowling closer and closer to civilization. A begrudged home, with a hundred averted eyes and a thousand superstitious platitudes about sin and expiation, but a home nevertheless.

The Sisters never predicted me discovering a secret meant to stay hidden. The secret lurking in my bloodline. The secret that drove me far from the only home I ever knew toward a world bursting with possibility.

"Oi!"

A deft figure clambered up the side of the transport. I caught a glimpse of black curls and golden-brown skin.

Luca.

Just spans older than me, Madame Rina's son was the only friend I'd made on this cursed journey. Heir to his mother's chartered ore convoy, Luca had spent half his life traversing these brittle, sun-reddened plains. He'd been the one to catch me when I attempted to stow away in the convoy at Piana, the mining town near the edge of the Dusklands.

It had already been nearly a span since I'd run away from the Temple of the Scion, and although I'd tried to secure passage to the Amber City with half a dozen convoys and caravans, everybody took one look at my hungry eyes and torn dress and turned me away without a second thought.

"Not enough coin," the kinder guides said, pity slicking the lie and making it easier for them to swallow.

"No Duskers," the blunter ones said, pointing to the crude signs etched into the prows of their transports. "Imperial Law. Refugees might be carrying Dominion taint."

I gritted my teeth and tried to explain there was no such thing. Dominion shadows might hunt and kill, but they were just shadows. And the people fleeing toward the light were just people. But my words did nothing to lessen the fear slithering behind their eyes as they glanced toward the horizon.

I watched Madame Rina's convoy for three days as it stockpiled ambric and other provisions. Her transports numbered nearly twice the other convoys, and the smaller wagons carrying kembric and dristic were rarely touched—there was no demand for those precious metals out here on the edge of nowhere. I didn't relish hiding between crates and stealing food from hardworking laborers for six spans, but I was running out of other options.

I waited until third Nocturne before dashing across the shadowed stockyard and hurling myself beneath the canvas siding. I froze, squinting into the dense shadows. I almost didn't hear the whisper of leather ties against canvas as the door behind me fell open, splashing violet light across the floor of the wagon.

"Can I help you?" said a voice, crisp with laughter.

I spun. Silhouetted against a sweep of fire-scorched clouds, he was easily the best-looking boy I'd ever seen. He had none of the waxen, dull-eyed pallor of the Dusklanders I'd grown up with; energy seemed to pulse out of him, brash and buoyant in the seething dim.

"I was just—" My tongue was suddenly too fat in my mouth. I didn't have a good reason to be here, and we both knew it. "Looking for something I lost?"

"That so?" His eyes gleamed with amusement. "And how did a fine lady such as yourself happen to misplace sixteen quintals of raw kembric ore?"

I licked my dry, cracked lips as I rolled lies and truths and excuses around the ragged furrows of my exhausted mind. For all my bravado during that past span, I had very little left to lose. Desperation made me brave, or maybe a little mad.

"I'll tell you," I promised, giving my chin a vain twist, "in exchange for free passage to Posette and the return of half my riches."

Luca had laughed until his face turned purple, then dragged me into his mother's tent and insisted she accept my contract as a free traveler, despite my lack of coin or supplies. And to my surprise, Madame Rina had rolled her eyes in resignation and drawn up the paperwork.

Now Luca plopped down beside me. Below, in the center of camp, someone had lit a bonfire, and the crimson glow sent ruby sparks glinting from the tri-metal bar bisecting Luca's ear—his signat, the mark of his profession. He dug his elbow into my ribs. "Where've you been? Avoiding cleanup duty?"

His tone was light, but I remembered the hunted look in his eyes when he couldn't find his brother, Vesh. Both boys survived the attack unharmed, but something twisted in my stomach and kept me from returning the jibe.

"I tried to help," I muttered. "But I figured I'd be better off staying out of everyone's way."

Luca chuckled. "Why?"

"Because I saw the way everyone was staring at me."

Luca's shoulders stiffened. I instantly regretted my petulant words.

"Sylvie." Luca's hands were gentle, unknotting my fingers and unclenching my fists. "Look at me."

I hesitated, then obeyed. Sometimes I thought Luca was born to laugh, with his broad white smile and eyes that crinkled with humor even when he was trying to be serious.

He wasn't laughing now.

"You saved us, Sylvie." Luca's voice was soft but clear. "I saw the way you stared down that Skyclad captain. Without you, we might be dead. We all know it—Vesh, Maman, me. *They* know it too. But they don't know *how* you saved them. What you did or said to drive the platoon away. They don't know who you are. And that frightens them."

"I didn't—"

"Listen. Out here—where the dust twists itself into monsters, and mirages dance on the horizon, and the shuttered eye of the Scion stares down on us from Matin to Nocturne—we fear the things we cannot fathom. We use that fear as a shield against the dusk and hope we can survive long enough to understand. It's not about you."

I swallowed a bitter retort. I knew he was right. I knew it when I was a strange, lonely child in a shoddy Duskland village full of roughnecks and bullies. I knew it at the Temple, where the Sisters shunned me in favor of the cold, silent comfort of prayers and penance. And I knew it when I held out my hand and made the Skyclad captain see something that wasn't there.

"I know, Luca." I forced a smile and buried the old resentment. "I'm just tired of being a castoff. My parents abandoned me. The women who raised me despised me. The villagers feared me."

"Is that why you're going to the Amber City? To start over without hate or fear?"

I tore my eyes away from Luca's inquisitive gaze and glanced back toward the western horizon. Toward the sun, frowning from its rusty throne. Toward the Amber City, where I'd find either a world where I truly belonged . . . or more disappointment.

"You ask me that every Nocturne, Luca," I reminded him.

"And every Nocturne I hope you'll finally tell me," he retorted. "Now come down off here—it's getting late."

"I'm not ready for bed."

"Who said anything about bed?" A warm breeze kicked up the edge of Luca's tunic and ruffled his hair. "Noémie's telling the Meridian tale. By the bonfire."

"Again?" I wrinkled my nose. "I don't want to listen to that same old story."

"Yes, you do." Luca jumped into a crouch and wrapped his arms around my waist, sweeping me off my feet. I let out a surprised whoop when the world tilted upside down, spinning the sun in a blurry circle.

"Luca!" I was breathless with laughter. "Put me down!"

Finally, he set me gently on my feet, then vaulted off the top of the transport in a spinning leap. I gasped, but he landed neatly and took off at a run.

"Coming?" he called.

I dragged my dark tangle of dusty, sun-faded hair into a knot on the top of my head, then clambered off the transport.

The camp hummed with tension. Free travelers and workers clustered in knots, sipping from the precious stores of tize, honey-eyed wine imported from the Sousine Coast. The bonfire burned low, choking down offerings of battered wooden wheels and shattered furniture. One of the slaughtered animals roasted on a spit above the embers, a grudging boon from a cursed day.

A cluster of children scattered around my legs like wind around a tree trunk. One bouncing mane of coal-black curls caught my eye.

"Vesh!"

The boy skidded to a stop, his eyes brightening before he threw his arms around my waist and knocked me off-balance. At least this boy wasn't strong enough to lift me off my feet and spin me around.

Yet.

"Sylvie!" Vesh took a bite out of whatever he was holding in his hand, then talked around a mouthful of food. "Did you see the Sky-horse people?"

"I did." I crouched. "Did you?"

"No," Vesh said, a frown creasing his liquid eyes. "Luca made me hide beneath one of Maman's transports. So I didn't see nothin'."

"Luca was only trying to keep you safe," I explained. "He's a good brother, you know."

"Say that to my face!" Luca danced out from behind me and swept his little brother onto his shoulders. The younger boy shrieked with laughter, clinging to Luca's neck as he frolicked toward the edge of the fire.

A smile crept onto my face. I never had a sibling, but even if I did, I couldn't imagine being as close to anyone as Luca was to Vesh. Not only did they resemble each other physically—with their coloring and easy laughs—but even when they were apart they seemed to move in the same manner, and with the same intent. Two marionettes, fashioned from the same material and moved by the same hand, dancing always to the same silent rhythms.

Melancholy tugged at my heart. I reached for the amulet around my neck—the only thing I truly owned, the last relic of the anonymous parents who discarded me like trash at the edge of the daylight world. The pure ambric glowed dully between my fingers, and I wondered what it would feel like to belong. To be part of a family, whether by blood or by choice.

Part of me wanted to ask Luca, but with his warm eyes and quick smile, I couldn't imagine him ever knowing what it felt like to be unloved.

THREE

The sound of strings being plucked pulled me out of my bitter reverie. Noémie—a storyteller who'd joined the convoy at Posette—knelt by the bonfire, her fingers deftly tuning the wizened knobs of her ancient luth. Behind her, her dancer daughter Audé had begun to stretch, lifting a lean leg above her head as her husband, Henrique, grasped her waist for balance.

Finally, Noémie swept a hand toward the crowd, fingers splayed.

"Listen!" she cried, voice sonorous.

We listened. The only sound was the crackle and purr of the fire.

"Listen!" Audé and Henrique paced slowly forward, the outlines of their long limbs sinuous in the flickering firelight. "Listen, and hear the beginning of the longest day. Listen, with your ears. Listen, with your eyes. And listen, with your heart."

A warm hand brushed mine. My pulse jumped, and I sliced my eyes to the side. Firelight heated Luca's gaze as he leaned in, his lips nearly grazing my ear.

"Thought you didn't want to hear this story again."

"Who says I'm here for the story?" I teased.

I turned back toward Noémie, pretending not to see Luca's cheeks flush dull red.

"Long before the Amber Empire," she began, "or the Midnight Dominion, or any of the lands today, the world was ruled by two gods. The Sun, and the Moon. The Sun was a beautiful god, and where his holy fire fell, the earth was fruitful with joy and plenty. His heart was generous, so every day he spun around to all faces of the world, drenching new lands in light."

Henrique performed a dizzying series of graceful pirouettes. The bonfire scattered sparks.

"The Moon was a beauty like no other, a bright creature shining like polished dristic embedded with diamonds. When the Sun left behind darkness in his wake, she lit the sky with her calm, pale light."

Audé's arm arched above her head, and in her open hand nestled an opal, sparking with a cold, muted glow. The children cooed with delight and leaned closer, but Audé twisted the stone away into the folds of her silken dress.

"The Sun loved the Moon with a passion. But the Moon was indifferent to his gaudy light. Still, the Sun chased the Moon around the world, and whenever he caught her he touched her hand or stole a kiss, hoping to win her heart." Henrique and Audé orbited each other in the dusk, their steps so light they almost seemed to be floating. "But the Moon always ran away again, and the Sun became bitter and jealous.

"The Sun decided if he could not be with the Moon, he would kill her. But he could not bear for the Moon's pain to be on his own conscience. So he searched as he spun, until he found a man strong and ruthless enough to do the terrible deed in his stead."

We all leaned forward, caught in the haze of legend and fire sparking between Noémie's words and the dancers' choreography.

"The man's name was Meridian, although you may know him by other names. Scion. Evening Star. Skybender. Some say he was a god himself. Or even a demon." The fire popped, and someone gasped. "His legacy was strong, stronger than any who have walked the world since. He could summon the rain from the skies, or command a wind to cease. The dirt trembled when he walked, and the waters shivered away from his touch.

"The Sun saw all this and knew Meridian would do as he asked. He summoned Meridian to his skyborne palais, and gave him three objects. First: a net woven from fine golden filaments, to capture the Moon. Second: a spear made of metal forged so hot it would never break, to pierce the Moon's chest. And third: a vial made of glass, to catch the blood from the Moon's heart.

"Meridian rode his flaming chariot across the sky in pursuit of the Moon. For a tide and a day he chased her. Finally, she could evade him no longer. And in the velvet night, surrounded by a thousand weeping stars, she turned to face Meridian. But even as he lifted his spear to strike the fatal blow, Meridian saw the Moon's exquisite form, bathed in pale light and near enough to touch. Overcome by adoration and unable to murder something so beautiful, Meridian turned the spear on himself, piercing his heart with the deadly metal.

"Meridian's flaming chariot plummeted, and with him fell his terrible tools. The net, delicate and golden, spread across the lands of men. *Kembric*." Audé sent a glittering chain of burnished kembric spiraling into the dust. "The spear drove veins deep into the Meteor Mountains. *Dristic*." A polished bracelet of the strong, silvery metal slipped off Henrique's wrist and landed with a puff. "And the shattered glass vial, stained with Meridian's own blood and infused with his great power, pierced shards deep into the heart of the world. *Ambric*." Audé blew across her palm, and a billow of shimmering amber dust swirled up to fly above the empire that was its namesake.

"Meridian hurtled to the earth. The Moon fled deep into the comforting darkness of night. And the shameful Sun, wracked with terrible guilt for his evil deed, turned his face from the world, hiding within the flaming towers of his palais. And from that day forth, the daylight world became as you know it. The Sun does not traverse the skies. The Moon remains hidden in the shadowy gloom of the Midnight Dominion. And Meridian—Meridian is lost."

I leaned forward, gripping my knees as a shiver teased my spine. This was my favorite part of the legend. The familiar words never failed to raise the flesh on my arms and tickle the hairs at the nape of my neck.

"Some claim Meridian is not dead, but merely sleeping. Deep within the bosom of Midnight he sleeps, waiting for a time when mankind needs him most. Only then will he awake from slumber and use his legacy to force the Sun to rise and set once more.

"But some say Meridian is neither dead nor sleeping. Meridian, impassioned by the beautiful Moon, trekked deep into the shadows of Dominion to seek forgiveness from his love. There he shines still, a bright star at the Moon's side. And one day, when darkness spreads across the land and Midnight rules the earth, he will watch as the vengeful Moon finally snuffs out the light of her greatest enemy. And the Sun will shine no more."

A sudden hush sifted secret fingers through the dusk. The only thing I heard was a low, distant humming in my ears. A humming like—

Unease grasped my throat. I glanced down at my lap, and sucked in a sharp breath.

A pennant of shadow yawned between my hands, velvety and fathomless. A million brilliant flecks of light danced within the darkness, still and cold and impossibly remote.

The third bell of Nocturne chimed across the camp, breaking the spell. Children giggled, and Noémie accepted a sprinkling of applause as Audé and Henrique bowed. The free travelers dissipated to their tents and wagons, eager for sleep.

Panic stitched cold threads down my back. I clamped my hands in the folds of my skirts and squeezed my eyes shut. A swarm of invisible insects hummed in my ears. I reached for something to distract me from the vision of an ink-black night studded with diamonds of light. Words and images flickered across my mind's eye.

A bloodstained sun, peering between flags of livid clouds.

Dristic streaks in the hair of a frowning Skyclad captain.

A tumble of black curls above kembric-flecked eyes.

A shining city, and the promise of a new world.

"Sylvie?"

I lifted dizzy eyes to meet a familiar gaze. Warmth stained my cheeks, and I turned to stare into the fire, forcing my breathing to slow.

"Is everything all right?" Luca asked. "You're pale."

"I'm fine," I lied, scrambling to my feet. "I thought I . . . saw something."

"What did you see?" A mischievous smile pushed Luca's frown away. "Was it a *mulo*? A dust devil? They haunt these lands, and if they catch you, they'll use your hair for a necklace and your blood for wine."

"Luca, don't." I hated the peevish tone of my voice, but my ears still hummed, and my fingers itched, and my heart thrummed uneven in my chest. "There's no such thing as a *mulo*, in these lands or any other."

"It was a joke, Sylvie." Luca's smile faded. "Are you sure you're all right?"

"It's been a long day." I scrubbed a hand over my brow. "It's past third Nocturne. I should sleep."

"Of course." Luca stuffed his hands into the pockets of his tunic. "Will you ride with me and Vesh tomorrow? You know how he loves your stories."

"I will." I forced a thin copy of a smile, guilty for being so unkind to my friend. My *only* friend. "I'll even promise to tell a new story."

"A promise I'll hold you to."

I was almost to my patched tent when Luca's voice reached out and stopped me.

"Sylvie?"

I turned.

"Every day I ask why you're traveling to the Amber City. Every day you brush me off with jokes or half-truths. Why won't you answer me?"

In the harsh glow of the silent sun, Luca could almost be a *mulo* himself, a spirit crafted from dust and wind, restless and wild as the parched earth that spawned him.

"Maybe you're not asking the right questions, Luca."

"I've asked every question I can think of." Luca gave his curls a rough shake. "Everything I know about you I had to coax out of you. Even your name I had to guess. You tell me nothing. I just want to know you. Why can't you give me something real, Sylvie?"

"I'm not sure there's anything real to give, Luca," I whispered into the dusk. "Blink, and I might return to the shadows I came from."

I ducked into my tent, tugging the flap closed before I could see the hurt on my friend's face.

I flung myself onto my meager pile of blankets and examined my hands in the gloom of the narrow tent. My slender fingers tingled, and I curled my hand into a fist, watching the tapestry of blue veins beneath my skin pump blood I shouldn't have. Blood I *couldn't* have.

Mother Celeste and the other Sisters swore I was an aberration, a judgment from the Scion himself meant to test their piety. They begged me to stop, praying over my deviant hands as radiance poured forth, impossible as sunshine in that dim-cold dusk at the edge of Dominion.

It's for your own good, they hissed, desperation crowding out the terror in their eyes. *Do not tempt the wrath of the Scion, child!*

And when I couldn't—or wouldn't—stop, they kept me locked in my room for days at a time, conversing in hushed whispers outside my door.

That was the first time I heard the word: *legacy.*

Legacy. A word I barely recognized until a tide ago. A word I'd never uttered aloud. A word that shuddered through my bones with a familiarity I couldn't name.

Legacy meant magic. Legacy meant power. Legacy meant birthright.

Only the aristocracy of the Amber Empire claimed the gift of legacy. It was an inheritance bestowed upon the descendants of Meridian, bloodline of the Scion—the great families who held court upon the Amber Empress herself, in Coeur d'Or, the palais at the heart of the Amber City.

I wasn't highborn. Or if I was, whoever sired me disowned me, dumping me in the shadows at the edge of the world like I was worthless. The thought stoked the ember of rage burning always within me, a bright kernel hard and polished as a ruby.

When I opened my hands illusions spilled out, beautiful and terrible and impossible to control.

Trees of kembric, draped in garlands of jewels.

Bouquets of skyflowers.

Bracelets of stars.

I wasn't worthless. I wasn't an aberration, a freak, a *monster*. I was a *legacy*.

I ran away from the Temple of the Scion because I knew I deserved better than merely being tolerated. Much as I'd tried to follow in their footsteps when I was young, I had never belonged with the Sisters, and they had certainly never loved me. They had taught me many things: that to laugh too loudly in the presence of the Scion was a sin, and that the bruises and scrapes inflicted by the ignorant village kids were my own fault, and that dreaming of anything outside the dank walls of the Temple was too dangerous to be allowed.

They had taught me that being alive was not the same thing as living.

They had tried to stop me from leaving, when I finally fled. They had burned the Imperial Insignia and tried to lock me in my room, panic churning their studied tranquility into chaos. But I'd escaped. Jagged satisfaction tinged with guilt burned through me when I remembered how I'd repaid a lifetime of their indifference.

But I deserved the chance to find where I belonged. To find a world where my gift—my *legacy*—did not frighten superstitious Sisters or enrage cruel children. To find a world forged in sunlight and honed on dreams, as perilous and intoxicating as the colors spilling jewel-bright from my fingertips. To find a world where I wasn't a freak or a monster.

That's why I was traveling to the Amber City: to join the court of the empress in Coeur d'Or. As a legacy of the Amber Empire, I would be embraced and celebrated. I would finally be around others like me, who understood what it was like to *burn*—with magic and wonder and the heady thrill of impossible visions.

I twisted my hands again, and a shower of ghostly petals drifted down to brush against my lips, soft as a kiss.

A kiss that tasted like a promise.

FOUR

A breeze scudded clouds across the somber sun, and the convoy slept.

I huddled at the edge of a guttering cook fire, warming the gristly scraps of dried meat I'd wheedled out of Löic, the kindly drover of one of Rina's transports. I'd tried to be tough, gnawing on bitter ginga root to keep my hunger at bay, but it was getting harder to ignore the jut of my ribs and hipbones. I was running out of food, but so was the rest of the camp. Barrels of tize diminished as stores of lavas and meat thinned.

The convoy had trudged westward for another span, churning our spirits in its wake until they were as dusty as the earth. The hours of Matin bled into Prime, then drifted into Compline and Nocturne until the bells rang out for Matin once more. The sun appeared to creep higher above the horizon, lightening the sky to tangerine. The dusty prairie had finally given way to endless meadows of green maize swaying beneath pristine flocks of cygni soaring overhead. We passed men trudging through stunted villages. Their hair and clothes were black with smears of the soot produced in the smelting of kembric.

But we were still nearly a span's ride from the Amber City.

"Sylvie?" A voice sliced through my tangle of anxiety. "What are you doing out here?"

I whirled. Luca stood in the silhouette of the biggest transport, hair mussed. I clenched my fist around the handle of the borrowed skillet and almost tried to hide it, before realizing it was too late. Luca's sleep-heavy gaze had already narrowed on the meager scraps of meat.

"I told you to tell me if you ran out of food," he growled. He crossed the space between us in a few long strides, his drowsiness dissolving into exasperation. "If this is all you're eating, you're going to starve before we reach the Amber City."

"A romantic way to die," I said, and laughed.

Luca didn't.

"I don't want to bother your family," I explained, sobering. "You and your mother have already done too much for me."

"You aren't a bother. You need to eat."

"I'll never be able to repay you."

"You don't have to repay anything. We want you here. *I* want you here."

I cut my gaze to Luca's. The scudding clouds threw pennants of light and shadow across his face, and I could almost pretend I didn't see the ruddy flush rising in his cheeks. I looked away, and silence stretched out between us, brittle as metal hammered too thin.

"You once spoke of a *mulo*, a dust devil," I muttered, reaching for something—anything—to ease the tension. "Will you tell me the story?"

Luca gusted a sigh, crouching to flip my scraps of meat before they burned. "There isn't much of a story. It's just something Tavendel mothers tell their children to frighten them into behaving."

"I want to hear it anyway."

"They say a *mulo* is born from dust, christened in fire, and cursed with an eternal thirst. Back home, we left saucers of wine in front of our tents, to stop the *mulo* from sneaking inside and drinking our blood."

"Wine?" A shiver curled cold fingers around my spine. "But why would the *mulo* drink the wine when it could sneak inside and drink your blood instead?"

Luca's fire-bright eyes met mine, and he shrugged. "Maybe by paying a demon what he needs, you keep him from stealing what he desires."

A fierce breeze kissed my neck. My palms thrummed, and I felt the dire image heaving through my consciousness. *Dust. Fire. Blood.* I saw its terrible eyes, ringed in fire; heard its silent, billowing footsteps; felt the metallic gnaw of its bloodlust hollowing out my stomach.

"Home," I gasped out, seizing that word and using it as a shield against the dream pummeling strange fists against the prison of my ribs. "You mentioned home. Where is that?"

Luca's brows came together, and he glared into the fire. "It's less of a where than a *who*. My people—we are Tavendel. Time was, we traversed the length of the Tavend flatlands, following the rains to the best grazing. These days, few among us follow the old paths, choosing instead to seek out more lucrative trade in the cities."

I nibbled on a bit of jerky as cautious curiosity surged within me. I'd heard Luca mention Tavendel, but this was the first time he'd spoken of what that meant to him.

"So you were herders?" I asked.

"We bred and grazed horses, yes." A sudden radiance gripped him, and he grinned. "But we were also cartographers, and astronomers, and poets. Vesh ôn Khorin, my grandfather many times over, wrote a thousand poems—quite a few are still famous, sung often among the Tavendel."

I tried on a smile. "Sing me one?"

Luca uncrossed his arms and gazed at the sky. His voice spilled out, timid at first, then more confident. I didn't understand the language, but the fire-fretted melody curled desolate against my skin. Finally, the song trailed away on a soft, low note. I shook myself, and swiped at my suddenly damp cheeks.

"Beautiful," I murmured. "What does it mean?"

Luca shrugged, suddenly shy. "My Tavendel is rusty, and the translation is complex. But it's about something precious being stolen away, and the hollow wind at the edge of heartbreak."

I nodded like I understood. "Why did you and your family leave? Your Tavendel homeland, I mean."

Luca tensed, the muscles in his forearms going rigid as bars of dristic. I immediately regretted my thoughtless question.

"Luca, I'm sorry." I choked on a tough scrap of meat. "I shouldn't have—"

"No." Luca's voice was puckered as an old scar. "It's a story that deserves telling, just so it's never forgotten." He paused, and smoothed his fists open onto his thighs. "I was eleven. Vesh hadn't been born yet. My father had chosen me to follow in his footsteps as a Guardian—I would learn the ways of weaponry so that I might one day be able to protect my tribe from any dangers it might face. But first, I had to be tested. So I was blindfolded and taken into the Chabrol, a maze of rock formations sacred to the Tavendel. They left me there, bound, with no food, water, or map. I had to use my wits, my endurance, and my bravery to find my way home, or die trying."

You were only a child! I wanted to shout. But I bit my lip and listened.

"It took me four days, and by the time I returned I was sun-burned and bleeding and half-dead with thirst. But I didn't get the victor's welcome I had expected." He paused, and the sooty dregs of some ancient shame passed over his face like ashes. "While I was gone, a Skyclad platoon had raided the camp and stolen all our horses. They slaughtered my father, as well as my aunt, uncle, and older cousins. They only spared my mother because she was heavy with child."

Shock and pity struck me mute.

"Maman wept for a week, then went cold and hard as forged dristic. We walked to the nearest sand port in Dura'a, where she sold every last piece of her bridal jewelry in order to purchase a Charter Writ. Vesh was born on that first expedition to the Duskland mines, and we've worked to grow the convoy every tide since." He spread his arms to encompass the tents, travelers, transports, and crates of ore. "And so I will spend my life travers-ing this harsh land, instead of becoming an honored Tavendel warrior like my father wished. All because the Amber Empress's hired thugs didn't feel like paying for fresh mounts."

"Luca—" I dug deep for words to express the roil of disgust and sympathy and fury souring my stomach, but only unearthed platitudes. "I'm so sorry. I can't imagine how terrible that must have been for you and Madame Rina."

For the space of a breath, a pall of bitterness seemed to tower over Luca, twisting his features and hunching his spine. But in another moment it was gone, banished by the sudden carefree blaze of his smile.

"Past is past." He surged to his feet. "Convoy's moving on in two hours—best get some rest."

I groaned out loud, pushing away the uneasy weight of shared sorrow. Luca was right—there was no point in dwelling too long on past tragedy. But as I trailed him back into the heart of camp, I wondered for the first time whether his near-permanent grin masked a different face—a face scarred by misfortune and pocked with spite.

A face I'd glimpsed in the space between heartbeats, and hoped never to see again.

FIVE

I rode in the back of Madame Rina's transport, teaching Vesh a silly guessing game I invented. Brightly dyed curtains swayed in the breeze, casting a patchwork of colored light and shadow. Vesh laughed as I dragged a nub of charcoal across a scrap of parchment, sketching a rough design.

"Horsey!" he shouted, breathless. "Fluterwing! No, wait— giant!"

I shook my head, giggling over the sound of my rumbling stomach.

The transport swayed to a halt. The curtains trembled, and a stack of copper pots fell to the floor with a thud. Voices raised outside, then silence.

Vesh and I stared toward the front of the transport.

"Vesh!" Luca's head popped between two green curtains. Excitement lit his face. "Sylvie! Come out and see."

I clambered to my feet, tamping down a ripple of nerves. Vesh's small hand was hot in mine as I lifted him out to his brother. He was gone before I could blink, sprinting away to find his friends.

"What is it?" I asked, craning my neck.

"You'll see." Luca slid his hands around my waist to help me down from the transport, the touch sending a shiver lancing up my spine. He twined his fingers in mine and tugged. Curiosity and unease warred within me.

Arrayed along a stony arête, the convoy gazed out across a valley. Grass swept away from our feet, dotted with purple heliotrope. The ruddy sun hung a few fingers' breadth above the distant spine of ambric-streaked massifs, and nestled amid gentle foothills sprawled the Amber City, towering and glittering and vast.

We made it.

Sudden panic tore the breath from my throat and chilled my bones. Part of me never believed I'd make it this far. Part of me believed the Amber City was nothing more than a dream, a mythic world conjured up by travelers to soothe the drudgery of an interminable journey. Part of me believed I would wake up one Matin, blanketed in creeping shadows and surrounded by indifferent Sisters.

I blinked to dispel the mirage. The Amber City didn't budge, solid and commanding in its position of majesty across the plain.

So close.

"*Vitza!* Stop gawping!" Madame Rina was a whirlwind of billowing robes and tight braids, rounding up laborers and free travelers like unruly goats. "Do you want to look at it, or do you want to get to it?"

Luca whooped, swinging up onto the roof of the transport as the ambric apparatus belched orange and the convoy trundled toward the distant city. I trotted to catch up, but the air tasted thin in my lungs and I couldn't take my eyes off the distant glitter of domes and spires.

It took us another two days to arrive at the gates of the Amber City, but it might have been an eternity. I did nothing but stare and wonder as the convoy crawled closer. The Amber City was huge. My mind could hardly comprehend the vast metropolis reaching up toward the smoldering sun. The labyrinth of streets and alleyways twisting and converging across the city. The bright smear of the river, its network of canals gleaming red as rivulets of blood.

And surrounding everything, a great wall, with soaring ramparts built from black ironstone and barred in dristic. Sullen ambric lamps pulsed from stern towers, sending shards of red and gold to pierce the sky.

I asked Luca whether an army could ever breach those battlements.

"Any army foolhardy enough to approach the Amber City would have to face ten thousand Skyclad long before even setting eyes on the wall," Luca laughed. "But it makes a statement all the same."

"Is it noisy inside?" I pressed. "Crowded? Where do all the people live?"

"There are different quartiers, see, each with its own character." Luca leaned close enough that his stubble rasped against my cheek. I fought to control my breathing as his hand sketched precise arcs against the outline of the city. "To the south, Unitas: a place of learning where students pore over ancient tomes written in dead languages, staining their fingers with ink and swilling kachua to stay awake."

"Kachua?"

"Like tea, but black and bitter." Luca wrinkled his nose, then pointed to a cluster of glittering spires. "That's Jardinier, where the wealthy clothe their children in the feathers of rare birds and adorn their pets with priceless jewels. That arched boulevard is Concordat, where great fountains spew and the hooves of a thousand Skyclad destriers ring out on kembric-lined streets. North of that is the Mews, where the rich rub shoulders with the poor in vast marchés. You can buy anything: stardust, or the tears of a lovelorn maiden, or a tamed *d'haka* all the way from Dura'a."

"A *what*?"

"A flying desert serpent with wings of flame and eyes so bright they'll make a man go blind."

"Luca, that's not real."

"How do you know?" Luca's smile flashed before he pointed back to the city. "That chaotic mountain of shanties and hovels and ill-made huts, climbing the foothills? That's the Paper City. Slums, where the poor live on top of one another, clambering on roofs and across rickety bridges. Vice goes hand in hand with poverty. You're as likely to get bitten by a starving orphan as a stray dog."

But I was barely listening anymore. My eyes snagged on Coeur d'Or, gleaming at the center of it all. Set atop a rise overlooking the river, the palais of the Amber Empress seemed to shine like a sun. Built from glass and ambric and gilded in kembric, Coeur d'Or dazzled and beguiled. Crystalline towers sent splinters of light dancing across the city. A thousand filigreed arches twisted and spiraled toward the sky.

"And Coeur d'Or? What about the palais?"

Luca's eyes sharpened on mine, and his smile wilted.

"What do you care about coddled aristos dancing attendance on a spoiled empress? My friend Garan is a servant in the palais— you should hear how they prance around in silks and velvets, primping and preening and never venturing beyond the walls of their private paradise." The rusty sun sparked in his eyes and turned his expression harsh. "Those legacied fools don't realize how big the world is. What I wouldn't give to have that blood running through my veins! Maybe I'd find a way to protect the world from evil, instead of holing up in a château in face paint and high heels."

I lowered my eyes, sudden shame battling with the hot thrill singing through my veins. Colors burned the edges of my vision: craggy violet and river red and the intoxicating translucence of seething sunlight through amber. My hands itched, and for the first time since I joined the convoy at the edge of the Dusklands, I actually wanted to show him. Show him the many-hued illusions pulsing at my fingertips, the daydream fancies beguiling my mind.

Coddled aristos. Luca's voice echoed in my mind, dripping with scorn. *Legacied fools.*

I bit down on the colors, shoving them into the cage of my ribs.

"Sylvie?" The brush of Luca's palm against the back of my hand was both a question and a sort of answer. "You're trembling."

I curled my traitor fingers into my palm and stared toward the shining city. I swallowed a wave of sour guilt, ignoring the hurt pooling in Luca's eyes.

I was so close. I couldn't let myself get distracted.

SIX

We felt the gates thunder open in our bones.

The convoy joined the imperial boulevard, steering transports and wagons onto broad flagstones thronged with travelers. Horses stamped as a profusion of livestock squawked and hollered from crates and cages. Women and men of every color and garb jostled for space, and the hum and chatter of a thousand voices crowded my ears and weighed on my chest.

"All right, Sylvie?" Luca's concerned eyes brushed my face. "We're almost there."

"I know," I gasped out. The crush of humanity was nearly too much to bear—I'd never seen this many people in one place.

"Don't be frightened," he said, and grinned. "I've come here so many times I've lost track. You're safe with me."

But when I glanced toward the gleaming domes of Coeur d'Or, I wasn't sure I wanted to be safe.

Through the gates, the city burst with even more sights and sounds. Terraced houses loomed over stately, tree-lined boulevards. A quartet of plumed horses pulled a lavish carriage, gilded shutters pulled tight. Laughing fountains arched beneath looming monuments sculpted from ironstone and gilded in kembric. Tall posts topped with ambric lamps lined the road, hung with banners emblazoned with the image of a face.

Soft, delicate features. Rosy lips curled into a gentle smile beneath eyes violet as the heliotrope blossoms dotting the plains outside the city. Lustrous auburn curls falling beneath a diadem jeweled with a faceted cabochon of purest ambric.

I didn't need Luca to tell me who she was: Severine, the Amber Empress.

I could hardly take my eyes off her. Luca's lips thinned when he noticed me staring, but I gazed at the brightly dyed banner until another reared up to take its place.

We left the dignified boulevard behind, diving into the sprawl of the Mews. Streets and avenues unfurled, reaching in every direction like a many-fingered hand. Vast marchés spilled over sidewalks, colorful tents and stands draped in food and clothing and jewelry and ambric artifices. My nose crinkled at the scent of unfamiliar herbs and spices. Vendors shouted and waved at the convoy, offering up their wares: gemflowers from the Meridian Desert; fur from the mythical white tiger, hunted on the snow-draped peaks of the Meteor Mountains; a lock of the empress's hair, certain to bring good fortune.

Finally, we reached the depot, a dilapidated cluster of storehouses where Madame Rina staged her convoy. Dazed, I gathered my few belongings and threaded through the throng of bonded workers and free travelers hugging and weeping fond goodbyes. Luca and Vesh had disappeared with their mother. I assumed they had business with the comptroller of the warehouse—duties to pay and bribes to dole out.

A trough by the gate held clear water, and I felt suddenly caked in grime after spans on the road. I thrust my hands in the cool liquid, scrubbing at the crusted dirt with my nails. The ruffled surface flung shards of my own image back at me—a blue-grey eye, chapped lips, a length of lank hair. Once, Sister Anouk had admitted I was pretty, with my thick, dark hair and wide eyes. *But sometimes the prettiest people can possess the ugliest souls*, she'd demurred, fading back into the tenets of her faith. *A body is an illusion and a face is a lie.*

What would she think of my soul now, now that my body was dirty and malnourished after spans on the dusty road?

My eyes wandered across the crowded rooftops to the gilded domes of Coeur d'Or, shining above the maze of narrow streets. I imagined pristine jardins and courtyards, ringed in flowers. Glittering hallways, awash in the coral light of a thousand ambric lamps. Elaborate feasts. Gowns. Fêtes.

I clenched my itching palms.

I glanced back at the hunched storehouses. The narrow doors and dark windows. The peeling paint and rusting metal.

I should wait for Luca. I wanted to say goodbye to him, and his strong mother, and his sweet brother. I wanted to tell them how much their kindness meant to me, when I had nothing else.

But then I remembered the look on Luca's face yesterday when he'd spoken of Coeur d'Or. I remembered the brush of his fingers against my hand. His honey-warm eyes, flecked with kembric. The easy brush of curls against his brow. His bright smile.

I bit my lip so hard I thought I might draw blood.

Maybe it would be easier not to say goodbye at all. A poor reward for a good friend, but better than a path to a broken heart.

I turned toward the gate.

"Sylvie!" Luca's shout rang above the clamor of the courtyard.

I spun. Relief battled with regret in the fathomless corners of my heart.

Luca wore only an undershirt—the sweat-damp fabric clung to the muscled planes of his torso. He pushed damp curls out of his eyes and frowned. "Where are you going?"

"I'm leaving." I sucked in a sip of air and forced myself to meet his gaze. "You and Madame Rina have been more than kind to me. I owe you both so much. But I can't impose any longer. I should be on my way."

"Leaving?" The crease between his brows deepened. "Why didn't you tell me?"

"I couldn't find you," I lied, swallowing against the lump swelling in my throat.

"I was just unloading crates with Anaïs."

"Anaïs?"

"The comptroller's daughter," he explained, glancing to the left and raising a hand. I squelched an absurd flare of envy when a voluptuous, golden-haired girl waved cheerfully back. "Many of the bonded laborers and free travelers are staying at the inn next door before moving on. Why don't you do the same?"

"I don't have any money. I can't afford it."

"Then where will you go?"

I opened my mouth to tell him, to explain, but my voice was trapped in my throat.

"Sylvie." Luca grasped my shoulders. The scent of sun-warmed metal and sweat clung to his skin, and my pulse jolted. I wasn't sure whether I wanted to break away, or lean closer. "I don't know where you're going. I don't know why you're here, in the city. But I don't think you know either."

I shook my head, trying to find the words to explain how wrong he was.

"I don't care." He tilted his head. "I know you're proud. But we can take care of you. Me, Maman, Vesh. Stay with the convoy. Stay with me."

My gaze slashed up to meet his. In the faded light, his eyes glinted like coins.

"The ore trade is a hard life," he continued, fervent, "but a good one. Our charter takes the convoy from one end of the Amber Road to the other, traveling through more towns and provinces than you can imagine. You'll see things you've never dreamed of before. Cities made of glass. Oceans with waves of light. Blue men. The infinite sweep of the Tavendel grasslands. I want to show you all of that. I want you to stay."

"Stop," I choked out, finally. "Just stop."

Luca's hands fell from my shoulders. His brow furrowed, and his hands squeezed into fists.

"Please, Luca." I clenched my jaw, still struggling for the right words. "Don't ask me for that. Even if I wanted to, I can't."

"Why?" His voice rose in pitch. He shook his mess of dark curls. "I've asked you every Nocturne for six spans, Sylvie. What are you hiding? Why are you here?"

Dimly—distantly—I heard a buzz, like beetles crawling over metal. I rubbed my prickling hands together. And before I could change my mind, I held them out, palms up, like an offering.

"Because of this," I said.

I conjured Coeur d'Or, in perfect miniature. Spires and arches and domes vaulted into the empty space between us, glittering in the light of a faded sun. Spiral stairways. Delicate ogees. Pillars. Fountains. For a moment I could barely believe that I had created this—*this wonder*—from nothing more than imagination and the legacy swirling in my blood.

I sustained the illusion for the length of a held breath. Then the exquisite palais drifted apart like paint washed away by water. A wave of vertigo blurred my vision, and I gasped in a reedy breath.

Only then did I dare look up at Luca.

His head jerked back like I'd slapped him. His nostrils flared with a rough breath. Pain darkened the edges of his eyes before his face shuttered.

"You never told me." It wasn't a question.

"I didn't know how."

"How?" Contempt twisted his face. "It didn't seem so hard a moment ago. What were you afraid of? Did you think I would spit at your feet and call you *witch* or *monster*?"

"No! I just didn't think—"

"I am Tavendel," he interrupted. He trawled a shaking hand through his hair, scraping sweaty locks from his temples. "When we sing, the clouds weep, and our own eyes spill raindrops. When we stamp our feet, *mulos* dance across the plains. When we are cut, we bleed poems full of magic. I would as soon call you a witch as I would disown my own mother."

"That's not it at all," I said, struggling to keep my voice even. "What I just showed you—that's my legacy. I thought you might not understand how much a part of me it is. How it changes the way I see the world. How it changes the way I see *myself*."

"You're going there, aren't you?" He wrenched his gaze toward Coeur d'Or. The palais sparked spears of light into a sky stained with plum and ocher. "You want to join the empress's court. To dance attendance on that horde of sniveling nobles. To find the parents who abandoned you."

"You're not listening to me." I swallowed, dousing a sparking kernel of rage. "I'm already one of them. Coeur d'Or is where I belong. I have noble blood flowing through my veins—the bloodline of the Scion. I deserve this chance to change my world."

"You think your *blood* defines where you belong? You think being highborn means you deserve special treatment?" He sneered. "Our blood is nothing without the will that moves it. You can choose your own life."

"I didn't mean—" I snapped my teeth in frustration, cutting my words to pieces. "I can't control my legacy. It either pushes out of me against my will or makes me tremble with exhaustion. I want to learn how to use this power living within me. Imagine the splendor I could create, the dreams I could make real! The people living in that palais are the only ones who can show me how."

"That's not why you're going." Luca's eyes narrowed to slits of fire. "I just offered you friendship. Security. *Family.* Splendor and dreams are just fancy words for wealth. You want silks, refinement. Fine wines and feasts. Parties that last from Compline to Matin. Kembric dinner plates and high heels. And worst of all, you want *power.*"

"So what?" The words burst from me louder than I expected. "What's wrong with being ambitious? I do want a world full of beauty and grace. I do want power. And what's more, I *deserve* it. It's my birthright, and I'll be damned if I don't claim what's mine!"

Luca rocked back on his heels. I twisted trembling fingers in the fraying hide of my knapsack. Silence stretched between us. Luca finally tore his eyes from mine, staring across the courtyard toward the shadowed warehouse.

"I hope you find the world you're looking for, Sylvie," he said heavily. "I really do. But I've heard the stories about what goes on in Coeur d'Or. Those poisonous courtiers will never accept someone like you. You may claim a legacy, but you weren't born in their world. They will humiliate you with twisted pranks. They'll contaminate your soul with toxic games. You will never truly belong."

Unease gnawed at my ribs.

"So after they leave you broken, think of me. Remember what I offered you—family, security, friendship." His broad shoulders tensed. "More, if you wanted it."

And then he strode away. Disquiet clambered up my throat and choked me with a cold certainty: I hadn't expressed myself well at all.

I didn't want to leave Luca like this. Part of me didn't want to leave him at all. But I'd made myself a promise, back in the grim, pallid dusk—I would find where I belonged. Not just a place to survive, but a place to flourish, surrounded by people who understood the blaze of strange colors staining my soul. A place anchored in beauty and steeped in wonder. A place where magic could bring dreams to life.

Did wanting that world make me vain, or greedy, or ambitious?

Maybe.

But even if it did, was I willing to sacrifice that world for the love of a boy? A boy with heat in his smile and a song on his lips. A boy who'd had his own perfect world stolen away, in exchange for the bitter drudgery of an unwanted life.

I clenched my teeth, sifting my hurt through the shifting sands of my uncertainty.

Luca paused halfway across the courtyard, caught in a narrow swathe of sunlight. Motes of dust glittered like pale stars in the vermilion light. The tri-metal signat in his ear glinted as he turned his head to glance over his shoulder.

"We'll be in the Mews for another half span," he muttered. "Gathering supplies and contracts for the convoy. If you change your mind—"

For a moment I thought he was going to say something else. But then he shook his head and disappeared into the cool, hay-scented dusk of the stables.

Where Anaïs was waiting for him.

I squeezed my eyelids against a prickle of tears. I wouldn't think like that. I was making the right choice.

I cut my gaze toward the center of the city, where Coeur d'Or perched, aloof and ephemeral as an unspoken secret. I still couldn't believe I was here, so far from the dusty, shadowed village where cruel children kicked me for being different. So far from the tomb-quiet Temple where impassive Sisters quelled all my hopes and forbade me from dreaming.

I squared my shoulders and imagined forged dristic pouring into my veins and strengthening my bones. I wasn't that weak, neglected, abused girl anymore. And I'd traveled too far to let regret stop me from finding where I belonged.

So what if I lost a friend? Surely that was a small price to pay for finding a brand-new world.

SEVEN

The gate to Coeur d'Or was a thing of outrageous beauty. Wrought in kembric and shining like a beacon, the portal loomed from the spiked fence abutting it. Gleaming vines of filigree twisted along slender bars. The Imperial Insignia glittered from the ornate finial, the sunburst set with a faceted bijou of ambric that caught the low light and magnified it, splintering radiance across the courtyard. A platoon of Skyclad Gardes flanked the gate, pale armor polished mirror-bright and silvery cloaks stirring.

I tore my eyes from the magnificent gate to look back the way I'd come. The palais occupied a steep hill like a queen atop a throne, and the city spread out below in a vast tapestry, woven with the warp and weft of unfamiliar colors and sounds and smells.

Without knowing the way to the palais—and too embarrassed to ask—I found my way to the gates by sight alone, along alleyways and across parks and up endless flights of stairs. The Amber City was vast and vivid; each new sight and sound shivered through me like the thunderous pulse of a colossal heart.

Satins rippling with sky-lit colors: vermilion and magenta feathering toward a sapphire twilight. A mechanical eagle, twice as big as my head, with articulated wings and ambric eyes as red as the sun. Feral-eyed vendors selling bottled curses and stoppered wealth, mirrored kisses and scented secrets. Clear ponds full of giant lotus flowers, their silky-soft petals pale as the mythic Moon. Jewels and colored glass. Laughing children.

I sucked in a deep breath, letting the sweat dry on the nape of my neck. Up here, the air was clear and fresh—none of the wonderful, shifting scents of the city: perfume and garbage, cooking food and rotting fruit. Up here, everything was expensive and manicured. Controlled.

Perfect.

I curled my fingers into my frayed skirts. My heart beat an uneven pattern against my ribs, and I brushed a strand of greasy hair out of my eyes. A trickle of nerves raised gooseflesh along my arms.

I should have bathed before I came here.

To desire is to sin, Sister Anouk's voice whispered. *Be content with all you have.*

I should have prepared a speech.

Dreaming breeds misfortune. Sister Cathe. *Dominion shadows will seek you out.*

I should have—

No.

I forced the insidious whispers away. I had no reason to feel insecure. I belonged here. The exceptional blood in my veins flowed within the nobles who lived inside the palais. Even the empress herself, whose exquisite face hung in shopwindows and on banners across the city, was of that same bloodline. Meridian's royal, magical line. And if my uncaring parents hadn't dumped their infant in the Dusklands with nothing more than a vague note and an ambric amulet, I would have grown up in this world.

This should have been my home.

I marched forward before I could change my mind.

Beneath their shining helms, the Skyclad Gardes' eyes were flat and distant, registering me as neither threat nor interest. I approached one, taller than me by a head, muscled and powerful. Another worm of uncertainty wriggled along my spine, and my eyes skittered the length of the tall fence.

There had to be another way. Another gate, or a smaller door, or someone I could talk to—a palais liaison, or—

Stop it, Sylvie, I snarled at the coward sniveling in the back of my mind.

My face swam distorted in the poor mirror of the Garde's breastplate. The soldat finally registered my presence, glancing down her nose at me, a raggedy urchin covered in half the dust and grime of the Dusklands. Her lip curled into a sneer.

"Hello," I stammered, cursing the high squeak that emerged instead of my normal voice. "I'm here to join the court of the Amber Empress as a legacy. The Scion's bloodline flows through my veins."

The soldat cocked her head to one side, a tiny motion that nevertheless nearly sent me running back to the Mews. Smirking, the Garde banged a sword against her shield with an efficient clang, summoning a Skyclad officer from a small hut beside the gate. He strode forward, raising a hand to keep the sun from his eyes. He was young, but he wore his command around him like a cloak, his every movement breathing power and contempt. My skin itched with a chill when I saw his frown.

The Garde clicked her boots and gestured to me.

"A prankster, sir," she muttered.

"A prankster?" The officer's frown deepened. "What manner of prank did the girl play? I see no props or other silliness."

"She claims she is of the bloodline," explained the Garde, disdainful. "A legacy, sir. She wants to join the Imperial Court."

The officer's brows shot up toward his hairline before he

schooled his features into passivity. His eyes took in my ragged clothing, my unwashed hair, the grime collected beneath my fingernails. Heat climbed up my neck toward my cheeks.

"And what proof do you have, girl? Writ of birth? Patents of nobility? Anything to prove this absurd claim?"

"N-no," I said, hating the stutter in my voice. Humiliation flared through my veins, and I reached for the soothing planes of my ambric pendant. "All I have is my legacy. I can show you."

"Fine," snapped the officer. His eyes were keen on my face. "Make it good, or you'll be spending this Nocturne in the palais dungeons."

I scrubbed my palms against my skirts. I closed my eyes, listening for that familiar, faint buzzing. My palms tingled. I focused on an image, holding it in my mind's eye until I could see nothing else.

I held out my palms, and showed the officer something that wasn't there.

The same illusion I'd shown Luca: Coeur d'Or in miniature, delicate and gleaming and even more perfect than before. Spires of glass. Arches twisting with porcelain vines. The stunning golden gate, sunlit ambric glinting from the finial. I willed the illusion to hold, but like before, the toy-sized palais melted away in the space of a breath.

I dropped my arms, fighting a wave of dizziness.

The officer stared at the scraps of color evanescing into thin air.

"Worthless trick," he snarled. "Clockwork legerdemain. Ambric and mirrors. I've seen such things before, in the labs at Unitas. A person can even buy such an apparatus in the marchés of the Mews, if one has the money to pay."

Thunder roared in my ears, and I reeled a step back. *No.* I'd imagined a million different ways this day might go. Simply not being believed was never one of them.

"It's not a trick," I said, pouring the last of my strength into the words. "I'm not using a device. It's my legacy. I create illusions."

The officer hesitated, then threw back his head and laughed. The Garde did the same, her straight white teeth gleaming red in the ruddy light. The other Skyclad Gardes within earshot chuckled, shaking helmed heads.

"A worthy attempt," mocked the officer. "Leave now, and I won't punish you for it. Come here again, and I can't promise I'll be so lenient."

He turned on his heel and marched back toward the gate, his cloak swinging in the breeze and his laughter echoing in my ears.

"Wait!" Desperation was a living thing inside me, choking my lungs and squeezing my heart. "I can do better. I'm not lying!"

Something in my voice reached the officer. From across the courtyard, his eyes touched mine, and I thought I saw a glint of uncertainty in his cool gaze.

"Look at me," I ground out.

This time, when I closed my eyes, I let my mind soar through the days and weeks and spans, back to the Temple at the edge of nothing where I was abandoned as a baby. Back to the bullies who kicked me in the ribs when barely formed shapes and colors spilled unbidden from my hands. Back to the sanctimonious Sisters who prayed for hours over my unrighteous fingers.

What if we took them? I once overheard Sister Anouk whisper. She didn't seem to realize the careless cruelty of the suggestion. *The magic would go, and she'd have to stay.*

But I never believed the magic ended with my hands. And I don't think they did either.

I dug my ragged fingernails deep into the skin of my palms. My fingers tingled, but I ignored the feeling, concentrating instead on the space between my ears. Concentrating on the feeling of my skin, covering my muscles and bones. My face.

I hadn't looked into a mirror for a tide. I could almost forget what I looked like—my sable locks; my blue eyes, tinged with grey Duskland shadows. Instead, I imagined another face. A face I'd seen more times than I could count on my journey through the city.

A face with even skin and sharp cheekbones, framed in a luxuriant tumble of dark auburn hair. Lips stained rose red. Luminous eyes the precise color of heliotrope. And a circlet bedizened with a single jewel of flawless ambric.

A swarm of insects droned in my ears. The skin on my face prickled before my cheeks went numb.

I imagined I had that face. I imagined *I was* that face.

I lifted my eyes to the Skyclad officer.

Everything stopped. My breath caught in my throat, and I felt balanced on the edge of something terrible and beautiful and terrifying. I teetered, caught between one world and the next. The past, and the future, intersecting in this single, breathless instant on the cusp of failure and hope.

I toppled.

The courtyard broke out into chaos.

Blood drained from the officer's features. His mouth dropped open, and his palm fell limp by the hilt of his sword. The stocky Garde shouted, then dropped to one knee, her dristic armor clanging loud against the cobblestones. Behind her, other soldats did the same, dropping like a line of Vesh's precious dominos. A muffled whisper sprinted across the courtyard, followed by shouts of *Your Majesty!* and *It's the empress!*

The illusion melted away.

I knew I was me once again.

The officer sprinted toward me, fumbling at the hasp of his cloak. The silvery material bloomed around me, snapping and billowing. He wrapped the silky fabric over my shoulders and face until I couldn't see anything but his shadow, muted on the pale cobbles of the courtyard. I pushed at the cloak, but the officer reached out one gloved hand and captured both my wrists.

"Curse you," he hissed, his words razoring through the shroud of heavy fabric. Then, loudly: "Back to your posts, you ingrates! Have you forgotten your training?"

The Skyclad platoon snapped to attention, shuffling and straightening.

"You," muttered the officer. Polished boots stepped into my limited view. "Nothing happened here, do you understand me? If anyone speaks of this, they will be flogged."

A grunt of agreement. "What will you do with her?"

"Chevalier Devall. He'll know how to proceed."

"Dowser?" A low whistle. "Better hope her mind is stronger than her body looks."

Dread coiled in my belly as the officer tightened his gloved hands around my wrists. I opened my mouth to ask *Who is Dowser?* but the golden gates swung open, silencing me.

I passed between their ornate arms into the glittering heart of the Amber Empire.

EIGHT

O ut of sight of the gate, the Skyclad officer ripped the silvery cloak from my shoulders. His eyes weren't kind as he led me swiftly through the evolving labyrinth of the palais compound. Down shallow steps glinting with mica. Through a shimmering copse of jewel-flowered trees. Past a jardin that seemed to breathe in time to the distant chime of crystal bells. Gilded archways. Coiled staircases, golden and white. Stained glass. Mirrors. Chandeliers.

My mind spun at the blur of unfamiliar sights, and though I clung to each new image, I was soon overwhelmed. Struggling to keep up with the strident gait of my captor, I stumbled, my knees cracking against marble. I stared at my grimy hands splayed against the immaculate pattern twisting in the marble. A trickle of dread shivered along my spine, and I scraped my tongue around a mouth suddenly dry and foul-tasting.

"Get up," the officer commanded. I did as he said, swallowing my fear as he dragged me down yet another anonymous hallway. A long line of arms hewn from pale, translucent stone grasped guttering torches wrought in kembric. The officer burst through a hidden door and snapped to attention, raising his arm in a salute.

"Chevalier Devall!" he barked. "Pardon the interruption, but I bring you a matter of some urgency."

I squinted into the room. After all the white marble and gilt and blazing torches, the low-ceilinged chamber was dim and gloomy. A tall figure rose from the corner, face veiled in shadow.

A glowing ember flared, then faded as the person sucked smoke from a curving pipe.

"Is that so?" The man—Chevalier Devall, I assumed—spoke slowly, his deep voice rich and refined. "Please explain."

The Skyclad officer tersely recounted my behavior at the gates, but his words faded as I stared around the new room. A row of curtains shrouded a bank of windows—only a sliver of vermilion bled in from outside, illuminating dust motes suspended in the air. Books thronged jumbled bookcases. Vast spreads of paper swarmed the walls, but in the gloom I couldn't see their contents. Maps, perhaps. The scent of tabak hung like a pall in the room, tinged with a cloying perfume. I smothered a cough.

The officer and the chevalier fell silent, and when I looked up they were staring at me. I pushed a thread of hair behind my ear, and shifted my feet.

"You may go," said Chevalier Devall. The Skyclad officer bowed before stalking from the room. His steps echoed away, leaving me alone with the chevalier.

Anxiety twisted my stomach into a skein of knots. All I could see of Devall was the flare of his pipe. The stench of tabak clambered up my nostrils and sent sickly fingers down the back of my throat. I squeezed my eyes shut, fighting away nausea and a sudden feeling of weightlessness. When I opened them, the chevalier was standing right in front of me.

I muffled a shriek and lurched backward. Devall was tall, and broad in the shoulders. He wore a long, unadorned robe, like a monk or an ascetic. His bald pate was a smooth, deep brown—like polished ironwood—and his features were refined, almost severe. Lines sprayed from the corners of his eyes, and a deep furrow dug between his brows. His black eyes, hidden behind slender spectacles, betrayed no emotion.

"Your name."

"Sylvie, sir," I muttered. "I mean—Chevalier Devall—"

"Call me Dowser," he said. "Everyone else does."

"Dowser," I repeated, bobbing my head like an idiot.

"You traveled far," he said. It wasn't a question.

"Yes, sir," I managed. "From the Dusklands."

"A long journey. From the edge of Dominion to the heart of our empire. Because you believe you are special."

A cold hand stroked my spine, and I shivered.

He's just guessing.

"Maybe you are. But most likely you aren't. Few deserve what they were born with. Even fewer deserve what they weren't born with."

"I'm a legacy, sir," I managed, ignoring the fingers of ice caressing my heart. "I belong here. At Coeur d'Or. At the empress's court."

"Ambition—I like that." A precise smile creased Dowser's face. "But that exhibition you put on at the gates doesn't guarantee you are a legacy. Magic is not the sole domain of the highborn."

My head jerked up, my nostrils flaring.

"Surely you knew that." He studied me, not unkindly. "This world is full of strange things. The bewitching songs of the Gorma can just as easily lure a fish into a trap as they can dash a frigate against the rocks. I've known Aifiri who could bend metal with a touch. Among my people, the Zvar of the Meridian Desert, there are those who can command armies wrought from sand and nightmares. No, the bloodline of the Scion is not the only magic in this world."

"So I've come all this way for nothing?" I clenched my hands to stop them shaking with fury and embarrassment. "But—but I could be a valuable asset to the empress and her court. I create illusions—I can make you see things that aren't there. I could act as a double for the empress at public events, or perform for the people, or—"

"And what of your family?" Dowser interrupted. "Won't they miss you when you abandon them for wealth and prestige? Or perhaps they are in on the plot."

"I have no parents." My tongue was a lick of flame, turning my mouth to ash. "Only a highborn sire or dam who deserted me at the edge of the darkness and never returned."

"Interesting." Swift as a viper, Dowser reached out his hands and placed them on my temples.

"What are you doing?" I tried to jerk my head away, but his grip was like a vise.

"Didn't you wonder why they call me Dowser?" His expression flickered. "Because I dig deep, and what I find is nearly always precious. Now hold still. This won't be pleasant."

My mind imploded.

I might have screamed, but my own voice was distant, like an echo from another time. I fell inward, spiraling. I felt him there—here—dredging inside me, digging relentless fingers into the crevices of my being.

Images surged around me, a whirlwind tumble of noises and smells and sights and feelings. I couldn't breathe. I couldn't think. I was drowning beneath the cascade of my own memories.

And at the center of it all was Dowser, watching.

Sifting.

Luca smiling, reaching for my hand. Warmth. The Skyclad platoon. Violence. The shadowed dusk at the edge of nowhere. Home. The bruised clouds above Dominion, bright with slashes of silvery lightning. Frenzy. The slap of a dusty hand on my cheek. Pain. The smack of knees in packed dirt. Misery. Ugly laughter. *Monster.* The pointed toe of a boot in the ribs. Fear. My own urine, warming my trousers and staining the dust. Humiliation. A chilly Prime—

There.

The whirlwind slowed. A dingy, frigid room. Dull, livid light oozed from the window. An ancient desk. Heavy drawers creaking open beneath my hands, empty of anything but dust. One locked. I grabbed a bent letter opener, jamming the tip into the lock. *Snick. Click.*

There.

A sheaf of parchment lined in handwriting so elegant I barely recognized the language. My eyes skittered down the page, but my rudimentary skill in reading could only decipher half the words. *Remit of the empire . . . martial enmity . . . protective custody . . . Order of the Scion.* The sentences didn't make sense. The Imperial Insignia filled my eyes, ornate and unmistakable— a sunburst bigger than my hand, stamped in amber wax and gilded with kembric.

And below that, a signature scrawled in vermilion ink, looping and illegible. A puzzle to my squinting eyes.

The scene whirled away, scattering into dust. I rose, soaring up through the swarm of thoughts and images.

Me. Only me.

I stumbled, and fell to my knees. My breath was a harsh rasp. I swallowed a surge of bile.

Dowser took one shaky step back. His chest rose and fell as quickly as mine. He straightened the immaculate lines of his robe and swept one uneasy hand over his smooth crown.

"Show it to me." His voice was rough with gravel.

"I can't," I whispered, stricken. "They burned it—when I found it, the Sisters burned it. They thought it was the best way to keep me from leaving."

"There's something else. Let me see it."

Recollection poured over me, and I reached with shaking fingers for the only thing I truly owned—the only thing the Sisters never dared take. The only thing that was all mine.

The amulet hanging between my breasts, skin-warmed and timeworn.

I held it out, reluctant. The ambric pendant dangled from its chain, glowing faintly in the gloom of Dowser's study. I'd brushed it with my fingers so often that its sunburst shape was nearly obscured.

Dowser nodded, once. His face hardened with a decision.

"Put it away," he growled. "And get up."

"What does it mean?" I gasped, shoving the amulet beneath my shirt. "Who gave it to me? Whose signature was on that imperial decree?"

"Ambitious, and inquisitive," he said, but this time there was no humor in his tone. "The signature was mine. Now rise."

"*What?*" Surprise wrapped hands around my throat, nearly choking me. "You? How—"

"No more questions. Get up. We're going."

I dragged myself to my feet, cursing my trembling muscles. A waterfall of questions blotted out my thoughts. I came to the city to find the world where I belonged. I swore to myself I didn't give a Scion's eye who my parents were—why should I? They abandoned me, cast me off like nothing. But this—this was new.

Dowser signed the writ passing my guardianship to the Sisters. And even if I didn't care who my parents were . . . I did care *why* they abandoned me.

Dowser swept out of the study, a blot of shadow against the spill of saffron light gilding the marble hallway and stinging my eyes. I hurried to keep up with him.

"I hope you have a better trick than what you showed the Garde tucked up those filthy sleeves," Dowser said without looking at me. "They'll expect something more impressive."

"They?" I felt suddenly dizzy with hope and uncertainty. "Who? Where are we going?"

Dowser twisted to face me. In the ambric glow, his eyes gleamed red as the sun.

"I'm giving you what you said you wanted. I'm presenting you to the Amber Court."

NINE

Entering the Amber Atrium was like waking into a dream of paradise.

The spacious room was airy and full of colors. Potent sunlight streamed in through a curving ceiling paned with colored glass, tossing jewels across the creamy floor. Flowers spilled across walls and along fluted pillars, filling my nostrils with a dense perfume.

Arrayed along a series of shallow tiers rising toward the throne was the Amber Court, strutting and preening like exotic birds. Even the flowers seemed drab and plain beside these courtiers. Everyone was young, and lovely. Silk nestled against velvet, and satin whispered secrets to great sweeping feathers pinned to headdresses or draped along sleeves.

Courtiers lounged along divans and among scattered pillows, lithe and elegant, jeweled fingers waving and fans twisting. Soft chatter rustled the air. A young woman gowned in tangerine strummed at a lyre, while another girl with blue-tinged skin sang. The sound sent a frisson of delight tripping down my spine. A young lord with hair like glass tossed a glittering crystal decanter toward the ceiling, where it exploded in a cloud of glittering fragments. Prisms danced across the floor. When the shards hit the floor, the decanter was whole once more. I stared at a billow of opalescent orbs. A tangle of vines, sprouting roses that bloomed in seconds.

And perched above it all, like an orchid among weeds, sat Severine, the Amber Empress herself.

She was beautiful. Her neck was long and elegant, the imperious tilt of her chin softened by the gentle smile on her ruby lips. Dark auburn hair made complicated coils around her head. She wasn't wearing the famous ambric-set crown, only a simple circlet. The pale fabric of her dress caught a spill of colored light, and for a moment I could almost believe her gown itself was wrought from stained glass.

"Stay here," Dowser grunted. "Don't say or do anything unless I tell you to."

I jumped. I had nearly forgotten why I was here. Nervousness sent threads of fire stitching down my arms to itch against my palms. I squeezed them into fists.

Not yet.

Dowser cut through the jardin of indolent courtiers, severe as a raven among songbirds. He bowed to the empress, then stepped forward to whisper in her ear. She leaned toward him, and for a long moment they were still as a tableau. I thought suddenly of a moldy tapestry in the Temple of the Scion, an illustration of the story of Meridian and the beginning of the longest day.

Dark and light, side by side.

Night, reaching ever for the day, separated only by dusk.

The empress glanced at me.

Even from across the room, those violet eyes fastened on me with all the power and capability of the empire they presided over. I gasped, sucking in a sip of perfumed air. I was pinned to the spot, caught in the space between those eyes.

Finally, she looked away. I took a shuddering step back, my heart racing in my chest. The empress said one last thing to Dowser, then rose to her feet with a sighing sweep of her luxurious gown.

"Come closer, child," she called out, her voice sonorous as the Nocturne bell.

Nobles raised drowsy heads crowned in curls and braids and feathers. Jewels winked from hats and throats and hems and fingers. Red lips twisted into smiles and grimaces. A giggle sprinted around the room like a naughty child.

Embarrassment heated my blood, followed by an icy rage. I took one step, and the sound of my ragged boot on the priceless marble was like thunder in my ears. Another step. I climbed toward the throne. The court scattered before me, flower petals blown before a high wind. Fluttering fans hid smirks and winks.

I gritted my teeth so hard I thought my jaw would crack.

These are your people, I reminded myself. *This is your world.*

But I wasn't as sure as I'd been yesterday.

I paused a few tiers below the empress, and dropped into what I hoped was a passable curtsy. Another delicate laugh scampered to and fro. My fury grew cold and hard and smooth, a river stone polished by tides of wear.

The empress smiled down. This close, I could see she wasn't as young as her banners made her out to be, although she had many tides yet before she turned grey. Thirty, at least. Nearly twice my age, but certainly not yet old.

"So." She waved an iridescent fan in a lazy circle. Her eyes touched mine, but this time there was none of the forbidding power of an empress, only gentle humor. "My Dowser tells me you have an interesting secret to share with my court."

"Yes, Majesty," I forced out, my voice barely above a whisper.

"Why don't you tell us all?" Her fan made a sweeping motion to include the assembled courtiers. "We love a good secret, don't we?"

Someone shouted a mocking "Hear, hear!"

More laughter.

Nausea bloomed in my gut, hot and sour.

"She traveled far, Majesty," supplied Dowser, sensing my discomfort.

They all sense your discomfort, said a nasty voice within me.

"Pray tell us why?" cooed the empress.

"I'm a legacy," I managed. "I've come to join your court."

Stunned silence. Slippered feet shuffled on luxuriant carpets. Whispers coiled behind raised fans. I dared a glance over my shoulder, and saw nothing but eyes staring like livid jewels from a sea of blank porcelain masks.

The empress didn't flinch.

"Delightful!" She dropped me a slow wink. "Perhaps you'll favor us with a demonstration? I've been longing for a distraction from all these dull legacies you see before you."

A feminine titter scraped sharp nails down the back of my neck and struck sparks on my growing anger. They were making fun of me. The courtiers. The empress. Did Dowser bring me here to be humiliated? I sliced my gaze toward the black-robed chevalier, but his expression was shuttered behind the lenses of his spectacles.

Those poisonous courtiers will never accept someone like you. Luca's bitter words echoed in my ears, muffled only by the sick pounding of my own heartbeat.

What if I'd been wrong about where I was meant to belong?

No. I survived tides of indifferent Sisters locking me in my room just so they didn't have to look at me. When the ragtag Dusklander bullies called me *monster* and poked me with sharpened sticks, I snarled back. I escaped the creeping claws of Dominion, traveling spans with no money and little food. All for this—this world of enchantment and beauty and bright-eyed accomplishment. And it was exquisite. Astonishing, not because it existed, but because I hadn't even been able to imagine it without seeing it for myself.

I would just have to prove that I belonged here. That I deserved a place in this sunlit sanctuary filled with jewels and daydreams and perfect faces.

I let my eyes flutter shut. A distant hum drowned out my panicked thoughts. Images crowded against the backs of my eyelids. Colors. Pictures. Emotions. I discarded each in turn. Too small. Too ugly. Too obvious.

Until I was left with only one.

I remembered fire, and lithe limbs sliding through complicated choreography. Charred meat, hard eyes. A plucked luth. A flash of kembric chain and ambric dust.

And a story. A story of a wicked Sun, and an innocent Moon, and the god-king who changed the world forever.

My palms tingled, but I clenched them together, willing the tingle to spread up my arms. To creep toward my shoulders. To tease the nape of my neck.

I spread my arms, and thought of Dominion. That ominous shadow staining the horizon of my childhood home. I imagined it bigger. Purer. Consuming. I poured every ounce of anger and fear and confusion into that darkness. I *became* it.

Night poured out of my hands, thick and velvet. Impenetrable.

I strewed pebbles of silver into the blackness, pricking it with bright points of light.

A high whine filled my ears, drowning out a chorus of gasps. The illusion was barely bigger than the space between my arms, but it was greater than anything I'd ever attempted. Already I could feel it wearing on me.

My arms trembled. My breath gasped.

The ringing in my ears trebled, becoming something like a scream.

Not yet.

I had never seen the moon. No living soul had. So I made it like Noémie had described it, huge and glowing. Silver light streamed through the blackness, pale as marble and sharp as dristic. It sliced through the edges of the darkness and splintered against sunlight, scattering shards of mirrored glass and amber across the Atrium.

I held the illusion for one blistering, aching, tortuous moment.

And then I collapsed.

TEN

I flickered through the dusk. Words and images echoed in my head, distant and incomprehensible. Space seemed to expand and contract, breathing in time to my own exhalations. I tried to move, but I was held fast in the womb-like dark, buoyed by the amniotic embrace of silence and shadow.

Reality came thundering back.

Light and sounds and smells shredded my senses. I lurched onto my elbows.

"She's a fantast!" someone exclaimed.

"Dexter or Sinister?" The clink of coins.

". . . most *certainly* a trick!"

"What does she smell of?"

I tried to follow the flicker of confusing conversation. Smeared faces swam in and out of my sight, blurred and leering.

"Silence!"

The empress.

The conversation died away with a grumble.

"You are a surprise, aren't you?" The empress's smile still oozed benevolence, but there was a tightness around her eyes. "And such a mystery! Dowser claims your bloodline is true, but it seems so unlikely. An outcast, from the edge of the world! Your mother must have been unsuitable indeed for your father to go to such lengths to get rid of you."

The ensuing laughter heated my blood. I struggled to my feet to hide my blush.

"But of course you know a mere legacy isn't guaranteed a place at my court." Her fan flicked, like the tail of an irritable cat. "I've handpicked my court from among the children of my most powerful nobles. Each has something extraordinary to offer. Talent. Wit. *Beauty*."

She said the last with such languor that it inspired another round of laughter. I rolled a tongue around my dry mouth and bit back scorching fury. Part of my mind screamed at me to run, to escape this excruciating humiliation.

But another part reminded me that if I could only wait—*wait* a few painful moments longer—I might be deemed worthy enough to stay. To walk these halls and call this glory *home*.

"But your legacy is so unusual. A fantast, in the flesh! Perhaps an exception can be made." She tapped her lacquered fingernails. "Perhaps we can even make a game of it. Who fancies a wager?"

A male whoop shattered the silence, and I heard whispers and giggles. To my right, a shower of golden coins arced into a shaft of low light. The courtiers laughed as they shielded their faces from the fall of money. I glared at the kembric écu rolling toward my boots.

Those few coins were more money than I had seen in my entire life.

"This is how it will go," the empress went on. "The girl will join the court, provisionally. She will live among you until Carrousel, in three spans' time. During this period, she will work with Dowser to hone her legacy. Then, at the Fête du Carrousel, she will display what she has learned, and I will personally decide whether she is fit to join my court."

Hope loosened the dristic clamp around my chest.

"Here's the catch." She dropped her voice, and the nobles leaned in. "She has no money. No wardrobe. No breeding. For her to live in Coeur d'Or, one among you must sponsor her. If she earns a permanent place at court, you will be rewarded. If she doesn't, a portion of your personal fortune will be forfeit."

The metal vise tightened, squeezing my heart. I didn't know much about money, but as an untrained legacy I was probably worth little to these courtiers. No sane person would take such a wager.

"Not only that," she continued, a smile coiling in the corner of her mouth, "but whoever chooses to sponsor her also takes her on for their dynasty. Dexter or Sinister. If she succeeds, that dynasty will win my favor for an entire tide. If she doesn't—well, I will let the opposing dynasty choose the forfeit."

Heated conversation sprang up around the chamber, accompanied by a few vicious glances thrown across the hall.

I frowned. Dynasty? Dexter? Sinister? The words spilling from the empress's mouth had devolved into nonsense. I glanced back and forth between the young nobles, a flicker of memory teasing my mind.

Dexter. *Sinister.* Where had I heard those words before?

The image pounced. Another of the Sisters' moldering tapestries, recounting the story of the Scion's prized hounds. The dog that sat at his right hand was loyal but meek. The dog that sat at his left hand was protective but vicious. Their names were Dexter and Sinister.

Right hand. *Left hand.*

And that's when I saw it. Although the divide was not perfect, the courtiers sitting to the empress's right were arrayed in warm, pale colors. Cream. Rose. Apricot. And the courtiers to the left of the throne wore darker, richer hues. Indigo. Steel. Viridian.

A divide, in the empress's court. Two houses in opposition, always pitted against each other.

And me, thrown between them like a bone between two dogs.

"Well?" Severine's voice pealed out above the arguments and insults hissing across the Atrium. "Who will have her? Dexter? Your hearts must bleed for her plight. Or Sinister? Surely you sense the ambition seething within her. Perhaps she will surprise you."

Silence. I forced myself to look around the room, but the courtiers' eyes flicked away from mine like startled flutterwings.

Someone finally stepped forward. A young man, tall and lean and achingly handsome. He wore a doublet of deep violet. Fine brocade glimmered from the sleeves, and silver braid winked across the chest. A black surcoat hung from one louche shoulder, a stark contrast to his slash of white-gold hair.

Hope blossomed in my chest. Someone saw my value. I wasn't going to be cast back out onto the streets after all.

The lord glanced at me. His eyes—pale green edged in dristic—narrowed.

Pain slashed me from head to toe. Sudden. Fierce.

I opened my mouth to scream, but the pain was gone nearly as soon as it came. Nothing remained but a memory of cold, brilliant agony.

The lord's eyes drifted away. His fluid gesture to the empress spoke a subtle language I couldn't understand.

"I will, Majesty." His voice, though soft, rang across the room. "I will sponsor the fantast."

"You, Sunder!" Surprise tinged the empress's voice, and her eyebrows winged up, marring her perfect mask. "I confess you astonish me. You are willing to let her stand for Sinister?"

"You mistake me, Majesty." He bowed. I thought I detected a note of disdain in the line of his back. "I will sponsor her. But I sponsor her for *Dexter*."

"Dexter?" echoed the empress.

The queen's exclamation was underscored by a burst of noise from the Dexter side of the room, accompanied by a hiss of pleasure from Sinister. The young man rose from his bow with a flourish, the sculpted lines of his aristocratic face impassive.

A slab of granite sank into the pit of my stomach. It was one thing to be bandied about like a lame mare at auction. Another thing to be sponsored, but only for the opposing team. This young man—Sunder—was essentially wagering money that I would *fail*. And he was so certain I would fail on behalf of the opposing dynasty that he was willing to forfeit part of his personal fortune in the process.

How rich *was* this young courtier?

"I did not forbid such a thing, so I will let it stand!" The empress raised her voice above the clamor of protestations and congratulations. "Trust our Sunder to always find a way to improve upon a wager!"

She winked at Sunder, who inclined his pale head.

"Nevertheless, if not a sponsor, then the fantast will still need a mentor in Dexter." Her violet eyes scanned the room. "Lullaby. Present yourself!"

A slight girl with gleaming black hair to her waist detached herself from the Dexter side of the room and glided into a curtsy.

"You haven't been at court long yourself. You'll show our new little fantast how she is expected to behave in Coeur d'Or."

"Yes, Majesty." The girl's fluted voice was soothing, loosening the tightness in my chest.

"Keep close to her. I blame you for her mistakes," the empress said, turning back to her throne.

The girl approached on gliding feet, and I saw she was the one I'd noticed singing with the lyre. Against her spill of ink-dark hair, her blue-tinged skin was lovely and otherworldly. Her eyes were also blue, dotted with flecks of green. The expression in them was nothing but mutinous. My ribs clenched as her cool, soft hand circled my wrist.

"One more thing," called the empress. "What is your name, little Dusklander?"

I opened my mouth, but a thread of defiance tangled in my belly. I felt suddenly overexposed and outplayed. The minute I stepped into the Atrium I had ceded all control to these scheming nobles, who didn't seem to care who I was or where I truly belonged. I dared a glance at Dowser, the only person who knew my real name. He wasn't looking at me, but amber reflections danced from his spectacles, and I felt him listening.

I didn't want to tell them. Not the empress, not Sunder, not the girl who radiated anxiety beside me. I wanted to keep something for myself—one thing they couldn't take from me, even as I willingly stepped across the threshold into their world.

My world.

"Rina," I whispered, choosing on impulse the name of Luca's powerful, composed mother.

"A Tavendel name?" Severine's laughter chimed. "How

quaint. Perhaps you meant to present yourself at the stables, instead of the Atrium?"

A wave of amusement rippled in my ears. The empress smiled, pleased by her own joke.

"Well, *Rina*, we don't use our given names in Coeur d'Or. In my world, nothing is more important than your gifts, and how your legacies come together in service of my empire. Each member of the Amber Court has chosen a new name to reflect the spirit of their legacy. Even if you are only with us for a few short spans, I expect you to do the same."

The empress—and the rest of the court—turned waiting eyes on me. I reached for something—*anything*—that would do for a name. A word. A phrase. But only echoes danced in the empty cavern of my mind.

"I—" My voice rasped like gravel in my throat. I ran a tongue across my lips. "I don't know."

"Sunder?" The empress's voice was too sweet. "As her sponsor, perhaps you'll do the honor of choosing in her stead."

The lord stepped forward, and the vise around my ribs tightened. I should have chosen. Something. *Anything.* Because I had no doubt whatever this cold-eyed, pale-haired man chose, it would only be intended to cause me pain.

"She shall be called Mirage," drawled Sunder. "Because, like a mirage, she promises something that is likely not there. And because, with any luck, she will disappear as swiftly as the illusions she creates."

Fire flashed white-hot on my cheeks and roared in my ears, drowning out the accompanying roar of laughter from Sinister. I watched with slitted eyes as Sunder sketched a mocking bow, then turned to clasp gloved hands with a tall girl behind

him. Ice-blond hair looped high around her head, and her amethyst gown was edged in black velvet. She favored him with a
cool smile, then turned to pin me with eyes like emeralds.

I jerked my gaze away.

"Mirage it is." Severine sank into her chair, her expression
suddenly bored. "Now go, the both of you. You have much to
attend to. Neither of you will be expected at Salon this Nocturne."

The girl beside me—Lullaby—dropped another deep curtsy.
I didn't even make the attempt. Blood stung my palms and
rushed hot in my ears.

I allowed myself to be propelled toward the gilded doors at
the end of the Atrium. Lullaby's liquid eyes flickered toward
mine, silently begging for me to leave quietly. She could probably feel the hot jump of the pulse at my wrist. Or sense the anger
and humiliation rolling off me like yet another stench.

As the doors swept open, I skidded to a halt. Lullaby jerked
my wrist, but I twisted out of her grasp and turned to face the
chamber. Already, the nobles had returned to lounge on cushions and divans, limbs languid and heads swaying.

"And you, Majesty?" I called out. Defiance made me bold, and
for once my voice was strong and powerful. "Severine Sabourin,
Empress of the Amber Empire, Protectress of the Dusk, Warden
of the Shore, and Glory of the Setting Sun? What should I call
you, here in Coeur d'Or?"

The empress's smile was sharp: a blade forged from dristic
and whetted with secrets.

"If you're very, very clever, little Mirage," she said, "you'll
make sure to call me nothing at all."

ELEVEN

The door whispered shut behind us. Lullaby turned on me immediately, her lavender gown billowing.

"What was that?" she hissed in my face. "Are you absolutely mad?"

"Sorry," I muttered. Already that lunatic burst of daring was fading, leaving me hollowed out with unease. "I know I shouldn't have spoken so brazenly in front of the empress, but I—"

"Her *legacy*, you idiot," she spat. "Has your head grown bored of its place atop your neck?"

"What are you talking about?" Confusion chased away the last of my anger. "I don't know anything about her legacy."

"Scion be damned." Lullaby rocked back on her heels to study me with depthless eyes. "You really are a country gamine. Although I suppose you'd have to be ignorant, fighting your way into the palais like you did."

"This is where I belong." I squared my shoulders. "Isn't it?"

Her mouth twisted. She slid her eyes down the empty corridor.

"We have much to do." She turned on her heel, her movements graceful as a dancer's. I trotted to catch up, my ratty boots loud on the tile.

"There are rules here, *Mirage*," she muttered, emphasizing the strange syllables of my new name. "So many rules. I've been here two tides and I still don't know all the rules, much less when I'm allowed to break them. If you have any sense, you'll keep your head down and watch, and listen, and maybe you won't be ostracized or killed."

"Killed?"

"You think this is paradise. That we're all powerful and wealthy and beautiful." Lullaby's voice swelled with caustic humor as she swept through a portico and down a flight of gleaming stairs. "You're wrong. Living here is like living on the edge of a sword. One misstep and your reputation is ruined. And your reputation is the cheapest thing to lose."

Luca's words echoed through my mind. *They'll contaminate your soul with toxic games.* Unease tiptoed into my heart.

"You shouldn't have come." Lullaby's lovely face warped, then smoothed once more. "But you're here now, for the next few spans at least. So. The first rule is never—*ever*—allude to Severine's legacy. And that's exactly what you did when you asked for her court name. You're lucky you're still alive. The last lord who dared ask wasn't so lucky."

A shiver wrenched at my spine. "She had him executed?"

"Worse." Lullaby bared a set of small white teeth. "She set her dog on him."

"Her dog?"

"You're familiar with his name." Her gaze was full of blunt fear. *"Sunder."*

I stopped in the middle of the room, my head too full of thoughts to walk and think at the same time. Lullaby paused too, the set of her shoulders impatient. Around us, a living chamber of vine-wrapped pillars and leaf-drenched ceilings sighed in time to the trickle of a thousand clear rivulets branching across the floor.

"Sunder. Lullaby. *Mirage.*" I took a deep breath, as though I could absorb all the new information through my lungs. "What do the names mean?"

"The names represent the essence of a legacy. Take me: When

I sing, my song affects the emotions of those who listen. I can just as easily inspire a dance or encourage sleep. So—Lullaby. You are a fantast—your power lies in illusions. While your new name was intended as an insult, *Mirage* is nothing if not accurate."

"And Sunder?"

"Pain." Lullaby walked on, hiking her skirts to avoid the skitter of water across tile. "He can tear flesh from bones, rip limb from limb, tighten your skull until your brain liquefies. *Sunder.*"

I shuddered, remembering the slash of his hard eyes across my face. The shrieking pain in my mind, over nearly before it began.

Sunder. My sponsor. For better or for worse.

I couldn't help but think it was probably for worse.

"And Dexter? Sinister?" I hurried to catch up with Lullaby, who moved much quicker than her high-heeled slippers should allow. "The empress called them dynasties. Are they separated by blood?"

"No. Our dynasty represents our dispositions and motivations. I have seen siblings and cousins split between dynasties. Our dynasty is defined by who we are on the inside, not the manifestations of our legacies."

"So—" I chewed on my lip, remembering the bright garb of Dexter, and the sneering, calculating gazes of Sinister. "Dexter is good, and Sinister is evil?"

"I doubt Sinister would appreciate that judgment." Lullaby's soft bark was barely amused. "It's more complex than that. Take Blaze and Spark, for example. Their legacies manifest in essentially the same way—they both create fire. But while Blaze enjoys setting conflagrations to devour buildings and eat away at forests, Spark prefers sending glimmer-lights to dance spirals against the ceiling. Which of them do you think belongs to Dexter?"

"Spark?" I guessed.

"Exactly."

"But what about me? I didn't get to choose. Sunder sponsored me for Dexter."

"Don't remind me." Lullaby frowned over her shoulder. "Scion knows where someone like you belongs."

I buried a spasm of horror. "And why is everyone so young? No one looks older than twenty-five. Where are your parents?"

"Most of the highborn families keep to their estates, monitoring harvests and trade and taxes," said Lullaby. "Only the most beautiful and talented of the noble children are hand-selected to remain at court. Jewels in a crown."

Lullaby led me down a curving set of steps into a subterranean grotto set behind artfully tumbled boulders and a curtain of ferns. Hidden fountains filled the air with the sweet music of water. The scent of lilies hung heavy.

"Where are you taking me?" I whispered.

"The baths," Lullaby replied, with a faint twitch of her nose. "Now hush, and do as you're told. If you're even able."

Blood heated my face, but something stopped me from releasing the rising flood of angry words. I stared at my new mentor, chosen for me from Dexter at the empress's whim. For all her sharp words and sidelong glances, she spoke to me without scorn, and had answered my barrage of questions with no small degree of forbearance.

She was treating me like a peer. Like an *equal*.

She might find me dirty and rude and uncultured. But she wasn't trying to pretend that I didn't belong in Coeur d'Or.

Rose-scented steam from the baths caressed my skin, promising hot water and perfumed soap and escape from half a tide's sweat and grime. A keen burst of satisfaction warmed my chest, loosening my ribs and conjuring a smile to my face.

I made it. I crossed half an empire to find a world I'd only dreamed of, and it was more spectacular than I could have imagined. Despite Luca's misgivings and Lullaby's daunting words, I knew this was where I was meant to be. My legacy swarmed against my palms, a beguiling promise of a better future yet to come.

I'd made it to Coeur d'Or. I belonged here—I knew that. Now I just had to convince everyone else.

"A bath sounds lovely." I lifted my chin and tossed my head. "Lead the way."

TWELVE

The underground corridor opened into a broad, tiled chamber. Perfumed air caressed my face, hot with steam and lit with a thousand glowing ambric lamps.

Attendants led me behind a screened alcove, where my clothes were stripped away. The way they handled the foul scraps of my ancient dress, I doubted I'd ever see the garment again. I wrapped a panicked hand around my amulet when the attendant reached for it, but the girl pursed her lips and insisted I'd get it back when I finished bathing. She brushed out my hair with deft fingers, then, without warning, drenched me with a spray of lukewarm water. I spluttered and dashed the water out of my eyes, but another cascade drowned out my protestations.

By the time the attendant was finished with me, I was cleaner than I'd ever been. I reached for the robe by the door, but the girl slapped my hands away and gestured for me to return to the main bathing chamber.

I gritted my teeth, fighting a blush as I snatched a hanging towel.

I guess I needed a bath . . . before they would let me take a bath.

Lullaby was already in the steam-swirled pool. I clutched my towel closer when I noticed she was perfectly naked beneath the water. She laughed and sipped from a jeweled goblet.

"Another rural habit?" she asked, quirking a slender eyebrow. "Modesty is a choice, Mirage, but prudishness will get you nowhere in this place."

I sucked in a lungful of humid, fragrant air, then dropped the towel to my feet. I darted down shallow, tiled steps, only releasing my breath when I was safely neck-deep in warm water.

In the shards of light dancing around the chamber, Lullaby's eyes looked paler, and her skin deeper, so that they were both nearly the same color as the water. Her long black hair trailed behind her, twisting like a strange aquatic plant. Her gaze on my face was reflective.

"What?" I demanded. "Is something wrong?"

"Nothing," she murmured, then smiled. It was the first time I'd seen her smile, and it was lovely, like the sun breaking through a dark cloud. "You're passably pretty, you know. Although much too thin. Perhaps things aren't so dire after all."

She ducked her head beneath the water. A stream of tiny bubbles burst upward as she surfaced with a splash and a giggle.

"You seem . . . more relaxed," I ventured.

"I am." The thought seemed to sober her. She pushed sopping hair out of her eyes. "It's the water. I shouldn't let it get to me."

I stared at her, at the tint of her skin, the lively coil of her sleek hair. I'd never seen anyone who looked like her. Not that my life experience was particularly broad.

Lullaby caught my gaze, and blew out a loud sigh.

"By the Scion, you don't know anything, do you?"

"I didn't mean to offend you."

"It's all right." She grimaced. "People talk about it, but usually behind my back. Have you at least *heard* of the Blue Men of the Sousine?"

I had, in Luca's fanciful legends. Men with skin like blue ink; women with the scales of fish, and wings of glass.

"I didn't know they were real," I said. I reached for the twin to Lullaby's glass sitting on the edge of the pool, and breathed the aroma of sweet wine and rare spices. The cool liquid burst on my tongue.

"They are," said Lullaby, "although they call themselves Gorma, and they are neither as fearsome nor as magical as the stories tell. My father was one of them."

"Your *father*? How?"

"My mother is a baronne. She trades extensively in the Sousine Isles, along the empire's southern coast. She met my father on one of those journeys. They loved each other, but he would not leave his home. And she would not give up hers. And so they parted. But not before he gave me these." She touched her hands to her tinted cheeks. "These." She ran slim fingers along the lids of her cool eyes. "And this."

She opened her mouth, and sang. It was a song of overwhelming longing. It rippled through me, and suddenly all I could think of was the water. Of ducking my head beneath the surface. Feeling the warm liquid embrace me. Drifting between the currents. I slid down to the edge of the water. My chin touched the surface. I closed my eyes.

The song broke off. I blinked, my mouth half-open and filled with perfumed water.

"It's beautiful," I whispered, after I'd stopped choking. "I've never heard anything like it."

"Nor had anyone else." Bitterness spoiled the sweet tones of Lullaby's voice. "I only came to Coeur d'Or two tides ago. The empress has known of my legacy since I was a child, but my gift was stained with my father's origins. I wasn't *pure*. She didn't want me. Not until my mother secured trading rights with Lirias."

My brow furrowed at the sudden change in subject. "I don't understand."

"Of course you don't." Lullaby looked away. "Otherwise you never would have come here. We—the children of the empire's wealthiest noble families, gifted with unusual legacies—we are more than her court. We are her crown jewels. Hers to flaunt to the world, and use as she desires. But most importantly, we are her insurance."

"Insurance?" I echoed. I knew the word, but I'd never heard it used to refer to people.

Lullaby hesitated, dropping her voice to a whisper.

"We live here at the empress's pleasure. Our presence guarantees that our noble parents and families behave according to her wishes. Do you understand?"

I struggled to wrap my mind around this new information. "She keeps you all as hostages? But why?"

Lullaby smoothed her mouth into a smile. Her light laugh danced across the rippling surface of the warm water.

"Scion, how should I know?" she asked, loudly. Her gaze moved toward the pale-garbed attendants drifting like phantoms through the haze of steam and perfume. "I never pay attention to politics. Why should I, when there's so much fun to be had here in Coeur d'Or?"

I opened my mouth again, but the sudden flint in Lullaby's eyes silenced me. I subsided into the bath, a whirlpool of questions swirling in my mind. I ducked down, and as the surface of the water closed over my head I felt as though I was drowning in a world I had spent most of my life longing for.

Politics. Lies. Games.

I had yearned to be welcomed with open arms and kind words. No—I had *expected* it. And why wouldn't I? These were my people. This was my world.

But they didn't see it that way. I was an outsider to them—an unwanted complication dirtying the pristine floors of the palais. I could see it in Dowser's calculating eyes, in the empress's gentle, mocking smile. In the sneering gazes of Sinister, and in the pitying glances from Dexter.

I dashed water out of my eyes, and gazed up at marble pillars twisting toward a ceiling of cracked green agate. I breathed deep the scent of cleanliness, edged with the perfume of opulence—pomade and crushed pearls, privilege and entitlement. And I compared it to the taste of my own desire, thick as the sweet wine in my jeweled goblet.

This world still felt right to me. I knew it in the way my blood beat like a drum in my veins, bursting with possibility. In the way my insatiable mind inhaled the incredible magnitude of that first, tantalizing sip of *belonging*. And I knew it in the way my legacy glided soft against my fingertips, sifting shards of color between waves of liquid glass.

I curled my hands into fists, and made myself a promise. If this world liked games, then I'd learn the rules. If intrigue bought friends, then I'd collect secrets. If Dowser could teach me to control the kaleidoscope of colors blooming like jeweled flowers from my fingertips, then I'd endure the tabak stench of his gloomy chambers.

I would not falter.

And whether it was the wine or the wonder, I felt suddenly light-headed; the world pulsed against my eyes, tremulous with promise. I leaned back, letting the warm water buoy me up as the world spun on its axis. I drank in the mosaic of unfamiliar colors, painting their rich pigments upon the cadence of my heart: sun-streaked marble, sapphire water, emerald agate—

Sunder's eyes, green with poison, invaded my mind. I suppressed the shudder running from the tips of my ears down to the base of my spine.

No. Not even a man with pain in his gaze and chaos in his heart could stop me from earning the world I'd always deserved.

THIRTEEN

When the sweet wine was drunk and my limbs were so heavy I thought I might collapse, Lullaby led me to an overgrown courtyard striped in long ruby shadows. Gleaming stone pathways meandered toward terraced villas tucked behind lush foliage and trellised flowers.

"This is Lys Wing," Lullaby said. "All the Dexter girls live here."

"My lady." A severe woman appeared at Lullaby's elbow. The silver tray balanced on her gloved hand bore a slim envelope. "Lord Sunder's steward brought this."

"Madame is the châtelaine of Lys," Lullaby explained. Then, eagerly: "Promissory notes, I hope?"

"Not until the transaction is complete." The woman handed me the envelope without meeting my eyes.

I recognized my new name, inked in a hand so fine it sent a wave of helplessness coursing through my veins. *Transaction.* I turned the envelope over, fitting my thumb beneath the flap.

"In private!" Lullaby hissed at me, eyes narrow. "Are your manners really so vulgar?"

My hands stilled. My cheeks flamed.

"No promissory note?" Lullaby whispered to the châtelaine, a note of desperation straining her voice. "How on earth am I supposed to prepare her without money? Her failure falls on *my* head. I can't possibly afford one new dress for the girl, let alone a wardrobe!"

"Her Majesty has approved a line of credit in the meantime," murmured Madame. "Worry yourself with regard to the girl's wardrobe and comportment. I will handle the financials."

Lullaby inhaled, then stalked away across the shaded court-yard, her silky mane whispering around her shoulders. I hurried to catch up.

Tucked behind a screen of blooming vines, my new chambers were lovely. Coiling pillars braced carved stone archways. Gauzy drapes billowed in a fragrant breeze. Plush carpets caressed my tired feet. But that wasn't what made the chambers so wonderful.

On every surface in the room—from the walls, to the low tables set around the room, to the decorative finials above the door—flowers were painted in a deft, clever hand. Sun-tinged jessamin amid leaves of green. Shy violettes, hiding beneath sills. Gaudy columbine, stained with port. Not even the panes of the windows had escaped the artist's brush; muted sunlight splashed brilliant petals across the polished floor.

"Who did this?" I murmured, spinning in place to soak in the imaginary jardin. "Are all the rooms in Lys like this?"

"No," replied Lullaby. Her voice was choked and quiet, and I spun on my heel to look at her. To my surprise, tears prickled in her stricken eyes.

"Lullaby?" I asked, reaching a tentative hand toward her. "Are you all right?"

"Sorry," she whispered, dabbing moisture from her cheeks. "This was a friend's room. She painted these. The châtelaine must not have had time to remove them before you arrived."

"Why would I want them removed?" Shock made my voice shrill. "Please let Madame know I want them to stay. They're beautiful."

"They are, aren't they?" Lullaby took one more look around the room before setting her jaw. "I'll need to put in a rush order for gowns. Blues, I think, to match your eyes. Be prepared to rise with first Matin. We must transform you into a lady before we can present you at court again."

She half turned. Her gaze narrowed on my chest, where my ambric amulet swayed. She curled her fingers around its time-polished curves. "What is this?"

"Oh." Apprehension coiled a hand around my spine. I remembered the heavy twist of Dowser's expression when I showed him the amulet. What if the pendant meant something to Lullaby as well? "It's just something I wear for luck."

"It looks old." Lullaby released the necklace to thud against my rib cage like an extra heartbeat. Her lip twisted. "And ugly. The empress would hate it. Never wear it again."

Relief tinged with outrage stained my cheeks. Lullaby turned on her heel.

"Lullaby!" I pushed away thoughts of Dowser and the amulet I'd worn since birth. I thought of the vow I'd made myself: my personal pledge to earn my place at Coeur d'Or, at whatever cost. If I wanted this mentorship to work—if I wanted Lullaby to support me, to fight for me to succeed as hard as I intended to fight—then I would need her friendship. I *wanted* her friendship. "Your friend. What's her name?"

Lullaby paused with one hand on the door. Her inky hair floated around her shoulders as she bowed her head.

"Her name was Blossom." Her voice was so quiet I could barely hear her.

"You said these were her rooms. Where is she now?"

Silence hung taut between us, and for a moment I thought

Lullaby wasn't going to answer me. Then her hands tightened on the doorknob, and she fixed me with eyes as forbidding as the shadows cloaking the Midnight Dominion.

"She's gone," Lullaby whispered. "And unless we're both careful, we can expect the great pleasure of following right behind her."

She swept from the room with a whisper of silky skirts and resentment, leaving me alone in a fanciful jardin of made-up flowers, the only memorial to a girl who no longer existed.

A finger of trepidation trailed down my spine. *Gone.*

Whether that meant banishment, death, or worse, I dared not guess. I just knew I would do everything in my power to escape that fate.

My hands shook as I dragged the brittle chain of my amulet over my head. I stared at it, memorizing its soft edges and burnished patina. Then I crossed to my bed and shoved the pendant beneath the soft mattress, ignoring the needle of regret piercing my heart. I already missed the comfort of its warm weight between my breasts.

I would do what needed to be done. If this world required Mirage, then I would forget Sylvie. I would abandon her in the Dusklands with the indifferent Sisters and the cruel, ignorant children. I would say goodbye to her in the bustling courtyard of an ambric warehouse. I would sponge her off and scour her clean, until she was exactly who she needed to be.

I'd gone from *nowhere* to being *here.* The last thing I wanted was to be *gone.*

FOURTEEN

I woke to the disorienting splash of colored light across my face. For a long moment, I thought I was back in Madame Rina's transport, with the livid light of a dying sun peering between colored curtains. But then the bright, clear chime of first Matin pealed through the chamber, and I remembered.

Coeur d'Or. I was in the palais of the Amber Empress.

Excitement tainted with anxiety surged through my veins, and my eyes snapped open. A young woman in a servant's uniform smoothed open another set of drapes, letting a necklace of bright jewels spill across the marble floor.

"Time to rise, my lady," said the girl, bobbing a quick curtsy toward the bed. I glimpsed dark hair pulled away from a soft-featured face. "Apologies, but the châtelaine made it clear you must awaken early this Matin."

"I'm up," I murmured, watching the girl move through the room with practiced efficiency. "Who are you?"

"I'm head of your personal staff, my lady," she replied. "I'll coordinate your wardrobe, activities, and appointments, as well as any other errands you require. Your staff includes two other handmaidens to dress you, plus access to the entire staff of Lys Wing, as necessity demands."

"My—my staff?" The words felt strange in my mouth. Staff meant *servants*. Entitlement waged war with mute horror. *What would Luca think?* I shoved the thought away. "Why do I need so many handmaidens?"

The girl ducked her head to hide the smile stretching the corner of her mouth. "I assure you, my lady, three servants is fewer than customary."

My lady. Those two words wakened a foreign thrill in a chilly corner of my heart. I'd spent more than a few dim, lonely Nocturnes dreaming of servants and soft pillows, hot meals and heeled slippers. I twisted my fingers in the fine sheets and waited to feel guilty.

"Do you have to call me that? It sounds so—so formal."

"And what would my lady prefer instead?"

"My name is—" *Sylvie.* No, it wasn't. I snagged my lip between my teeth. "Mirage. Call me Mirage."

"Of course," she replied, impassive. I studied her face, bleached pale by the faded sunlight streaming through the window. Did she know I was different from the other courtiers? I searched for some sign that she saw me as just another girl—a commoner, like her, from the edge of the daylight world.

But you're not just another girl, whispered the voice deep inside me. The voice that made me run away from the Sisters and stow away on a convoy. The voice that made me leave Luca behind in the Mews. The voice that longed for kembric fancies and dristic smiles; a million ambric dreams honed on sheer impossibility. *You belong here.*

"And what's your name?" I asked, mostly to smother the mess of uncertainty roiling within me.

I saw surprise behind the girl's deferent brown eyes. But then she returned to her task, arranging a bouquet of lilies in a crystal vase.

"My mother calls me Louise, my lady," she said, at last. "But here in the palais they mostly call me 'You, Girl.'"

Horror flickered through me, followed by a flash of amusement. *My servant made a joke.*

"Louise," I said, choking on a laugh. "I think we're going to get on just fine."

"You say that now," said Louise, and a smile transformed her face. "Let's see how you feel after I have a go at your hair."

Two other handmaidens bustled into my chambers, laden with fabric and jewels and enough cosmetics to make my head spin. I jumped out of bed, itching to feel the fabrics beneath my fingers, the sheer breadth of color against my skin. But I was summarily deflected. The girls maneuvered me into layers of garments, pulling and prodding and cinching until I felt like livestock trussed for slaughter. I might be seventeen tides old, but I was apparently not expected to dress myself.

"What do I call you?" I gasped between brutal tightenings of the torture device they'd strapped around my waist. "Louise says I shouldn't ask, but it seems odd that you've seen me undressed and I don't even know your names."

The girls darted glances at each other. One was tall, with dark circles beneath her pale eyes. The other was plump and pretty, but her fine mouth wore a pout.

"I'm Matilde, m'lady," said the tall girl, her voice timid. "And this is Elodie."

Elodie gave me a tight smile before returning to her task of making my waist as small as possible. Fortunately for her, I'd barely eaten in the past few spans, so I was thinner than I ought to be. The thought conjured up a sudden image of Luca, grinning like a fool as he snuck me tidbits from his and Vesh's dinner. Barely more than crumbs, but more than the nothing I had to eat. A sour hand squeezed at my throat. I clenched my eyes shut and pushed the memory away.

I certainly wouldn't go hungry here.

After I was dressed and cinched to the girls' satisfaction, they began my cosmetics while Louise tore my hair out by the roots.

At least, that's what it felt like.

Louise's touch was even less gentle than she promised. My scalp screamed as she twisted and yanked, grumbling the whole time. My strands were nowhere near her standards, which I imagined were the glossy, thick, impeccable strands of the wealthy and well fed.

"At least it's long," she muttered, and I knew that was as close to a compliment as I was going to get.

Elodie smeared creams across my face, staining my cheeks and lining my lashes until tears prickled at my eyes and threatened to spill down my newly painted face.

"Don't you dare cry," Elodie hissed, her eyes dangerously insolent. And in that moment I realized she must know what I was and where I came from, and that she hated me for striving, hated me for climbing, and most of all, hated me for achieving what she never could.

I pasted a look of cool serenity on my painted face and ignored the roiling sea of pride and shame and ambition carving out my insides.

Finally, the girls moved back, their work finished. Three sets of eyes examined me as I swiveled my head, unused to the heavy weight of my hair. I took a tentative step in my heeled slippers. Dense layers of fabric rustled against the tile. I craned my neck, looking for a mirror.

Instead, I found the face of a stranger in a pane of polished glass. A lady, with blue-grey eyes framed by long black lashes. Lush-dark curls piled high above a flaming splash of vermilion feathers. Lips as red as the rubies strung around her neck. Cream lace frothing above the collar of a carmine gown.

I pressed my palms together, but there was no buzzing in my ears, no restless itch. This was no illusion.

At least, not one made by me. Pleasure swaddled me in warmth.

"You'll do," said Louise, and I thought I heard a note of satisfaction in her dry tone. "Now the lady Lullaby requires you in her chambers for breakfast."

At the mention of breakfast, my stomach growled, hungry as a wild animal. I realized with sudden horror that Elodie had left no room for anything resembling food to pass between the stalwart stays of my corset. She smirked, as though reading my thoughts, then dropped a mocking curtsy before disappearing into an alcove with the other girls.

I sucked in as much air as the corset would allow, and took a tentative step toward the door. Every step was strange in this costume; my body felt as though it had been dissolved and reconstituted in some new configuration. My feet felt small, pointed and delicate. The corset and the tight sleeves of the gown forced my shoulders up and back. The tower of hair balanced on my head required me to hold my neck long and straight. Even my center of balance had changed, tightening my hips and lengthening my spine.

I was newly made.

Sudden melancholy swept over me, prickling my skin with hot little fingers. I spun, searching for something—*anything*—in these chambers to remind me of my old life. Of the old me. But everything I saw was beautiful and spectacularly expensive, crafted with skill and purchased with unimaginable wealth. Even the press of painted flowers was a constant reminder that *this was not mine.*

Why not? I railed against the traitorous thoughts diffusing doubt through my mind. Why should I lament a change I myself had fostered? Why should I apologize for seeking, for striving, for transforming? I was evolving. Every step I took was a step *away* from a life I hadn't chosen, *toward* a life I had. A life bursting with wealth and wonder and a thousand unimaginable possibilities.

The bell chimed for third Matin as I moved out into the shaded jardins of Lys Wing. Half-masked by crimson-streaked clouds, the brassy sun sent spears of muted light to stripe the pebbled pathways. Gentian and cerise slapped against my full skirts, raining petals behind me. The sight of the broken flowers conjured thoughts of Blossom, Lullaby's erstwhile friend.

Gone.

I shoved the thought away as a servant in what I was beginning to recognize as the uniform of Lys Wing bowed me into Lullaby's room.

Lullaby's chambers were laid out like mine, but instead of being decorated in a thousand imaginary flowers, hers were drenched in shades of blue. Cerulean glass paned the windows, striping the walls in aqua. Gossamer drapes undulated in the breeze, casting shadows across the floor. My palms itched with fluid fancies.

"It reminds me of the sea," Lullaby said. "It's soothing."

The rumpled mess of Lullaby's inky hair and her gaping yawn told me she'd just risen. One of her servants draped a dressing gown over her outstretched arms. She meandered toward a low table set with platters of fragrant buns and carafes of steaming liquid, then plopped into a plush chair and shoved a cake into her mouth.

My stomach growled again, louder than before. Lullaby glanced toward me. Her sleepy eyes widened and her mouth popped open, revealing her half-chewed breakfast.

"What?" I snapped, hunger quickly transforming into resentment. When would these people stop staring at me like I was a curiosity?

"Nothing," muttered Lullaby, but her eyes didn't leave my face as she devoured another bun. "Your girls didn't disappoint. You look—well, *beautiful*."

"Oh." Her words cooled the indignation boiling inside me, but only barely. Her loose hair and breezy dressing gown reminded me of the satin prison compressing my ribs. "Why did I have to get primped and prodded at first Matin, when you got to sleep in?"

"Sleep in?" Lullaby snorted. "This is the earliest I've been awake since arriving at Coeur d'Or. Even the early risers don't get up until at least Prime."

"Why not?"

"Because most of us have been feasting and drinking and dancing until the last hours of Nocturne," explained Lullaby drily. "You'll see."

I mulled over this new information as I reached for a bun that smelled as delicious as it looked sticky. But Lullaby slapped my hand away, hard.

"Scion's teeth! What was that for?" I demanded, cradling my stinging wrist.

"You're not here for breakfast," said Lullaby, and I saw a wicked light ignite in her liquid eyes. "And I didn't crawl out of bed at third Matin to watch you stuff your face. You're here to learn court manners, and that's your first lesson."

"I'll be damned—"

"Ladies never curse. Second lesson."

Fire burned my cheeks, and I dug newly buffed nails into my calloused palm. "I haven't eaten since yesterday."

"Then you should have asked your staff to feed you. That's why they're there." Lullaby's eyes softened when she saw the expression on my face. "Oh, fine. I'll tell you what—we'll make a game out of it. Yet another court lesson for you—when there's an opportunity to make a game or wager out of something, take it."

"A game?"

"A game." Lullaby's mouth quirked. "Today we're covering comportment and address. For every question you answer correctly, or task you perform well, I will reward you with an item of food or a sip of tea. Will that do?"

Humiliation battled with hunger. Hunger won.

"I'll play your game," I huffed. Both sides of the wager were in my best interest. I was desperate to master Lullaby's refined graces, and I was starving to boot. Still, pride flared hot in my belly, souring whatever pleasure I'd anticipated in learning how to play courtly games. "But I won't like it."

"Fourth lesson," crooned Lullaby. "Never, *ever* let anyone know you're not enjoying something. That will only make *them* enjoy it more."

And so began the first of many lessons on manners and courtly conduct. Curtsies, *depth* of curtsies, angle of the head, and inflection of the wrist. Unending lists of the types of nobility, and the customary address for said nobles. Duc de Beltoire: *Your Grace*. Comptesse L'Aumont: *Your Ladyship*.

"But *why*?" I asked, around a mouthful of berries Lullaby had grudgingly doled out as the reward for a curtsy she deemed *not the worst*. "If everyone at court uses their dynasty names, why do I need to know how to address them by their official names?"

"It's hard to explain." Lullaby pursed her lips. "Sometimes the most important reason for understanding a courtly convention is knowing when and how the rule may be broken. Does that make sense?"

"Not at all!"

"Comportment matters, but only *really* matters when someone *isn't* doing it. Because when everyone knows the rules of *politesse*, any breach in decorum is always intentional. If I, as the illegitimate daughter of a baronne, know I'm required to curtsy lower to a duchesse, with a deferential twist of my chin, like so"—Lullaby dipped into a graceful, almost obsequious bow—"but I choose instead to curtsy as to a peer, without lowering my gaze"—she adjusted her bow, rising up and adding an insolent inflection to her chin.

"It's an insult," I finished. Realization dawned as I watched the subtle effect of Lullaby's movements. "By going against the protocol of decorum, you're insulting the person you're meant to be paying your respects to."

"Exactly." Lullaby sank back into her chair, sipping on her fragrant kachua. "But most courtiers learn these subtle rules from birth. So trust me when I say you're better off watching and listening until, well, forever. The only thing worse than insulting someone intentionally is insulting them accidentally."

I slid into a clumsy curtsy, trying to mimic Lullaby's gestures.

I felt anything but graceful; with sweat prickling at the base of my neck and unruly tresses slipping out of my careful coiffure, I felt like a dirty swine who'd accidentally stumbled into a stable of fine thoroughbreds.

"Mirage?" Lullaby rolled her eyes at my poor attempt at poise. "I'm going to say that again, in case you weren't listening. Please, *please*, whatever you do—don't insult anyone. Not the empress, not Sinister, not even your servants. Do you understand me?"

I nodded, slowly. But when Lullaby turned away to demonstrate yet another form of social grace, I couldn't help but catch my lip and worry it between my teeth, fighting a rush of resentment and humiliation that was beginning to feel familiar.

I knew this was where I belonged. But would I ever be able to learn the intricacies of a life I wasn't born to? And if I couldn't, how long until the gilded teeth of this opulent court chewed me up and spat me back out into the dusk?

FIFTEEN

When the bell chimed second Prime and the sweet buns from breakfast were a fond but distant memory, Lullaby dismissed me back to my chambers. Due to my being a *shockingly rude and graceless rustic*, Lullaby had requested we both be excused from all court gatherings until I was fit to be presented. Which meant we'd be training together, dining together, and—if yesterday was any indication—bathing together.

Lullaby seemed less enthused by the prospect than I was.

"Go explore, or read, or practice your legacy," Lullaby sighed when I asked what I was meant to do until our next lesson. "Sleep, for all I care. Just don't bother me."

So I eased my way along the perfumed paths of Lys toward my chambers. There were signs of life among the residences; delicate laughter wafted from an open window, and more servants flitted between the shadows.

My own rooms were empty save for a breeze sweeping the pale curtains. I let out a disappointed breath; I'd hoped Louise might take mercy on me and unlace the Scion-cursed contraption squeezing my waist into oblivion. I wandered into the parlor area, my heart leaping when I saw the plate of dried fruit and breads laid out on the low table. I sank to my knees, gobbling down delicacies with an aplomb that would disgrace Lullaby.

My chewing slowed when I saw the envelopes laid out beside the decanters of fruit juice. The first was familiar: a small, cream-colored note addressed in a spiky, effortless hand. The delicious bread turned to ash in my mouth when the châtelaine's words echoed in my mind: *Not until the transaction is complete.*

Sunder.

I remembered his sharp, aristocratic profile, his slash of white-gold hair. What exactly did he think he paid for? Outrage soured with shame rolled over me, and I scraped my tongue around my mouth. I pushed the envelope away, ignoring the dread coiling in my belly like a poisoned serpent. I had no desire to learn what my so-called sponsor wanted in exchange for the funds he'd promised.

The second envelope was larger, exuding the faint scent of tabak smoke and leather.

Dowser.

I tore open the letter, letting the envelope flutter to the floor. Heavily inked letters stared back at me, and I squinted with the effort of making out the words.

Mirage—
Welcome to the palais. Your training will begin at once. Make
your way to my chambers at your earliest convenience.
Dowser

A thread of excitement stitched its way down my spine.

Finally. I hadn't forgotten that the terms of my arrangement required me to hone my legacy as well as my courtly skills. How could I? Curtsies and niceties would help me fit in at court, but my true worth—the reason I belonged here at Coeur d'Or—lay in the secret of my blood. My legacy—the gauzy visions spilling from my fingers like half-remembered dreams, jewel-bright but whisper-thin.

Dowser would show me how to improve and control my powers.

A different thought brushed chilly fingers against my heart. Dowser also knew why I'd been abandoned in the dusk. Scion, he might've even been the one who left me there.

That's not why you're here, I hissed at the frigid specter of ancient heartache. Nothing in my past was of any use to me here. I'd come this far using only my wits, my determination, and my legacy. I didn't intend to start looking backward now.

I paused only to shove Sunder's hateful note into the pocket of my skirts before striding out into the jardins of Lys Wing, through the shaded grotto and up a shallow flight of stairs, beneath a veiled entryway and toward—

I stopped, my heeled slippers skittering on the slick floor. This hallway looked unfamiliar. I glanced behind me, but I'd already lost sight of Lys Wing. I tried to conjure up memories from yesterday, when Lullaby led me from the Atrium to Lys, but all I remembered was a jumbled hodgepodge of gleaming floors and burnished ceilings and carved reliefs.

I had no idea where I was going.

And there was no one around to ask.

I took a few tentative steps. A pillared arcade opened out to a vast botanical jardin stretching toward the distant roofs of the Amber City. Grassy boulevards bordered glassy ponds. Pruned hedges twisted into shapes so lifelike I could almost believe they were real: a Skyclad chevalier atop a rearing destrier; a dancing maiden; a strange, hulking beast with a nose so long it twisted like an arm. And beyond that, a pretty wilderness of fruit trees and flowering shrubs whispering secrets into the warm air.

I was so enchanted I almost didn't notice the sound of

footsteps behind me. I whipped my head around, eager to find someone who might be able to show me how to navigate this lavish labyrinth. I spotted a slender, velvet-clad back quickly retreating behind the colonnade of tiered archways.

"Hey! Wait!" I gathered up my cumbersome skirts and dashed forward. The loud staccato of my heels on tile caught the man's attention more than my shouts, and he turned, raising his hands in surprise as I skidded to a halt in front of him.

"Thank the Scion," I gasped between shallow breaths. The corset was cutting off my air supply, and a wicked stitch sliced my side. I bent over, pressing a hand to my rib cage. "I might have wandered forever in this maze if it wasn't for you."

"I beg your pardon?" The gentleman's voice was tinged with concern. "Mademoiselle, are you unwell?"

"No, it's just this damned—" The words died in my throat when I glanced up into the face of the most handsome man I'd ever seen.

He was obviously a courtier, dressed in a stylish dove-grey coat over a shirt of dark blue silk. Ambric and sapphires glittered from the hand he extended toward me, and iridescent feathers in green and blue swept from a rakish hat perched on bronze curls. Hazel eyes blinked from a richly tanned face dusted in freckles. Plush lips parted in surprised amusement.

"This damned *what*?" he prompted, with barely contained laughter. "And is it alone in its damnation, my lady, or can I expect a similar fate?"

"Sorry, I shouldn't have said that," I managed, straightening to my full height. I pushed back an unruly strand of hair and forced myself to stop staring at his perfect features. "I've been admonished that ladies shouldn't curse. I've also been told that ladies oughtn't talk about their underthings."

The man stared at me for a moment longer before throwing his head back and letting loose a whoop of laughter.

"Well, aren't you a fresh breeze in a stuffy room," he smiled. His eyes skimmed my face before examining my new gown, the cobweb-thin bangles whispering around my wrists, the blunt nails on my tanned hands. "You can only be the new legacy everyone is talking about."

"Is it that obvious?" I fought the urge to pull an unladylike face, and hid my rough hands in my skirts instead. "Do I still have dirt stuck under my fingernails?"

"Not at all." His eyes softened on mine. "Rather, I cannot help but remark on such a beautiful new face when I've been sur-rounded by the same hundred people since I was born."

I ducked my chin to hide the stain heating my cheeks. I assumed it was courtly flattery, but after yesterday's dubious welcome, it was more kindness than I'd been taught to expect.

"May I ask what you're doing out here alone?" He graciously ignored my blush. "And why you feel the need to go chasing after strangers along the Esplanade?"

"I'm lost," I explained. "I was trying to find the way to Dowser's chambers, but this palais is a maze. I hoped you might be able to point the way."

"Indeed," he murmured. He bowed absurdly low, sending his gaudy feathers flying. "Perhaps the lady will allow me to do even better, and lead her to her destination?"

I stared at the handsome lord, and swallowed hard. Already, Lullaby's lessons on comportment and decorum had flown from my head, leaving me with the awkward knowledge that I was almost certainly missing important social cues.

"You were on your way somewhere," I hedged.

"Nonsense." A broad smile creased his face, displaying a row of white teeth. "Allow me."

He proffered an arm clad in richest velvet and ringed with jewels. I hesitated the briefest second before reaching out and grabbing his arm with my hand.

"Easy!" he said, grin widening. "I'm not a crutch. Here: lightly, and from the inside."

Deftly, he showed me how to tuck my hand into the crook of his elbow, drawing me closer against him in the process. A rich, spicy perfume filled my nostrils, along with a subtler scent, like burnt grass. He led me firmly in the opposite direction, away from the open arcade and the sweeping jardins.

"I'm sorry," I blurted after a few minutes of walking in silence. "I apologize if I've offended you in any way. I barely know anything about courtly protocol."

"I noticed," he chuckled. "But I find it endearing. It serves to make the rest of us look rather foolish, prancing and bowing and preening like so many perfumed *paons*."

"*Paons*?"

"Ornamental birds we keep in menageries," he explained. "Slender and serene, with great sweeping tail feathers in kembric and blue. Ridiculous, as they cannot fly."

"Ridiculous?" I eyed the drooping feathers on his hat, and decided to lie. "Impossible. And I've seen the court. I can't imagine ever being so graceful and elegant."

"You're making a lively start, my lady," he said, with an incline of his plumed head.

A curving staircase choked in wisteria stole my breath for a few moments, and I took the time to mull over my new acquaintance's words. While his fashion and demeanor marked him as a courtier, he didn't seem overly concerned with my poor manners or rustic bearing. My behavior in the past few minutes would have sent poor Lullaby into a fit.

"I hate to pry, but you didn't recognize me when we met back in the hall," I said. "Weren't you in the Atrium yesterday? When I asked the empress for a place at court?"

"Ask?" he echoed. "From what I heard, your *request* took the form of an unmitigated demand, my lady Mirage. But no—I wasn't in the Atrium yesterday."

"Why not?"

"We take it in shifts."

"Why?"

"To better fulfill our great ruler's demands on us, of course." The smile on his face remained even despite a sudden tightness around his eyes. "And so she doesn't grow weary of our tiresome faces."

"Is that likely to happen?"

"It's happened before." He dropped me a sideways wink. "Although with such a face as yours the empress will surely be clamoring to see you more often than the rest of us."

I frowned, trying to see past the flattery.

"It's happened before?"

His laugh was a few seconds too late.

"Of course not. Merely a figure of speech, my lady." He released my elbow and bowed toward a passage glowing with quartz, where milky statues cupped blazing torches. "I'm afraid I must leave you for other, far less enjoyable pursuits. But Dowser's chambers are just down this hall."

"Oh!" A glimmer of recognition sparked in my mind. "Thanks for your guidance. I don't know how to repay you."

"No need. Your company is payment enough."

He dipped into another ludicrous bow, the feathers on his hat dancing. I tried to smile at the handsome man, but the expression felt forced. Beneath his courtly demeanor, I sensed he was avoiding some truth with his careful words.

"Then I am in your debt."

"And I yours."

He turned to go. And as his velvet-clad back disappeared between the crystalline chancels edging the luminous hallway, I remembered my vow to do whatever necessary to earn my place in this court of wagers and intrigue. As Lullaby had pointed out countless times, I was an unsophisticated gamine with no skill for secrets. I could use a friend like him. Someone shrewd, and glib, with a skill for flattery and a notion for guile.

It also didn't hurt that he hadn't been expressly ordered by an empress to treat me with civility.

"Wait!" I called. "One more thing!"

He spun, hazel eyes ripe with cautious curiosity.

"Your name," I said. "You never told me your name. I ought to know who to ask for when it comes time to repay my favor."

"Ah." The perfect smile faltered once more. "Of course. The empress and her court see fit to call me Reaper."

"Reaper?" I frowned. The name seemed uncharacteristic of the smiling, flattering young man standing before me. What could such a name represent? I imagined shining scythes cutting through fields of golden wheat, stealing plenty from the earth. My palms itched, scored by invisible blades.

"But since we're friends," he continued, reading the uncertainty on my face, "I hope you'll call me by my given name—Thibo." He brushed my chin with soft-gloved fingers. "Our little secret."

I meandered toward Dowser's rooms, lost in thought. I'd only spoken to a few courtiers at the Amber Court, but both Lullaby and Reaper seemed consumed with an inner turmoil I found puzzling. In the bloom-beribboned Atrium, everyone had seemed content in the luxury of the palais. And why wouldn't they be! Coeur d'Or was like paradise, glittering with wealth and magic and the promise of a thousand sun-smeared spectacles.

I was overlooking some intrigue or scandal. But did I risk my future at court by prying into business not my own?

Dowser's door of darkened wood snapped open of its own accord. The heavy scent of tabak underlaid with the tang of kachua assaulted my nostrils. I sneezed, wincing when the stays of my corset dug furrows between my ribs.

"Come in." His voice was as inscrutable as the layers of shadow swathing the study. I squinted, and stepped into the dimness.

SIXTEEN

"You're late," Dowser said. He leaned on a desk laden with dusty scrolls.

"I was busy," I said, cautious.

"Nothing you could have been doing is more important than learning to master your legacy," Dowser said. His voice was free of intonation. "Isn't that why you came? Or did you just want a new gown and a few spans of good feeding before crawling back to the Dusklands?"

"No!" My hands twisted into hard pebbles. "I want nothing more than to master my birthright."

"Birthright," he repeated, stepping closer. The light at the edge of the shrouded windows striped my gaze and hid Dowser's expression in silhouette. "Do you truly believe you deserve a place at court, by blood alone?"

"You tell me." The old familiar cinder of resentment flared to life, heating my blood. "You're the one who signed that writ, transferring my guardianship to the Sisters. You clearly know more about my past than I do."

"So you want to uncover your parentage," he said, shrewd. "You came here to find out if you're highborn, if you belong to a noble family. To claim a dowry? To marry a lord?"

"Frankly, I don't care about my parents." The ember burst into a bonfire, crackling through my veins and spinning runnels of smoke through my thoughts. "They abandoned me, discarded me at the edge of the daylight world like so much refuse. Even if they were still alive, even if they wanted me back, I wouldn't care. They don't deserve me."

"*Deserve.*" Dowser tasted the word, rolling it on his tongue. "And what, lady, do you believe *you* deserve?"

My breath caught. Staring around Dowser's closed-off chambers, I felt suddenly imprisoned within my own anger, a being of smoke and shadow trapped behind heavy curtains of resentment and humiliation. I scrubbed my aching palms down the front of my dress, fighting the sudden press of unpleasant memories: stinging slaps from children who could have been my friends, detached stares from women who should have been my mothers. I reached for the certainty I had riveted to my bones with each toiling step away from the Dusklands.

"I am a legacy of the Amber Empire." I forced my voice to stay calm. "You said so yourself—my bloodline is true. I may not have been born in a palais, but my bones were forged in the dusk and my veins are alight with dreams. Do not ask whether I deserve a place at court. Ask whether this court deserves me."

Dowser was silent, nothing more than a flash of spectacles in the smoke-dimmed chamber.

"You said the Sisters who raised you burned that Writ of Guardianship, to keep you from leaving," he murmured at last. "And yet here you are. Why didn't you obey them?"

"Obey the distant and sanctimonious Sisters who hid the secret of my heritage, denied my legacy, and locked me away when I dared ask questions?" I swallowed bile. "I'd had enough. I conjured shards of piercing sunlight and billows of glittering clouds. I blinded them with colors they'd never dared imagine, and escaped while they prayed for mercy from their Scion. I never looked back."

A frisson tripped brokenly down my spine: satisfaction prickled with guilt. I lifted my chin, and didn't tell Dowser about the waves of bone-deep exhaustion that had slowed my fleeing heels, or the jagged screams and curses that haunted my dreams for weeks after.

"You're ambitious," Dowser remarked. "You're arrogant. Perhaps even a little cruel. Whatever gave you the idea that you were owed so much, when you offer so little?"

My nostrils flared, and a low ringing teased at my ears.

"Poor abandoned highborn lady," Dowser said. "If only anyone wanted her around, she might be able to do great things."

I choked on my fury. "Why are you saying these things?"

"You have no discipline, barely any control over your thoughts or emotions. I want to see what happens when you lose what little control you have."

My breath hissed in my throat. Thorns needled my palms, and a familiar numbness coursed from my wrists toward my elbows.

"I'm not losing control!"

"Aren't you?" Dowser's hand lashed out. The flat of his palm struck my cheek. Pain exploded behind my eyes.

Shock twisted into rage in one dizzying instant. The sting at my cheek blended with the buzzing numbness coursing up my arms until I was roaring. Images and colors flickered and flooded and pulsed out of me in a perilous cascade.

Flaming sunlight. Cursed wasteland. The translucent whisper of jeweled fingers, pale as opals and sharp as glass. Flashing eyes. Runnels of shadow, unspooling like threads of smoke.

Darkness, hot and pulsing behind my eyes.

I must have fallen, because my knees were hard against the tile and my palms were slick with sweat. I shuddered, my head bursting with spikes of color and shadow.

"What were you saying about control?"

Dowser's voice was inches from my ear, composed as ever. My hands twitched with the urge to reach out and pitch him to the ground like the savage Dusker kids used to do to me. But I fought the urge, clamming my fingers and setting my jaw.

"You made me do that," I whimpered. "I was fine before you goaded me."

"I didn't make you do anything," Dowser replied. "No one can make you do anything, Mirage. Everything is a choice."

"That's not true." I pulled my feet underneath my shaking body and dragged myself upright. "I didn't choose to be abandoned at the edge of the world. I didn't choose to be raised by unloving zealots, praying to Meridian like he's about to swoop out of Dominion and save us all. I didn't choose this legacy coursing through my veins."

"Perhaps not. But you chose to abandon everything you'd ever known to travel halfway across the daylight world. You chose to reveal your legacy in a bid for recognition. And when I hit you barely hard enough to smart, you chose to lash out at me with the one thing that makes you powerful."

"I didn't *lash out*—"

"Which is it, Mirage?" Dowser's voice sliced my argument to shreds. "Did you lose control, or did you want to hurt and disorient me?"

Silence mingled with the rich scent of leather and tabak. The tremors wracking my chest subsided, and I forced my breathing to slow.

"I was angry," I finally admitted. "But I can't always choose when I use my gift. I don't know how to control it."

"And that is the most frightening thing of all." Dowser shifted in the shadows, a wraith in his black robes. "You let your legacy control you, instead of the other way around. That makes you powerless. And without power you have no control, no choice."

"I know." I shuddered in the dim. "That's why I need your help."

Dowser contemplated me. "Are you willing to work?"

"Yes."

A smile ghosted across his face. "Then let us begin."

SEVENTEEN

Dowser's lesson consisted of sitting, blindfolded, in the dark.

"Be still!" he snapped, again. From the ever-changing direction of his lashing tongue, I assumed he was stalking around his study like a cat.

I tried to obey, but I'd been sitting like this for what felt like an eternity. My neck ached with the effort of holding up my elaborate hairstyle, and I was reasonably certain the corset was cutting off blood flow to my legs.

"How much longer?" I whispered. "I thought we were working on my legacy."

"I am teaching you discipline," Dowser repeated. "Discipline comes before control. And control comes before capability. You have none of any of these things. So we begin with discipline."

"Is everything a moral lesson with you?"

"Must you insist on approaching every lesson with petulance and insubordination?"

"I'm trying—!"

"Find the stillness inside, Mirage. Still your mind, and the body will follow."

I lapsed into frustrated silence. Dowser's unceasing footsteps circled me. I chewed on my lips, and forced myself to think of nothing. But the instant I tried to think of nothing, every doubt and worry squawked and clamored for attention. Lullaby's lessons on etiquette, eddying into one giant pool of curtsies and addresses. The forced smile on Reaper's—*Thibo's*—handsome face when I asked for his court name. The sting of Dowser's palm on my cheek.

Sunder.

The bell for fourth Prime shattered the stillness, dispelling the images swirling between my ears.

"Enough. Get up."

I stumbled to my feet, dragging the blindfold off my face and swinging my arms to get my blood flowing. Dowser had lit long tapers in a burnished candelabra, and the guttering flames fractured his face into a patchwork of red and black.

"That was terrible, Mirage. You'll have to show more initiative if you ever hope to prove yourself for Dexter and win a permanent place at court."

Disappointment soured my stomach. "Tell me how."

"That's exactly what I'm talking about." He pursed his lips. "Come back tomorrow before Prime. We have a great deal of ground to cover."

I swallowed against the bitter tang of failure and reached for the clear-glass certainty that had carried me all the way from the Dusklands. *I belong here.* But the sensation was fractured and distant, like looking into a broken mirror and seeing someone else's face.

A flick of Dowser's fingers dismissed me. I plodded toward the door, confusion and dismay eating holes in the dristic cage I'd built around that ancient, desiccated heartache.

Discipline. Choices. *Control.*

"Dowser?" My voice sounded hoarse. I cleared my throat. "I know I said I didn't care about my parents, and I don't. But your signature was on that writ. Do you know why they left me? Why I was abandoned in the Dusklands?"

His obsidian eyes stared at me over spectacles flaring with reflected candlelight. Silence stretched chilly fingers to push at my chest.

"I'll say this, Mirage," Dowser said, at last. "It wasn't because your parents didn't want you. The rest of it, I would advise you to forget."

"I can't forget what I don't know."

"And what you do not know is less likely to hurt you."

"Hurt me?" A spark of curiosity burst to life inside me. "How—?"

"Merely a figure of speech," Dowser interrupted. "There is nothing in your past but forgotten ghosts and bad memories."

I shivered. He had no idea.

"If you truly wish to earn a place at court, you must focus. Learn the rules of your legacy. The rules of your station. Everything else is a distraction. Do you understand?"

"Yes," I said. I nodded my head, as much for myself as for Dowser. "I do."

Stepping out into the scarlet-striped passageway of Coeur d'Or was like being reborn. I leaned against the smooth alabaster wall and lifted my face to the shafts of coral light glimmering through a row of carved spandrels. Dowser was right. I had made myself a promise, in the shimmering waters of the baths, to do whatever it took to earn my place here. Too-tight corsets and mean little games and unspoken secrets—these were small prices to pay for the endless exhilarating exuberance of belonging. I was willing to work, I was willing to cooperate, I was willing to—

I jammed my hand into the pocket of my gown, where a small, smudged note had been burning a hole in the fabric since I shoved it there hours ago. The writing on the creamy envelope was nearly illegible at this point, crumpled and smeared. But I could still make out my name—my *new* name—spilling across the paper.

Mirage.

I gusted a breath and slid my fingernail under the edge of the envelope. The note inside was written on the same rich parchment, and when I lifted it to my nose I caught a whiff of something sharp and clean, like genévrier needles.

"Money," I muttered, to distract myself from the skein of trepidation unspooling in my belly. I wasn't sure I wanted to know what terrible price Sunder had decided to ask for his dubious sponsorship.

And wasn't sure I wanted to find out whether I was willing to pay it.

I sounded out the elegant words sauntering across the page. There were only a few.

Come to my residence. Belsyre Wing. Now.
Signed,
Sunder

I sucked in another gulp of that searing perfume, but this time, it tasted of bitterness and pain. My stomach soured. The vermilion light pouring in through the glass stained the fingers on my right hand, triggering a memory of Luca, and a guttering cook fire, and iron clouds scudding across a dim sun.

What had Luca said, when he'd told me the tale of the dust devil, with its terrible eternal thirst?

Maybe by paying a demon what he needs, you keep him from stealing what he desires.

I crushed the terse note into a crumpled ball of paper, and shoved thoughts of Luca from my mind. From what I'd heard and seen, this Sunder was little better than a devil himself. But what did he desire?

To inflict pain? To see me suffer? To watch me fail?

I tossed the hateful note behind a gilded statuette and stomped through an archway draped in velvet and strung with diamonds.

I wouldn't give him what he desired, and I might not be able to give him what he needed. But maybe I could give him a little something of what he deserved.

EIGHTEEN

Sunder's chambers were a wing unto themselves, a sprawling residence I only found after an hour of wandering in circles and cursing whatever vindictive architect had designed Coeur d'Or's curving hallways.

A blank-faced servant in black-and-white livery bowed me into a verdant foyer. Hanging terrariums spilled tendrils of green from a vaulted ceiling. Invisible fountains filled the air with the drowsy splash of water. A songbird trilled a soprano glissando that lingered sylphlike among the drooping heads of lush flowers.

"This way," prompted the servant.

We threaded down a hallway lined with polished silverwood and studded with carved ambric, and I couldn't help but wonder how rich my suspicious benefactor was. Just one of these exquisite finials or precious ornamentations was worth more than my life. And all of this together? A treasure trove unlike anything I'd ever imagined.

The servant led me out beneath a pergola draped in foliage. A crystalline chandelier dashed prisms against a pillar slim as a cygni's white throat. Gauzy veils tangled with rubies splashed blood across a glossy floor.

And at the center of it all was Sunder.

He was sleeping, draped along the curving tongue of a white chaise. His head was thrown back, and strands of pale kembric hair caressed the collar of a charcoal surcoat. Tall black boots left stark smudges on the couch. His lips, curled into a sneer the last time I'd seen them, were parted ever so slightly. Black lashes stained his high cheekbones with ink.

He was beautiful.

"I employ a portraitist, if you care to use his services."

He was also apparently not sleeping.

Sunder swung into a seated position, brushing hair out of his eyes. His gaze slashed up to meet mine. I glimpsed a vivid burst of pale green ringed in dristic before agony shuddered down my spine and clawed at my mind.

I gasped, clapping a hand to my forehead. But like before, the pain was gone in an instant, no more than a memory of suffering foaming on an ocean of unease.

"I apologize for the tickle," he drawled, rising to his feet and crossing to a low table tucked between two vine-wrapped pillars. "Some legacies are more volatile than others. And try as I might, I can't seem to look at you without wanting to hurt you."

A thrill of outrage heated my blood. Sunder sloshed liquid into a goblet before draining the glass in one long gulp. He refilled the cup, then turned to face me. I braced myself for the flare of pain, but it never came. He inspected me, cool eyes raking me from head to toe.

"A miracle indeed," he murmured. "You really are a talented fantast. An illusion to hide all that dirt—I'm amazed you didn't think to use it before."

A searing heat crept up the column of my throat. Sunder smiled at me over the rim of his goblet.

"Or did someone finally tell you about bathing?"

My newly buffed fingernails cut semicircles into the palm of my hand. The cursed corset tightened around my lungs. I couldn't drag enough air into my chest.

"You summoned me here, Lord Sunder," I managed between clenched teeth, dipping into what I hoped was the appropriate curtsy befitting his rank. I wouldn't respond to his insults. I knew he was trying to make me lose my temper, but I refused to let him know it was working. "And, as your note requested, I came."

"Forgive me, but did I neglect to specify a time?" His voice feigned innocence. He stalked closer. "When did I say you should come?"

He paused close enough for me to smell that sharp, clean scent wafting off him. I could see the dark embroidery etched along the ridges of his sleeve, and count the rings on his fingers.

"Well?" he prompted.

"*Now,*" I admitted, reluctant. "The note said I should come *now.*"

"Yes. And when was that?" His voice was an unstrung bow.

"Yesterday."

"Ah!" He snapped his fingers. His voice grew taut. "How strange, *now* being *yesterday*. Are Dusklanders unfamiliar with the concept of time? Or are you just as stupid as you look?"

Flames zinged out toward my fingertips, raising the hairs along my arms. My eyes cut up to his. "Sinking to my level, Lord Sunder? You insult my looks and intelligence so bluntly that no one would claim you are adept in the art of dealing pain." I dragged an insolent gaze around the lavish chambers. "Although subtlety hardly seems to be your forte."

His hand snapped out to wrap around my chin. His skin was cold. A low thrum of discomfort vibrated along my jaw, burrowing into flesh and bone. I met his gaze with as much malice as I could muster, and he smiled sharp as a knife's edge.

"It's alive," he whispered, leaning closer. "And it bites."

I held my breath against a choking flood of fury. Too late, Lullaby's warning about comportment echoed in my head. *Whatever you do, don't insult anyone.*

Too late.

"Tell me, my most clever lady Mirage." Sunder's hand trailed a cool, aching line along the column of my throat. "Do you understand the concept of reciprocity?"

I swallowed, hard, fighting the urge to shove his creeping, stinging hands away. Dread cooled the anger heating my blood. I'd promised myself I would do whatever it took to earn my place here. Corsets, cruel games, cold secrets—these were things I could endure. But this—this was asking too much.

"Let me remind you." He leaned closer. I felt the whisper of his breath in the shell of my ear, the brush of his hair against my cheek. "I offered you money. Power. Position. Now you offer me something in return."

I sucked air into my captured lungs, but still I couldn't seem to breathe. A shudder climbed my spine, vibrating against Sunder's fingers. His hand tightened, sending an icy twinge lashing along the plane of my collarbone.

"No," I choked out, taking one huge step backward. My skirts gasped along the slick floor as I wrenched my throbbing shoulder out of Sunder's grasp. "I owe you nothing."

"Nothing?" Sunder's hand drifted to his side. His smile was little more than a ghost. "You owe me everything."

"Your wager was with the empress, and so my debt lies with her."

"You will not repay me, then?"

"Only in vindication, lord."

He stared at me for a long moment, his gaze calculating. And then he swept me a deep bow I distantly recognized as being reserved for the most illustrious of nobility. But what must surely be mockery barely stung through the haze of surprise and confusion.

What just happened?

"Bane!" he shouted over one shoulder. "I win!"

I took another involuntary step backward as a willowy girl appeared from behind a curtain of blushing eglantine. She was the same lady I'd seen with Sunder in the Atrium, a chilling beauty with blond hair coiled high above her head and eyes like cut emeralds. The midnight damask of her gown made her skin look like marble. She wore satin gloves stretching to the elbow.

Sunder bowed over her elegantly proffered hand, then straightened with a half smile.

"You owe me." He gestured to the clock, which chimed as if on cue.

"I do not," she said. Her lovely red mouth twisted into a moue of derision. "You said it would take half an hour. Not that she wouldn't give in at all."

"But *you* wagered it would take only ten minutes. I think I win by default."

"If you insist." She reached into a delicate little purse to hand her companion something that glinted in the light. "But I'll have it back before the last hour of Nocturne."

"Care to wager on it?" Sunder shot back.

"Pardon me!" My voice was loud and raw. The two courtiers turned to me with looks that implied they'd forgotten I was even there. I twisted my fingers in my skirts so they wouldn't see me shake. "What just happened? Did you wager on how long it would take—how long—"

I choked, fury burning the words to ash even as I tried to force them from my throat.

"How long it would take me to seduce you?" Sunder cocked his head to one side and smiled like a serpent. "Why, does that bother you?"

Rage paralyzed every muscle in my body.

"Well, you did better than anyone dreamed." He lifted a sun-gilded eyebrow as he reached into a pocket and drew out a slim sheaf of parchment. He didn't even glance at the papers, just tossed them to the ground at my feet. "Apparently the Dusklands aren't populated solely by whores and thieves."

He turned on his heel and offered his elbow to the lady.

Every inch of my body trembled. I stared down at the sheaf of paper, catching a glimpse of sums inked on parchment. Carelessly scrawled signatures.

Promissory notes. Money. The sponsorship I was promised.

Tossed at my feet like so many scraps.

A sudden vivid memory seared my mind's eye—Sister Cathe's drawn white face, her trembling fingers as she'd unlocked the door to my room. She, of all of them, had been most frightened of me, of what I could do. Maybe she'd meant to set my dinner on the ground, but instead she'd flung the plate into the room, scattering morsels of food before slamming the door behind her.

I could still feel the dirt clinging to my scrabbling fingers, taste the dust coating my tongue. My vision flashed white.

Lullaby's warning sprinted like a mantra through my head. *Don't insult anyone. Don't insult anyone.*

Don't.

"Sunder," I called out, my traitor voice funneling all my furious thoughts into calmly uttered words. I couldn't think of anything beyond the blood pounding in my head, beyond the enormous sum of money thrown to me like leftovers to a begging dog. I couldn't remember why I wasn't supposed to insult anyone.

I just wanted to hurt him. Like he'd tried to hurt me.

Sunder paused, glancing over his brocaded shoulder. His lady followed suit, and I found myself admiring her smooth skin, her frosty hair, the jewel-bedizened choker collaring her white throat. She was perfect, and so different from me, with my faded dark hair, my travel-rough skin, my ungraceful manners.

"Are your lady's tastes so singular, then?" I asked, sweetly— and even as the words formed, I knew it was weak, I knew it was dull, I knew it wouldn't sting. "Or did you have to wager on her virtue too?"

His eyes widened, and I glimpsed a sudden, searing bleakness: a futile gasp of poisoned air, the cold moment before a last hope is dashed. For an aching moment, it was like staring into the violet-dark clouds above Dominion, dangerous and breathtaking and wild with impossible things.

I braced myself for pain.

But in another instant they were just eyes, and Sunder was just himself, arrogant and aloof and cold. He stared at me for one last moment, then stalked from the pergola with his lady, his boots loud as thunderclaps on the glassy floor.

I stood immobilized for what felt like an eternity before I found the will to crouch and retrieve the promissory notes. I felt particles of dirt stick to my numb fingers even though the marble floor was pristine. I thumbed through the sheaf, and even with my poor knowledge of numbers and finance, I knew the sum was enormous.

More money than an ambric mine could expect to earn in ten tides. More money than a Dusklander family would see in twenty lifetimes.

I took two shuddering breaths, then fled. I ran back through the porticos and vaulted halls, fighting the icicles stabbing at my eyes. No one stopped me, and the only sound to splinter the chirping of distant birds was the faint tap of my slippers on the pristine floors.

I made it nearly all the way back to Lys Wing before I collapsed between two carven pillars, shivering and shaking. Tears streamed down my cheeks, my eyes stinging as carefully applied kohl dissolved into salty mud.

I cried so hard I thought either the stays of my corsets must break, or my chest would explode. And when at last the tears subsided, the realization dawned.

I was rich. For the next three spans, at least, I was fabulously, ridiculously, unimaginably wealthy.

NINETEEN

When I finally made it back to my rooms in Lys Wing, Lullaby was waiting for me.

She wore a silver-blue gown, and matching metallic fingernails drummed a staccato on the arm of one of the many blossom-encrusted chairs thronging my chambers. An elaborate meal was laid out on the low table in my parlor; I smelled fresh bread, and dumplings, and more spices than my nostrils were used to.

Even caged in its prison of boning and silk, my stomach gave a yearning moan.

"You're an hour late," Lullaby snapped, water-blue eyes swirling. "Didn't you hear the bells for Compline? Or did you simply not care if I was kept waiting?"

"To set the record straight," I mumbled, folding onto a divan and giving my tearstained cheeks one last swipe, "I do know how to tell time. Despite what anyone says to the contrary."

"Pardon?" She leaned forward, her delicate brows coming together. "Who have you been speaking with? I thought I told you to keep a low profile."

"I tried," I said. "But Dowser thinks I'm a disappointment and a failure, and Sunder thinks I'm a mewling lowlife fit only to be tormented."

"Sunder?" Lullaby jerked out of her chair, and the delicate color of her skin drained to ash. "You saw Sunder? When? *Why?*"

"He summoned me," I reminded her. "He wanted to see me before he released the funds he promised me."

Lullaby relaxed a hair. "And?"

I jerked the cursed sheaf of parchment out of my pocket and flung it onto the table, where the pages lay wilting between charred greens and saffron rice. Lullaby hesitated for barely a second before grabbing them up, eagerly rifling through the pages. Her skin regained its color, then brightened with tinges of sapphire on her high cheekbones.

"Scion help us," she murmured. "I never dreamed it would be so much."

"Worth the price, I hope," I grumbled.

Lullaby's head snapped up.

"What did you say?"

"Nothing."

"Mirage." Her lovely eyes narrowed. "What did you do? Is there something I ought to know about?"

"More like what did *he* do," I said. Lullaby's gaze drilled holes in my forehead, and finally I sighed, fighting the urge to rip the pins out of my hair and tear the stays from my corset. "He slandered my birth, my intelligence, and my looks, then made a poor attempt at seducing me."

Lullaby's lips tightened.

"But that turned out to be nothing more than a sick wager between him and that icy witch he hangs around with, so he gave me the money and I left."

"And that was all that happened?" My mentor's dristic-flaked fingernails crushed the parchment. "You didn't say or do anything to punish him? For insulting you? For scheming to get you into his bed?"

I snorted. "I doubt there would have been any beds involved."

"*Mirage.*"

I blew out the air from my nostrils and jutted my chin forward, feeling like Luca's favorite brindled mule.

"I barely said anything at all. I only insinuated that his lover might not warm his bed by choice."

"Lover? What lover?"

"The girl. The frosty one. They're always together—I assumed—"

Lullaby jolted, then went still. "Mirage, no."

"What?" I rolled my eyes. "It's hardly even an insult, they're actually—"

"She's his *sister.*"

Shock sent a bolt of lightning up my spine, and I sat up so straight my corset ground against my ribs.

"His sister?"

"Worse." Lullaby's face was so pale I thought she might faint. "His twin. And they are most certainly not lovers."

"Oh." I cast my mind back over the events of the past two days, every second shifting in hue and shade until everything was awfully, blindingly clear. "Oh, no."

"Scion help us both." The multicolored light from the flower-stained windows turned the walls an ugly shade of mauve. "Oh, they will have their revenge for that slight."

"Who *are* they?" I had to ask. "You called him the empress's dog. He deals pain with a glance. He wagers on seduction with his *twin sister.* They're unimaginably rich. What am I missing here?"

"Who are they?" Lullaby's harsh laugh sent chills skittering down the back of my arms. "Only you would dare to ask that. Only you would dare not *know.*"

I waited.

"Most of Dexter refers to them as the Suicide Twins," she said, finally, a suggestion of fear in her lovely voice.

"Why?"

"Because you'd need a death wish to be on intimate terms with them." She took a breath. "Sunder and Bane. Pain and poison. They were born Aubrey and Oleander de Vere, and they're the last living heirs to the estate and great fortune of the Marquisate of Belsyre."

She looked at me, as if these names meant something significant. I had to shake my head. She sighed, deeply.

"Belsyre is the largest producer of dristic and kembric ore in the empire. Vast mines in the Meteor Mountains pump out nearly half the imperial supply of precious minerals. It's the wealthiest region in the land, and before the Conquest, the de Veres were dauphins in their own right."

I frowned, thinking of the gorgeous blond twins, tossing away fortunes to foundlings and wagering on intrigue. "If they have all that wealth and power, why are they here?"

"Is that a joke?" Lullaby stared at me like I'd sprouted extra eyes. "Their personal wealth rivals that of Severine herself. Their private militia is legendary in size and prowess. They control hugely valuable resources. Why would the empress want them anywhere *but* here?"

"Where she can keep an eye on them?"

"Where—" Lullaby's mouth twisted, and she dropped her voice, as though worried someone might be listening. "Where she can control them. Where she can use their power. Like she uses all of us."

"Uses you?" A memory nudged its way to the front of my mind—a handsome young man in a ridiculous hat, his smile fading when I asked why he and the other courtiers took it in shifts to dance attendance on the empress. *To better fulfill our great ruler's demands on us.* "What does she use you for?"

Lullaby's face shuttered like one of Dowser's darkened windows, and then she was prattling about place settings and cutlery and types of crystal and table manners, and I didn't have time to think about anything but keeping my back straight and my elbows in and my mouth shut.

But later, when the bells struck for second Nocturne and I was finally released from my aching tower of hair and my mask of cosmetics and my cage of a corset, I couldn't think of anything but the chilly slash of a gaze hard with dristic and infinite with green. And the sharp, clean scent of genévrier and pain.

TWENTY

The next week acquired something of a routine, and I was grateful for it.

I spent Matins with a grumpy Lullaby, rehearsing curtsies and niceties and flicks of the wrist, which seemed to be a language unto themselves. Comportment and address and carriage and diction. I tried on new clothing—Matin gowns and leisure gowns and Compline gowns and ball gowns. Underclothes and outerwear and shoes and accessories. Sunder's money had paid for a luxurious wardrobe that I—insulted but slightly relieved—was forbidden from having anything to do with selecting.

And there were my sessions with Dowser. Hours spent in that darkened study, breathing in the heavy scents of tabak smoke and kachua while he made me sit and focus, silent and unmoving, until I felt like one of the corridor statues forced to hold guttering torches from now until eternity. Hours dragging illusions from my uncooperative hands: a potted plant dissolved into flickers of ropy greenery; a glass paperweight snatched at the light before fading into shadow; a horn comb was a wisp of fog evanescing like a ghost at dusk.

I wasn't getting better.

Only once, after I managed to conjure the suggestion of an imaginary flutterwing, body like a diamond and wings like lace, did Dowser deem my work halfway satisfactory.

"Where do your illusions come from?" he demanded, frustrated. "What binds them to your mind, your body? Magic requires control, Mirage. Magic requires rules."

Rules. There had only ever been one rule with the Sisters—hide my legacy at all costs. Don't imagine, don't hope, never dream. And I'd tried. For so long, I'd tried to bind my power with the sinew of my will and suppress it beneath the weight of my fear. But control had always meant oppression. I didn't want rules; I wanted *freedom.*

I clenched my buzzing hands. Dowser was trying to help me hone my gift, and I'd sworn to do whatever he said. If he required control, then I'd learn control. I didn't know what the rules of my legacy were, but I'd find a way to learn them.

After my lessons I returned to my chambers in Lys for more hours with an increasingly nettled Lullaby, learning the differences between suppers, dinners, teas, and banquets. Socials, fêtes, soirées, and galas. The steps to dances long forgotten and yet to become popular. Card games. Gambling. Polite banter. Singing.

And although Lullaby swore the Suicide Twins would have their revenge for the slight I unwittingly—but not involuntarily—delivered, I saw nothing more of either Sunder or his icy sister.

But sometimes, when I woke at third Nocturne in a sweat and the edges of my shutters bled crimson, I knew all my nightmares were about pain and poison.

I burst into Lullaby's rooms without knocking, eagerness winning out over manners. After a whole week of practice, I'd finally mastered a complicated dance step, and I couldn't wait to show Lullaby. I hoped the progress would soothe her frazzled nerves—she'd developed purple bags beneath her eyes, and her once-manicured nails were bitten nearly to the quick.

I skidded to a halt in the foyer. Lullaby's sleek dark head was bent close to a cap of bronze curls under a rakish hat.

She was with someone.

Embarrassment heated my face, and I lifted my skirts to back out of the door. It was too late. Two faces stared up at me with matching expressions of guilty astonishment. And I recognized the second face—it was Reaper. *Thibo*. The gorgeous gallant who showed me the way to Dowser's. I glimpsed a flicker of parchment disappearing into his velveteen pocket, but I glanced away before they could catch me staring.

Even with my inferior manners and inelegant graces, I knew I'd interrupted something I shouldn't have.

"Oh, Lullaby," I mumbled. "I'm so sorry to barge in. I didn't know you had company, and—"

"Mirage?" Thibo's beautiful smile showed off every one of his perfectly white teeth. "Is that really you? I'd begun to think I dreamed you up in a fever, so deeply did you dazzle me with your beauty."

I knew it was worthless flattery, but his sugary words heated my cheeks. I ducked my head, embarrassed, but Thibo had already crossed the room on lavender-clad legs to bow over my hand. The feathers on his hat—silver today, edged in tiny black pearls—nearly brushed the ground.

"Thibo, stop," snapped Lullaby, from across the room. Annoyance darkened her turquoise eyes. "The last thing I need is for all that fawning to go to her head."

"Oh?" Thibo straightened with a flourish and a wink. "And what could possibly be the problem with her head?"

"The problem," sighed Lullaby, "is that no one else at court is going to treat her like that. I don't want her getting the wrong impression."

"Lullaby, it's fine," I cut in. "I'm not an idiot. I know it's just flattery—I know it's not true."

Thibo slapped a jeweled hand to his heart. "You wound me, fair lady! I would never say anything that wasn't true."

Both Lullaby and I fixed him with pointed glances.

"Fine," he pouted. "Perhaps I will leave the business of illusions to our famous fantast. Since mine seem so transparent as to be thought lies."

He sketched a bow before heading for the door.

"Thibo, wait!" In spite of the contrived compliments, I enjoyed his company, and after a week of no one but Lullaby and Dowser, I was antsy for fresh companionship. I wanted to hear about Coeur d'Or, about the parties and balls and courtiers. I was also desperately curious. Their whispered voices. The shred of paper shoved hastily into a pocket. "Won't you stay?"

He cocked his head, bronze curls swaying.

"Lullaby says your politesse is unparalleled," I lied. "We're practicing tea service and polite inquiry. Perhaps you'll lend some insight?"

He raised skeptical eyebrows at Lullaby, who stuck out a tiny pink tongue.

"Such beauty can brook no argument," Thibo said. "And by beauty, I mean you, not that fish-colored water sprite who delights in my pain and drinks all my wine."

"Fish-colored?" Lullaby's eyes narrowed into slits. "I'll have you know, songs have been written about the rare color of my exquisite skin."

"Now she's writing songs about the color of her own skin?" Thibo's wide eyes feigned shock. "The vanity!"

"I did *not* say—"

The pair devolved into comfortable squabbling, sniping at each other's insecurities with a skill that spoke of long familiarity. I rose and crossed to the bar, pretending not to listen as I poured a few generous glasses of ice wine. I might have invited Thibo to stay on a whim, but now that he was here I realized I was desperate for friends. Lullaby had been more than patient with me, but we hadn't exactly crossed the boundary into friendship. I didn't blame her. I was more an assignment than a companion, and my progress—or lack thereof—fell on her shoulders as well as mine. And she had more to lose.

But Thibo—Thibo brought forth an ease in Lullaby that I'd barely even glimpsed. Watching them bicker made me think suddenly of Luca and Vesh, separated by tides in age but so close in spirit. Melancholy clambered up my chest and tightened my throat. I could still only imagine what it must feel like to be so close to another person, to be understood so completely and loved so indescribably. To *belong*.

"Did you pour all three glasses for yourself?" Thibo quipped from the chaise. "Or is one of those for me?"

I snapped out of my reverie to see Lullaby and Thibo staring at me from across the room.

"She's a lightweight," Lullaby said, hiding a smile. "If she passes out drunk you have to carry her home."

"I won't," sniffed Thibo, indignant. "Besides, if anyone's passing out drunk, I can assure you it will be me."

I laughed, handing out the glasses before sinking onto the couch.

"You two seem close," I ventured, eyeing their arms, interlocked at the elbow. "How long have you known each other?"

"Too long!" Lullaby rolled her eyes. "Thibo is here when I need him the most, and want him the least. He's a terrible friend and an outrageous nuisance. I've listened to his extravagant tales and outlandish compliments more times than I care to count."

"I would pretend to be offended by that." Thibo sipped from his glass. "But I really am an outrageous nuisance."

"Are you two—?" I cleared my throat, belatedly realizing it was probably impolite to ask such things.

Thibo frowned. Lullaby stared blankly at me for a moment before her face fractured into amusement. Her laugh was the sound of clear water rushing on stones, lovely and merry.

I couldn't help but laugh too.

"Oh, Mirage," she giggled, "that's not it at all."

Thibo choked on his wine. "Scion, you thought we were lovers? Lullaby, where did you find this simple-minded rustic? Does she also think babies are delivered by Dominion star maidens in the night?"

I flushed to my hairline.

"Don't be cruel," scolded Lullaby. Her soothing tones cooled the heat climbing my face. "Thibo prefers his, ah, *intimate companions* to be—hmm. Similarly male to himself?"

"Oh!" Another wave of embarrassment flared in my veins. "Why in the daylight world didn't you just say so?"

"I'm not sure Thibo's ever had to explain before," shrugged Lullaby, her tone wry.

"Speaking of which, I'm in love!" Thibo flung a mournful

hand over his heart, then sat up with an eager light in his eyes. "Lullaby, do you remember Mender?"

"How could I forget?" Lullaby shot me a spiky glance. "Mender is heir to the de Médeux estates."

"Compte de Médeux?" I wracked my brain. Just because we had company didn't mean Lullaby was going to stop being my mentor. "Cousins to the Isamberts? They export beech lumber from the Arduinne Forests."

"I'm impressed!" Lullaby turned back to Thibo. "What about him?"

"He's returned to court, and he's more beautiful than when he left!" Thibo sighed. "I want to steal the Moon herself from Dominion so I might hang her above his heart."

"I doubt the Sun would appreciate that," said Lullaby.

"Nor Meridian!" I added.

"Nor the Moon," we both said at the same time, before dissolving into giggles.

"This is why I don't fall in love with women," snapped Thibo. "You're so practical. No sense of the romantic."

"At least I know the difference between love and infatuation!" Lullaby scoffed.

"Did Blossom know that?"

Lullaby stiffened. Thibo froze.

Blossom. I sat up straighter. The girl who painted my rooms. The girl who was—*gone.*

"How *dare* you," Lullaby hissed. "If you had only done what I'd asked—"

"Now it's my fault?" Thibo's shoulders bunched. "You were the one who couldn't control her outbursts, it's no wonder—"

Thibo's white teeth snapped, slicing the words to ribbons. He cut his eyes to me, and Lullaby followed his gaze. I watched as courtly façades of feigned nonchalance descended over both their faces.

"It's well past Nocturne," murmured Thibo, rising to his feet. He bowed over my hand. "Mirage, let it be known your company was as exquisite as your visage. I hope to impose upon your pleasure time and again."

"The pleasure was mine!" I demurred, barely hearing my own words over the thunder of questions boiling inside me.

Lullaby didn't move as Thibo slipped out of the room. Her slender fingers were clenched in her lap, and her eyes shone like sapphires.

"Lullaby—" I began.

"Don't ask," she whispered, her voice cold as a frozen lake. "Please, Mirage, don't ask me to explain."

So I didn't. I eased out into Lys Wing's sun-bleached jardins, skimming my fingers over the heads of orange-painted callas and flushed asters. *Blossom.* The girl whose flowers crowded my walls might be gone, but she wasn't *gone.* Her presence rippled through my days, intangible but undeniable. Who had she been? And where was she now? What had happened to her, that she should be so discussed with so few actual words?

It's none of your business. I tamped down the curiosity spiraling through me. My place at court was still unsure. My progress with Dowser was almost pathetic, and I'd only recently made any headway with Lullaby. Whoever Blossom had been, she wasn't here now. And I couldn't let myself get distracted. Not now, not when I was so close to earning my place here, in the world where I belonged.

TWENTY-ONE

"What do you know about—?" I was already talking as I pushed my way into Dowser's study, waving my hand to clear the smoky haze souring the air.

Another week of twice-daily sessions with Dowser had cured my habit of knocking. But my voice shriveled in my throat when I saw who was already in my teacher's rooms.

Sunder stood across from Dowser, his arms braced on the broad desk. His suit was a crisp, stark blue: the color at the edge of the eastern sky. In the oppressive gloom of the study, he seemed uncanny—a creature blown from clear glass, or an icy breath on a cold morning.

They both looked up. Sunder's green eyes locked on mine, and I braced myself for pain. But there was none—just his cool, sheer regard and the throb of my own pulse in my ears.

"You're early," said Dowser.

"I'm sorry, I didn't—" I choked on my own words, suddenly flustered. "What is he doing here?"

"He," said Sunder, "happens to be your sponsor."

"Yes, but—" I struggled to maintain my composure, which felt suddenly frayed. "Why are you here?"

"To check on your progress."

"But you wagered against me. You're betting that I'll lose."

"That's a very simple way to think of a very complex investment." Sunder's voice was like polished marble, elegant and lavish and too slick to get a grip on. "And win or lose, the whole thing is bound to be entertaining."

The ember of resentment flared to life inside me, releasing a billow of rancorous smoke.

"Calm yourself, Mirage." Dowser stood smoothly, reading the mutinous fury that must have warped my features. "As your sponsor, Sunder does have the right to check on your progress. I would have updated him privately, but I'm afraid you interrupted us."

"And what were you going to tell him?"

"There's no need to tell me anything," said Sunder. "Why not just show me?"

Panic shivered hot through my veins, surely painting my skin in fevered shades. Since coming to Coeur d'Or, I had barely been able to conjure more than pathetic suggestions of illusions. Scraps of color, pulses of light. I would rather die than display my abundant failure in front of the lord who'd gambled on my virtue and wagered on my defeat.

"No."

"What are you afraid of?" Sunder bared his teeth in what might have been a smile. "Surely not me."

"Lord Sunder," Dowser interrupted, stern. "She is under no obligation to perform for you before Carrousel."

"I'm under no obligation to perform for you *ever*," I snarled, suddenly livid. "I don't care how much you paid—"

"Mirage."

"—if you think I'm some kind of dancing—"

"*Mirage.*"

The unexpected edge in Dowser's voice made me swallow my fury. My teacher was right. I shouldn't be wasting my time or my energy on this spoiled, sadistic man who called himself my sponsor. He was just a distraction, a stumbling block on the way to earning my place at court.

"No need to mince words on my account." Sunder cocked his head, amused, and the light from a guttering candle turned his hair to kembric. "I'm inclined to let the lady speak her mind."

"That's enough, from both of you," growled Dowser. "If you'll give us the room, my lord?"

Sunder tensed, and for the space of a breath I thought he might lash out. But then he bent into a practiced bow, inclining his bright head with such a degree of respect that even I recognized it as a taunt.

"I'd hate to be an impediment to genius," he murmured, brushing past me toward the door. I strained to keep my eyes unfocused, but the refined grace of his movements caught my gaze with jagged precision. He paused in the foyer.

"Lady Mirage?"

I gritted my teeth. "Yes, Lord Sunder?"

"Why are *you* here?"

The raw curiosity in his voice shredded my predictions. I dared to meet his eyes, and once again glimpsed the churning border of a bare kind of desperation I didn't have a name for. My heart lurched strange in the cramped cavern of my ribs.

"There's no need to tell you anything." I flung his words back at him. "In three spans' time, at Carrousel, I'll just show you."

Sunder's smile was a sharp blade in the dim. And then he was gone.

I exhaled.

"Have you heard nothing I've told you?" Dowser's voice was hard. "We've spoken of little else besides discipline. Restraint. And yet you lost every ounce of composure the moment you saw Sunder, and made no effort to regain that control."

"Did you hear what he was saying?" Pride quickened the coals of my resentment. "How could I allow him to treat me so disrespectfully?"

"You are so naïve." Dowser's words stung, more now than when he'd slapped me. "You understand nothing of this place, this world you are now a part of. You came here with your heart held in your palm, never realizing that this court was full of carnivores who would devour it in an instant. The things that mean nothing whip you into a frenzy, yet the important moments slip through your fingers like desert sand. You are weak, and simple."

"That's a lie!" Horror gripped me, and I fought for the words to explain how wrong Dowser was. "I am strong enough. I was raised in the grasping dusk. I discovered my legacy when a pack of feral village children beat me bloody into the dust. I survived a lifetime of being locked away and ignored by superstitious Sisters who treated me like I was cursed. I traveled a thousand miles with no money and little food to come to this place. I proved myself. Why isn't that enough for you?"

"Proved yourself?" Dowser chuckled grimly. The sound curdled my stomach. "If you've proved anything, it's that you still have everything to prove."

I tried to douse the dueling flames of humiliation and resentment.

"I don't know what else I'm supposed to do." I turned my head so he wouldn't see the gleam of tears in my eyes. "I came here because I thought this was where I belonged. Where I would be accepted. Where I would find the family I never had. But you're telling me that none of that means anything, and I'm just some weak child too stupid to understand the intricacies of a world she wasn't born into."

Dowser's expression softened, and his black eyes touched my face with something not too different from sympathy.

"You are weak," he said. "And you are a child. But none of that matters if only you could admit to yourself that you're both those things. Then try to be better. And try again, until you are wiser, and stronger. No one is born belonging anywhere. Nothing valuable is ever given. You deserve nothing that you haven't first earned."

"I am trying!" My gut ached. *No one is born belonging anywhere.* What if that was my fate—to belong nowhere, forever? Not at the frigid edge of daylight, not with the rumbling convoy of ore transports, not here in the palais surrounded by the legacies of an empire.

"Stop that." Dowser stepped closer. "Feeling sorry for yourself won't help."

"Why shouldn't I feel sorry for myself?" A hot hand clenched my throat. "I've been working as hard as I know how. But my illusions are just as weak as they were when I first arrived. *Weaker.* I'm supposed to be transforming into the Amber Court's prize fantast, not languishing in this study waiting for the empress or Sunder or whoever to toss me out on the street!"

Dowser sighed. He pulled his narrow spectacles off his face and polished them slowly on the hem of his robe.

"Your illusions," he said, after a long silence. "Where do they come from?"

"My bloodline." He'd asked me this question before—I didn't have a new answer. "Isn't that how legacies work?"

"That's not what I mean." His snapping eyes were a nighthawk's, keen as knives. "Where do the illusions originate? How do you conjure them?"

"I'm not exactly sure." I hesitated. "I pull them from inside me. There's a buzzing in my hands, and I push the illusions through my palms. Once I made a mask of a face—"

"How do you control it? What are its rules?"

I hesitated, struggling to find the words to explain. Every illusion I'd ever conjured was wrought in the dream-bright pulse of my quickening heart. A dream made real: ethereal symmetry unbound by earthly anatomy. Something of my very soul bursting out on the world. How did that have rules?

"I don't know," I whispered.

"How can you expect to master something you do not control?" Dowser shoved his spectacles back onto his face. "Perhaps if you assigned steps to the process, it might give your illusions structure."

"Steps?"

"You begin by imagining the object in your mind, yes?" That sounded right, so I nodded. *"Envision.* Then you must somehow use the energy of your body and mind to give the image shape."

I shrugged. "Maybe?"

"Empower." Dowser looked pleased with himself. "And then you project the illusion outward. *Express.* Perhaps if you run through each step of the process with each new illusion, your legacy will adhere to the structure it so clearly needs."

Envision, empower, express. I rolled the words around my head. Dowser's new steps made logical sense, I knew that. Rules I hadn't intuited myself were probably better than no rules at all. But something rebellious and implacable railed against the rigidity of those three words. Three steps—three *rules*—for each new illusion, every vision I ever created.

"I'll try," I whispered.

Dowser studied me. "Perhaps that's enough for today. We'll give it a go tomorrow."

I bowed my head, gathering my skirts to leave. Surprise jolted my gaze back up when a heavy hand fell on my shoulder.

"Mirage." Something softened the spare, stern lines of Dowser's face. "I'm not unaware of what this means to you. You may think me harsh, but I only ask of you what I believe you can achieve. I have high hopes for what you might accomplish."

I scanned his face, but his eyes were unreadable behind his spectacles. "Why?"

"These Nocturnes, I dream too often of cold, pale faces and fractured heartbeats and invisible thieves," he mused. "But sometimes, come Matin, the sun breathes an ambric smile and I remember what it was like to dream in color."

Surprise pressed a shivering smile against my skin. I waited for Dowser to continue, but the only sound was the hiss of guttering candles and my hitching breath.

"That's not an answer," I said, at last.

"I suppose it isn't," Dowser agreed, before turning away to his desk. "Come back tomorrow, and be prepared to work."

TWENTY-TWO

"You're still mistaking the address for a duc with that of a compte, Mirage," complained Lullaby. "It's not complicated."

"Easy for you to say!" I groused. "I still don't even know what the difference is between the two."

"A compte—" Lullaby flattened her slender hands. "On second thought, I give up. Let's move on to wines, because frankly, I think I need a good, strong drink. You're hopeless."

But she was hiding a smile, and we both knew it. I had spent so many Matins ensconced with Lullaby that I was finally—if too slowly for my mentor's taste—acquiring something resembling good manners. My curtsies were no longer the wobbling stumble of a half-drunk goat, and I could pour a cup of tea without dumping hot water all over the table. Although I was still frankly incapable of telling a Belsyre ice wine from a coastal Cartoinne red, or a Devangelis ruby from a Sousine garnet.

"Goddesses!" Thibo swept into Lullaby's chambers with insouciant grace, clad in an outrageous suit the color of daffodils. "I come bearing gifts."

He tossed a few boxes of bonbons on the low table and flung himself dramatically on the chaise. Lullaby cooed over the patisseries, popping a handful of confections into her mouth. I'd asked her once how she ate such a staggering amount of sugar and maintained her slim figure, but she just patted her blue-tinged skin in obscure explanation.

I almost didn't notice the slender young man lurking in the foyer. I rose, curtsying in the manner appropriate for new acquaintances, and shot Thibo a questioning glance.

"Scion, I forgot you two hadn't met!" He popped back up, curling a proprietary hand around his friend's elbow. "Mirage, meet Mender. Mender, Mirage."

The name caught my attention, and I took the opportunity to study Thibo's new infatuation. He was indeed beautiful, all cool-dark skin with jeweled undertones, and firebrand eyes. He leaned forward and brushed a fleeting kiss on the back of my hand.

"Mirage enjoys being flattered," Thibo said to Mender in a theatrical whisper. "Here, I'll show you. Mademoiselle, today your beauty is as green and pliant as a newly grown leaf."

I snorted. Mender's eyes gleamed with humor as he leaned forward.

"Don't worry," he murmured in my ear. "Even I think he talks too much."

"I heard that!" Thibo griped, but the lithe young man was already slinging his arms around Thibo's lace-frothed neck and pulling him in for a kiss.

"Yeauch," Lullaby muttered, around a mouthful of chocolate. "Not in front of the children, please."

But I didn't mind. I liked Thibo, and I liked Mender, and I liked seeing them happy with each other. I tried to ignore the cold, dusky taste of loneliness coating my throat with dust. Once I earned my place here at court, then surely I'd find someone of my own. Someone who wanted to breathe my secrets and taste my hopes. Someone to share my world with, every soft-edged kiss and bittersweet sigh and pulsing promise.

"Let's play cards," said Lullaby. "Or something else. Anything, really, to force you two to keep your hands to yourselves."

"How about a game of peine?" Thibo extricated himself from Mender's embrace. "I only play cards if there's gambling involved."

Mender groaned. "But you always win."

"Do I?" Thibo favored me with a salacious wink. "That couldn't possibly be the case."

"I'm afraid I don't know the game," I admitted.

"Penance?" Thibo looked shocked. "Well, it's not difficult to learn."

"Not difficult to learn," said Mender, voice smooth as velvet. "Only difficult to avoid losing the entirety of your fortune to this thief."

Both were difficult for me, as it turned out. I had no head for cards nor for gambling, but I sipped my wine and obediently tossed Sunder's bronze écu on the pile of coins. Thibo won hand after hand of the viciously complicated game, bluffing and lying and cheating as the game actually required.

"Scholars at Unitas are predicting a Blood Rain," Mender said, eerily calm after losing yet another stack of coins. "Later this span."

"What's a Blood Rain?" I asked.

"Once per tide, a storm blows in from the Meridian Desert," Mender explained. "The deep red droplets deposit valuable minerals and nutrients across the land. Without it, crops wouldn't be able to grow beneath our dim sun. So it's usually a time of celebration and plenty."

"I think it's vulgar," said Thibo, nose wrinkling.

"That's just because you hate when your clothes get stained," Lullaby pointed out.

"I do at that." Thibo perked up, a wicked grin sliding across his face. "But a Blood Rain usually means a ball."

Lullaby jerked, nearly knocking over her wineglass.

"What's wrong?" I asked.

"Nothing," she lied. But sudden fear wreathed her gaze and sent a chill skipping down my arms.

"It's a good thing, Lullaby," insisted Thibo. I frowned—as usual, Thibo had leapt to some realization while I was still learning to walk. "Better a ball than the Gauntlet! Even if she makes a mistake—"

"How can you say that?" Lullaby looked stricken. "You heard what the empress said in the Atrium—"

The bell rang for Prime. I jumped to my feet before Lullaby and Thibo's bickering deteriorated into a brawl.

"I'm late for my lesson with Dowser. Anyone care to walk me across the palais?"

Lullaby shot Thibo a glance heavy with meaning, but Thibo returned the look with a peevish stare, throwing his cards onto the table and rising to his feet.

"I should be pleased to escort the fairest lady at court. Mender?"

"I'll stay for a bit." Mender gave Lullaby a smile like cool water touched with sunlight, and curled her hands in his. She instantly relaxed, her face smoothing like stretched silk. "We two should get reacquainted."

Thibo shrugged, and led me from the room.

"What was that about?" I asked as we strolled through a hallway streaked with malachite.

"It was nothing," said Thibo, but a muscle feathered in his jaw.

"You can tell me," I insisted, peering into his face. A frown marred his symmetrical features. "I know how to keep a secret."

"It's not a secret." Thibo shook his head, and his disgruntled expression slid away. "That's just Lullaby and me. We've fought like brother and sister since the day we first met. We disagree on practically everything. But we understand each other. And I would never trade that relationship with her, even if it is turning me grey before my time."

"Do you have blood siblings?" I asked. Thibo never spoke about his family.

"Yes," he said, with a queer finality in his tone. He glanced at me, and something softened in his eyes. "As I'm sure Lullaby told you, my father is Gilbert Montrachet, Duc de Beltoire. We are a notoriously fecund family, and my siblings and cousins are legion."

"And where is your estate?" I wanted to keep him talking—there was something strange behind his eyes, some apprehension or fear, faint as a whisper but dark as a Dominion shadow.

"South," he said, and brightened. "Come, I'll show you."

"Show me? But I'm late for my lesson with Dowser!"

But Thibo was already dragging me toward an unfamiliar annex of the palais. A narrow parlor opened into a sweeping hall, lined with high glass windows along both sides. A massive fresco soared in a grand arch high above—a stylized retelling of the Meridian myth. The Sun in his pale blue palais, the Moon surrounded by her starry-eyed handmaidens. And soaring between them, the Scion on his chariot of flames, flanked by his hounds and luminous with his Relics and his righteous fire.

"Not that." Thibo, impatient, tapped on the floor with the toe of his shoe. *"This."*

I stared at the collection of tiny colorful tiles beneath my slippers for a long moment before I realized they were tesserae in a grand mosaic. I squinted at the vivid shards—emerald, turquoise, ambric, and pale glass—but I couldn't make out the picture. I didn't think it was a reflection of the Meridian myth above.

"What is it?"

"A map of the daylight world, of course!" Thibo stared at me. "You're telling me—"

"Don't," I snapped, holding up the flat of my palm. "I was raised by superstitious Sisters in the middle of nowhere."

"So I've heard," said Thibo, unsympathetic. "Here, I'll show you."

He dragged me toward the far wall, then spun me to face across the mosaic.

"This line of black tiles demarcates the edge of Dominion," he explained, pointing to our feet before nudging me forward. "This is you crossing the Dusklands." I nearly tripped over a hunk of ambric set into the tile. Thibo smiled. "The Amber City, of course. To your right—northward—are the Meteor Mountains. And to your left—southward—is Beltoire, the Montrachet lands." He pointed to a few sapphire-blue tiles scattered like jewels among the green. "*Terre du Lacs*. The lake country. Pretty women, *beautiful* men, and the most delicious delicacies you've ever tasted."

But I'd almost forgotten the original question. I stood transfixed by the daylight world, glittering with a million tiny colors. I could see it now, the sweep and flow of grasslands into forest, rivers trailing slow fingers toward the vast dazzle of infinite ocean. In the ruddy sunlight the mosaic glowed, chatoyant with light and depthless with shadow.

"Tell me more," I whispered.

"As you wish." Thibo led me around the room in a slow pavane, our slippers dancing between land and sea, desert and mountain. "Here—just off the southern coast, the Sousine Isles, where Lullaby's father lives. The water is blue as sapphires, and the worms who spin our silk are protected by powerful colonial warlords." We stepped into a vast golden stretch of mica-dusted tiles. "The desert ports across the Dura'a Valley, where the sand barges of Aifir and Lirias stop for supplies on their way to the Amber City."

"If you're planning on running away from Coeur d'Or," drawled a low voice from across the hall, "you're going to need a smaller map."

Thibo froze, his palm tensing against mine. We turned around at the same time, but I already knew who that refined tenor belonged to.

Sunder, flanked by his twin sister, Bane, and followed by a bouquet of finely scented lords and ladies. I faintly recognized a few from that day in the Atrium, but besides Lullaby, Thibo, Mender, and the oh-so-charming twins, my acquaintances at court numbered zero. The Suicide Twins were dressed to match—the rich verdure of Sunder's waistcoat made his eyes dark as genévrier needles, and Bane's pale green and silver gown looked sewn from frosted new leaves.

"Sunder." Thibo bowed with barely the appropriate level of respect due to the blond lord's rank. "Off to rip the tails from newborn kittens, I assume?"

"Reaper," replied Sunder, his tone acid. "Have you run out of lords to seduce, and so moved on to ladies? Narrow hips do not a boy make, despite what you may have heard."

Someone among the Sinister entourage giggled. I heard

Thibo's rough intake of breath, but couldn't look away from Sunder as his green gaze inevitably cut to me. I fought the urge to flinch as his eyes raked me up and down, lingering on my chevron-patterned gown of cobalt and rose.

"I see my money bought you clothing, but no taste." He quirked a disdainful eyebrow. "What are you doing roaming about the palais? I thought you were confined to your rooms until you learned to spell your name."

I did flinch then, and anger flared white-hot inside me.

"Wagered on any more seductions recently, my lord Sunder?" I made my voice as sweet as possible, ignoring the rage sending flames to burn my fingertips. "Or did they finally ban you from the stables?"

A courtier behind Sunder guffawed, elbowing his neighbor and sending a gratifying rush to cool my fury. But I was surprised to see most of the courtiers glance at each other with confusion. I was even more surprised to see Sunder flush nearly to his hairline before dipping into a low bow, his wrist quirked in an attitude I recognized as *points awarded*. When he rose back to his full height, he'd schooled his expression to its usual haughty scorn.

"As subtle and charming as always, demoiselle," he said, before turning on his heel and crossing the room, his cohort trailing him in a colorful convoy of satin and organza.

And as I watched his velvet back recede beneath the mural of Meridian, I wondered—why hadn't he told anyone about his sadistic plot to humiliate me in exchange for his sponsorship? I'd expected that to be the talk of court by now. But instead, my allusion to the wager had embarrassed him.

Who was Sunder? And what did he hope to gain by insulting and toying with me at every turn?

TWENTY-THREE

I arrived at Dowser's chambers late, flustered, and distracted. The room reeked of coquelicot resin, thin purple smoke lingering hazy in the air. The stench tickled my throat and burned my nostrils. I coughed.

Dowser jerked up from his chair, but when his eyes found mine across the room, they were dull and unfocused. He tried to rise to his feet, but his movements were jerky and uncoordinated.

"You're early," he groaned. His head lolled on the back of his chair.

"I'm not," I said. Surprise made my words slow. "You're just high."

I frowned, stepping farther into the chamber and waving the smoke away from my face. I'd met men and women like Dowser before, folk in the dusty villages along the Dominion border who sought refuge from the dusk in this insidious smoke poisoning them from the inside. Folk who called the stuff joie, or rêve, or lotus. Folk who thought they touched magic or foresaw tantalizing futures, but only found death.

"This place stinks." I flung the heavy curtains open. Ruddy light poured into the murky room. Another push sent the smooth panes of glass swinging outward. Cool air swirled the smoke into drifting specters, then banished them. Inexplicable disappointment shuddered through me. I had no right to scold my teacher, and yet—"How can you expect to serve your empress when you're floating in shadows like a nighthawk?"

"It helps . . ." Dowser's words were as sluggish as his movements. ". . . with the dreams."

Dreams. What had he said, the last time I was in his study? *These Nocturnes, I dream too often of cold, pale faces and fractured heartbeats and invisible thieves.*

Sympathy pierced my heart, reluctant but sharp. I'd never bothered to wonder what kind of life my teacher led. I'd been too busy disliking him. I'd hated the way he'd rifled through my memories, sifting shrewd fingers through shrouded secrets and drab dreams. But he couldn't have enjoyed it any more than I did. Was that how he spent his days? Diving deep in the resistant minds of spies and thieves and subversives, plowing their thoughts and harvesting their secrets?

He turned his head toward me, and beneath the blur of drug-induced stupor, there was pain in his eyes. Nausea soured my stomach. Perhaps if I dreamed in the splintered fragments of other people's stolen memories, I too would seek solace in a pipe of joie.

"Come on," I said, wedging one organdy-clad arm under his shoulder. He groaned again, but allowed me to haul him to his feet. His black ascetic's robes were long, and threatened to trip us both. "Let's go for a walk. This place needs to air out."

"Where?" he protested when I shoved him through the door and out into the gleaming corridor. It was still early in the day—hopefully we wouldn't run into anyone. I didn't want anyone to see him like this.

Unless . . . A thought sent outrage prickling in my belly.

Unless everyone already knew, and didn't care.

A broad hall narrowed into a corridor lined with agate and striated with amethyst. Beyond lay my favorite discovery since I'd arrived in Coeur d'Or—a sheltered grotto crafted from crystal. Mirrored trunks sent shards of burnished light to flicker between delicate leaves blown from clear glass. Prisms danced along lacy fronds. Water slithered down the walls like the phantom tears of invisible sylphs.

I eased Dowser onto one of the benches, then perched beside him. He stared around at the translucent jardin for a long, long moment. Finally, he smiled.

It was the first time I'd ever seen Dowser smile—really smile—and it was like a sunbeam slicing between thunderclouds, radiant and bright. It didn't matter that his teeth were stained with tabak and kachua, or that his lips were dull and cracked. He was happy, if just for an instant.

The smile disappeared, replaced by a more familiar frown. Though his eyes were still distant and a little cloudy, Dowser's gaze had regained some of its usual clarity.

"Why here, Mirage?" he asked.

I answered his question with one of my own.

"How often do you get out of your chambers?" I asked. "Be honest."

"Does escaping into hallucinations count?" His voice cracked, and he sighed, removing his spectacles to polish them on the front of his dark robes. "I'm sorry you had to see me like that. I never intended—"

"Don't apologize," I snapped, interrupting my teacher. "I've seen what that rubbish can do to a person, you know. If you truly felt sorry, you'd stop."

"It's not that simple," he growled. "It's never that simple, and if you've truly seen the effects of coquelicot, you'd know that as well."

We sat in silence, the only sound the chiming whisper of crystal petals.

"Who else knows?" I finally asked.

"How should I know?"

"Severine?" I pressed. "Does she know her closest advisor is an addict?"

Dowser was silent, but the corner of his mouth twitched. Horror prickled through me.

"She gives you the stuff?"

"That's enough!" Dowser surged to his feet, and in an instant I was reminded of his size and breadth, usually hidden behind a desk and a dark robe. His eyes were clear once more, as though he had willed away any lingering effects of the drug. "There are limits to the things you may discuss with me, and you would do well to remember that."

I took a deep breath, gazing around. The sky, a bruised mauve. The dazzle of a thousand crystal leaves. Glass flowers, beveled and faceted like diamonds. Water, streaming down gleaming walls.

"I know why I am kept at arm's length," I murmured, fighting against the drowning sensation of being always *outside*. "I know I haven't yet earned my place. But how can I play a game if I haven't been taught the rules? How can I navigate a web of intrigue if no one shares their secrets? Belonging is more than just existing somewhere."

"How can you be so sure this is where you belong?"

"How can you be so sure it isn't?" I spread my arms. "You spoke of sunlight and ambric smiles, of dreaming vast, colorful dreams. That's why I came here: to be part of that world. They named me Mirage, and that is what I am. Not a faint illusion that will quickly disappear, but a desire, and a promise, and a dream of something impossible. But only if I'm given the chance."

Dowser stilled. Beneath the ethereal shimmering branches, he was stark as a nightmare. Expectation glossed his gaze.

Control. I hissed Dowser's favorite word at myself. The dristic prison around my heart clenched. *Rules.* I bit my lip and tried to remember Dowser's steps. *Envision. Empower. Express.*

I squeezed my eyes shut and conjured up an image. *Envision.* I held it in my mind's eye as I tried to suffuse it with power from—where? I gritted my teeth as I imagined my blood pulsing with life, with *animation.* A tatter of energy was torn from my center, rent from my being. *Empower.*

And then I lifted my arms, and tried to create something that wasn't there. *Express.*

A cascade of crystal in a velveteen sky. Diamonds and dusk, ice wine and ambric. A dream of sharp edges, of hopes flown too high.

The illusion dribbled between my fingers like water down a drain.

Dismay hollowed out the space between my ribs even as vertigo blurred my vision and weakened my muscles. I dragged my heavy gaze to Dowser, but he wasn't looking at me, or even at my hands, where the illusion was barely a memory. He stared at the trees, at the smooth, polished trunks, mirroring our movements in distorted swoops and curves.

"Mirage," he murmured. "Where do your illusions come from?"

"I don't know," I said, choking on the hot tears smearing my rouge and clogging my throat. "I don't know."

"Go home," he said gently. "We'll try again tomorrow."

TWENTY-FOUR

Sleep was like the Midnight Dominion, near enough to see but impossible to reach.

I drifted toward the window in a nightgown pale as the mythical Moon and soft as a lover's touch. The sunlight creeping beneath the curtains was red as the cinnamon Lullaby sprinkled on her kachua, and its touch on my skin made me feel feverish, as though I was burning up from within.

I didn't know how much longer I could do this. I'd come here believing so fully in the promise of a new life that I hadn't made space for the horrible possibility that none of this would work out. I might never step in time to the intricate choreography of courtly life. I might envision a thousand reveries—midnight and cold fire, bright sand and cobalt, amber and dusk—only to have them drift like wisps of fog from my fingertips. I might have dreamed of a perfect world that simply didn't exist.

A soft scuff at the door to my chambers jerked my attention toward the foyer. It was past second Nocturne. My staff never came to my rooms this late, and I thought I'd heard rumors of a big soirée tonight.

"Who is it?" I called softly.

There was no response, only another tap at the door. I gathered my dressing gown closer and ignored a warning throbbing in time with my heart.

Surely it's only Lullaby or Thibo, I assured myself. *Who else could it be?*

I opened the door, letting in a sliver of crimson light. I glimpsed a streak of white gold. A glitter of green.

Sunder.

Shock strung my bones at hard angles. My heart shuddered against my ribs.

"You." The word escaped me in a narrow hiss. The specter of remembered pain spangled white-hot against the back of my eyes, and I clenched my fists.

"Calm down," Sunder said, words clipped. And then, as though reading my mind: "If I wanted to murder you in your bed I probably wouldn't have knocked."

I gaped.

He glanced over his shoulder into the red velvet light, furtive, then brushed past me into my chambers. The scrape of his brocade jacket against my bare arm reminded me in an excruciating flash that I was dressed only in my flimsy nightgown.

"How dare you!" I snapped, crossing my arms over my chest and trying for haughty.

"Dare what?" Sunder turned on his heel, taking in my blooming chambers with slow disinterest.

"Dare—invade my privacy!" I spluttered. "What are you even doing here?"

"Offering you an opportunity." He gave an indolent shrug, and tossed a bundle of cloth at me. "Now get dressed."

I unfurled the cloak in a heavy exhale of green damask and black velvet. Curiosity and fear mingled with the sharp glossy tang of genévrier and frost, making me light-headed. I curled my fingers deeper into the cloth, remembering Dowser's admonishments. *Discipline. Control. Composure.*

"And why," I forced out, "would I want to wear this anywhere?"

"It doesn't much matter what you want. You're not supposed to be going where we're going. So you'll have to go disguised."

"Oh?" A flutter of intrigue tickled the nape of my neck, and I suppressed a shudder. I was suddenly desperate to leave my chambers—to go somewhere, do *something*. I'd been nearly a span at the Amber Court and had barely ventured out of Lys Wing. I didn't particularly fancy Sunder as a chaperone, but . . . he was the only one offering. "And where, pray tell, are we going?"

"I'm disinclined to ruin the surprise."

"And I don't like surprises." My voice was flat. "Tell me now, or I'm not going."

He hesitated, his eyes bright and rigid as polished dristic.

"The Gauntlet," he said at last. The word was a knife honed too sharp; brittle at the edges and so thin it might have been translucent. "Now hurry, or we'll miss the start."

❦

It was after third Nocturne as we passed through eerily deserted palais halls. The constant glow of the sun steeped through glazed windows and stained panes, but torches and ambric lamps were extinguished, and gloom lurked in the silhouettes of things.

I hurried after Sunder, nearly trotting to keep up with his long, spare strides. The borrowed cloak was too long, flapping around my ankles and threatening to heave me onto the floor. It smelled like its owner too—a disconcerting bite of ice and greenery that crept up my nostrils and conjured vague visions of shadowed forests and frozen lakes. I shook my head, fighting the urge to hurl off the cloak and run in the opposite direction.

Sunder stopped suddenly in the shadow of a marble pillar along the Esplanade, flinging out an arm to halt my progress. I stumbled, knocking into his outstretched palm with my shoulder. I jerked away, but not before a coil of pain rippled down the length of my arm.

"Don't do that!" I yelped. I curled my hand around my wrist, but my fingers were cold and trembling and offered no comfort for a chilly ache that had already disappeared. "Don't you ever touch me like that again."

Savage shock pulsed raw across Sunder's face before he looked away. When he glanced at me again, his mask of practiced indifference was intact.

"You ran into me, demoiselle." His words were piercingly polite. "Perhaps you ought to ask Lullaby to school you in the sophisticated art of walking in a straight line."

"Perhaps *you* ought to—" I began, but Sunder's attention jerked away from me, and my hot words died in my throat.

Beyond the colonnaded arcade of the Esplanade, the terraced jardins of Coeur d'Or had been transformed into an arena. A broad oval court had been flattened and sanded, ringed by tiers of delicate benches draped in flaming pennants. Braziers of fire roared at both ends of the arena, melting the armor of stiff Skyclad Gardes into shades of amber and blood. I watched openmouthed as courtiers paraded past in wild, revealing costumes and extravagant headdresses. I glimpsed a bare, muscular stomach painted like the gaping maw of a vicious beast; necklaces of thorns and bracelets of coals; tiaras of sharp glass and slippers of obsidian.

"What is this?" I whispered, but Sunder had already told me. *The Gauntlet.*

The court began to file into the tiers of benches and seats. Their taut whispers filled the air with uncanny music, and their crystal goblets chimed like a hundred tiny bells. I reluctantly scanned the crowd, and recognized Thibo with a dreadful jolt. He stood with his arm slung around Mender, who was practically carrying his beau as Thibo sagged at the knees. I squinted: Thibo's eyes looked glazed and unfocused. I frowned. Even from here I could tell he was blind drunk.

I took one step forward.

"Don't." The quiet word was a dristic-tipped lash; when I turned my head Sunder's gaze was unforgiving. "Stay."

A manic energy throbbed through the crowd, and my own heartbeat quickened as my gaze fell upon the last courtier to join the gathering.

Severine. The Amber Empress.

She rode slowly out of the jardins on a massive chestnut destrier, wearing a dress of purest white and flanked by six feather-plumed chevaliers. The blazing braziers gilded the horse's coat with molten kembric and dazzled across the diamond-bright gown until Severine was a celestial vision astride a tongue of flame, outshining the dim sun. I could hardly breathe for the beauty of it.

She dismounted in a swirl of amber and took her place in a draped chair at the head of the arena. The crowd quieted.

"Tonight," Severine said, her voice ringing like the Compline bell, "we welcome the delegation from the Sousine Isles to our humble court. With vast bolts of rich silk and coffers full of jewels they thank me for my patronage—I intend to repay that thanks with hospitality! Let no request go undenied, no whim go unindulged, no fantasy go unrealized."

Sousine Isles. I scanned the faces of the group Severine indicated, looking for a hint of pelagic skin or aqua eyes, but besides the heavy medallions hanging around their richly clothed chests, the party looked no different from the courtiers. I frowned again. Why wouldn't the Sousine delegation include any native Gorma?

"So with no further ado," Severine was saying, "from Sinister, I choose . . . Bramble!"

A tall girl extricated herself from the crowd and prowled to the center of the sand court. She had sable hair coiled in a towering chignon and brown eyes ringed in kohl. Living vines entwined her torso, the creeping tendrils of green stark against her fair skin. She lifted her arms, and Sinister cheered and stomped. Her answering smile was cool with confidence and ripe with ruin.

"And from Dexter," purred Severine, "I choose . . . *Rill.*"

A cascade of some unspoken sentiment surged through my dynasty. Thibo lunged forward, only to be dragged gently back as Mender whispered hurriedly in his ear. I craned my neck to spot whoever the empress had selected. My stomach curdled when I saw him.

Rill couldn't have been more than fourteen. He had a man's height but a boy's body, all gangly limbs and skinny shoulders without an ounce of muscle. His eyes were huge in his face as he slowly descended to the arena. Bramble hissed at him, and he jerked away, trembling hard enough that a brisk wind could have blown him over.

"But, Sunder," I heard myself say, "he's just a child."

"Yes." Sunder's eyes went glassy with the reflection of some ancient torment. "Once upon a time, we were all just children."

"Let the pas de deux begin!"

The empress's cool clarion jolted my attention back to the ring. Bile climbed my throat in an acrid stream as I watched the duel progress, and end mere moments after it began.

Bramble dived at Rill like a desert cat pouncing on prey, shrieking with glad fury. Ropes of black-thorned vines sprouted from her fingertips, whipping through the air at the boy. They wrapped around his wrists and climbed his arms. Where they traveled, they raised painful welts that dribbled blood onto the sandy arena. Rill screamed, jerking his arms ineffectually against the tangle of barbed tendrils. A burble of clear water squirted from his palms in a pathetic attempt at defense, but that only seemed to egg Bramble on.

"Come on!" she screeched. "Is that the best you can do?"

Rill was crying now, leaking water from his face and skin as he fell to his knees in the sand. The thorns had climbed over his shoulders and snaked around his chest, pinning one of his arms to his side. He jerked, managed to free a hand, and with a sobbing gasp, pointed it directly at Bramble. A surge of water, stained pink with Rill's blood, punched the girl in the face. Her kohl smeared, and her tower of hair collapsed in a soggy mess. Fury contorted her face into harsh lines. She sneered, and stalked closer, whipping more green-black vines at Rill.

They slapped around his shoulders. Coiled around his neck. Climbed the sides of his face, punching ragged holes in his cheeks. He screamed with agony as the brambles invaded his mouth. He gagged as he wept for mercy. Still Bramble pushed forward, curling vines toward his nose, his ears, his *eyes*—

"Enough!" The empress's voice pushed through the choking silence. "Victory to Sinister!"

The vines retreated with Bramble, leaving Rill sobbing and broken and bleeding on the sand. A girl with Mender's cool-dark skin and lustrous eyes pushed out onto the court, dropping to her knees beside the boy and smoothing her hands over his lacerations.

With a sudden burst of vile heat I realized I was livid. My fingernails sliced into palms burning with fire, and when I glanced down I saw a jardin of creeping vines skulking at my feet. Their spiny leaves had long thorns that sprang sharp as needles from fat trailers. Drooping flowers hung tattered like Dominion shadows. Ichor dripped black as venom onto the marble.

Control. I bit down on the wash of hues. My chest contracted. The illusion disappeared. I looked up to find Sunder staring at me with brittle incredulity.

"Time to go," he said.

TWENTY-FIVE

I dashed after Sunder, hiking the borrowed cloak around my knees. Confused emotions roiled thick and sour through my head, slowing my thoughts to sludge.

"Wait!" I hissed as I struggled to catch up with his receding back. "Stop!"

He paused beneath an archway carved with crystal arabesques. I skidded to a halt beside him.

"Why did you show me that?" I demanded. "Why did you bring me to the Gauntlet tonight?"

Sunder opened his mouth to say something, but the raucous sounds of celebration ricocheted down the passageway. The shouting and laughter was gaudy in the muted Nocturne hush. My jaw hardened when I glanced over my shoulder and glimpsed smeared eye makeup, damp black hair, and a tight, gloating smile.

"Not here," said Sunder, and grasped my wrist.

I steeled myself for the jolt of pain. It never came. There was just the bracing frisson of his cool fingers against my hot pulse. My outrage at his touch bled away as my curiosity took over, and I let him lead me through a tangle of hallways. Finally, he pulled me into a shaded alcove dripping with breezy silks. They breathed and bloomed around us like captured clouds, caressing our skin with sleek, soft fingers and hiding us from view.

"Why didn't that hurt?" I blurted out.

A muscle in his cheek leapt as he clenched his jaw.

"Politic as ever, demoiselle," he said. "That's the question you want to ask me?"

"Now I do." A mulish stubbornness gripped me. "Can't you control your legacy?"

His eyes were metal. "Can't you?"

A blush painted my face with restless heat. "I'm an untrained fantast from the edge of the world. You've lived in the palais your whole life."

"You know nothing about me."

"I know they call you Severine's dog."

His head jerked back, sifting his pale hair between the drapes. His nostrils flared. He wordlessly turned to leave. I reached out, suddenly repentant, and snatched his wrist. This time, a sting zipped up my arm to my elbow. I dropped his hand like it was on fire.

"Your feelings," I guessed. I thought of how my own legacy ebbed and flowed with the tides of my emotional states— bursting out of me unbidden when I was frightened, or angry, or awestruck. I swallowed the uncomfortable sensation of having anything in common with the arrogant blond lord. "You can't control your legacy when your emotions are heightened."

"Our *gifts*"—he spat the word like it was poison—"are a reflection of our inner selves. Our inclinations, our experiences, our emotions. None of us are ever fully in control of our legacies. Some of us never are."

"But—"

"Enough." He forced a listless smirk. "Don't you have packing to do?"

"What?" Confusion rocked me off-balance.

"Packing," he repeated, enunciating the word until it was sharp and bright. "The process by which one readies one's belongings for departure."

"Departure?" My face twisted into a knot. "Who's leaving?"

"I assumed you would be." One burnished eyebrow lifted. "After everything you just saw—?"

"So *that's* why." Realization swelled, hued in faint shades of humiliation. "That's why you took me to the Gauntlet. To intimidate me. To frighten me away from the palais. To manipulate me."

"To give you an opportunity." Sunder stepped closer in the sighing silk sanctuary until we stood toe-to-toe. "The Gauntlet is more than just a political maneuver disguised as entertainment. It is a show of power. To the Sousine delegates, to the world, but most importantly, to *us*. At any moment, for any reason, any one of us could be called to the Gauntlet. Dexter versus Sinister. And the Gauntlet always has a winner. And a loser."

I shivered.

"I don't know why you came here, *Mirage*." His voice was barely audible. "Whether you want fortune or fame or you just have some dusk-addled fantasy about what it means to be aristocracy, I don't know. I don't care. But I don't want you here. And you shouldn't want to be here."

"I chose—"

"Make a different choice," he interrupted. "Leave the palais. Unless you're eager to find yourself lying in the sand of the Gauntlet in a pool of your own blood."

"Is that a threat?"

"No." I could taste his cool breath on my cheek. "But it might be a promise."

We faced off, as stiff as the breathless silks were pliant. I tried to banish the image Sunder's words had conjured back up—poor skinny Rill, covered in vicious vines as tears and blood and the water from his useless legacy pooled around him. Was that my fate? To be trussed up for slaughter and fed to another legacy, all for someone's twisted idea of entertainment? That wasn't the world I'd promised myself.

But no. Lullaby, Thibo, Mender—they were nothing like that. And I'd barely been at court a span—taking a single event like the Gauntlet out of context was jumping to conclusions at best, and social suicide at worst. I still had time to hone my legacy, to find my strength. Rill was young, nervous, weak. I'd gotten worse treatment from the mean brats in the Dusklands—I wouldn't let myself surrender to that fate.

What good are illusions against an army of thorny vines? whispered a traitorous voice in the shadows of my mind.

"I'm staying," I breathed. "This is where I belong."

Sunder loosed his breath and pushed his hair back from his forehead. His eyes blistered my skin where they touched my face.

"Who cares where you belong," he said, "if you're dead?"

And then he was gone, disappearing like a phantom in a shifting forest of silken trees. I almost pursued him, but a sudden fierce intuition rooted my feet to the ground, and I knew that if I followed him I would fall. Fall through a brittle glass floor onto bright, mirrored spikes, fall from a fragile dream into a waking nightmare, fall like an incandescent Meridian through the sheer blue riot of lingering dusk.

He isn't your friend, I reminded myself. *And he would see you ruined.*

I was nearly back to Lys Wing before I realized I still wore Sunder's borrowed cloak of midnight and pine. And even when I shucked it off and kicked it into a corner, I knew that I must now smell like cold fire and dristic and the sharp blade of anguish at the edge of cruelty.

I entered my chambers to find Lullaby perched on a cushion beneath the window. The colored glass cast such lovely shapes and contours on her face that for a long moment I didn't see how pale she was. Or notice her expression.

Dread was a living thing inside my breast.

"Where have you been?" Lullaby stood, and shoved something at my chest. It was a crimson envelope stamped in gilt and smothered in looping calligraphy. I couldn't have read it if I'd tried.

"What is it?" I asked, although some cowardly part of me didn't want to know, especially if Lullaby was so terrified.

"It's an invitation." Lullaby crossed behind me and glanced over my shoulder at the thick paper. "A grand ball, a week hence. Astrologists are predicting a Blood Rain. Everyone is to wear red, in honor of the occasion."

I frowned. "So?"

"So." Her lower lip trembled. "So, the invitation is for you, Mirage. The empress wants to see you. She wants to see your legacy."

"But—" Fear gripped me as my skin flashed hot, then bitter cold. "But what about Carrousel? I thought I had more time."

"Time is as fickle as a courtly game, Mirage." Worry made Lullaby's eyes stormy. "And the empress never plays by anyone's rules but her own. You'll have to be ready by the Blood Rain Ball. If not, we'll all pay the price."

And as she turned to leave, I heard the echo of her unspoken words: *I'll pay the price.*

TWENTY-SIX

nxiety stole my sleep, and trepidation followed me on silent footsteps.

The following days were a flurry of activity. Fittings for an ornate gown in a fabric as scarlet as temptation. Instruction in the latest dances: tempête, jaconde, angoisse. Lullaby's eyes brimming with panic as I practiced the tiny twists of the wrist that meant much, much more than I would ever truly understand. Dowser, haunting the corners of his rooms like a ghost, insisting I *envision, empower, express.* Hours sitting on the floor of Dowser's study and attempting to conjure each of the objects he set before me: a small horn comb, delicate and fragile; a tabak pipe, smoothed with age; an old book, its spine broken and shredded by overuse.

I barely managed snippets of shapes and dribbles of color.

I couldn't bring myself to tell Lullaby that she'd have to be responsible for my failure.

Thibo sensed our collective unease, and attempted to distract me and Lullaby with various picnics and outings and adventures around the palais.

"I thought I wasn't supposed to roam Coeur d'Or yet," I hedged. Normally I would have jumped at the chance to escape my rooms, but I was sullen with dread.

"You received an invitation to the Blood Rain Ball from the Amber Empress herself," Thibo said, making his eyes comically round. "No one is going to bat their eyes at afternoon tea."

I glanced at Lullaby, who managed a brooding shrug.

"Come *on*," insisted Thibo. "We're going to the Solarium. If there's one thing that will cheer you two preening lumps, it's some sunshine and the mirrored images of your own vain faces."

Set in a little wilderness beyond the Weeping Pools, the Solarium was a tall, circular pavilion with a curving dome filigreed in bronze and kembric. We stepped through huge, swinging doors into a space thunderous with light. I gasped, throwing one arm up to shield my eyes from the brightness. The interior of the pavilion was edged and winged with mirrors—a hundred, a *thousand* mirrors, angled and curved and flared. Sultry sunlight poured in through an oculus above the door, striking one mirror, then reflecting again and again until finally it seemed to hang in a spectacular orb of kembric at the center of the dome.

I was so transfixed by the light that I almost didn't see Sunder. With one leg propped on a low bench against the wall, he leaned down to flirt with a lovely maiden in a cerulean gown. The hair pushed back from his brow glowed molten in the spectacular rays.

"It's Sunder," I said, grabbing Lullaby by the elbow. Wrath and embarrassment beat twin pulses in my heart when I remembered the last time we'd met. His cool fingers on my hot wrist, the taste of his derision in the back of my throat. *Who cares where you belong if you're dead?* "Let's go."

But it was too late. The blue-gowned lady's eyes had flickered to us across the room, and Sunder straightened to follow her gaze. His smile froze on his face.

"The most fearsome trio at court," he drawled. His low voice echoed around the dome, seeming to originate from everywhere and nowhere at once. "The Blue Man's daughter, the caterwauling Casanova, and our own filthy-faced Dusklander."

The familiar ember of rage scorched my blood. I stepped forward, quelling a brief flash of rational panic.

"Lord Sunder." I dropped into the curtsy reserved for royalty and hoped it looked sardonic. "I confess I'm not surprised to find you here, the one place in the palais where you can view your own reflection so many times. You must be in raptures."

Sunder prowled closer, until he stood with me beneath the false sun bathing us in brilliance. Behind him, his flirt edged closer, unease and curiosity warring on her face.

"So you admit," he purred, "that I am beautiful to look at."

"He who admires himself so confidently," I demurred, ignoring the hot throb at my temples, "must surely know more about beauty than one such as me."

Behind Sunder, the girl's mouth popped into a little O. Lullaby inhaled.

"You accuse me of vanity and poor taste in one breath." Sunder's droll tone hid an edge. "Perhaps, then, you might begrudge me your own explanation of beauty?"

I sucked in a breath of cool sunlight. Sunder's smirk oozed condescension, but there was something in the straightforward weight of his eyes that made me think he might actually care what I was about to say. But this line of bantering had grown far too philosophical for my tastes. Were we talking about vanity, or taste, or beauty? I didn't think so.

I only wished I knew what we *were* talking about.

"Beauty," I began, before abruptly deciding to be honest. "Beauty is all the things we can see, but cannot touch. Beauty is a way of seeing the world, unsullied by convention and free from coveting. Beauty is a stripe of amber light on a shoulder dusted with kembric. A breeze chiming through petals of glass. A distorted sun in a mirrored room."

"Beauty, by that definition," murmured Sunder, with a searing flare of his unfathomable eyes, "is your legacy manifest, is it not? What we can see, but cannot touch?"

I swallowed, and frost feathered the length of my spine.

"Perhaps you will favor us with a sample of beauty, then, my most talented lady Mirage?"

The ice turning my blood to sludge told me I'd made a mistake. I'd backed myself into a corner. I was trapped. There was no way to say no.

Control. I reached through the haze of panic for an image. Any image. *Envision.* A horned comb, or a jardin full of glass flowers, or an amber throne, or—

I dared a desperate glance at Sunder, expecting a sneer of scorn. But he just watched me with cool regard. Waiting.

I took a sunlit breath and let myself drift toward the well of impossible colors latched away in the dusky prison around my heart. They pulsed, hazy as amber and lazy as a heartbeat. These were the dreams that had carried me from the edge of the daylight world, but they were scorched with humiliation, shackled with thorny vines, stained with the gratuitous blood of gangling youths. I'd beaten them down so many times, throttling them and denying them, smothering them with rules even as I begged them to obey me.

Why couldn't I control them? It wasn't that the power wasn't there. I remembered a dim dusk edged in shadows, and then colors bursting blithe and brazen through the gloaming. I remembered the reverent cadences of an ancient myth, and then a lush blackness opulent with argent light. I remembered a vile burst of fury, and then an impossible wilderness of spiked vines and grasping tendrils.

The empress's voice echoed in my mind: *Let the pas de deux begin!*

A cruel joke; a beautiful veil for a hideous reality. Wrath burst to life within me, but so too did a bright, cold hope, clean-edged and gleaming like a silver thread in the dim. Another world, laid like a veil above our own: a scintillant hush of peace and harmony and calm.

A world where grace reigned. Where compassion dwelled. Where children weren't forced to fight to the blood.

I can do better than she can.

"Mirage?" Lullaby's voice, uncertain, pierced my reverie.

Envision. Empower. Express.

And I suddenly knew—I didn't want to mirror this world. I didn't want to conjure horn combs or paperweights or even glass jardins. I wanted to create my own worlds. Impossible, ephemeral, elusive worlds at the edge of imagining. Dreams, reborn and rebranded, set free from reality.

Something like that didn't have rules. And it certainly couldn't be controlled.

I opened my eyes and let instinct take over. A pair of dancers appeared with a gasp of light. I shaped them from breaths of rose-colored air and the contours of featherdown. I left them translucent, and the gilded edges of the false sun's rays cut them to ribbons before stitching them back together again. They glided, pellucid and lambent, through a breathless duet. Their feet never touched the ground. The mirrors caught their reflections and echoed them across the edges of other mirrors, until a hundred dancers whirled whisper-quiet through a world beyond touch.

Finally, the dancers drifted into oblivion. When I dared look at Sunder, I caught a glimpse of dazzled bemusement before his face smoothed into its cool mask once more. His eyes etched lines of fire on my face as he bent over my hand. The brush of his lips was the graze of a razor.

He returned his attention to the other lady, a gracious hand at her elbow. A second later Lullaby dragged me backward, away from the brilliance of the Solarium and out into the scorched dimness of our real sun.

"Scion, Mirage!" Lullaby burst out the moment the doors were closed behind us. "That was—why didn't you tell us you'd come so far? That was exquisite."

A whisper of pleasure heated my chest.

"But what in Dominion's name were you thinking, challenging him like that?" Practicality crept back into Lullaby's voice. "A philosophical discussion on the ideals of beauty with *Sunder*? That's like standing on the edge of a cliff and asking Meridian himself to push you over!"

"I think," said Thibo, smothering a gust of laughter and looping his arm through mine, "that you have proven yourself socially invincible in the most spectacular fashion on your first outing at court. I'm taking you everywhere from now on."

But as we trekked back to the palais, my friends bickering and laughing over my head, I couldn't think of anything but the chilly weight of Sunder's astonished gaze, and the perilous, tremulous sensation of working with my legacy instead of trying to control it. Look what I'd done: A new world had spilled jewel-bright from my fingertips. An impossible world, woven from patterns of dappled sunlight and the threads of old dreams.

A world that belonged to me, instead of the other way around.

TWENTY-SEVEN

I found Dowser almost by accident, after spending nearly all of Compline searching for my teacher to tell him the good news.

He stood in a broad hall with his arms loosely clasped behind his back. I'd never been to this wing before, and I couldn't help but catch my breath. Huge arching windows splashed rivers of amber light across a parquet floor. Lithe gilded statues twined themselves between jasper-limned pillars. Magnificent crystal chandeliers hung from a frescoed ceiling. And everywhere were portraits.

A hundred unfamiliar faces stared down at me. Smiling faces, severe faces. Laughing children with flower garlands and stern generals with medals spangling their jacket breasts and cool-eyed dames who'd seen the world. Dauphines astride destriers. Emperors dressed all in kembric. For a moment it seemed as though the weight of all that history and heritage would crush me to the earth and grind me into dust. But then I squared my shoulders, and strode toward my teacher.

"I heard about what happened in the Solarium." Dowser glanced away from the portrait of a man with laughing eyes and a peppery beard. A smile lingered around Dowser's mouth, a small ghost of the grin he'd given me that day in the glass jardin. "Congratulations."

I gaped at him.

His smile cracked wider. "News travels fast at court, Mirage. And I have eyes everywhere."

I turned toward the wall of portraits to hide a sudden awkward dazzle of mortification mixed with pride. *News travels fast at court.* Was everyone talking about me?

"I confess myself curious," Dowser continued. "What was it, in the end, that set your illusions free? Incandescent sunlight? The mirrors? Lord Sunder's unique attention?"

I barely registered the light teasing. Dowser's question had struck to the heart of my own seething conflict: What exactly had I done, and would I be able to do it again? All I knew was that I had relinquished the control I'd fought so hard for, and magic had happened. I chewed on my lip for a long moment. Finally, I flicked my wrist at a diamond-bright mirror wedged between two hulking portraits and dug deep for the words to explain.

"When I was a child, I kept a scratched and tarnished mirror under my pillow." I leaned forward until my own features loomed close. It was still a shock to see myself gowned and gilded, my hair an elaborate coiffure and my lips rouged. "I'd nicked it from a village kid and used to take it out when the Sisters thought I was asleep. I would trace the lines of my nose, the edges of my eyes, fascinated by the sensation of being in my own body, and no one else's."

Dowser gave a slow nod.

"But though my reflection may *look* identical to me, it is not me. She has no flesh, no blood. No thoughts, no opinions. No substance. She's not alive. She's merely a reflection of something that is alive." I sucked in a breath, focusing on the brilliant certainty that had soared through me at the Solarium. "Back in the Dusklands, the Sisters taught me that to control my legacy was to deny it. And when I came here you taught me that to control my legacy I had to give it rules. So I tried to bind it to reality—chain it up in the blood-hot space between sinew and bone. Make it *real*. But I am not a mirror, nor am I a god. I can neither reflect life, nor create it."

Dowser turned his head to regard me with quiet absorption.

"I am a fantast. My legacy is illusion—a blaze of strange colors born to rail against the pallid dusk. I *burn*, Dowser— with marvel and magic and a yearning I can't name. I finally stopped fighting for control. I surrendered to the impossible. I stopped trying to create the world I saw, and chose to create a world I wanted to see."

"And in that surrender, you have triumphed." Dowser's eyes glittered behind his spectacles, and I suddenly felt as though I was plummeting through a fathomless twilight: the boundless space between bright mirrors, lit by stars and hope and distant laughter. But then his eyes went flat and colorless once more, and he looked around the hall as though remembering where he was. Who he was. "Your success is my success, although I seem to have led you more wrong than right. I suppose you will no longer be needing my guidance now that you've found your own guiding light."

Disappointment plundered my heart. I looked up to stem a sudden well of tears, and caught a glimpse of the arching fresco adorning the ceiling. Another Meridian story—a fallen star and black mountains, the Blasting of the Wastes. I remembered another Scion fresco, and beneath it the spread of colorful tes- serae in a mosaic of the daylight world. Thibo's easy explanation of lands I'd never heard of, never dreamed of. Lullaby's cool tones, picking out the weft and weave of the empire's political tapestry. The scrawled ink of Sunder's haughty hand.

I'd only just learned that the key to wielding my legacy was not control but surrender. Still, I allowed myself to hope. If I could finally prove I belonged here . . . I wanted all that—art, artifice, knowledge—for myself.

"Quite the opposite," I murmured. "I've unlocked my legacy, but I'm far from mastering it. I think I will need your guidance more now than ever. Also . . . it will come as no surprise to you that the Sisters were remiss in my education. The basic scholarship highborn sons and daughters attain—geography, politics, art—was denied me. If you wouldn't be opposed, I wonder if you'd be willing to spend some time . . . catching me up."

"I'd be more than willing." Dowser smiled again, but the expression looked suddenly strained. A tremor shook his fingers as he adjusted his spectacles. "But perhaps we can begin another day."

I frowned, glancing more closely at my tutor. Although it was hard to tell in the harsh blanch of amber sun, his eyes looked shadowed, and grey stubble flecked his jaw.

"Are you sick?"

Dowser splayed his hands, then clenched them tight. Another spasm feathered the muscles along his jaw.

"Only of you," he said, but the comment carried neither malice nor humor.

And then I remembered Mamie, the woman who used to sweep for the Sisters. When the peddlers were late or weather delayed the convoys, she would turn grey and quivery, her teeth chattering even in the warmth. *The ague*, she used to insist, *it's just the ague*. But when the peddler jangled through the village and replenished her secret stash of coquelicot—rêve, joie, lotus, whatever you wanted to call it—her face warmed and her muscles strengthened.

"Thank you," I whispered into the sun-washed crush of strange faces and untold stories. "Thank you for trying."

Dowser didn't say anything, just lit his tabak pipe with trembling fingers. The ember flared as he turned to leave, releasing a billow of sour smoke that followed him out of the portrait gallery.

I took the winding, less-populated route back through Coeur d'Or to Lys Wing, caught in the colorless wasteland between pity and compassion. An imprecise sensation nettled me, like being given a gift I hadn't known I'd wanted. For I had never known anyone quite like Dowser: the man who cloaked himself in black robes and resided in the shadows, searching for magic in everyone but himself.

TWENTY-EIGHT

From my perch on the roof of Coeur d'Or I could see to the red river where it burned between the foothills. Bloated clouds rolled in overhead, snarling like shadow wolves. The wind whistled, tasting of moisture and foreign lands and the distant brush of midnight.

For three Nocturnes I'd practiced my illusions here, amid the gleaming spires of cool crystal and brushed bronze. Bribing the Gardes had cost me more of Sunder's kembric livres than I cared to admit, but it was worth it. Up here, I could almost imagine I was an empress of bright dreams and brittle hopes, awash in the clamoring perfume of a million soul-safe secrets drifting upward from the city below.

I had practiced surrendering to my legacy, slowly unraveling tides' worth of restraints upon the power belling inside me. I shattered fetters forged from fear and unlocked shackles chained with humiliation and inhibition. It was thrilling, to feel the unencumbered swell of strange pictures and dreamworlds, bigger and more fantastical than ever before. But it was unnerving too, to release the control that for tides had been a safeguard against punishment and a weapon for survival. The sensation was almost like falling: I felt as though I flung myself from the lip of the roof, again and again, with nothing but the pliant promise of ephemeral hope to catch me.

But it was working. Illusions of cities: glass spires and jeweled staircases, faceted with crisp clarity and translucent in the fantastical haze of an inky night. Great birds with feathers of onyx and wings of cold fire, sheared sharp as flaming swords. Liquid landscapes, rippling like pale honey below azure skies. Milk-white plains beneath cobalt mountains. Thrones of amber, drenched in blood.

I blinked, and scrubbed my palms against the slick brocade of my gown. High above, the wine-dark clouds grumbled, promising a deluge. And soon.

I'd nearly reached the edge of the palais roof when the thunderheads burst and showered me in blood.

Fat droplets splatted down, liquid roses blooming on the slanting tile. They struck my face and my arms, staining my bodice and skirt. The liquid dripped along my spine and between my breasts until I was red, as if my skin had been flayed from my body and I was nothing but glistening muscle. I imagined that soon even the muscle would disappear, and I would be nothing but bone, gleaming pale and white.

And when I looked down to see Coeur d'Or drenched in blood, I felt remade, as though I was forged of illusion, and always had been. An illusion of muscle draped over bone, covered in an illusion of flesh and hair and clothing. And at the heart of it all, an illusion of a soul, of a being, of a person.

I was nothing but what I had made myself.

❦

The chime for sixth Nocturne hung in the air like a warning.

I hesitated near the top of the staircase leading from the roof to Lys Wing and glanced over my shoulder. The storm cast a pall of purple shadow over the unlit stairwell, and my scarlet footprints glittered dull like a trail of real blood.

Scion, but it looked like someone had been murdered. I muttered a curse. The Gardes would never let me up on the roof again if I trailed a broad river of red from their abandoned post straight to my rooms. Or worse—they'd be punished on my behalf, flogged for indulging the well-paying whims of flighty aristos.

I sent a prayer toward the Scion, and stripped. My ruined dress slapped to the ground, and I kicked the gown and my slippers behind the archway leading to the roof. Even if the Gardes discovered the garments, I'd paid for silence as well as discretion. I shivered for a long minute in nothing but my underthings, my bare feet cold against the floor. Then I made a dash for it, sprinting through the echoing halls of the deserted palais with my heart clogging my throat.

I shoved into my chambers. The panic clutching at my chest loosened, and my limbs turned liquid with relief.

"The Dusklander has wheedled her way into someone's bed," drawled a voice from the depths of my shuttered room. "Will wonders never cease?"

I started, violently, banging my shoulder against the corner of the foyer. My eyes dredged at the gloom. A streak of white gold. A glitter of green.

Sunder.

Fury turned my blood molten. I sucked in a breath of twilight-tinted air, remembering at the last second that I was essentially naked. I wrapped my arms around my torso, ignoring the shudder wracking my spine.

"Lurking in dark corners?" I hissed. "Appropriate behavior for a spider like you."

Sunder's splash of pale hair loomed closer. I glimpsed a midnight-blue waistcoat, a glint of amber, and those fierce, fathomless eyes.

"I came to surprise you." He lifted a languorous hand toward my shoulder and trailed a gloved finger along my collarbone. The tip of his finger came away scarlet, as if he'd dipped it in blood. His voice twisted in a taut spring—if he had been anyone else in the world, I would have named the intonation jealousy. "I confess, demoiselle, that you have surprised me instead."

I took a purposeful step backward. My skin buzzed as though he was still touching me.

"Surprise me?" I made my voice chilly. "And what, pray tell, have I done to deserve such an honor? Insulted a beggar? Kicked a small animal?"

"Do I seem like a man who needs a reason to do anything?" A smile stretched his voice but stopped short of his eyes. He pivoted on his heel and stalked behind me. I followed him with my eyes, insolent. "I'm your sponsor. I wanted to give you something for the upcoming ball."

"I don't want anything from you." I shoved the words between clenched teeth.

"And here I thought women enjoyed being showered in gifts." He stepped close, pushing the sopping mass of my hair over my shoulder. His splinter of a laugh raised the hair on the nape of my neck. "Drenched, even."

A snake of chilly metal slithered around my throat. My breath hissed between my teeth, and every muscle in my body tensed. Sunder's cool hands coiled the chain, clasping the necklace at my nape. I glanced down. A waterfall of kembric and rubies nestled between my ichor-striped breasts, topped by an ambric jewel the size of a bird's egg. Its facets caught the dim light, hinting at shadows in its depths.

Confusion prickled in my chest. Despite Sunder's taunting tone, the gesture was almost . . . *kind*. A gift, for the first ball I was to attend as a courtier. It was the sort of thing a sponsor was supposed to do.

I remembered words flung like weapons across a room draped in ivy and glass. A sheaf of money, tossed at my feet like trash. Sand and blood and barbed words. The touch of blue silk, the taste of misplaced hopes.

Why would Sunder come to my room in the dead of Nocturne bearing gifts of expensive jewelry? What new intrigue could he be planning?

"You'll wear the necklace to the Blood Rain Ball." It wasn't a question. He cocked his head to the side, white-gold hair drifting ghostly around his face. Another ice-honed smile bent the corner of his elegant mouth.

"What?" I demanded when he continued to stare at me, standing half-naked in the center of my chambers.

"Perhaps I ought to remind you," he said, in a voice like satin, "to wear actual clothes too."

He slipped from my rooms like a bad dream, leaving nothing behind but that piercing scent of him and the cascade of jewels at my throat.

I dragged off the necklace, tossing it to wink moodily on my vanity. But when I climbed into bed and dragged the blankets over my head, I could still feel the pressure of it around my neck, the slinking weight of it between my breasts.

Did he intend it as an ornament? A collar?

A declaration of intent?

My blood frothed thick as the rain bathing the city in crimson. I could craft worlds from pale portents and promises, forgotten follies and remembered dreams. But not even I could think up a world in which he and I—

Enough. I squeezed my eyes against the feverish memory of his hands at my throat: cold metal and a profusion of jewels. I had finally forged the dristic bones of my own fortune in this pristine palais. I would not squander that on a man whose truths were laced with lies, whose face was a mask, whose price was power. He could only be a curse.

TWENTY-NINE

The Blood Rain bewitched Coeur d'Or with a dark, sweet languor.

I barely recognized the palais as I trailed Lullaby to the ball. The ink-stained clouds had darkened steadily all day, thrumming thunder through the halls and birthing secrets in the shadows. Ambric lamps pulsed a sullen red, and my heart quickened to match the throb of the light. We passed beneath two heavy doors into the transformed Atrium.

It was like standing inside a Devangelis ruby. The glass ceiling arched high above, stained crimson by the bloody rain falling from the wounded sky. The air tasted thick as nectar and sweet as wine. A curved and coiling chandelier hung from the apex of the ceiling, glass tendrils in black and scarlet grasping toward the floor. Silhouetted against a churning sky of violet and tangerine, Severine sat atop her ambric throne.

I glanced around the Atrium, fighting a nebulous sensation of exposure and shame. I tugged at the bodice of my gown, cut viciously low. I'd wanted a higher neckline, but the moment Lullaby set eyes on Sunder's dubious gift she summoned my seamstress and demanded she slit the bodice nearly to my navel. Satin skirts billowed around my legs, the color smoothing from black at the hem to a lustrous maroon near the hips. A grindingly narrow waist. That obscene plunge of a neckline. Bare shoulders. Sunder's jewels, heavy as iron manacles around my neck.

I suppressed a shiver. Courtiers pressed close, bedecked in the same brazen finery as me. Gowns in ebony and violet and scarlet. Wine-red lips and lusty eyes. Some danced slow, purposeful steps to the sultry strains of unseen musicians. Others lounged on cushions strewn in purposefully dim corners. Still more whispered behind their fans, watching me with brutal deliberation.

Lullaby shoved a wineglass into my hand. The liquid was sweet, and cool, and I drank gratefully. My throat was parched, and the air in the room seemed too thick—too solid—to drag into my lungs.

We edged around the room. Lullaby introduced me to friends and acquaintances, and I curtsied and nodded as politely as possible, striving to obey the modes of decorum demanded by the politesse of the court. No one mentioned my infamous introduction that day in the Atrium, and I was glad. But curious glances followed me around the room, and I heard my name murmured behind my back more than once.

Finally, Lullaby pulled me behind a gilt-limned pillar.

"Stay," she ordered. "Don't talk to anyone if you can help it. I'm going to get us both something to eat."

Her words roused an answering grumble of hunger from my cinched stomach.

I waited, taking everything in. Nearby, a pale statue of a half-naked man acted as a strange candelabra; lit tapers of red and black dribbled waxy trails down his shoulder and around his uplifted wrist. I drifted closer, admiring the sculpted contours of his marble torso. His eyes cut to mine. He shifted his weight.

I jumped backward, shocked and embarrassed. It wasn't a statue—it was a person, wearing real candles pouring hot wax onto skin painted to look like marble. I forced my gaze away, but when I gazed around I saw other men and women posed as living candelabras, tapers clinging to their skin.

Disgust battled with curiosity. How dare the empress order

these servants—these *people*—to stand for hours as melting wax stained the planes of their well-formed bodies? Didn't it hurt? I imagined the sensation, a hot drizzle prickling across my skin before cooling and solidifying. The thought sent a burst of warmth through my belly, and my eyes skittered across the room. I realized who I was looking for a moment too late.

Sunder, standing elegant and unsmiling beside his sister. Their pale hair gleamed diamond-bright amid the churning sea of red and black.

I shuddered. It was impossible not to admire the Suicide Twins, so alike in appearance and demeanor. But I couldn't help but curse my traitor gaze, seeking my sadistic sponsor out across a room full of people just as handsome and rich.

I rubbed an absent thumb against the faceted cabochon of ambric resting over my heart.

Almost as handsome and rich.

❦

The lazy hours of Nocturne crept by. I ate, and drank more wine. I met more courtiers—Vida, Mender's curvaceous sister; a glowering Sinister lord named Haze; River, a young man with a laugh like sunlight on water. I drank a little more wine. I danced, my too-high slippers an easy excuse when I fumbled a step. I flicked my wrist and simpered; my dance partner laughed and handed me another glass of wine. Finally, I stumbled upon Thibo, tucked beneath a rose-draped alcove with a deck of cards and a coterie of rakishly handsome young men.

"Mirage!" he cried. In his poppy-colored suit studded with rubies, Thibo looked every inch the libertine. His ringed hand rested on Mender's slender thigh. "Tonight you are exquisite in the way of new flowers and old money."

I curtsied. "And your compliments are as fleeting as wind in the desert or a roué's kiss."

The gentlemen all laughed.

"We're playing peine, Mirage," said Thibo. "Would you care to join us?"

"I have no head for gambling, nor a face for bluffing," I mused. "But I am of a mind to waste some Belsyre coin."

"A noble ambition," Mender said, nodding gravely.

"Indeed!" A wicked gleam brightened Thibo's eye. "Altruism at its finest."

I'd just been cleaned out when the empress rose from her throne of luminous amber and waved to the musicians, who ceased their slow sarabande. I raised my sluggish head from where I'd propped it on my hand to watch Thibo bluff his way into another stack of livres.

"A bountiful Blood Rain to you all!" the empress called, her voice as fluted as I remembered. She was resplendent in a gown glowing like molten kembric. "May it bring you luck in love and audacity in ardor!"

The courtiers all clapped, and turned to plant light kisses on their neighbors' cheeks. One of Thibo's foppish friends leaned in, but I pushed him away, wrinkling my nose. Not a tradition I cared to ascribe to.

"The Blood Rain comes but once a tide, carrying with it important nutrients and minerals from the Meridian Desert. Without this rain, our crops could not flourish. So it is a time to celebrate fertility and fortune." Severine paused, and cast her eye over the crowd. "It so happens that my greatest fortune is you! My prized court, full of beauty and wit and talent. But we should also remind ourselves that sometimes fortune comes from afar, and we don't know we have it until it knocks on our door." She smiled. "Sometimes literally. Mirage, where are you?"

I was pleasantly drunk, warm and buoyant with wine. The sound of my name ringing like a bell across the silent Atrium sobered me in an instant. Thibo and his friends stared nervously at me over their cards. I stood up automatically, a marionette with strings attached to my arms and legs. The courtiers in front of me moved away, clearing a path to the raised dais where the empress waited.

My unsteady steps in my precarious shoes rang loud on the marble floor. I swallowed against a throat that felt suddenly dusty, and I cursed the amount of wine I'd drunk. What I wouldn't give for a cool glass of water. I clenched my trembling hands in the skirts of my revealing gown, wishing I had fought harder to keep the design modest. I felt excruciatingly exposed, as though the assembled courtiers could see through all the satin and boning into the kaleidoscope cavern of my soul.

I reached the bottom of the dais. I slid into my best curtsy, lowering my coiffed head in the posture of utmost deference. I waited there, spine screaming and waist aching, for a long, miserable moment.

The empress's chiming laugh rang in my ears like a seductive curse.

"How our fantast has changed!" she exclaimed. "What a difference a span makes! Those eyes! This dress! That necklace!"

I fought the scarlet flush climbing my exposed décolletage. I didn't know whether to be flattered or offended.

"Rise, child."

I obeyed, forcing my tottering knees to behave as I pasted a smile on my face.

"You are much changed in appearance, Mirage," remarked the empress. "But tell us, are you so changed in ability as well? The last time you appeared before us, your abilities seemed to render you . . . rather faint."

Yes, if you called collapsing on the Atrium floor *rather faint*.

"I beg Your Highness not to torment me so," I simpered. "Surely my teacher keeps you apprised of my efforts."

"But you're wrong," said Severine, a bite to her tone. She tapped her closed fan against the side of her thigh. "My Dowser has maintained an irritating silence on the matter. Perhaps he hopes to shield me from disappointment."

"Or perhaps he hopes merely to raise your anticipation."

The court sucked in a shocked breath. Someone laughed. It rang in my ears, sounding appreciative, but I knew it must be mocking. I dropped my gaze and silently ran through every curse word I knew.

Why are you bragging? I snarled at myself. *This is your opportunity to prove you've earned a place here, not act the arrogant upstart with absurd ambitions.*

"Perhaps," agreed Severine, but her voice was too smooth, a desert pard closing in on its long-awaited prey. "Either way, we're all dying to know. Won't you favor us with a little sample of your talent?"

"I'm at your command, Majesty," I murmured around a mouthful of ashes. *You knew this was coming.* "But perhaps another evening? I wouldn't want to diminish the glory of this exquisite ball."

Again that braying laugh, loud and earnest. And with a sinking feeling, I realized I'd done it again—I was *bragging*. I insinuated that my legacy was so astounding that the ball would pale in comparison. My pride conspired with my mouth and left my brain out of the decision.

"Impossible," purred the empress. "Really, Mirage. I must insist."

No escaping that.

I sucked in a deep breath of crimson air. Around me, courtiers retreated, leaving a wide berth. I trawled my gaze around the room one last time, looking for a familiar black robe and smooth pate.

Dowser wasn't here.

I didn't expect him to be. Ever since he learned I would be presented at the Blood Rain Ball, Dowser warned me he might not be there. He insisted I practice my chosen illusion over and over, until it was perfect. Perfect from every angle, in every light, under the tightest scrutiny, since I wouldn't be able to rely on his presence to calm and strengthen me.

No one wants me there, he said. *And I don't want to be there.*

I closed my eyes. I didn't expect it, but part of me had hoped he would show up anyway. For my sake.

I slowed my breathing, focusing on the cool cluster of icy whites and blue golds swirling in the space beneath my heart. In honor of the Blood Rain, I had decided to show the court a vision of a world bursting with vast, wild oceans and cold cascades. It began simply enough: a pool of clear spring water bubbling up from the floor. I closed my eyes and focused on the glass-bright water, the murmuring plash, the blush of sullen light on a ruffled surface. I tasted the fresh, cool kiss of water against my lips.

I surrendered to the sensation, falling into the illusion as I waited for the glister and gleam to spill forth.

Nothing happened.

THIRTY

A snake of dread coiled around my spine.

I tried again, dredging the coruscant reservoir of light and color.

Nothing happened.

Panic shoved my composure to the side and dug pointed fingers between my ribs.

I pushed away the carefully choreographed illusion and reached for any of a dozen half-dreamed reveries. *Control.* The treacherous thought slithered into my mind, and I obeyed it without thinking, tethering the images to the sinew of my will. I throttled my legacy, forcing grand, impossible visions into its silent depths. A flying ship with bones of glass and wings of steel. Kembric cliffs slicked with lakes of obsidian. Alabaster skin and crinoline eyes, hewn from pale rock and towering like a mountain.

Nothing.

My hands, cold as ice, dropped to my side. A bare few seconds had passed, but already the court was beginning to rustle and whisper, curious and contemptuous. I dared not raise my gaze, but I could feel the empress's keen eyes on me.

Reality, heavy as a slab of iron, compressed my lungs. It was no use. Despite the intoxicating thrill of finally unlocking my impossible dreams, my legacy had refused to perform when I needed it most. Anything would have been better than this. A small, simple illusion. A pathetic half illusion followed by unconsciousness—even *that* would have been better than this. This . . . nothing.

I had failed.

"Mirage?" Severine's voice forced my gaze up to hers. Her smile was luminous. "Is something the matter? Did you misunderstand my directive?"

I shook my head, slowly, putting off the terrible moment of admitting my failure. *Failure.* Oh, Scion. *Lullaby.*

She stood to the side of a grinning Sinister lord. Even from here I could see she was crying—her lovely face wet with tears and her mouth twisted in a grimace of disappointment. I hadn't just failed myself—I'd failed my mentor. *Keep close to her,* the empress had said that day in the Atrium. *I blame you for her mistakes.*

I took a deep breath and shoved my pride beneath the sickly blossom of failure and dread blooming in my chest. I dipped into a deep, fawning curtsy.

"Majesty, I apologize," I murmured. "I seem to have forgotten how to conjure the smallest illusion. I can only account for it by saying that I have drunk far too much wine."

"Too much wine?" The empress raised a delicate hand to cover her smile. "Indeed. I can safely say there are many here this Nocturne who understand the feeling. Drinking too much wine can often lead one to, ah, *underperform.*"

The assembled courtiers roared with sudden laughter, and all the tension drained from the room. The empress gestured, and a sprightly minuet cascaded from the corner, sending men and women lining up across the Atrium. A young lord shoved me out of his way, not unkindly, but without a second thought. I turned a shocked stare to the empress, but she wasn't even looking at me as she returned to her throne, gilded skirts gathered in jeweled hands.

I was the entertainment of a moment ago. A disappointing one, at that. Time to move on to the next momentary pleasure.

Disappointment and shame and relief and irritation boiled up inside me in a great, heaving stew. I turned on my heel, scanning the crowd for Lullaby. After everything she'd done for me—all the work she had put into my appearance and my comportment—I had to apologize for my pitiful performance.

But my eyes didn't find Lullaby.

They found Sunder.

He stood by the heavy Atrium doors, a sullen ambric globe brightening his hair to a halo. He was staring right at me, his dristic-ringed gaze a sharp lash in the dim.

My hand flew to my throat. My fingers closed around an expensive jewel, set in kembric and edged with rubies. Sunder smiled like he'd break the world, if only he could grasp its bones.

My heart faltered, then jolted forward in double time. Sunder's words echoed in the rough-hewn valley between my sense and my sentiment.

You'll wear it to the Blood Rain Ball.

A command. He ordered me to wear his gift to the ball, and like a rustic half-wit, I obeyed. For a span, Lullaby had warned me the Suicide Twins would exact their revenge for my insults. Yet I had blindly agreed to wear his talisman in front of the entire court. I had even thought well of him for it.

But now—now it seemed so painfully obvious. I didn't know how it worked—or even what it *was*—but this waterfall of gems and precious metals around my neck was no mere ornament. I closed my fist around the necklace, the crisp facets of the jewels biting into my palm. I'd pull it off, I'd march back over to the empress, I'd insist I was enchanted, I'd demand another try, I'd—

Sunder was gone.

A raging beast frothed in my chest. I shoved through the crowd, pushing dancers and servants out of my way as I marched toward the end of the Atrium. Sunder's sword-sharp smile carved a bleeding gash in my composure, and I couldn't banish the sound of his voice convincing me to accept his gift. What had possessed me to trust him?

Part of me already knew. I had dreamed him up. Not the hard line of his jaw, or the chilly slash of his evergreen gaze, or the elegant sweep of his broad shoulders. But I must have imagined the uncertain pulse of bleak remembrances behind his eyes, the jealous tone that cracked his voice like agate, the blur of hesitation whenever he touched me.

That Sunder had to be an illusion. Because I couldn't fathom a world in which both of these men existed.

I stalked Sunder through the palais.

Outside the Atrium, it wasn't hard to spot his bright head bobbing between the sultry red lamps lining the dusky halls. He didn't glance over his shoulder as he strolled through bands of gloom and glow, although my heels clicked loud on the marble behind him. He knew I was following him, and his indifference stoked the flames of my fury like a bellows. By the time we reached the collection of suites I'd come to know as Belsyre Wing, I burned with a rage that blistered my skin and hollowed my bones.

Sunder pushed through a gate that appeared to be fashioned from long runnels of ice. I followed, curiosity drawing my gaze and pouring cold water over the embers of my anger. It wasn't ice at all; the gate was cunningly crafted from glass and jewels and suffused with moisture to make it gleam. My fingers, when I dragged them along the pointed spines, came away wet.

Sudden doubt raised the hairs along my arms. I ignored it, shoving through the flimsy gate into a jardin made from winter.

We had winter in the Dusklands, where the earth froze hard as forged metal and the rugged vegetation bloomed with flowers of frost. But I'd heard stories of other kinds of winter, in the Meteor Mountains—where blankets of white fell heavy on broad-limbed trees, where waterfalls froze into châteaux of ice, where the cold was a living thing. I'd dreamed of that winter world.

Sunder's jardin was like waking up in that dream.

Pillows of purest white piled high on the glazed trunks of black trees. Shimmering blossoms of bright ice dangled like secrets between the stark boughs. My breath clouded the air before me. Silence hung thick enough to taste, a hush as tangible as a name or a wish.

"What is this place?" I breathed, and Sunder turned to face me.

In this white womb of ice and solitude, Sunder finally seemed fathomable. His black waistcoat was the same stark ebony as the trees reaching bare, mournful arms, the silver tooling like frost trellising bark. His defined cheekbones were carved of ice, his skin like snow. And his eyes—his eyes were winter. Cold metal and harsh memories, frozen behind frosted glass.

Abruptly, I remembered I was supposed to be livid with anger. I grimaced, wrapped my hand around the hateful necklace hanging from my neck, and pulled. The clasp snapped with an audible pop. Jewels cascaded into my palm. I raised the necklace to catch the flat white winter light, then flung it at Sunder. It struck the ice-glazed floor and slid with a whisper to knock against his boots.

Sunder glanced at the jewelry, then returned his unreadable gaze to my face.

"Well?" I snapped, frustration making me impatient. "What are you waiting for? What do you have to say for yourself?"

"I beg your pardon," he said. "I was waiting to see if you were going to take off the rest of your clothes and fling them at my feet."

The gibe was rude, and consummately Sunder, but fell flat, as though his heart wasn't in it. A smirk died in the corner of his mouth. He turned on his heel and stalked farther between the snow-draped trees. I opened my mouth, then stormed after him. I would not be denied an explanation.

"You tricked me!" I snarled. "You gave me that enchanted necklace to stop me from performing illusions. You wanted me humiliated in front of the empress and the court. See?"

I held out my hand and conjured the illusion I'd practiced with Dowser. The clear, bright water poured from my fingertips, easy as breathing. I closed my fist, and the illusion trickled away. Sunder watched, unimpressed. His shoulders curled into a shrug.

"So?"

"So?!" I spluttered. I took another step, but I felt off-balance, as though every time I found myself on sure footing the path veered in another direction. "So why did you do it? Was it revenge, for what I said about you and Bane? Were you trying to punish me? Are you still trying to manipulate me into running away from the palais, like that Nocturne at the Gauntlet?" Another thought sidled into my mind, a thought that dragged my mouth open in horror. "Or did the empress *command* you to do it? Were you under orders to shame and humiliate me in front of the entire court?"

Sunder sighed, and lifted his gaze to the black trees. Wind whispered, and a shower of snow flurried between the branches. The flakes danced before my face, and when I looked close I could see the individual crystals, meticulous and fine. I reached out my palm, but the snow disappeared before it alit, insubstantial as one of my illusions.

"I had this place enchanted," Sunder murmured, and I wasn't sure whether he was talking to me or to the trees. "There was a girl—a Dexter girl—named Shiver. All she ever wanted to do was create places like this. Beautiful, cold, intricate sculptures. She loved the touch of ice, the brush of snow, the way winter never promises anything it doesn't intend to give. So I had her build this jardin for me."

"Why?" I asked, to fill the drowning silence.

"It reminds me of home." His eyes cut to mine. "Belsyre. It's not a forgiving place. Icy winds scream between valleys scooped from black rock. We tear out the bones of the earth and forge them into wealth. It's always cold. Death is a constant companion. But the pines are old and sturdy. The tigers are white as snow, and clever as men. There is something clean, and precise, and fair about winter. It has no patience for wealth, or power; it only values vigilance."

I listened, astonished. I'd never heard Sunder put so many sentences together in one breath, and there was none of the sneering lord in his tone. For the first time since our regrettable meeting, I believed the words falling from his mouth.

"And the girl?" I said, at last. "What happened to her?"

"She needed help." His fingers twitched tersely toward the edge of the trees. "So I helped her."

My eyes followed his indication. A white statuette of a slender girl leaned between the trunks. Her head was bowed, and icicles fell from her eyes and down her nose, making her look as though she was crying.

A corresponding trickle of ice trailed down my spine. Curiosity and horror battled for dominance within me. Horror won. I yanked my gaze away from what I thought was marble, but could just as easily be flesh and ice and impossible magic.

"No," I whispered. "You wouldn't. You couldn't."

"I helped her," Sunder repeated, and his gaze on my face was flat and unpitying. "Has the thought ever occurred to you that I might be trying to help you too?"

"Help me?" Disgust twisted my face. I fought for control over my expression. "If that's your idea of help, I don't want anything to do with it!"

"No, I suppose you wouldn't." Sunder's face hardened into its usual mask of disdain and cruel amusement. "You can leave now. You're bleeding on my snow."

Shock forced my gaze to the ground, and I saw he was right, in a way; the wine-dark hem of my gown, drenched in melting snow, had left great lacerations of dye across the bone-white floor of Sunder's winter jardin. I gathered the sodden hem in my hands, but that only served to smear the bloody gashes further. I bit my lip and did as I was told, retreating to the gate. Sunder paced a step behind me.

I paused outside the gate, emotions whirling within me. I only distantly remembered why I'd come in the first place, and the interaction had left me feeling cold and disappointed, as though I expected something different from what I was given. I whirled on my heel to once more meet Sunder's dispassionate gaze.

"Why—?"

"Do you know what my sister does, on evenings like these?" Sunder asked, his voice the unexpected slice of a sharpened blade.

My head jerked back. Again, I felt as though the path I took here had veered suddenly in a different direction, leaving me stranded in an unfamiliar wilderness. I shook my bewildered head.

"On evenings like these," Sunder murmured, "other courtiers, drunk on wine and lust, seek pleasure in each other's company. They flit behind pillars and steal sweet kisses. They use touch like a weapon, their hands on each other's bodies, stroking and exploring. Their breath mingles, warmed by shared desire."

His words ignited a thrill of heat in my veins.

"My sister, on evenings like these," Sunder continued, "retreats to her chambers. She tears pins from her hair and scrubs rouge from her lips. She hides in her bed, and she weeps. She weeps because her breath is venom, and to taste it would mean sickness and pain. She weeps because a single touch from her finger would drive a person mad. She weeps because her lips are poison, and a kiss from her turns a man or woman into a pile of rotted, putrid flesh."

"And you?" His words scored my heart with lines of ice, but I couldn't ignore one obvious fact: He was trying to manipulate me. As usual. "What do you do, on *evenings like these*? Play vicious pranks on unwitting Dusklanders? Deal pain with a touch? Make a game of seduction? Yes, my lord, you have my deepest sympathies for your sad plight."

"Do not mock what you don't understand." His eyes were a glacier, cold and unyielding. "We are bound to our power, just as it is to us. And every legacy has its consequences."

"Prestige, fortune, and admiration," I hissed. "Consequences indeed."

"You think you understand this world, demoiselle," he whispered, leaning closer. That sharp tang of genévrier needles slapped me in the face. "You think you hear Dexter, or Sinister, and you know what that means. Good, evil, *legacy*. Pain, poison, *power*. You imagine these words bound up and trussed away, with clear outlines and hard borders. But they are alive, seething with a complexity you refuse to acknowledge."

I opened my mouth to keep arguing, but Sunder reached a finger toward my lips. He hesitated at the last second, curling his hand back to his side. An involuntary gasp tore at my throat.

"There are worlds of understanding you have failed to envision," he said. "We are only as blind as the things we refuse to see."

The ice gate swung shut in my face, leaving me dripping scarlet dye in an empty hallway and wishing I'd never, ever come.

THIRTY-ONE

I tottered back along the Esplanade toward Lys, my thoughts choked with poison and ice.

I didn't want to believe one insidious word out of Sunder's twisted mouth. But I didn't think he was lying—not about Bane, at least, and the consequences of her legacy. I couldn't exorcise the image of her scraping cosmetics from her perfect face and weeping because she could never be touched, never be held, never be kissed.

What had he said, the Nocturne of the Gauntlet? *None of us are ever fully in control of our legacies. Some of us never are.*

Surely the touch of Sunder's hand was not inevitably laced with pain. I'd heard rumors of his conquests, his seeming parade of paramours. I doubted many maidens enjoyed a lover's gaze that seared with actual fire. I suddenly wondered what it would be like to kiss him, whether—

I tripped, the spiked heel of my shoe catching the soggy hem of my gown. I cursed, throwing out a hand to steady myself against a fluted column. I bent at the waist, reaching for my slipper.

A low moan snagged on the edge of my hearing. I froze.

Again—a throaty sigh, followed by a soothing murmur.

Blood rushed to my face, and Sunder's words rang in my ears. *Courtiers, drunk on wine and lust . . .* I had almost stumbled upon an assignation. I ducked deeper into the shadow of the pillar, gathering my skirts and preparing to make a stealthy exit.

One of the trysting lovers laughed, a melodious, bell-like

sound that struck a chord of familiarity even as it raised the hair on my arms.

Curiosity overcame discretion, and I dared to peer out from behind the column.

Caught in a wine-stained swathe of stormy light, the empress's golden gown looked mottled with blood. A luminous smile lit her face from the inside, and her violet gaze was fixed on the man in her embrace. He had his head thrown back with pleasure, and he was moaning, breathy and indistinct.

Fear prickled white-hot at my temples and pulped my muscles. If the empress caught me spying on her rendezvous, it wouldn't matter that I had stumbled here by accident. I couldn't afford her wrath, not after what had happened at the ball.

I tiptoed away, tensing at every rustle and sweep of my traitorous gown. Finally, I reached the edge of the Esplanade.

But as I turned to flee, I caught a glimpse of the empress's hands, her long, elegant fingers tipped in blood-red nails. And I realized she wasn't embracing her beau after all: She had her hands coiled tight around his neck, and his muffled moans weren't from pleasure.

They were sounds of pain.

❧

I waited for Lullaby in her silent, empty chambers as the bells chimed for fifth Nocturne, then sixth, then Matin. I waited for the chitter of footsteps on cobbles, the brush of satin in the marble foyer, the sweep of midnight hair. I waited for my friend to collapse beside me on the divan and stuff her face with chocolate while complaining about Thibo.

I waited until I was sick with guilt and unease.

I needed to apologize for my abysmal performance at the ball and explain why my legacy had failed me. Failed *us*. I needed to tell her about Sunder's ice jardin, about the strange things he'd said. About Bane's tortured ill fortune. To ask her about the consequences of legacies, the penalties for power.

But most of all I was desperate to tell her what I should never have seen in that darkened hallway. I couldn't banish the image of Severine's slim fingers wrapped around the exposed throat of a faceless man. Her blood-red nails. His moans. Lullaby must know *why*—why the empress skulked in shadows without a retinue. Why the sting of Sunder's touch made me shiver with a thrill I couldn't name. Why a legacy was sometimes a curse.

I must have fallen asleep.

The door slammed, jolting me awake. Soft, burnished light crept beneath the curtains. Lullaby limped into the room, leaning on Thibo's scarlet shoulder. I surged to my feet, and they both stopped. In the window's rosy flush I could see my friend was crying; tears cut channels through her makeup, and swollen pillows nearly hid her eyes.

"What are you doing here?" Thibo asked, not unkindly.

"I—" The apologies and explanations and questions choked me. "I waited for hours."

"Lullaby's not well." Neither his gaze nor his voice was as heavy as my heart. "She doesn't feel like talking. You should go."

I nodded, mute. My eyelids stung as I watched Thibo half carry Lullaby to her bed. I scoured her body for any sign of injury, a cut or scrape or brindled bruise that could make her whimper like that. I saw nothing. I dug my teeth into my lip and fled outside.

The storm had passed. Gauzy clouds draped a veil across a new-forged sun. Lys Wing rang with quiet birdsong and the patter of lingering red moisture. Sudden disgust soured my stomach as I hunched by Lullaby's door. How could a place so beautiful, so serene, be filled with so much pain and sorrow? I closed my eyes against the rush of images. A sandy arena stained with a child's blood. Bane scraping cosmetics from her face. Lullaby's cheeks striped with tears. Blood-tipped nails digging—

A hand brushed my shoulder. In the ruddy light, Thibo's face was drawn and exhausted.

"Go home, Mirage," Thibo said. "It's been a long Nocturne for everyone."

"What happened to her?" My voice sounded ugly in my own ears. "It's my fault, isn't it?"

"You couldn't have prevented this."

"That's not what I asked."

Thibo hesitated as he squinted into the light, hazel eyes distant.

"I won't be here much longer," he finally said. I frowned, not understanding. He unslung a locket from beneath his cravat and opened it to reveal the miniature portrait of a girl with his same deep complexion and bronze hair. "My youngest sister has come of age. She's talented, and ambitious. She wants to take my place here, to represent Beltoire at the Amber Court."

"But—" Shock slowed my words. "But there are other siblings at the palais. Sunder and Bane. Mender's sister Vida—"

"Mender's coming with me," he interrupted. He jerked his gaze to mine, his gorgeous features a discordant clash with the caustic anguish swelling in his eyes. "Scion, Mirage, can't you see? I *want* to go. This is my chance to have something for myself, for once in my miserable life. I haven't been back to my father's estate since I was a child, but I know there's an old farm south of the lake where the vines are unkempt and the fields lie fallow. And Mender—" Emotion choked him. "I would marry him, if he'll have me. We could look after my nieces and nephews, and maybe someday have children of our own. We could grow grapes, build barns, dance at country festivals. I want all those stupid, mundane, ordinary moments, Mirage—I want them so much it hurts."

I was quiet, but I was beginning to understand.

"And yet," he whispered. "And yet when I think about leaving I can't help but feel as though I am stealing something that doesn't belong to me, something I don't deserve, something I can never truly have."

"You're not a thief, Thibo," I interrupted, fierce. "Not for reaching for a world where you know you belong."

"We are all thieves here, Mirage," Thibo breathed. "We steal a thousand scintillating moments of drinking and dancing and laughter and pretend that there will never be any cost for the choices we make. But the price of love is heartbreak. The price of pleasure is pain. And the price of power is always corruption."

I shuddered. Thibo cupped my face in his hands, his touch tender. His fingers tightened against my cheekbones, and for a moment I imagined that sharp blades traced the edges of my memories, shining scythes slicing sheaves of golden wheat. But then Thibo dropped his hands to his sides and turned away.

"Sometimes—sometimes we all must pay the cost for what others have stolen," he murmured. "And the empress always collects when a debt is owed."

THIRTY-TWO

A breeze sifted motes of ruddy sunlight through a vivid curtain of bougainvillea. I leaned back on my elbows, letting fingers of light and shadow stroke my face. The air was redolent with hot honeysuckle and freshly mown grass. A fat bee hummed around my head, mistaking the silk flowers on my hat for real blossoms. I blinked drowsy eyes.

The day was hot, the sky clear save for a few salmon clouds bellying toward the horizon. Most of Dexter sprawled across the manicured lawn edging the Weeping Pools, sipping lemonade and munching on dainty cakes. The picnic was River's idea; I could see him floating great, undulating spheres of clear water across the grassy sward. A few courtiers, clad in gossamer skirts and light linen waistcoats, danced and darted after the liquid globes. They tried to pierce the limpid surfaces with the tips of their fans, shrieking with glee when the spheres exploded, scattering droplets across the lawn. Puppies borrowed from the palais kennels wobbled and flopped in their wake, bounding and nipping at skirts and heels.

The last fortnight had been *pleasant*. After the disconcerting events of the Blood Rain Ball, I'd expected a cascade of unpleasant consequences. But when I'd approached Thibo to ask how best to make amends to Lullaby for my failure, Thibo had cut me short.

"She doesn't remember." He'd drained the contents of his wineglass in one long slug, sending the feathers on his velvet hat sweeping. "So leave it alone, Mirage."

He'd been right. Lullaby was her usual self—if slightly glazed—and had no recollection of the night. And I didn't have time to ponder her lacquered smile, because my social calendar was suddenly and astonishingly full.

Events filled my days from Prime to the latest hours of Nocturne. Feasts with mountains of delicious foods: fragrant salmon with thyme and lemon crème fraîche; delicate tomato bisques; sweet, rich mousse. Salons where giant tabak pipes with sinuous necks smoldered, and guests drifted sylphlike between curtains of fragrant smoke. Soirées with literal fountains of spiced wine, which I learned the hard way made my head feel like it had been kicked in by one of Madame Rina's mules.

And if I sometimes glimpsed Sunder standing in the shadow of an opalescent pillar, sipping from a goblet and watching me, I bit my lip and lowered my eyes. Because when my eyes snagged on his, I saw they were full of a jagged expectation that made the tips of my fingers and the depths of my heart cold with ice.

I didn't owe him anything. I'd fought for my place in this world, and earned it. I deserved this serenity, this opulent luxury. Amid the flurry of graceful nobles and redolent perfume and gossamer fancies, I could almost forget the splatter of ruby blood on sand, crimson-tipped fingernails clutching bare throats, icy maidens weeping frozen tears. I could almost forget the chill of dread tripping brokenly down my spine when I counted the days until the Fête du Carrousel, where I would either prove I'd earned my place here, or shame my mentor and my dynasty before losing everything.

I could almost forget the word that lingered in my mind and stained the edges of my dreams: *gone.*

I shook my head to clear the miasma of worry, and looked for my friends. I spotted Thibo with his gaggle of preening pop-injays, regaling them with one of his favorite yarns—an embel-lished lark involving seven chickens, a prince in disguise, and one very long sword.

I saw the messenger before anyone else did—a palais courier, long-legged and tan. She crossed the lawn at a lope, cutting between the sphere chasers, who paused in their revels to watch her pass. The conversation and laughter died to a murmur as Dexter waited to see who the urgent message was meant for.

It was for Vida. I didn't know Mender's healer sister well, but she seemed kind, with her gleaming eyes and slow smile. That smile faltered now, as she reluctantly accepted the slim envelope from the courier. A bated hush descended over the courtiers. Her fingernail popped the seal on the envelope, and she raised the paper to her face.

The wail that ripped from Vida's throat was the sound of someone's world tearing apart. She collapsed to the grass like a marionette with its strings cut. The picnic shattered into chaos, courtiers rushing toward and away from Vida. A fight broke out between several young men; one of them yelled at the top of his lungs, while three others tried to catch his flailing arms and hold him down. Glass shattered, and the sound of weeping sucked all the light from the jardin, leaving it pale and colorless.

The hair rose along my arms, and I was suddenly cold. I hesi-tated for a moment, biting my lip between my teeth, before dashing out from beneath the fall of foliage toward the wrecked picnic.

No one paid me any attention. I cast about for Lullaby or Thibo, but in the mayhem it was difficult to tell one silk-clad figure from the next. Finally, I caught sight of Thibo, whose extravagant hat broadcasted his location. He was crouched in the group beside Vida.

"He's gone!" She screamed the words over and over, a terrible mantra that sent horror to claw deep fissures in my heart. "Mender's gone!"

Thibo stroked a hand over her bright head and whispered too low for me to hear.

"Did something happen to Mender?" I asked, my voice breathless. "What can I do?"

His eyes twisted to mine, but they were unfocused and sad. It took him a moment to recognize me.

"Go away," he murmured, without malice. "You don't belong here."

Hurt splintered through me like shards of broken mirror glass, leaving me empty and breathless and wretched. I careened up the grassy rise toward the palais, where lawn gave way to exquisite topiaries twisting against the rouged sky. The strange, leafy animals stared down at me and seemed to echo Thibo's words: *You don't belong here.*

I smeared an uncharitable tear from my cheek. Why was I crying? Thibo and Vida had just experienced a tragedy of unimaginable significance. I should be filled with compassion for their troubles, not consumed with self-pity and embarrassment for my own idiocy. Nothing that happened to me was anything but my own fault. I came here. I threw myself at the mercy of the empress. I begged to be a part of her court.

I should have known this world would always be out of my grasp.

I marched along the Esplanade, gripping my voluminous skirts. Dowser—Dowser would know what was happening at the Amber Court. Why my footsteps interrupted sibilant whispers and hurried conversations. Why Lullaby couldn't—or *wouldn't*—remember the empress punishing her for my failure at the ball. Why a place that had once seemed like a haven for magic and wonder had transformed into a nightmare of pain and lies and disappearances.

I rounded the corner. I recognized every crook and twist of the pallid arms clutching their fitful torches. I lifted my hand to rap on Dowser's door. My fist froze in the air when I heard voices floating from behind the door.

Voices raised in argument. One was Dowser's. The other was female, rich and cultured and authoritative.

The Amber Empress. And she was shouting at my teacher.

I knew I should back away—*I absolutely must not eavesdrop on the empress*—but my amber heels were glued to the floor. The image of slender, red-tipped fingers wrapped around a male throat haunted my mind's eye.

"I will not be put off any longer, Dowser!" Severine paced in front of the door, her voice growing louder and softer. "I want what you promised me, and I want it now!"

A low murmur indicated that Dowser had replied to his liege, but I couldn't make out the words.

"Time?" Dristic sharpened her voice. "I don't think you realize the urgency of this. We have only the briefest of windows, and the weapon *must* be ready in time."

Weapon? I leaned closer, struggling to make out Dowser's low voice, but it wasn't any use.

"No," snapped Severine. "There is no one else, and you know that as well as I. The Zvar corsairs are devouring my operatives nearly as quickly as I can conscript them, and that decision has not been without retaliation and reprisals from my nobles. Word has gotten around, and we've seen no new volunteers—"

Dowser's soft murmur interrupted her.

"Scion, who cares?" she snarled. "If I had to guess, it would be Reaper, but—"

A sudden ringing in my ears drowned out the empress's muffled words. *Reaper.* But that was Thibo's court name.

Panic jolted me away from Dowser's door. A shudder quaked through me, sending Severine's disjointed words skittering around my skull, teasing me with half-understood meanings.

I shouldn't be here. I couldn't be here.

I turned and fled.

My skirts whispered against the walls, and my heels tapped louder even than my panicked heart, flinging itself against my ribs. The outstretched sconces seemed to twist and reach in the dimness of the hallway, as real as the human candelabras at the Blood Rain Ball, ready to catch and hold me until the empress could punish me.

"You're imagining things," I whispered to myself. And I had to laugh, as I gazed around the halls of Coeur d'Or—at the marble veined with the blood of an empire, the murals depicting brutal battles and savage conquests. This whole world was an illusion, and I, the fantast, had been the only fool to believe it for so long. Lullaby, Thibo—all their actions and comments had hinted that everything was not as it seemed. But I'd been seduced by the glamour and the games and the heady, tremulous feeling of finally belonging to the world I'd always longed for.

Even Sunder had tried to warn me, that Nocturne in his ice jardin. *Has the thought ever occurred to you—*

The necklace. I thought he was trying to sabotage me, by dampening my legacy, but what if—like he said—he was trying to *help* me? To protect me?

But from what?

Or who?

I closed my eyes against the whirlwind of uneasy realizations and vague guesses. The only thing I knew . . . was that I knew nothing. And if I wanted answers, I was going to have to go right to the source.

THIRTY-THREE

By the time I arrived at Belsyre Wing my fancies had expanded into paranoias. Everywhere I looked, I saw curious eyes: the lowered gazes of servants flickering as I passed, the studiously blank eyes of the Garde suddenly keener. Even laughing courtiers seemed to mark my passage, their manners suddenly false and pretentious.

I fought to control my breathing as I was bowed into Sunder's residence, but my corset strangled my chest and my palms buzzed with Duskland shadows. I clenched my hands and calmed my expression.

"My lady?" asked the demure servant garbed in the black-and-white argyle of Belsyre.

"I will see Lord Sunder at once," I said, arching my eyebrow in the imperious manner I'd seen the court ladies use with the servants.

"I'm afraid he's—"

"I'll find him myself," I snapped, brushing past the girl. Her protestations fell on deaf ears as I marched through Belsyre Wing. I didn't know if I'd be able to find Sunder in this disorienting sprawl of opulence and splendor, but I was tired of only ever meeting him on his terms. This time, he'd be the one off guard and off-balance. I'd have the upper hand.

The idea sent nerves stitching up and down my arms. I shivered, and smiled.

I found him in the covered pergola where he had wagered upon my virtue. I thought he was actually sleeping, this time;

his lean frame was once again draped along the curve of the couch, but his hair was mussed, his fine features slack. His gleaming boots were kicked off, and his shirt was open, baring the pulse leaping in the hollow of his throat.

The servant made a nervous sound behind me, so I turned to her with a seductive smile and laid my finger gently across my own lips, hoping she'd assume this was a tryst. She hesitated for a moment, then curtsied and left the arbor.

I stepped closer to Sunder. In sleep, without his courtly mask of hauteur and sneering politesse, I could almost picture what he must have looked like as a boy. His lips were slightly parted, and his burnished brows slashed together in an expression both anxious and vulnerable. His pale hair drifted in the genévrier-scented breeze, and I imagined what it would be like to run my fingers through it, to smooth it away from his forehead and smooth away that frown with it.

Stop. I clenched my hand until my nails bit into my soft palm. The burst of pain cut through the absurd fantasy. *He's* Sunder. *Even if he actually is trying to help you, he'd just as soon hurt you.*

I uncurled my fist, reached for the half-empty goblet at his elbow, and dashed it to the ground in a shower of brazen prisms.

Sunder's eyes flew open. He jerked back against the chaise. For a long moment there was nothing but shock and fierce confusion in those sharp eyes. Then they narrowed, shuttering against emotion, and he was the Sunder I knew, cold and haughty. A smirk tugged at the corners of his mouth.

"Hasn't anyone ever warned you?" Sleep made his voice dark and husky. Cool fingers latched around my wrist, sending a whisper singing toward my elbow. "Never wake a sleeping tiger, unless you want to be bitten."

"Oh, I don't know." I made my expression scornful, and raked my eyes up and down his lithe body, lingering at his pale hair. "I've heard the white snow tigers of your precious Meteor Mountains are all born without teeth. I'm not particularly worried."

"I don't need teeth," he said, his smile sharpening into a knife, "to make you scream."

I snatched my hand from his grip and stepped away, willing my pulse to slow.

So much for the upper hand.

"I need to talk to you," I muttered, rubbing at my wrist.

"No," Sunder said. He dragged a hand through his sleep-mussed hair. "I don't *talk*."

"I'm serious," I hissed. "Something's going on in this damned palais. Everyone knows about it but me, but they refuse to tell me about it."

"That's because you don't belong here," said Sunder, without expression. The words were Thibo's, and they sent a streak of pain to bleach the colors swirling around my heart.

"But I am here."

"Unfortunately."

"Stop!" I clenched my jaw, battling against the ember of fury Sunder's needling words invariably kindled within me. "I know what you're trying to do, and I know why you're trying to do it."

"Oh?" Sunder leaned down to retrieve his boots, and his shirt fell open around his torso. I caught a glimpse of a lean, muscled chest and a hard stomach before I jerked my eyes to the floor, fighting the surge of heat climbing my cheeks. When I finally dared look up, he was watching me. Amusement glinted deep in his shrewd eyes. "A glass of wine."

"*What?*"

"Fetch me a glass of wine," he ordered, gesturing toward the shards of broken crystal glittering on the tile. I opened my mouth to retort in anger, but he added, "And get yourself one too, if you must," before leaning back on the couch and examining his fingernails.

I did as he asked, fighting to extinguish the slow burn spewing flames in my belly. If acting like his servant bought me some answers, I was willing to pay that price.

I sloshed what I now recognized as Belsyre ice wine into two glasses, then marched them across to Sunder. He accepted his glass without thanking me. I sat across the room with a huff of annoyance, and sipped gingerly at the crisp liqueur.

"Do you know what Severine's legacy is?" he asked.

The sudden change in subject paired with the casual and familiar use of the empress's first name rocked me off-balance.

"No," I said, remembering Lullaby's bright flare of panic when I alluded to it that first day in the Atrium. "No one does."

"Exactly," said Sunder. His eyes flicked left, right, and up. He gave a tiny shrug, as if to say, *You never know who might be listening.*

I narrowed my eyes on his face. Was he trying to tell me something about Severine? Or was he trying to tell me that he thought he—or I—was being spied on? I couldn't see past the courtly mask.

An idea occurred to me. I shut my eyes, and dreamed up a thunderstorm: the drowning thrum of ponderous rainfall, the hissing splash of a million raindrops striking parched earth.

A phantom tempest roared down, drowning out the whisper of leafy branches and the twitter of unseen songbirds. Surprise flickered across Sunder's face. He held a hand out between the dashing droplets, but the rain passed through his flesh, ghostly and insubstantial.

"Indiscreet, demoiselle," he shouted over the grumble of the storm. "Unspeakably so."

I huffed, and dissolved the illusion. I chewed my lip, dredging the lucid swirl of fantastical visions for something more appropriate.

"Go on," said Sunder, with half a smile. He ran one long finger around the rim of his goblet. "Impress me."

I imagined the sound of a soirée: voices raised in merriment, a trickle of laughter, the clinking of glasses, a strain of distant music. The pergola sang with it.

"You may be irritatingly loudmouthed," Sunder laughed, "but even you don't produce this much noise."

"Fine," I snapped. The ghostly party disappeared. I wasn't fond of these straightforward fancies, these fleshless daydreams. They reminded me of my early lessons with Dowser: pale copies of paperweights and leather-bound books drifting like ghosts in flat vermilion light. Worlds bound by terrestrial rules, the rules of reality. *Control.* I longed for oceans blazing with fire, armies wrought of diamonds and dust, clouded worlds cracking open like eggs.

I sighed, and surrendered to a world identical to our own in all but a few ways. The chirrup and warble of birdsong amplified. Sunder frowned upward at the arbor, searching for birds that weren't there. The slow trickle of the fountain splashed louder, almost distractingly so. A brisk breeze disturbed the lush foliage surrounding the veranda, and the leaves' whispered gossip grew louder. I imagined thick cotton blanketing the space between Sunder and me—a density of space where sound didn't carry.

Sunder blinked. I saw his mouth move, but the words were too muffled to hear. He rocked back in his seat, smirking as he beckoned me closer. I approached, dropping gingerly onto the edge of the chaise. The curve of the seat deposited me nearly in Sunder's lap. He didn't seem to mind, leaning closer so his mouth was at my ear.

"Better," he said. Even this close, his voice was distorted, as though we were speaking underwater. "Now, to sell the illusion. May I?"

I found myself nodding. Sunder reached up and yanked a few pins out of my coiffure, tumbling my hair around my shoulders. His fingers threaded through the locks, spreading them to drape around our faces.

"There." His cheek brushed mine, and he glided his hand around the base of my wrist. A frisson of energy raised the hairs along my arm, and I suppressed a shiver. "You wanted to talk. So talk."

I tried to focus on the reason I'd come in the first place, but it was hard to think with Sunder's cool fingers drawing zinging circles against my pulse. I swallowed, focusing on the edges of the illusion and ignoring his hands on my skin.

"What's happening?" I thought of Lullaby's friend, whose room I now lived in, and Vida's tears. *Gone.* I thought of Thibo's dour expression when he thought no one was looking. "People are frightened. Why?"

"Don't you remember the Gauntlet, Mirage?" Sunder's sardonic laugh was chilly on my cheek. "We are more than just legacies. We are weapons, wielded by our empress."

"Weapons?" I jerked with surprise. His arm tightened around my waist.

"Don't," he whispered. "Where do you think my sister is right now?"

I tensed. "How should I know?"

"She is with the diplomatic delegation from the Sousine, in the arms of the Compte du Verre."

"But—"

"Yes. He'll be dead by Matin. No one will dare question why. But without his vocal opposition, the Aifiri embargo will be signed by the remaining Senat, and Severine will have her alliance. Do you see?"

"Not really." I closed my eyes, trying to shut out Sunder's intoxicating closeness. I focused on the words he was saying, willing them to make sense. *Sousine. Senat. Alliance.* "The empress sent Bane to assassinate a political opponent?"

"Eloquent as ever, demoiselle," purred Sunder. "Now think of how many *political opponents* the empress of the most powerful empire in the daylight world has. Rulers of distant lands. Desert corsairs. Peasant dissidents. Her own unruly nobles."

"You're saying—" Sunder's words bloomed into realization. "We're an army."

"A silent, *secret* army," corrected Sunder, "beholden only to Severine herself. And not just the courtiers in Coeur d'Or. Most of the time, we are merely her insurance."

His words summoned up a conversation I'd had nearly two spans ago with Lullaby: *We are her insurance,* Lullaby had said. *Our presence guarantees that our noble parents and families behave according to her wishes. Do you understand?*

I hadn't then. But I thought I was beginning to. I shifted on the chaise to relieve a cramp above my knee. Sunder took the movement as an invitation, his hands smooth as quicksilver as he circled my waist and lifted me onto his lap. I yelped a protest, but it was too late; I was straddling him, my gown bunched around my thighs in a billow of floral chiffon. I glared down, my dark hair a curtain separating us from the world. His steel-edged eyes flashed with savage mirth.

He's just trifling with you, I snapped at myself. *It's all a game. Get your answers and get out.*

"Why now, then?" I hissed down at him. "If she's been leveraging her court of favorite sons and daughters all this time, why are courtiers suddenly disappearing? Why is she taking legacies from Coeur d'Or?"

"Skirmishes in the Dusklands: the shadows of Dominion, testing the strength of our borders. Zvar corsairs uniting under a single banner, threatening Lirian trade barges crossing the desert. Barges that are more valuable than ever before, because of the civil war in Aifir. Tensions rising between colonial government and natives in the Sousine." Sunder's face hardened, and the touch of his skin to mine vibrated with a stinging thrum. "We are on the brink, Mirage. The threat of war strains the empire's bones and hums in its veins. Severine is clutching at weapons she dared not use before."

"But—" A grim thought chased my words away. *Insurance.* The word had been burrowing deep within me, and suddenly I realized why—

I had no connections. No family, no relatives to keep in line or leverage as a weapon. I was just a penniless fantast who turned up out of the dusk.

"Me," I said, out loud, and the word resonated in my chest like a death knell. "She wants me. No one will care if I disappear. No one will weep when I'm gone. No one will threaten revolution if I die in the dusk or the desert."

Sunder's eyes on my face were empty of menace, only calm pity.

And that's when I remembered the necklace—a fat amber gem nestled at my throat, a waterfall of kembric and rubies swinging between my breasts. *Has the thought ever occurred to you . . .*

"You did help me," I said, forgetting the bracelet of his cool, nettling palms. "You weren't lying. You gave me that necklace to dull my legacy. To hide my abilities from the empress. So she wouldn't steal me away to fight her battles. Yet."

Sunder's eyes sharpened on mine.

"Carrousel is a span away," I whispered, and panic opened its eyes, a frightened beast awakening inside me. I clenched my hands into fists. "Like it or not, I'm going to have to perform for the empress. She'll know how far I've come. What should I do?"

"Do?" Sunder's expression didn't change. "I've been telling you since the Nocturne of the Gauntlet—*leave*."

"Leave?"

"Yes, you stubborn half-wit," he snarled. "Get out of this labyrinth of lies while you still can."

He shoved me out of his lap without ceremony. I stumbled backward, half falling before catching myself on the slick floor. Humiliation stirred my blood to a boil and sent flames to lick at my cheeks. The illusion shattered around us, birdsong and trickling fountain and stirring trees calming as the bubble of silence evaporated. I glared as Sunder crossed to his sidebar and sloshed out another glass of ice wine.

"How dare you—" I breathed, but Sunder turned a gaze so cool and disinterested on me that I jerked back in shock.

"Enough," he said. "You may go."

I rocked back on my heels, searching for something appropriately scathing to say. But my chest and throat were empty of anything but a sinking bewilderment. I smoothed my rumpled skirt with shaking hands and turned away without a word.

I was nearly to the edge of the veranda when Sunder's crisp voice halted me in my steps.

"Demoiselle?"

I turned, suspicion battling with a strange, sour hope. Sunder lifted his glittering goblet toward the elaborate chandelier turning lazy circles above his chaise. The low red light dappled one quivering teardrop of true ambric dangling from its base.

"Shield enchanted that pendant," said Sunder, naming a Sinister lady I'd never met, only seen from afar. "Its magic shields this room from prying eyes and ears. Anything said—or done— beneath its protection cannot be heard or seen by those without. But never let it be said I didn't enjoy your company."

He drained his glass and turned on his heel, disappearing between the blooming lianas.

My embarrassment was swallowed whole by fury. Images came thundering at me like a terrible tide. My lackluster joke of an illusion. Sunder's guile in convincing me his fingers in my hair were *necessary*. His lips brushing my ear. His hands gripping my waist, sending lines of fire racing toward my heart.

A game. A vicious game to take my trust and transfigure it into something else. Something that now nestled chilly against my heart, beckoning me even as I fought to shove it away. Something bleak and delicious and horribly, wonderfully tempting.

I never should have trusted him.

I stalked out of Belsyre Wing with desire seething in my blood and hate searing my heart. Nothing Sunder did or said was trustworthy. Even his words about the empress and her legacies could be nothing more than an elaborate ruse to drive me out of the palais. To win whatever sadistic bet he'd wagered on my failure.

And whether I left or stayed, I knew I'd been outplayed. I thought suddenly of peine, the complicated card game Thibo had taught me. No matter how good my cards were, or how sure I thought my win was, Thibo always found a way to beat me. And sometimes, the only way to keep a bluffer from cleaning you out . . . was to fold.

Scion damn him.

Has the thought ever occurred to you . . .

Something stopped me in my tracks. I stared up at an archway swathed in cold, undying flames, and reached for the notion teasing at the back of my skull.

Dark trees tracing calligraphy against a backdrop of white. Frost. An ambric necklace skittering across a floor of ice.

And I realized: I asked Sunder whether he gave me the necklace to protect me from Severine.

I never thought to ask him *why he cared.*

THIRTY-FOUR

The bell for third Nocturne was nothing more than a memory, and still I worried.

Light burned through Blossom's painted glass window, casting orange shadows on my face. I fingered the planes of my ambric amulet, throbbing in time to my hurried pulse. Its weight against my chest was unfamiliar, like a memory I thought I'd forgotten, only to recall when I least expected it. It was so different from the gaudy spill of Sunder's Blood Rain gift, and yet I preferred its ancient contours, worn smooth by unremembered lives and time's steady strum.

The scratch at my door was so soft I almost thought I imagined it. I jumped to my feet. Reluctant hope untangled the knots in my chest.

The door whispered open at my touch. A broad-shouldered man stood in the shadow of the doorframe, nothing but darkness edged in blood. He stepped closer. My lungs gasped for air.

I saw a palais servant's pewter livery. A mop of curling, dark hair. Brown skin kissed by the sun. And burnished eyes gleaming like kembric in the shadows.

He wasn't who I thought he'd be.

"*Luca?!*" The name ripped out of me.

He kicked the door shut and crushed me against his chest. I gasped, and curled my arms around his neck. The kiss he planted on my cheek was rough with stubble. He smelled of musk and incense and the city, a scent so different from the fine perfumes of the palais that I nearly wept.

"Luca!" I repeated. I could hardly think of any other words. He set me to my feet, although he seemed reluctant to release me completely—his hands lingered at my waist. Heat climbed my cheeks when I remembered I was wearing nothing but my filmy nightgown. "Do you *work* here now?"

"Of course not." His smile was a flash of white, startlingly bright and achingly familiar. "I came to see you."

"But—" I paused. I hardly knew what to say. I never expected— "But I thought you were leaving the city with the convoy over a span ago! And how did you get into the palais? What if—?"

"I get caught?" His smile, if possible, grew brighter. "I hoped you—the famous fantast the city can't stop talking about— might be able to help with that."

"Famous—?" I barely got the word out before shock bubbled up into laughter. I clapped a hand over my mouth. "You're joking."

"Care to find out?" Luca stepped closer, holding out a mass of fabric—the same color and weave as the outfit he wore. Servants' livery.

"How—?"

"My friend Garan. The servant. He snuck me in and lent me these." Mischief brightened his eyes. "Come on. The palais may be asleep, but the Amber City is still awake. The city is *always* awake. What do you say—a reprieve from this prison of silk and secrets?"

Reality sent a sharp knife slicing through my fizzing exhilaration. Luca shouldn't be here. Luca *couldn't* be here. Not in the palais, and certainly not in Lys Wing. And I couldn't leave, not mere weeks before Carrousel.

Couldn't I? Sunder's cool voice echoed in my mind. *Get out of this labyrinth of lies while you still can.*

"Sylvie. Don't you trust me?" Luca whispered, and the name froze me. *Sylvie.* Again, I caught that scent of him, like burnt wood and sun-kissed skin and infinite skies. The scent of outside.

My teeth worked at my lip, and I remembered the day we arrived at the Amber City. The convoy transports, rattling along broad boulevards and narrow alleyways. The rush of unfamiliar sights and sounds. A thousand colors glittering like jewels in the ruddy light of a dim sun. A million people, with joys and pains and secret dreams.

I never got to see any of it.

"Just an hour." I grabbed the servants' livery from his hands, fixing him with my sternest glare. "If I'm not back before Matin I will personally have you executed by the Skyclad Garde."

His muffled laugh sent a flare of pleasure blazing up my spine. I ducked into my room and dressed quickly, shucking off the gossamer nightgown to step into the linen livery. After spans of dressing in only silks and lace, the fabric was rough on my skin. I repressed a shudder of doubt, and shoved my carefully curled hair beneath a nondescript cap.

"Ready," I whispered, ducking out. But Luca had moved toward my sitting room. His long, dark fingers splayed against the jardin of painted flowers draped about my chambers.

"Did you do these?" In the dimness of my shuttered room, his eyes gleamed like the bronze écu in my chamois purse. "I didn't know you could paint."

"The girl who lived here before me painted them."

"Where's she now?" He caressed a splash of white lilies.

"I don't know." *Gone.* I swallowed a bright burst of grief. *Mender.* I still hadn't been able to bring myself to approach Thibo after the picnic, but I wanted— No. I shoved the moil of emotions beneath the unexpected thrill of seeing Luca. "She . . . left before I arrived at the palais."

"Ah." Luca nodded, as though he understood something I didn't. He crossed to my side, twisting his arm through mine. "Let's go."

"Luca—" I hesitated one last time, but Luca spun to face me. He pressed one warm finger to my lips, his calluses brushing the tender skin. I swallowed, hard.

"Hush," he laughed. "No more excuses."

❧

We drifted like shadows through the halls of Coeur d'Or, keeping to the inner passages and secret doors the servants used to get quickly from one wing to the next. I jumped at every footstep, but Luca's hand was firm on the small of my back, pushing me forward.

A flight of hidden steps; the quiet whisper of a wooden door; the dank press of an ill-lit tunnel. And finally, a splash of burnished light on pitted cobblestones. The distant murmur and chatter of a city that never slept. A breeze laden with the complicated smells of a million citizens and their daily lives.

Outside.

Luca didn't let me catch my breath. We raced down streets where close-set houses frowned like distant Sisters. We squeezed along alleyways slick with moisture, where unseen creatures scuttled in the shadows. The air screamed in my lungs, and I was utterly lost.

"Where are we going?" I hissed at Luca's pewter-clad back,

barely visible in the shadow of a warehouse with busted windows like a gapped smile. "We shouldn't go too far!"

"Don't worry." Luca tossed the words over his shoulder. "I want to show you something."

I swallowed my uncertainty and followed my friend, avoiding the refuse beginning to slop at my boots. I breathed through my mouth to avoid the insidious whiff of waste teasing at my nostrils.

Finally, we wedged between two twisting heaps of scrap metal, and then all of my senses were simultaneously assaulted by noise and light and smells and the crush of thousands of people. Hundreds of booths and tables and blankets crowded together. Smoked meats and candies and breads piled between glorious bursts of exotic fruits and spices and wines. Cloth and jewels and food and trinkets and junk. People of every race and age and height and breadth moved between them, shouting and laughing and chatting.

So many people.

And behind the vast market, humped like the massive head and shoulder of a sleeping giant, was another city. Buildings and houses and streets and ladders, stacked and heaped and towering like the violet mountains at the city's back. My palms itched with a sudden tremor of delight.

"What is this place?" I heard myself shout. The crowd picked us up in its current and yanked us into the throng.

"This is the Thieves' Emporium," Luca shouted back at me, "and *that* is the Paper City."

Thirty-Five

I stuck close by Luca. After I was nearly carried away by the shove of the crowd, he laced his callused fingers in mine and tucked me against his side. I could hardly believe it was third Nocturne—the Emporium was as lively and crowded as if it was Prime.

"You should see it at Prime," he shouted when I said as much. "It's deserted!"

Luca paused at this stall and that stand bartering and negotiating in garbled dialects I didn't understand. Coins flashed between fingers, and keen eyes flashed toward my face, my clothes. I yanked the cap farther over my hair, panic stitching hot threads down my arms.

Finally, when I couldn't bear the crowd any longer, Luca ducked between two booths, down an alleyway, and up a flight of rickety stairs. An alcove in the shadow of a dead vine brushed cool air across my face. I could still hear the shouting of a thousand voices, and smell the crush of unwashed bodies and perfumed hair, but people no longer pressed against my shoulders and stepped on my feet.

Luca's face swam into view. Worry dragged his brows together. "All right?"

"Fine," I whispered, sucking in another lungful of humid air. After two spans in the palais, I wasn't used to the sounds and stenches pouring over me like a waterfall. "Now can we go back?"

"Back? No." Luca's mouth lifted in a crooked grin. "Now, we go up."

The Paper City was a mountain made of the debris and detritus of an entire civilization. Tiny cottages of wood and stone were crushed beneath towering suites built from corrugated metal. Dristic and steel were neighbors to slipshod masonry daubed between vast tracts of cobbles. The city was alive beneath my feet, breathing like a slumbering beast of legend.

Luca took a circuitous route of ladders and ledges toward the roof of the city. We were never alone—faces peered from behind tattered curtains, and untethered voices drifted like phantoms. A flock of startled birds flew at our faces, and we had to beat away the barrage of feathers and beaks. The creak of improvised levers and pulleys warned us to whizzing buckets full of refuse and dirty water. Dampness slapped cold, clammy hands on the back of my neck. A child wailed, and somewhere I heard the frenzied barking of a trapped hound.

And finally, when the muscles in my legs burned and the dank air seared my lungs, we reached the top. Luca clasped his hand around my forearm and hauled me up onto the final rooftop. A sudden wind yanked the cap from my head and flung it away. I turned to reach for it, and froze.

An ocean of rooftops fell away from my feet, heaving up toward the foothills and churning down to the city gates. An entire city laid out before me like a tapestry, many-hued and knotted with the threads of a million human lives.

It was awful, and beautiful. I'd never seen anything like it.

Luca's muscled arm curled around my waist as the wind whipped his dark curls against my cheek. The press of his chest against my back was warm, but a shiver wrenched at my spine. I trained my eyes on the horizon, where a line of wine-stained clouds billowed in a honeyed sky.

"Careful," Luca whispered, his breath hot in the shell of my ear. "We should sit. The Amber Empress would never forgive me if I pushed her prized fantast off a roof."

❧

We sat on top of the city, our legs pressed against each other and our hands entwined.

Luca spread his trove of purchases around us. A small jug of tize, enough for two. Tiny fireworks that shrieked and spun circles before sputtering into nothing. Sweet buns bursting with fruit and honey and tasting nothing like the rich, fine foods of the palais.

"Do you like it?" Luca's eyes flitted, grazing the dirty bricks and the flushed horizon and the glowering clouds. "Living in Coeur d'Or, I mean."

The question caught me off-balance, and I swigged tize to delay answering. The tangy fermented liquid heated my blood and loosened my words.

"It's not what I expected," I admitted. I reached for my throat, where my old amulet hung for the first time in spans. I felt suddenly split in two—the innocent Dusklander with towering dreams and a hundred incandescent worlds living inside her, and the pampered courtier with muddled doubts and mounting secrets. How could I be both girls, and yet neither? "Everything is so beautiful—a paradise. I can still hardly believe I live there."

Luca's eyes glittered. "And the Amber Court? Have you found your place bowing and scraping at the empress's feet?"

"That's not—" Air hissed between my teeth. "It's complicated. I'm still navigating the intricacies of court life."

I thought Luca would say something—something like *I told you so*, or *What did you expect?*—but he just bared his teeth at the city ebbing away from our feet.

"And you?" I asked. "That day in the Mews, you told me your mother's convoy was leaving in two weeks. You were meant to go with it. Why are you still in the Amber City? What about Madame Rina? Vesh?"

Luca surged to his feet, stalking to the edge of the rooftop, where the wind snatched his hair from his face.

"Maman and Vesh are safe in the Mews," he said, "until the whispers of violence are silenced."

"Violence?"

Luca's eyes on my face were filled with curiosity, disappointment, and something else—something like pity. Even when I was poor as the dust rolling beneath the wheels of his mother's ore transport, I never saw that look in Luca's eyes. It sent the scant sips of tize roiling in my belly. Bitterness coated my throat.

"They sure keep you sheltered, up there in the Heart of Gold," he said. "How can you not hear the murmurs? Civil conflict in Aifir restricts shipments of the valuable weapons and machinery the empire trades for its natural resources. Famine and plague ravage colonies in the Sousine Isles, forcing up the price of luxury commodities like silk and kachua. More Zvar corsairs in the Meridian Desert, scuppering imperial sand skiffs and threatening trade along the Amber Road. Moneylenders are struggling to raise enough capital to fund the pursuits of honest merchants and traders like Maman. The empire is hemorrhaging capital even as the empress raises taxes and encourages her nobles to bury themselves in debt to finance continuously lavish lifestyles."

I leaned back. Sunder's words echoed through me. *We are on the brink, Mirage.*

He'd told me of the troubles in Aifir, and the threat posed to trade across the Meridian Desert. But Luca made it sound so much worse. I gnawed on my lower lip, thinking of the sheaf of promissory notes Sunder had tossed at my feet when he sponsored me. It was hard to imagine anyone in the palais being in debt to the empire, but now that I knew how Severine treated her legacies, I wasn't too surprised to hear she encouraged her nobles to rely on her financially as well as politically.

"You and those—those *courtiers*, and the empress—none of you bother to see how your actions affect the people," Luca spat. "The people like me, and my family, who eke out a living from the meager castoffs of the rich and never ask for more than we deserve. When contagion blackens trade ships, we are the sailors who sicken. When corsairs launch fire globes at sand skiffs with only a few weak legacies for protection, we are the men who must fight with swords against magic. When soldats require free mounts, we are the horse breeders who die."

"Legacies?" My heart gave a bewildered leap toward the word. "What legacies?"

"Of course you would only care about the legacies." Luca's harsh laugh scraped inside my chest. "I shouldn't have expected you to stay the same. How could you? You have everything, when you used to have nothing."

"I *was* nothing." I found my voice. "Penniless and indigent, with nothing to my name but bad memories. Now I have a place where I belong. Would you really begrudge me that?"

We stared at each other. My pulse throbbed with the rumble of thunder, and I imagined my heart as dark and purple as the horizon. I clenched my fists against a sudden buzzing thrum.

"There's more." Luca dragged a hand through his mop of curls. "Maman postponed our departure date indefinitely, saying it would give us time to gather supplies and contracts for a more prosperous trip. But I was restless. I wandered the city from Matin to Nocturne, from Unitas to the Concordat, Jardinier to the Paper City. I visited teahouses and wine bars and lotus dens. And in the shadows—wherever the light of the palais doesn't reach—there are whispers."

"Whispers?" My throat rasped dry. "Of what?"

"Of revolution."

"Revolution?" The incredulous word slipped out louder than I intended.

Luca's expression flamed. "For tides the Amber Empire has flourished enough that even the poorest of her citizens didn't want for much. When your children are fed and your house is warm you may gripe about the excesses of the aristocracy, but taking up arms to overthrow an imperial family with a vast and powerful army is nothing short of madness."

"It *is* madness. The Skyclad Garde is highly trained and armored. Any attack on the palais would fail. A war would never—"

"Not a war. *Assassination.*" The word had been forged by unrest and cooled with patience.

"Assassination?" I repeated. The word tasted like poison on my tongue. "The empress?"

"Who else?"

"But what will that do?" I was on my feet, my voice a fierce hiss. "She isn't even the reason most of these things are happening. Like you said—it's civil war in the Aifiri Archipelago, plague in the Sousine Isles."

"Why are you defending her?" Luca was on his feet too, a bonfire in his eyes. "In the seventeen tides since she came to power she has run the empire halfway to the ground. She dissolved her Council ages ago. Any nobles who defied her promptly disappeared or met with accidents, only to be replaced by a farce of a Senat filled with the nouveau riche. She personally instituted the harshest immigration and refugee laws in history. Taxes on ores have soared, while technological innovation has plummeted. She's a tyrant, Sylvie. She needs to be stopped."

"I'm not defending her," I protested, swallowing down the taste of bile. I closed my eyes against the sick rush of images Luca's words conjured. I hadn't had the most pleasant experiences with Severine, but these revelations brought her into clearer focus. But even if she was a despot, did she deserve to die? Did anyone deserve to die without a proper trial, without justice? "Assassination just seems—*extreme*. And like you said, there's no Council. She has no heir or consort. Murdering her will leave a hole at the heart of the empire. Who will fill it?"

"Not another power-hungry aristo, that's for damned sure," Luca snarled. "Maybe we can finally throw off the yoke of imperial rule and build a government ruled by the people, for the people."

Realization finally hit.

"We," I repeated, rolling the word over my tongue and tasting everything it implied. "This isn't theoretical. You're not just telling me what people in the city are saying. You're a part of this. You want to assassinate the empress."

I couldn't ignore the froth of eagerness in Luca's eyes.

"You're not a revolutionary, Luca!" My voice came out shrill and desperate. Every muscle in my body trembled. "I remember the day you told me that your father chose you to be a Tavendel Guardian. You were handpicked to honor the ways of your land. To remember the songs of your people. To honor your family by defending them. Where is the honor in assassination? In revolution?"

A shadow darkened Luca's face. "There is honor in standing up for a cause. In protecting people who cannot protect themselves. There is honor in making the world a better place."

"There is also little to no chance you will ever succeed," I hissed. "If you fail—if you're captured—you will be tried and sentenced as a traitor, Luca. You will be publicly executed."

"I'm not afraid to die."

"What about Vesh?" I whispered. I felt a shred of jagged satisfaction when Luca flinched. "Your brother is barely seven tides old. You may not be afraid to die, but how will your family survive seeing your head mounted on a spike by the city gates? Who will teach your little brother how to be a man after you throw your life away on a futile cause?"

"Stop," growled Luca. His hot hands cuffed my wrists, his pulse thrumming in counterpoint to mine. "You're making this about something it isn't. Revolution is a distant possibility. War could not be further from my mind."

"Then what is this?"

"Do you agree the Amber Empress needs to be stopped? She's tearing her empire apart from the inside out."

Luca's words opened a yawning chasm between my ribs. I closed my eyes, and sifted through the bloodstained images painting themselves against the back of my eyelids. Sand and flaming torches, black vines and torment. Wine-scorched clouds and sharp red nails gouging a bare throat. Lullaby's swollen eyes and stolen pain, a scar of oblivion on the landscape of her mind.

The empress always collects when a debt is owed.

"You want something from me." I didn't pretend it was a question.

"I snuck into your wing by disguising myself as a servant," Luca said. "But that won't work with a bigger group. And Garan said the empress is heavily guarded from Matin to Nocturne. We won't get halfway to her chambers before being slaughtered by Skyclad."

"Bigger group?" Horror strained my voice. "How many of you are there?"

"Enough to make sure the job gets done, and well." Luca's voice was grim. "But we can't do it without you."

"Me?" Surprise rocked me backward. "What can I possibly do?"

"You're a fantast—an illusionist. You could shield us. Make us invisible. Lead us there and back without anyone seeing us."

"So you can kill the most powerful woman in the daylight world?"

"And possibly save that world in the doing."

"Luca—" I snatched my hands out of his grasp, choking on a hundred objections. "Even if I wanted to help you, this plan is insane. My legacy creates worlds from dreams—I'm not sure I'm capable of cloaking one person, let alone a group. And even if I could, I'm far from Severine's inner circle. I can't go waltzing into her private chambers unguarded."

"Planning can overcome all sorts of limitations. Just say you'll do it."

"I won't." I plucked at my collar, sudden heat burning me up from the inside. "I can't."

"If you won't do it for me, Sylvie," said Luca, and his face was suddenly hard, "and you won't do it for the citizens of the empire, poor and starving and diseased as they are, then do it for yourself. I've heard about your precious legacies disappearing in the night, whisked away to fight *her* battles. Those who have the most to lose are always the most selfish."

"And manipulating a friend to do your dirty work?" I stared at him. Dread cast a shadow over my heart. "That's not selfish at all."

Luca's eyes dropped. I clenched a hand to a belly suddenly roiling with nausea.

"I want to go home," I whispered. "You promised to have me back before first Matin."

Luca gathered up the last of our scanty picnic without meeting my eyes. When he helped me from the rooftop his hand was chilly against my palm. I imagined ice creeping upward from my fingernails all the way to my heart, and when frosted lace crackled like cobwebs around my wrist, I hid my hand behind my back.

We descended through the Paper City. We slipped down on loose shingles, and caught ourselves on rusted railings torn from listing balconies. Ladders fashioned from creeping lianas. Mortared shells curled tight like ears full of secrets. It grew warmer, the miasma of the city settling around us like a humid, stinky cloak.

I stopped Luca at the pitted wooden door leading to the servants' wing.

"I wish you hadn't come," I whispered. "Our friendship was made for guttering campfires and dusty songs and half-remembered legends, not assassination and intrigue and manipulation. I wish you would have let me remember you the way you were."

"Sylvie—" Luca sucked in a deep breath. "You must know I didn't want it to be this way. I wanted—"

"Go back to Madame Rina and Vesh," I pleaded, daring to press my hand against his chest. I couldn't feel his heartbeat beneath the layers of cloth. "The convoy. Go back to the girl at the depot—what was her name? Anaïs? Let this talk of revolution and assassination die before it destroys you."

"I would, Sylvie." He inhaled. "If you came with me."

"What?"

"My offer still stands. Same as it was in the Mews. Run away with us. With *me*. I would be willing to forget all this—radical discourse, revolution, assassination—if I knew it meant having a chance to be happy with you."

I forced my gaze to meet his. And when the sun-bleached kembric of his eyes dulled with sudden uncertainty, I knew he was lying. He realized it the same instant I did. Panicked denial jarred his expression. His fingers found my wrist. His arm curled around my waist. My heart lurched. His fingers cupped the side of my face, and his lips pressed against mine.

A taste of salt, and grit, and bitter discontent. A clash of tongue and teeth and lips. The tang of desire, soured by the promise of violence.

He jerked away first. I stumbled back, and pressed an involuntary hand to my mouth. My gaze cut up to his, and when our eyes met something stretched and snapped in the air between us. Something delicate, and barely formed, like hope or a dream of distant stars.

"Garan says the court ladies hang handkerchiefs in their windows to signal their lovers," Luca said. "If you change your mind, hang a red one. I'll know what it means."

Tears prickled the back of my eyelids. We both looked away at the same time. Luca nodded once, then disappeared around the corner.

We both knew that was hardly a kiss.

That was goodbye.

THIRTY-SIX

I didn't sleep that Nocturne, nor the next.

My conversation with Luca raged like a storm within me, thundering through my bones and striking lightning in my veins. The need to do something—*anything*—was a pulse within me, but with every thrum of that pulse I was thrown in another direction. Side with Luca. *No.* Betray my erstwhile friend to Severine. *No.* Confide in Dowser. *No.* Run, run, run away and never look back.

And so I did nothing. I let my servants coil black Sousine pearls in my lacquered hair and varnish my lips until they gleamed like Devangelis rubies. I trod on polished marble shipped from quarries in the foothills of the Meteor Mountains. I perched on divans and drank Belsyre ice wine from crystal goblets crafted by artisans in Lirias. And every gesture—every glint of polished ambric or brush of fine silk—reminded me that just by being here, I was complicit in all the evils my empress committed.

Every miner dead in a mine blast—*my fault.*

Every sand skiff scuppered by Zvar militants—*my fault.*

Every child starving in the stinking shanties of the Paper City—*my fault.*

But when I passed through the gilded halls and peered from beneath my darkened lashes at the woman who ruled over us all, laughing behind her fan and tossing her auburn head, I didn't think I could do it. Did she deserve to be overthrown? Possibly. Did she deserve to die? Maybe. But could I be the one to do it?

Could I forge the sword that spelled her destruction, and hold it to her throat?

I came to this place because I believed in a towering, tremulous, intoxicating world of beauty and grace. The world where I knew I belonged. Much as I'd fought for it, I hadn't found that world here, where shadows spawned secrets and justice was a kind of farce. Hope smeared sunlit colors against my heart when I thought that maybe it wasn't the world at fault, but *her*. If I destroyed the empress, cut out the cancer at the heart of the empire, maybe this world could fulfill its uncertain promise.

But even contemplating the assassination of an empress meant that the world I'd sought from the start might simply not exist.

And I wasn't sure I was willing to admit that to myself.

❦

"Scion's breath, Mirage!" snapped Dowser, yanking his spectacles from his face and fixing me with his sternest glare. "I said show me a tree bending in a breeze, not shred a forest with a hurricane!"

I dragged my attention away from the illusory tempest spinning cyclones of black mist through copper-boughed trees. I imagined the tangled branches lashing at my arms and face, raising painful welts on the delicate skin.

"What did you say?" I shouted over the sound of the wind.

"I said, *stop!*" roared Dowser.

I released the illusion. Pennants of fog drifted away into the shadows. I rubbed my hands together to dispel the faint sensation of nerves buzzing along my palms.

"What's wrong with you today?" Dowser's eyes flickered with annoyance. "Your worlds are all spinning out of control. It's less than a span until Carrousel."

"I haven't been sleeping well," I said, which was miles away from admitting the truth. I shuddered to think what my teacher would say if he knew I had spent the past few Nocturnes staring at the ceiling and contemplating treason. "Bad dreams."

Dowser's expression softened. "I don't blame you for being nervous, after what happened at the Blood Rain Ball."

That wasn't my fault, I wanted to scream. But how could I explain that to my teacher?

"You must focus on the illusion you intend to perform at the fête," he continued. "Your empress, not to mention your dynasty, is counting on you to be your best. As am I."

One of Luca's accusations against the empress surfaced in the muddied ocean of my irresolute thoughts. *She dissolved her Council ages ago . . . any nobles who defied her promptly disappeared.* But Dowser had been a chevalier to the imperial family since before Severine's coronation. His signature on that Writ of Guardianship proved as much. Surely he would know the truth about such an accusation.

I couldn't forget that Dowser was the empress's creature. What would he do if he suspected I plotted against his mistress?

"Everyone speaks of Severine with such admiration and pride," I mused, making my way to the wall, where maps new and old clustered thick as wallpaper. I examined the crisp edges of continents dark against pale oceans. I traced my fingers along charter lines vivisecting the land. Names swam into view, names of cities and oceans and mountains.

"But what of the old emperor?" I continued, casually. "What was his name?"

I dared a glance at Dowser, and saw his eyes flatten with something like surprise. He hesitated, then sank into his worn leather chair. He polished his spotless glasses on the front of his black robe.

"Sylvain Sabourin was a decent man, and a good emperor. He died too young, and with many things left undone."

"Too young?" I frowned. "How old was he?"

"Barely forty tides," Dowser murmured, "and until his heart gave out on him we thought he'd live to see eighty. A stronger, healthier man you never would have thought to meet."

"How did the empress take it?" I asked. "She couldn't have been older than . . . ?"

"Severine was seventeen," Dowser replied. His eyes sharpened on my face. "She was your age. And she was as distraught as any young dauphine losing her father ought to be. What have you been hearing?"

"I haven't heard anything." My pulse quickened, and I cursed my lack of tact. "I just wondered—"

"You shouldn't listen to rumors, Mirage," Dowser interrupted, fixing me with a severe stare. "Every palais physician ruled Sylvain's death as nothing more than a weak heart and bad luck."

I tried to hide my surprise. "I didn't—"

"And before you even ask, the dauphin was always a sickly child. He never would have been considered an appropriate heir to the throne even if he had lived to see his majority. And even had any *natural* children existed, they never would have been deemed suitable to succeed Sylvain."

What dauphin? What *natural children*?

I turned back to the wall of atlases to hide the twin serpents of curiosity and dread coiling around my heart. My fingers trailed toward the north of the empire, to the range of hard-edged peaks jutting from the earth like giants' teeth. The Meteor Mountains. I traced the tips of those snowcapped mountains, sounding out their strange names. *Dom. Le Brigand. La Belladonne.* And there, nestled in the cupped valley between two massifs: *Belsyre.*

I snatched my hand away as if I'd been stung.

"You're right," I said to Dowser. "I shouldn't have listened to the rumors. It's none of my business."

Dowser's gaze searched my face. "If you must know, you're better off asking someone who knows what really happened."

My head snapped up, and I stared at my mentor. Was he trying to tell me something? Was he giving me an opening to ask whatever I wanted? I opened my mouth to ask the question I was dying to ask—*Did Severine disband her Council and murder her dissenting nobles?*—but the bell chimed for Compline and Dowser looked away.

The moment was over.

"Get some sleep," Dowser commanded. "And come back tomorrow with your head full of illusions and empty of rumors. We're running short on time."

Dowser's bald pate gleamed in the dimness, and I couldn't help but wonder how many secrets were stored in that head, stacked like books and dusty with disuse.

"Your tremors," I remarked, tentative. "They've stopped. Should I be pleased, or worried?"

"Inquisitive *and* intrusive today." He rubbed an ink-stained thumb over his brow. "I still wonder why you feel obliged to care."

I thought of my teacher, sitting day after day—tide after tide—in this dim, musty study, tattered books and bad dreams his only company. A colorless life punctuated by demands on his legacy and his loyalty.

"Do you have a wife or husband? Children?" My words conjured something doleful in his gaze. "Well, then. Everyone ought to have someone who feels obliged to care. I guess you're stuck with me."

Dowser's eyes glittered behind his spectacles, and a tenuous understanding seemed to bridge the space between us.

"I'm trying," he finally muttered. "If you must know, I'm still trying."

<hr />

I paced back toward Lys, curiosity and frustration tangling within. Dowser hadn't answered any of the questions I'd intended to ask; he'd only raised more questions. How had I never heard the rumors about Severine? A father, dead much too young. A sickly brother, dead before his majority. Illegitimate half siblings. A Council, dissolved. Nobles, disappearing.

Maybe Dowser was right. Maybe it was cruel speculation and idle gossip.

Or maybe it was something more.

I thought of Luca's face, resolute in the light of our weary sun. His eyes bright with the promise of violence. His tongue heavy with conviction and death.

And for the first time, I stopped to consider if he might be right. Maybe violence did demand violence. Maybe death begat death. If the empress truly murdered and connived her way onto the throne of an empire, then what kind of world would I be condoning by letting her get away with it?

I gnawed on a lip already raw with my uncertainty. After everything he'd said to me, I wasn't sure I trusted Luca's judgment. I had to know the truth before I condemned anyone—empress or pauper, noble or thief—to the Scion's mercy.

Much as I hated to admit it, there was only one person I could ask. I didn't trust Sunder. But something about the unflinching way he looked at me made me think that maybe—if I could just ask the right questions—he might tell me the truth.

THIRTY-SEVEN

I stood in the shadow of a clematis-draped arch and watched
Sunder fight.

I'd only recently discovered that many courtiers made a
game of dueling with their legacies as a precaution against being
called to the Gauntlet. Angled sunbeams sliced the sandy arena
into wedges. It was hot, and most of the men had thrown off
their overcoats and vests in a pile of brocade. They loitered in the
long green shadows of boxy hedges, sipping from flagons of ale
and exchanging bets as they watched their friends spar. A coterie
of ladies lingered nearby, clad in pale linen and hiding their gossip behind colorful fans.

Sunder stood in the center of the arena, hair blazing gold in a
bar of ruddy sunlight. His white undershirt was rolled to the
elbow. Muscle corded along his forearm when he lifted his
hand. He saluted his opponent—a glowering Sinister lord named
Haze—then bowed. Anticipation hummed in the air as they slid
into crouches. The game turned dangerous.

Sunder lunged, his long fingers snaking toward his opponent's
heart. Haze blocked the blow with his elbow and aimed a pennant of dense fog at Sunder's face. He danced away, his steps quick
and sure in the sand. He circled Haze, wary, then lashed back in.
His fingers found his opponent's wrist. Haze roared with sudden
agony and kicked Sunder in the stomach. Opaque smog rolled
outward, disorienting Sunder as he searched for his foe.

It was a dance of death, meticulous and savage and ancient
as the sun. Each step was choreographed, each maneuver

deliberate. Point, counterpoint. Attack, parry, riposte. I was transfixed, hypnotized by the measured sway and dart, leap and flicker. They orbited each other in elegant circles, flashing in and out of bars of light and shadow. There was no sound, only their silent legacies singing promises of blood to the thirsty earth.

A misstep; an ankle rolling. My heart beat a fervent pulse as Haze stumbled. Sunder was a viper, striking fast and sure. He tackled Haze to the ground, who hissed with pain. Scarlet bloomed like a flower on a white shirtsleeve.

Sunder won first blood.

The pair separated, breathing hard. Polite applause scattered across the arena; coins exchanged hands. Sunder saluted. Haze did the same, although the look on his face verged on murderous. Sunder sneered and turned away, flagging an attendant as he dragged a hand through hair dark with sweat.

I swallowed hard, and stepped from the shadow of the archway.

I saw Sunder's face in the split second before the rest of the courtiers spotted me. And it occurred to me that if I had wanted to keep this meeting private I should have waited deeper among the hedgerows.

Sunder stalked toward me with a vicious smile. Behind him, I saw the courtiers turn to each other with raised eyebrows. One girl flicked her wrist at her friend in a gesture I recognized as *true love*. A sarcastic smile coiled in the corner of her mouth.

Sunder cut me an ironic bow, then pushed me back against the curve of the archway in full view of the courtiers. My breath caught as he captured my wrist with a hand and pinned it against the bricks. He covered my body with his own, sliding his knee between my legs and bunching my skirts against the backs of my thighs.

"What are you doing?" I gasped out. Every inch of me was molded to him. I could smell the hot musk of sweat and sand clinging to his skin, see the moisture beading the fine hairs at the base of his neck. I could barely think.

"Assuaging the rumors while saving both of our reputations," he breathed against my throat. I shuddered; I couldn't help it. "How dare you approach me here, in front of everyone? I'm not your friend, my most graceless demoiselle."

"I need to talk to you," I snapped. His insult cleared my head, and I shoved at his chest. He drew back, slowly, trailing his fingers along my wrist and his eyes over the curves of my body. He gave me a leisurely smile, but it didn't reach his eyes, and I knew it wasn't aimed at me.

"And I told you I don't talk," he replied, too soft for his friends to hear. "Did you come here to spite me? I can assure you—only your own position at court will suffer."

"This isn't about revenge." Spite was just an added bonus. "And I'm not concerned with either of our reputations. So if you don't answer my questions *now* I'll do something that will actually give you something to be embarrassed about."

Sunder's eyes blazed. Pain needled up my spine.

"Don't you dare," I commanded.

He clenched his fists, and the sensation was gone, nothing more than a memory.

"My apologies," said Sunder. "You make a compelling argument. But I'm going to need you to simper."

"What?"

"Do it."

I hesitated, then did as he said, dropping into a curtsy and tilting my head in a gesture of deference. I forced my wrist to swirl in the attitude for *quiet admiration*. I gritted my teeth at the sound of muffled tittering from the watching courtiers.

"That will do." He offered a hand to guide me toward the path. Out of the corner of my eye, I saw him turn on his heel and cut an extravagant bow to his friends. They all burst out in laughter. I fought a hot flush threatening to climb my cheeks.

"What was that?" I snarled as soon as we were out of sight.

"Window dressing," he snapped. "You may be content with the dubious state of your own reputation, but mine has been eighteen tides in the crafting. I will not allow an unrefined provincial upstart to ruin it with her meddling."

"I assume that's supposed to describe me?"

Sunder said nothing, just led me between the high walls of a hedged labyrinth. My captured pulse sang against his cool fingers. Finally, he dragged me up a shallow flight of stairs and through a set of glass doors, flinging me away from him and slamming the metal frame shut behind us.

I stared around, rubbing my wrist. Potted trees marched in regimented rows, globes of orange and yellow and green peeking between neatly trimmed branches. The air was cooler than outside, but humid; the strands of hair loose around my face were already starting to curl. Low honeyed light slanted in from the curved glass ceiling, casting dappled patterns across the tile. A marble fountain plashed pleasantly at the center of it all, echoing off the paned walls.

"What is this place?" I murmured, half to myself.

"The Orangerie," replied Sunder, before dunking his whole head into the basin of the fountain. He flicked his head back, and water cascaded down his neck and shoulders, soaking his white shirt and gluing it to the planes of his chest. I coughed and turned away, staring into the quiet army of citrus trees to avoid looking at the only thing I wanted to look at.

"Why did you bring me here?"

"There's no dress code," he drawled, raising an eloquent eyebrow at my blue gown, "and I can keep an eye on the door."

"What's wrong with my dress?" I snapped, indignant, before throwing my hands up and shaking my head. "Never mind. I won't let you bait me. That's not why I'm here."

"No?" He leaned against the fountain, propping one leg against its curving basin. "I'm dying to hear why you thought it appropriate to accost me publicly, in front of my friends, in the middle of my leisure."

"Fine friends," I muttered, before dropping my voice to a whisper. "It's about the empress. I heard something, and it's important to me that I find out whether it's true or not."

"Ask someone else."

"I did. I asked Dowser, but I couldn't tell whether he was trying to hide something from me, or tell me something else entirely."

"Clearly you didn't ask the right questions," said Sunder, looking bored. "Why in the Scion's name do you think I'll be any different?"

"Because—" I hesitated, suddenly uncertain. When I'd decided to ask Sunder—before I scoured half the palais looking for him—I'd thought my reasoning was sound. But now, standing in front of him, I wasn't sure I dared voice it. "Listen, I don't know exactly who or what you are. Some people say you're the empress's dog, and you bark or bite at her command. Some people say you're a dissolute libertine with decadent and depraved tastes."

The barest hint of a smile coiled in the corner of his mouth.

"And I know you don't care about me," I plunged on. "I could fall down a flight of stairs to my death and you'd call for another glass of wine. But I know what you do care about. Maybe the only thing you care about: Bane."

Sunder looked away, the smile dropping from his lips. With his wet hair slicked away from his face, he was a collection of hard lines and harder angles. He looked like someone who rarely slept, and never deeply.

"You're not the only one who understands pain, Sunder," I whispered, and ventured a step closer. "Bane's pain is your pain. And who makes Bane hurt? The empress. Severine takes the thing your sister loathes most about herself and uses it as a weapon. And Bane isn't like you, is she? She isn't as strong as you."

"Enough." Sunder's voice was rough, and when he lifted his eyes to mine they were empty of that familiar sardonic spite. They were empty of anything—an abyss I didn't dare stare into. "What do you want to know?"

"Severine's rise to power," I said quickly. I wasn't going to question my luck, or Sunder's cooperation. "I need to know what she did, and how it all happened."

"Sedition, seduction, and slaughter." Sunder's eyes flickered left and right, but there was no one here but us—nothing but a vast circle of orderly trees and a glass dome to eavesdrop. "But how else do you think the rulers of the daylight world get their power? They steal it."

"Did she—?"

"Murder the old emperor?" Sunder pressed his thumb and forefinger into the corners of his eyes. "By all accounts the young dauphine was whip-smart, persuasive, and ravenous for power. Sylvain was wise, merciful, and moderate in his government. Sacrifices had to be made. As a matter of fact, rumor has it my own father, Guislain de Vere, possessed a legacy strikingly similar to my own. I'd ask him if the empress ordered him to assassinate Sylvain, but of course, he's dead."

"She didn't—?"

"She did." Sunder's smile was a rictus of death. "Nearly half of her court—and most of her Council—suspected what she had done. There were . . . alternate opinions regarding succession, and plans in motion with those ideas in mind. But mere weeks before her coronation all of her dissident nobles dropped dead or disappeared in the dead of Nocturne."

"Your parents." Sunder's gaze flickered, a chink opening into the bleak expanse lurking behind his eyes. A dristic fist clenched my heart. "Sunder, I'm so sorry. I didn't know."

"I was barely old enough to remember them. It doesn't really matter."

The sudden silence was broken only by the plink of water in the fountain.

"What about—" I paused, fighting the sudden lump in my throat that threatened to crack my voice. "What about her sibling? Did she murder him too?"

"*Sibling?*" Sunder's laugh was a serrated knife. "Try siblings."

"There was more than one dauphin?"

"The dauphin was sick and weak, and if she hadn't killed him someone else would have," Sunder said without passion. "There were more pressing concerns. Sylvain had appetites. He married, once, but Seneca and Severine's mother died in childbirth, and let's say the emperor liked to keep his options open. Very, very open. By the time Severine came to power, there were seventeen tides' worth of options to worry about."

"Illegitimate children?" I gasped. Dowser's words trickled through my memory: *Even had any natural children existed . . .* "But if they were illegitimate—"

"In the Sousine Isles," interrupted Sunder, "the Gorma tell tales of a fearsome creature in the depths of the ocean. With its sharp teeth and cold eyes, it devours anything it comes across. But after it mates, a chilling ritual begins. A dozen littermates fight for space, and even in the womb, the unborn monsters have teeth. The biggest and strongest gobble up their brethren, growing larger and larger until finally, there is only one left to be birthed. Only the strongest, and the cruelest, and the hungriest offspring survives the womb."

A shudder wracked my spine. "How many?"

"No one knows," Sunder said with a shrug. "But rumors suggest that Severine makes that cannibal shark look like a magnanimous vegetarian."

A numb wave sent needles to prickle at my arms and legs. A low hum teased at my ears, and my palms tingled. I rubbed my hands together, shaking my head to dispel the buzz.

Luca was right. Worse—Luca's accusations were too kind. Severine wasn't just a tyrant, she was a butcher. Not only did she murder her father, her brother, and countless nobles, but she hunted down scads of children whose only crime was being sired by a lusty emperor.

I was beginning to think assassination was too kind.

"And you're sure about this?"

"Nothing is ever sure, especially not in Coeur d'Or," said Sunder. "But dig deep enough, demoiselle, and even beneath marble you are certain to find dirt."

I lifted my eyes to the glass ceiling. Spears of light lanced between the staid rows, and I felt suddenly as though I was one of these captive citrus trees, cultivated and pruned, my world reduced to the space between four glass walls and one arched ceiling. Luca was right to scoff at this place and everything it stood for. But revolution? Assassination? Could death and destruction ever lead to peace? To a world where dreams had wisdom and hopes had depth?

"Thank you." My words sounded distant and feeble to my own ears. "And for what it's worth, I'm sorry about your parents. I'm—I'm just sorry."

My footsteps were soft on the tiles as I turned toward the door.

"Mirage," said Sunder, and it was the first time he used the word as my name and not as a weapon. Surprise spun me toward the sound of his voice.

He closed the distance between us in a few spare strides. He looked down at me, and the press of his canny eyes on my face sent a thread of heat unspooling through my veins.

"I confess that I find you nearly as surprising as I find you annoying," he murmured. "But not all surprises are good, my most unexpected lady. So whatever decision I just saw cross your face, I suggest you reconsider."

"Decision . . . ?"

"On one so unerringly brash as yourself, coyness is an unflattering mask." He stepped closer, and a bar of low sunlight bleached his skin to marble and brightened his eyes to turquoise.

"However highly you may consider yourself, I can assure you: Whatever you're planning, you are outnumbered, outpaced, and outwitted. You are neither as brave nor as clever as you imagine yourself to be."

I couldn't stop the breath of air that hissed between my teeth. Was I so obvious? Or was Sunder bluffing?

"I'm not afraid," I whispered. "Not of the empress, and certainly not of you."

He bared his teeth in a laugh. "You should be."

"Isn't fear what allows people like her to seize power?"

"Fear is what keeps people like me alive," Sunder said, "when all around the world is dying."

"You're a coward," I hissed.

Sunder's hand jerked toward my face, and I flinched away from the anticipated jolt of pain. But he just brushed a strand of hair off my cheek. His cool fingers skimmed the curve of my ear.

"And you're a fool," he whispered. "And there's nothing I fear so much as a fool."

He brushed past me, tossing his brocade jacket over one shoulder and striding between the glass doors.

THIRTY-EIGHT

I stood for a few long moments, inhaling the sultry scents of mulch and bright citrus and sorting through the coil of emotions looping inside me. Maybe Sunder was right—maybe I should be afraid. But when I closed my eyes all I could see were the snapping jaws of an underwater monster, hungry for flesh and hungrier for power.

I pushed out into the jardins. A line of heavy clouds had rolled in over the palais, casting dull shadows over the crisp lines of rosebush and hedge. I didn't know exactly where I was—between the Gauntlet arena and the Orangerie, I'd gotten lost in Coeur d'Or for the first time in spans. Crystalline spires and ambric domes glinted over my left shoulder, so I headed that way, cutting through a wild copse edged in lavender and sedge. My broad skirts were loud in the underbrush, and I almost didn't hear the staccato rustle of someone else's footsteps retreating through the scrub.

I jerked my gaze toward the sound.

A maze of slender trees sliced my vision into shreds of brown and white and grey. I squinted. I glimpsed limp feathers clinging desperately to sharp twigs. I didn't understand what I was seeing. A bird, caught in a trap? Pity clogged my throat, and I lifted my skirts to move closer, scattering dried leaves and moss behind me. But no—beneath the silvery brush of pale feathers I saw dove-grey velvet and fawn-colored chamois. My bemused gaze lingered on a glister of jeweled rings before drifting to the curled sweep of bronze hair beneath a rakish hat. Hair I recognized. A hat I recognized.

The cold anticipation of trauma gripped my spine with barbed fingers and turned me on my heel. I took two shaking steps, as though I might undo a thing before it happened, just by walking away. But the thing was already done. I felt it in the drumming pulse at my temple, the sick roil of acid in my stomach, the keening horror unfurling thunderous wings inside me. I turned slowly back.

It was Thibo, beautiful and lavishly dressed and *empty*. He lay askew in the shadow between two trees. His hazel eyes stared toward the sky. I dropped to my knees beside him with a crunch of dead leaves. Terror bubbled hot below a slick sheen of denial.

"Thibo." I curled my hand around his shoulder. "Thibo, what are you doing out here?"

His only reply was silence.

"Is this supposed to be a joke?" I shook him, hard. His head lolled.

"Thibo, stop it." Panic made my voice shrill. I shook him again, my fingernails breaking as they crushed the rich nap of his waistcoat. "Thibo, this isn't funny!"

He blinked, slowly. Too slowly. My hands crept to his neck. His pulse—fast but even—throbbed in time to the desperate litany clogging my mind.

No, no no. No, no no.

But I couldn't wish this away. This—in the churning confusion of disbelief and nausea I could hardly fathom what *this* was. Thibo injured? Thibo dying? My hands fluttered uselessly, and I shook him once more, just to give them purpose. A burnished circle on a kembric chain slipped from beneath his cravat.

Thibo's locket.

I snatched at it with more force than I meant to, and the locket came away in my hand, the delicate chain slithering around my fingers. Disjointed words bubbled upward. *My youngest sister.* Mender. *I would marry him, if he'll have me.* Reaper.

And finally, like a boot to the gut: *gone.*

I jolted to my feet and took off at a run. I hiked my skirts around my knees and sprinted, faster than I'd ever run in my life. Branches slapped at my shoulders and raised welts on my face, but I didn't care. A strange, serene world of smooth velvet and chilled wine threatened to drown me in the dead, muffled silence of despair. I pushed the glassy calm away, forcing my leaden legs faster. The wilderness gave way to a sward of smooth green, and I glimpsed sky-bright chips of armor pacing calm along the palais wall.

"Help!" The word was jagged in my throat, a strip of raw metal tearing me from within. "Help!"

The Skyclad Gardes spared barely a glance at my rich jacquard gown and coiffed hair before jumping to my aid. They asked brief, pointed questions. I answered as best I could through the bewildering fog of grief and shock as I backtracked toward the copse, retracing steps that felt painfully slow. My thighs burned as my corset dug pitiless fingers into my waist. I fell to my knees in the grass, tearing with my fingernails at the prison of satin capturing my ribs, the rigid stays stealing away my breath.

The pair of Skyclad Gardes paused, confusion marring their trained impassivity as I shredded the bodice of my gown.

"Go!" I screamed at them. I realized I was weeping; hot tears left scalding tracks against my cheeks. I pointed a trembling finger at the pale trees rimming the copse. "Save him!"

They sprinted away. Others had heard the commotion and came running—servants in palais livery and courtiers in organdy and moiré. More Skyclad Gardes. They flickered through the trees like fireflies in the dusk, their calling voices a quivering lament.

Reaper! Reaper! Reaper!

And I—I churned with sorrow in the blanched glare of the staring sun. This was my fault. Instead of comforting my friend in the wake of his lover's disappearance, I had cavorted through the Paper City with a rebel. I had wrenched sick secrets from a lord who only spoke in riddles. I had thought only of my own desperate longing for an impossible world, dreaming of belonging when the people who mattered to me were scraping and scrambling to simply stay alive.

I should have kept him close. I should have watched his back. I should have protected him.

I wasn't sure whether it was minutes or hours before the Skyclad Gardes returned to me. Their eyes were full of pity and disbelief and a distant kind of scorn. I knew what they would say before they had a chance to say it.

They weren't able to find the body I'd *supposedly* stumbled upon. There was no one in the copse, or the jardins beyond. Their final verdict splintered my bones.

Thibo was *gone.*

I trudged to Lys Wing, where Lullaby greeted me with mussed hair and tearstained cheeks. And even before she flung her arms around my neck, my heart was shattered into pieces of broken mirror glass.

"He's gone," she wailed, her words garbled and hoarse. "She finally took him. Thibo's gone."

We held each other as we wept, but the tears streaming down my own cheeks seemed cheap in comparison to the grief of my friend. And when we finally broke apart, exhausted by grief, I could barely look her in the eye.

"I don't—" I choked on a fresh flood of tears. "I don't understand what *gone* means. Is this what happened to Blossom? Mender?"

"More or less. No one ever saw them . . . before. Or after. They just disappeared."

"Are they dead?"

"Dead? Probably," agreed Lullaby, and the set of her mouth was grim. "Or worse."

The skin on my face felt too tight. "What's worse than dead?"

"You're the fantast. Use your imagination."

We lapsed into silence.

"I think *she* takes them," Lullaby finally whispered. "Do you know what Thibo's legacy was?"

"I only knew his court name, and how much he hated it. I never wanted to ask."

"He stole memories." Her voice was terrible. "He could reach in and pluck them away. Gone. He loathed it. He used to say he was worse than a thief because no one even knew what he had stolen. But he was one of Severine's most useful tools. She'd been using him more and more, as a spy, as an assassin, for whatever she wanted. And he kept trying to refuse, but she knew how to get to him. She sent two of his sisters to the Dominion border, never to be heard of again. When Mender . . ." Lullaby paused, shaking her head. "Thibo was done, you know? Tired of fighting, tired of losing. Part of me wonders if he was ready to go. Ready for her to take him for good."

I shuddered with anguish, rolling my thumb over the dented surface of Thibo's locket. *I would marry him, if he'll have me.* He'd been so close to his perfect life, only to have that precious, mundane, ordinary world stolen from him.

It was almost too much to bear.

"I'm never going to see it again, am I?" Lullaby suddenly said. I jerked my eyes to her, and realized that she was staring at the curling drapes kissing the deep blue walls of her painted room. "The ocean. I dream of it every Nocturne, you know. The crash of the tide kissing the beach. The red sunlight piercing the waves. My father's voice, like coils of seaweed and echoing caverns and the infinite line of the horizon. But I'm never going to hear it again, Mirage."

"You'll see the ocean again," I said. The promise etched itself onto my ribs with pulses of light. "You'll hear your father's voice. I swear it."

And so too did I silently swear that this time, Severine had stolen too much. And if there was no one else, then I would be the one to collect the debt.

Oh, I would collect.

And when I finally returned to my chambers, my hands barely shook as I knotted a red silk handkerchief to flutter between my curtains.

I'll do it.

THIRTY-NINE

The next few days passed in a haze.

I didn't write to Luca for fear of my correspondence being opened or intercepted—I had no idea whether Severine was spying on me, but it would be stupid to assume she wasn't. But I took to wandering along the Esplanade in the last hours of Nocturne, and if more than one shadow lurked between the towering pillars there was no one nearby to notice.

We conspired in hurried whispers, sketching a plan that between the two of us might actually work. Luca crushed my hands in his and smiled like I'd been sent by the Scion himself. And with his lilting voice and eager eyes, words like *infiltrate* and *assassination* sounded less like sedition and more like a promise of change.

"And no one else will die?" An image of Lullaby's lovely face stained with blood instead of tears brushed the edge of my mind. "Promise me the courtiers will be safe."

"Only the empress," Luca swore. "There will just be a few of us. We'll be like ghosts."

But once he slipped back through the darkened halls in his stolen livery, doubt crept close. Regardless of the right or wrong of it, we were plotting treason. And if either of us was caught, we would both die.

I distracted myself by practicing my legacy with Dowser. It wasn't difficult to convince my mentor to help me learn camouflage instead of projection; when I suggested the idea of invisibility and cloaking, he stared at me in surprise.

"I don't know why I didn't think of it first," he muttered, polishing his spectacles.

Neither of us mentioned my questions from the day before, or the threads of obscure understanding stitching us closer together.

But mastering another aspect of my gift was more challenging than I expected. It was like learning to write with the wrong hand, or speaking an unfamiliar language.

I practiced long into the Nocturne hours, begging off parties and concerts in favor of standing in front of my mirror and trying to turn myself invisible. I surrendered to a world where I was made of glass, only to have my skin sparkle like crystal. I fell into an illusion where I was formed from breaths of air, only to have my skin smear on the breeze like pink paint in water.

I gritted my teeth and tried again. And again.

I awoke in the dead of Nocturne from a dream of rippling birdsong and ice wine and cool hands encircling my waist. Belsyre Wing. Epiphany slunk around the borders of my consciousness. I'd hated the literal practicality of that illusion, the passionless labor of reflecting a world that already existed. It was everything I'd loathed about Dowser's methods: reflecting the world I lived in, instead of creating my own. But I'd done it, and well.

I jumped out of bed and stood in front of the mirror. I closed my eyes, and imagined a bedroom identical to my bedroom, but without me in it. The gloom behind my shuttered curtains. The rumpled sheets. The constant press of hand-painted flowers. I surrendered to my absence, shearing away from the cavernous grasp of existential dread.

I opened my eyes. I wasn't there.

A cool smile of relief pressed against my skin. I squinted, and thought I glimpsed the outline of an arm, the impression of a grin. But it was faint, like a scrap of parchment scraped clean, only to be written on once again.

I released the illusion.

It wasn't perfect.

But maybe with a little practice, it would be good enough.

I spent every moment of the scant few days before Luca's plan was to go into effect practicing my illusion of invisibility.

I practiced in my room until the bells for Matin chimed, then kept on practicing until I was famished and my eyes swam with half-imagined illusions. I practiced in the halls of Coeur d'Or, standing stock-still and imagining another identical world overlaid on my own—a world that simply didn't show me. I practiced until my face didn't swim distorted in polished crystal vases and gilded statues.

Once, a Dexter maiden brushed too close, inside the bounds of the illusion. Her eyes flew open so wide I thought they'd pop out of her skull. I dropped the illusion at once, but she stared at me like I was an apparition of Meridian himself.

"Mirage!" she shrieked. "You came out of nowhere! I could have sworn—"

But I simpered, and made up a lie, and she laughed at herself, her unease turning into embarrassment. It was almost too easy.

Moving was the hardest part. Once I'd mastered making myself invisible at a standstill, I tried moving. Tiny steps, in one direction at first, slitting my eyes and imagining the illusion moving with me. Then faster, walking from one end of my room to the other, the world sliding around me as if I wasn't there.

So gradually that I hardly noticed it happening, the process of being unseen became like second nature. And when I realized that I'd intentionally rendered myself nearly as *gone* as Thibo, I had to laugh. Laughter that quickly turned to tears that turned to resolve when I remembered how ruthlessly my friend had been stolen from me.

The Matin before I was meant to let Luca into the palais with his cadre of assassins, I set myself one final test. Elodie and Matilde dressed and primped me, but the moment they left my room I undressed to my shift and corset. I shoved the gown in a wardrobe where no one would find it, then opened the door out into Lys Wing.

The sun burned a harsh red, unmarred by clouds. Razored shadows lined the passageways, untouched by the dull glow of ambric lamps. I breathed deep, and let the veil of my second world fall around me. I cleared my mind, ignoring the froth of my nerves, and stepped out into Coeur d'Or.

I drifted like a phantom through the halls. No one turned their heads or wondered why the newest courtier was prancing through the palais in her undergarments. And slowly, as instinct replaced control, I began to enjoy myself.

I eavesdropped on a group of servants gossiping about their vexatious mistress. I paused in the shadows and saw pretty Vida steal a kiss from Wing, who blushed to the tips of her bejeweled ears before returning the embrace with gusto. All around me, life in the palais kept marching forward. I was nothing more than a fleeting fancy, an unexpected breeze raising the hairs along napes. A whispered footfall and a distant laugh, a flash at the corner of an eye.

And even though I knew it was petty, I couldn't help but exact one small revenge.

I found Sunder leaving the Gauntlet, flushed and sweaty, a silver-embossed jacket slung across his shoulders. He seemed pensive, his brows slashed together over eyes focused on some distant thing. His stride was rapid, but I jogged up behind him, hugged my illusion tight around me, and jerked the jacket from his shoulders.

The expensive brocade fell to the packed dirt of the jardin with an audible thump, raising a cloud of dust.

Sunder turned on his heel, frowning at the limp pile of fabric. He bent, reaching for the collar.

I twitched the hem, and the jacket pulled away from his fingers.

Sunder's hand closed into a fist, and he raised himself to his full height. His nostrils flared, as though he were scenting the air, and he tilted his head. His glittering eyes narrowed to slits as he stared right at me. I stood perfectly still, every muscle tensed as I focused on making the illusion perfect—my very existence a hallucination.

Gravel crunched as he stalked from the jardin, leaving me standing trembling beside an abandoned pile of expensive embroidered jacquard.

Later, after I dashed back to my room and laced my gown with fumbling fingers, a churn of laughter bubbled up and spilled from my lips. I laughed until tears prickled at my eyes and my corset dug a painful groove into my waist. And when I stepped back out in the palais, fully clothed and entirely visible, I could almost convince myself that seeking out Sunder was a stupid prank, a childish bit of revenge.

Because when he turned on his heel and stared straight into my eyes, I almost felt like I was trying to say goodbye.

FORTY

The hours before first Compline passed so slowly I wondered if time was working against me.

Luca and I had agreed in one of our secret conferences that the only thing stranger than me marching up to Severine's personal quarters and requesting a private audience was me doing it in the dead of Nocturne. So I inquired, idly and discreetly, about the empress's daily rituals, and a courtier was more than happy to gossip about Severine's schedule.

She spent the hours of Matin ensconced with the cabal of cronies she called advisors. Prime, she whiled away in the Atrium with favored courtiers dancing attendance on her every whim. Most of Nocturne she spent sampling the pleasures of whichever salons, dinners, and concerts piqued her capricious interest. But first and second Compline she usually spent alone in her private chambers.

I scouted the Imperial Wing once I'd mastered my trick of passing unseen and unnoticed through the real world. Severine kept her chambers at the very center of the labyrinth of Coeur d'Or, past Belsyre Wing. The entrance was marked by a huge door, emblazoned with the Imperial Insignia: a massive sunburst gilded with kembric. Two Skyclad Gardes flanked the door, armed and alert. I waited until Severine exited her chambers for the delights of Nocturne, and caught a glimpse of a long passageway, curved like the inside of a shell and lit by ambric torches. Four more Gardes, two on each side of the hall. And one final door, slender and filigreed, edged in hard dristic.

Six Gardes, two armored doors. Getting in might not be difficult, not with my new ruse. But getting out was going to be a challenge.

Finally, sixth Prime tolled, and anticipation frothed within me, fueling the flames of my anticipation. I grabbed a cape with a deep hood and slung it over my shoulders, then turned to cast my eyes around my borrowed room. If everything went according to plan, I'd never return to this place. I lingered on the painted flowers slowly fading around the windowsills, and I couldn't help but think of poor Blossom's memory fading away with them. Bile burned in my throat when I thought of Thibo, passing in the same direction.

Would Lullaby miss me, when I was gone? Did I deserve to be missed?

I ran my fingers slowly over the surface of my vanity, touching the pots of cosmetics and jars of perfumes as if they were talismans. My collection of jewelry winked up at me, diamonds and rubies and amber purchased with Sunder's spare change. I considered shoving a few of the expensive necklaces in my pocket as insurance, but I clenched my hand into a fist instead. The less of this place I brought with me, the better.

I did one last sweep, then fished my amulet from its place beneath my mattress. The worn amber winked up at me, and I clasped the cool chain around my throat, tucking the pendant into the bodice of my dress. Then I stepped out into the last day I'd ever spend in the palais.

My steps carried me through Coeur d'Or, quiet in the lull before Compline. I paused at the Esplanade, gazing across the manicured jardins and vaulting topiaries. *Thibo.* Sudden sorrow knocked the breath from between my ribs. I'd met him here, that first day in the palais. He'd smiled at my mistakes and made me feel at ease in an unfamiliar place. He'd been *kind* to me, kinder than I probably deserved.

Coeur d'Or's insistent beauty crushed down on me, suddenly oppressive. I'd wanted so badly to belong here, for the promise of this place to be more than a wish or a dream. But I could no longer ignore the taint of death and violence lurking in this glittering heart. Wanting something badly enough doesn't make it real. And it certainly doesn't make it right.

I turned myself invisible as bitterness coated the back of my throat. Maybe it was easier to pretend I was already gone than spend another moment pretending I belonged.

I wound slowly toward one of the small gates set into the high wall surrounding the palais compound. It was rarely used, but I'd seen a few couriers ducking through it into the wealthy neighborhood just outside, and the palais side was wooded and shadowed. Unless Luca's group of revolutionaries were spectacularly imprudent, no one should notice anything amiss between when they arrived and when I made them disappear.

I crouched in the shadow of a crooked laurel to wait. The heat of the past few days had ebbed, and a bank of thick grey clouds shrouded the Amber City, turning the light of the sun eerie. A cool breeze kicked at my loose curls, and I dragged my cloak tighter.

Finally, I heard it: what sounded like a strange birdcall followed by a series of taps on the gate. I unlocked it quickly, using the code I'd memorized while surveilling an oblivious courier. I grasped a bare impression of height and breadth before a figure shoved by me, and then another, and another. Dread curled icy fingers around my heart as more and more hooded figures tromped through the gate. Finally, I spied a familiar crop of curling black hair over golden eyes, and I reached forward to grab Luca's hand.

"What's going on?" I hissed. I stared over my shoulder at the militia forming in the shadow of the palais walls: nearly twenty men and women, muscled and grim. Weapons glinted from belts and shoulders. Inked tattoos crept above collars and along corded forearms. "Who are all these people?"

"We call ourselves La Discorde," replied Luca. His fingers crushed my hand. "And we're going to change the face of the Amber Empire."

"I don't care what you call yourselves, there are too many of you. I can make you and one other person invisible. *Maybe* two." Panic threaded my voice as disquiet chilled my blood. "The rest of them can't come. What are they even doing here?"

"They have another mission," said Luca, his tone unforgiving. He motioned to two figures, a stocky man and a copper-haired woman. "Denis and Petra are coming with us."

"This is not what we discussed," I snapped, trying to infuse my voice with authority. "We planned a bare-bones mission. In and out. Simple, quick."

"Plans change, Sylvie." Luca's eyes shone with fever.

"But—"

"Stop whining," Luca snarled. "They're striking at the armory. None of your precious aristos are going to die. Not if they don't get in our way."

"The armory?" My knees were unsteady, as if the earth was crumbling beneath my feet. "I just told you, I can't turn them invisible. If anyone sees them, our plan falls to pieces!"

"If anything, it will be a diversion." Luca's voice was

impatient. "We're losing time. Our plan stays the same. Don't back out now, *Mirage*."

I stared at the dark-haired boy—*man*—and regret made my limbs heavy and weak. Regret for what I'd done. Regret for what I was about to do. I opened my mouth to say I wouldn't do it, I couldn't do it, but the words were distant and impossible. Something in my face must have given me away, because Luca nodded sharply to a muscular, bearded man.

The fighters disappeared into the hedgerows surrounding the outer jardins. I watched, mutinous, as the shadows swallowed them whole.

"Sylvie, come on." Luca gestured to Denis and Petra, standing silent and still as statues. "We don't have a lot of time."

I swallowed against the rock of dismay clogging my throat. *Our plan stays the same.* But I couldn't banish the image of twenty renegades cutting a swathe through the palais. I remembered the glint of weapons, the harsh tang of hatred souring the air.

I shook my head. It was too late to change that now. I had to trust that Luca wouldn't be a part of wholesale slaughter. They were here for weapons. They had their own mission.

Our plan stays the same.

"Fine." My voice was dry as a bone. "We'll take the quickest route to the center of the palais, to Severine's chambers. I'll be visible, but for you to remain unseen you'll have to cluster close together and move as one. You'll also need to walk in front of me."

"Why?" interrupted Petra.

"Because I don't have eyes in the back of my head," I growled.

"I thought you rich snobs had everything," the girl sneered.

"I'm not—"

"Petra, shut up," said Luca, a warning in his voice. "Sylvie, continue. We're listening."

"Luca, stay in front of the other two," I forced between my teeth. "If we reach a turn in the hall, I'll snap once for left and twice for right. If we meet anyone coming in the other direction you'll need to stop, and stay dead still. I'll take care of the rest."

"And once we get to the Imperial Wing?" asked Luca.

"Follow my lead, don't say a word, and wait until we're inside before you do *anything*." I fixed Luca and each of his comrades with a stare. "Do you understand?"

They each nodded. I sucked in a breath that didn't begin to fill the hollow growing shadowy as the Midnight Dominion between my ribs.

The bell for Compline rang.

It was time.

Sharp black clouds scudded across the curtained sun, throwing strange shadows as we darted across the lawn. The second we were beneath the pillars of the Esplanade, I cleared my throat, and the trio tightened formation, Luca standing in front with Denis and Petra flanking him. I conjured the illusion. The revolutionaries blurred against the background, then disappeared.

The palais was calm in the lull before Nocturne, and we kept to quieter passageways. I had to focus nearly all my attention on maintaining the illusion—it was far more complicated hiding three strangers than keeping myself out of sight. I concentrated on the gleam of the floors, the glow of ambric lamps, the flicker of torchlight on gilt. I couldn't afford to make a mistake. A mistake would mean death not just for Luca and his friends, but for me.

We were lucky. We only passed one servant, and he stepped

aside and bowed his head as I passed. I was so nervous I almost greeted the boy.

Stay calm, I whispered to myself, like a mantra. *You're in control.*

Finally, we were in spitting distance of the Imperial Wing. This deep into Coeur d'Or, the passageways curved inward, leading toward the most secure part of the compound. I couldn't see the sunburst door yet, but I recognized the color of the torches, shifting from pale gold near Belsyre Wing to the deep red favored by the empress.

I was so focused on what was around the bend that I didn't notice a pennant of shadow detach itself from an archway and step into the hall.

"Fairest Compline, demoiselle," said Sunder, and the smile on his face was as poisonous as his sister's touch. "What brings you to this side of the palais? At this hour? Pleasure, I hope."

Luca and his fellows stopped dead. I froze a bare second later. The illusion stuttered, but I clenched a panicked fist and the hallway was empty once more. Fury and fear beat twin fists against my heart. A trickle of sweat trailed cold from my temple down the line of my jaw.

"Sunder," I choked out. "What are you doing here?"

"How could you forget?" He quirked an eyebrow and stalked closer. So close his sleeve nearly brushed Petra's hidden shoulder. "I live here."

My voice was a caged moth in my chest, and I could only stare in mute horror at the catastrophe unfolding in front of me. Tension was a living thing, a grotesque specter hovering in the air between us.

"Not *here* here, of course," he amended, clicking his teeth. "Obviously I don't live in the hallway."

Sunder lashed out, one hand disappearing as he thrust it into my illusion. A horrible sound like grinding bones split the air. Someone screamed. The sound sheared off abruptly. Petra fell to the floor in a heap, the entire left side of her body bent at an unnatural angle.

Chaos splintered the hallway into fragments of shape and movement. Figures darted in and out of the illusion. I gasped, raising arms that felt heavy as bricks. The emptiness dissolved.

Denis punched at Sunder, and Sunder wrapped one long-fingered hand around his fist. I heard the sound of all of Denis's fingers breaking at once. Horror surged in Denis's eyes in the split second before Sunder's hand coiled around his throat and turned his head backward.

Luca leapt onto Sunder's back. A blade flashed like kembric in the torchlight. I opened my mouth and flung out a hand, but it was already too late. Sunder disarmed Luca in a flurry of expertly placed blows, and the dark-haired boy's knees hit the marble floor with a crack. Sunder twisted his arm behind his back, bones grinding in protest.

"So this is your Tavendel lover?" Sunder wasn't even winded. A flower of hostility blossomed in my chest. "I expected him to be taller."

"Please," I heard myself whisper. Water dragged cold trails down my frozen cheeks. "Don't hurt him."

Sunder sighed, and rolled his eyes. "An empire's trash is a revolution's treasure, I suppose."

His fingers dug into the space between Luca's jaw and

skull. Sudden agony flashed across Luca's face, then his eyes lost focus and his head rolled forward. Sunder dumped him in a heap on the tile.

"What did you do to him?" A sob escaped my chest, rising into a wail. "Is he dead?"

"Bane!" called Sunder. "Do you mind?"

Bane emerged from the opposite side of the archway where Sunder ambushed us. For once, the pale girl wasn't wearing gloves. Her bare fingers were long and white as albino spiders.

Bane gave her brother a questioning look. His shrug was fluid with apathy.

Fear poured adrenaline into my veins. I took a shaky step away, and prepared to flee.

Bane raised one liquid wrist to her mouth, and blew me a kiss. Her breath gusted across her fingers, black as dusk. I whirled as the inky particles glided toward me. My shoes slipped as I scrabbled for purchase on the slick floor.

It was like a bad dream. The cloud of poison surrounded me, and I was too slow. My steps clomped ponderous and strange, as though I was slogging through mud. My heart beat dull and sluggish, and I couldn't seem to draw enough breath. The vapor hemmed me in, clinging to my nose and prying at my mouth.

I collapsed to my hands and knees on the floor, coughing as Bane's venom invaded my system. My vision blurred.

Conviction crowded out any lingering uncertainty: This was the end.

I fumbled for my ambric necklace with numb fingers, and clutched its familiar, worn planes as darkness settled in.

FORTY-ONE

Consciousness dug sharp fingernails into the edges of my mind, and *pulled*.

My sense of hearing returned first, sending a constant clatter thundering into my brain. The sound was scraped raw of context or meaning, jarring me to my bones. I stirred. My muscles wailed in silent agony. I shifted my jaw and tried to open my eyes. Light screamed in like shards of glass. It prickled raw along my tender skin. I moaned, and curled away from the onslaught of sensation.

Slowly, the world settled around me. My head ached like I'd been drinking wine for three days straight, and I couldn't open my eyes more than a slit. I peered around, trying to make sense of the clatter and sway jolting me side to side. A carriage? I pressed my palms to the plush cushion beneath me.

"You're alive," remarked a cool female voice.

I forced my eyes to focus. A blurry face sharpened. Red lips. Ice-white hair coiled in complicated spirals.

Bane.

"What—?" I croaked out, but my throat was so dry I couldn't manage another word. I swallowed. It was like gulping razors.

"Pithy," said Bane. Her tone was cruel, with none of Sunder's bite of humor to warm it. "Sunder never said you were a philosopher."

"Water?" I managed. Pitiful.

Bane sighed, and tossed me a heavy skin sloshing with liquid. I raised it to my lips, sucking at the water like a greedy child. It was cold—so cold my teeth ached—but it was clean and pure and tasted like paradise. Finally, I capped the bottle and wiped a hand across my mouth to clear the droplets from my lips. My palm came away black.

Memory came flooding back. The Imperial Wing. Sunder. Violence and death. Luca. Bane, breathing poison, chasing me down the hall.

"What did you do to me?" I spat. The fingers I brushed across my eyes and nose came away filmy with fine black soot.

"Scion, you're a mess," she sneered. She looked away and curled a voluminous fur ruff closer to her face. She was clothed all in furs, pale grey and white framing her face and draping her slender figure. "Sunder's taste in women really has taken an unfortunate turn."

"Bane!" I snapped. She cut frigid emerald eyes to me, and her mouth formed a moue of scorn. "Feel free to insult me at your leisure, but would you mind telling me what happened? What did you do to me? Where's Sunder? What happened to Luca? Where are we, and where are we going?"

"Who are you? What time is it? What's a bath?" she mocked.

"You only *tried* to kill me," I hissed. Fury sent lines of fire to kindle my chest, and I felt suddenly myself again. "I can make you wish you'd succeeded."

"Ooohhh," said Bane, rolling her perfectly lined eyes. She lifted a velvet-gloved hand to tap idly at the white lace of frost spreading across the carriage window. "I didn't try to kill you. Sunder asked me to incapacitate you."

"But—you're—"

"Poisonous? Yes, I poisoned you. Don't worry, the effects

aren't permanent. You'll feel mildly ill for another day or two before you return to your natural state of loathsome vulgarity."

"And Luca?" I swallowed the wave of nausea rising in my stomach. "Did Sunder kill him, like he did the others?"

"The Tavendel ore trader?" Bane curled her lip into its accustomed sneer. "Sadly, no. My brother seemed concerned about how you might take that news."

I leaned forward, sudden hope fizzing in my chest. "Where is he? Luca?"

"In a great deal of pain, if I know Sunder." She smirked at my stricken look. "Oh, calm down. I haven't the faintest idea."

"And the empress?" The words were blades in my throat, and I dreaded the answer. "Did she learn of our attack?"

"I'm sure she'd be *soooo* surprised to discover the Dusklander trash she let into the palais turned out to be a traitor."

"Is that why I'm here? Are you taking me somewhere to torture me, or to—"

"Kill you?" Bane's eyes glittered. "Scion, I wish. But I'm afraid that's Sunder's decision."

I bit back the vicious words rising in my throat. She was baiting me—her eyes had the same savage glint as her twin brother's. I suddenly remembered what Lullaby called them when I first arrived at Coeur d'Or: *the Suicide Twins.*

I smothered a desperate, humorless laugh.

"Something funny?" Bane snapped.

"You are," I spat back, and was rewarded with a barely masked flash of curiosity. "If you're not going to kill me, then where are you taking me?"

"We're a day's ride from Belsyre," she said, returning her wintry gaze to the frost stitching a cold tapestry on the glass window. "I hope you like the cold."

✤

We spent most of the journey in uneasy silence, Bane and I.

Soon after our delightful conversation, I suffered a bout of nausea so intense I could do nothing but curl against the seat and close my eyes. The constant rocking and swaying of the carriage soured the empty cavern of my stomach, and for the first time in my life, I was glad I hadn't eaten anything.

When the nausea finally ebbed, the chills set in.

I shuddered in the corner with my teeth chattering before Bane finally took pity on me and tossed me a length of pale fur so soft and luxurious I could barely believe it wasn't an illusion. The moment I wrapped it around my shoulders my shivers faded away and delicious warmth folded me in its arms. I spared a thought for whatever fluffy winter animal gave its life for my comfort, and snuggled deeper into the fur.

The travel became almost hypnotic. I couldn't see anything out the frost-glazed windows, so I could only guess where we were. Sometimes I felt the pull of gravity as we crested a rise or turned a corner, but for all I knew we were driving around in circles a mile outside the palais. I settled into an uneasy stupor as my body slowly detoxified from the poison scouring my insides. I only moved when a leg went numb or the edge of the carriage jarred my shoulder. Bane seemed lost in her own thoughts, and neither of us was eager to engage the other in conversation.

We stopped only once, when—much to Bane's disdain—I had to relieve myself.

She rapped on the ceiling of the carriage, and the equipage slowed to a halt. A footman handed me down. Ice bloomed on the dark fur of his hood and rimed the tips of his mustache.

My palais slippers crunched through a thick layer of frigid snow as I trudged toward a copse of trees. But I barely noticed my cold toes or the chill air sucking the warmth from my cheeks. Hulking mountains rose up like giants, jagged heads and shoulders disappearing into clouds stained bloody by a hidden sun. Snow lined the branches of black trees. Everything was bright, and sharp, and crisp beneath the muted light. I stared around in awe even as the cold robbed the breath from my lungs.

"Hurry up!" shouted Bane.

But nothing could take away the mute wonder settling in my breast as we left civilization behind and climbed into a strange world of winter. And when I finally fell into a restless, broken sleep, I dreamed of red blood spilled across milky snow. Stone black as hate. Cold so fierce it snapped your bones.

And Sunder, with my name on his lips.

FORTY-TWO

I jolted awake to the sound of shod hooves striking cobblestone and the vague certainty that someone was trying to talk to me.

"Huh?" I grunted, shoving myself into a sitting position and closing my gaping mouth.

"Ever the poet," said Bane, but for once the jibe wasn't laced with poison. She rubbed the sleeve of her coat across the window and stared outside, joy polishing her face to a jewel and lighting her up from the inside. "I said, *We're here.*"

I reached for the handle of the carriage door. Bane slashed a hand toward me and frowned.

"Careful," she snapped. "Unless you want to lose a finger to wolfbite."

I snatched my hand away. "What?"

"It's colder here," warned Bane. "You're not used to it, and you're not dressed warmly. The cold steals from those who don't respect it." She tossed me fur-lined gloves and a pair of woolen socks. "Stuff those in your shoes. They're ruined anyway. We'll find you better clothes once we're inside."

I did as she said, swathing myself in layers of warmth. When I was cocooned to Bane's satisfaction, we stepped from the carriage.

Belsyre flung ice and light into my eyes, shattering my sight into razored shards of broken mirror.

Perched on a craggy rise nestled between two black ridges, Belsyre jutted strange and pale, slicing through a veil of icy fog like the teeth of some forgotten monster. The château seemed to grow up from the stone, rugged outcroppings smoothing upward into sharp towers and looming walls. Slender bridges arched across steep ravines, the crash of fast water thundering through a shroud of grey. Black trees drew lines of ink across a bone-white canvas of drifted snow.

And between the shadows of these looming mountains, I could almost imagine the sun had set forever.

"Isn't it beautiful?" whispered Bane at my shoulder.

And when I turned to look at her I realized she wasn't speaking to me at all. Her face was turned up in rapture to gaze at her home. The tears at the corners of her eyes were already frozen. They glittered like perfect diamonds.

I shivered deep in my borrowed fur, and watched as servants clad in the stark argyle of Belsyre unloaded the carriage. A team of ink-black horses, their forelegs and hooves flocked in white, stamped impatiently. Their breath sent clouds of steam to mingle with the fog.

"My lady." An older servant bowed low over Bane's gloved hand. "Welcome home at last."

"Thank you, Bertan," she replied. "How are your girls? Did Mireille ever coax that oleander plant to bloom?"

"She did, lady," said Bertan, "and its loveliness reminds us of you every day."

If I didn't know any better, I'd think the smile that ghosted across Bane's face was kind.

And as I trailed Oleander de Vere through the austere gates of her childhood home, I found myself wondering that I ever thought the Suicide Twins cold or cruel.

A wolf wasn't cruel when she killed for her meal. A

nighthawk wasn't cruel when he ripped his talons through the still-warm body of a mouse. Winter wasn't cruel when it blanketed the land in snow and stole the warmth from your bones.

Sunder and Bane might be cold, but they weren't cruel.

They were merely as nature made them.

❋

The inside of Belsyre was as forbidding as its outside.

Our footsteps reverberated strangely across the vaulted foyer. High above, white stone twisted in shadow-wreathed archways. Slender ambric lamps pierced down like blood-dipped icicles, throwing garnet jewels across the bare, smooth walls. I shivered.

Bane marched across the gleaming tile to a spun-sugar staircase coiling up toward a gleaming balcony. She didn't say anything as she took the steps at a trot, her gloved fingers skimming the balustrade.

"Wait!" My voice chimed like a bell in the echoing space. "What am I supposed to do now?"

"Do?" Bane paused, her face a blurry circle of white in the muted glow. "Why should I care?"

"Because—"

"You're not a prisoner." A huff of impatience. "Leave, for all I care. The wolves are always hungry."

"But—"

"Sunder should be here in a few days. He'll deal with you then."

She was nothing more than a flurry of velvet and fur

disappearing into the labyrinth of her frosty home. I considered following her, but she clearly wanted privacy. To ice her heart or bathe in milk, or whatever girls like her did to look like that.

So I wandered the empty halls of Belsyre like an unseen ghost. Many rooms were closed off—tables and chairs draped in thick white cloth. Still more stood empty of anything, except perhaps ghosts. I passed through a great audience chamber, where two ironwood thrones stood proud, limned in dristic and polished to a sheen, as though their occupants had only just left and might return at any moment. Banners chased with the stark emblem of the marquisate hung silent on the walls, untouched by wind or time.

In another wing of the château, a vast banquet hall played host to nothing but shadows. Unlit lamps glittered like unshed tears between the frosted boughs of captive genévrier. Grand empty dining tables were lined with perfectly maintained crystal and silver. Not even dust dared sit where royalty once feasted.

Belsyre was like an enchanted palais from legend, stark and elegant and eerie. I half expected to find a beautiful dauphine sleeping upon a bed of thorns, or a penitent king disguised as a monster. But beneath the crisp austerity lurked something desolate, and the bare walls seemed to pulse with the remembrance of lost things. And with every step I felt as though I was forgetting something important.

Or perhaps it was just the feeling of being forgotten.

Finally, a blank-faced equerry cleared her throat and led me up a twisting spiderweb of staircases to a fine bedroom with a bed piled in furs and a curving window looking out over the shrouded valley. A great fire roared with heat, and a plush carpet warmed my frigid toes. Toasted black bread lay beside a steaming pot of stew. The scent of mulling spices reached my nose, and I was suddenly starving.

Only later, when I was stuffed and clean and warm and tucked into a lush bed, did I let myself fall prey to the gnarled knot of worry and fear and sorrow pushing crooked roots into my heart. And when I swiped at my wet eyes with trembling fingers, I couldn't help but imagine my hands coming away red with the blood of lost lives.

❧

I spent the next three days pacing the halls of Belsyre in a haze of anxiety. I didn't catch a glimpse of my merciless hostess again, but Bane's words echoed in my mind.

Sunder should be here in a few days. He'll deal with you then.

Images of the fight in the hallway raged through my mind no matter how I tried to quell them. The scream of bones snapping. Petra and Denis dispatched with the ease of an assassin. Pain curdling Luca's gaze as his head fell forward and he slumped to the ground. Sunder, eyes unforgiving as he sent his sister to incapacitate me.

You're not a prisoner, Bane had promised. But then, what was I? Why was I here? The luxurious suite of rooms at my disposal was unlike any prison I'd heard of. I had food, and warmth, and a wardrobe full of gowns hastily altered from Bane's castoffs. But the natural environment of Belsyre was its own ruthless fortress. I shivered just looking at the austere banks of bone-white snow, the cold, leaden mountains, the hungry trees. I was as much a captive here as if actual bars of steel hemmed me in.

I considered finding Bane and demanding answers, but every time I approached her wing of the château, a gracious servant intercepted my progress and led me away.

So I was left alone to obsess about what Sunder did, and why he did it.

And most importantly, what he was going to do to me.

FORTY-THREE

The sound of footsteps jerked me from a nightmare of snapping jaws and breaking bones.

Furs fell away from my shoulders, and a chill kissed my collarbone. My eyes flew to the front of my room. A black silhouette skulked in the open doorway. Cold fingers ran the length of my spine.

Sunder stepped into the dim red light pouring through the window. He wore black furs and carried the scent of outside with him: ice and iron and pine. Melting snow puddled on the fine nap of the carpet, leaving dark stains beneath his boots. The flickering glow of the banked fire painted the angles of his face in shades of blood, and his eyes were forged dristic.

"Where have you been?" I asked, and immediately cursed my stupid traitor voice.

"Cleaning up your mess," he growled, voice hoarse. "Explaining to the empress how a score of rebel thieves managed to break into the palais compound without a single Skyclad Garde noticing. There's talk of canceling Carrousel."

"What about—?"

"Your foolish assassination attempt? You'd better hope she never finds out, or your lovely head will find its way onto a very sharp pike."

We stared at each other across the darkened room. Fear spackled my thoughts with mud and slowed the churn of questions within me.

"What are you going to do to me?" I asked finally. I'd thought of little else besides crunching bone and bursting blood since that awful fight in the hall outside the Imperial Wing.

"*Do* to you?" His startled brows clenched. "What in the Scion's name has Oleander been telling you?"

"Nothing," I whispered. "I haven't seen her since we arrived."

Sunder muttered a curse, then tossed off his coat and slumped into the fat-armed chair beside the fire. He lowered his head into his palms. His lips moved, but I couldn't hear what he mumbled under his breath.

Hesitantly, I swung my legs from under the crush of blankets and stood up, wrapping a length of snowy fur around my bare shoulders. I moved on quiet steps to the fireside, hovering an arm's length away from Sunder.

"How did you catch us? How did you know they were there, without seeing them?"

"My legacy. I can hear the throb of hearts, feel the rush of blood, smell the stink of fear."

I smothered a flash of revulsion.

"Where's Luca? Did you hurt him?"

"Your Tavendel beau is fine," muttered Sunder, without lifting his head from his hands. "Better than fine. He's back in the Paper City, probably planning the next ill-fated revolution."

"He's not my beau." My hands trembled with relief. "What happened to the other rebels?"

"The ones who weren't slaughtered by the Garde will be tried and executed as traitors."

"What if—"

"They divulge your involvement?" He sighed. "One of Bane's poisons blots out memories. It's not as elegant as—as some legacies, since it blots out most other cognitive functions too, but it gets the job done. By the way, the court thinks you were grievously injured during the attack and had to repair to Belsyre for recovery. When we return, everyone will assume we're lovers."

Silence clogged the space between us. I attempted to sort through the roil of opposing thoughts and feelings. Sunder had protected the empress from our assassination attempt, but hadn't told her of the danger to her life or the part I played. And if he was loyal to her, then why was I here, and not in some drafty dungeon awaiting my execution? Why was Luca alive?

"I don't understand anything," I said out loud.

"Never were truer words spoken!" He jerked his head up, fixed me with his sharp eyes, and barked a desperate laugh. "You inconceivable fool. You have no idea the trouble you've caused me these past spans. You have single-handedly and unwittingly dismantled tides' worth of planning, just by being you. You've nearly ruined everything."

"I don't know what you mean." Annoyance chased away my fear. "And if you were planning something so important, then you should have told me instead of letting me *ruin* it so efficiently."

"Tell you?" Sunder's eyebrows winged up toward his hairline. "Tell *you*, an ignorant, unreliable, loudmouthed provincial with delusions of grandeur and an entitlement complex as big as this château? Your grasp of the intricacies of intrigue boggles the mind."

"If you're just going to insult me, you can leave," I snapped, wrapping my fur tighter around me to keep from throttling him. "I'm sorry if my ignorance offends you."

"Everything about you offends me," Sunder said, and though his words rang harsh the look in his eyes was unguarded, ragged with expectation. "I don't understand how you can be the way that you are. You are brash, and thoughtlessly brave. You do exactly the thing that is the least expected and the most destructive. You are a puzzle and a curse."

"If I didn't know any better, I might think you were complimenting me," I snapped, lacing my tone with poison as I turned toward the door. "I'd rather sleep with the wolves than spend another moment being verbally abused by a haughty lord with knives in his fingertips and deceit in his soul."

"Stop." Sunder was on his feet in an instant. His fingers whispered around my wrist, holding me back from the door. I spun to face him. In the shadowed archway, his eyes glinted like silvery coins. "I—I'm sorry."

"Say it like you mean it," I hissed through my teeth.

"I do," he whispered, and the strain in his voice made me want to believe him. "I shouldn't have said those things. But you must understand the chaos you have wrought in my life since the moment you marched into that cursed Atrium."

"I don't understand," I said again. The familiar coil of ignorance and frustration soured my stomach. "You're going to have to explain it to me."

"I will." He suddenly looked unspeakably tired, as if the weight of the daylight world rested on his shoulders. "But you're going to have to sit."

Reluctant, I did as he said sinking into an armchair and tucking my legs beneath me. Sunder tossed a log on the banked fire, which spat yellow sparks before flaring. He poured himself a tall glass of wine from a decanter, raising a questioning eyebrow at me. I gave my head a hard shake. He shrugged, and paced to stand across from me.

"I'm astonished you haven't figured it out yet," he mused.

"Assume I'm as stupid as you imagine me to be," I managed around the resentment gluing my teeth together. "Start from the beginning. Don't leave anything out."

"If you're certain." Sunder cast pensive eyes to the crackling fire. "Dowser and a secret group of like-minded nobles have been plotting a coup against Severine almost since the moment she seized power. Recently, those plans have acquired a clearer sense of urgency and agency. Wheels are turning. Assets are in play. Everything is in motion to remove her from power. Or was, until you waltzed up the steps of the palais and announced yourself as a legacy in front of the court."

"Me?" I asked, incredulous. I felt suddenly dizzy as my world shifted beneath me. Dowser, plotting against the empress. *Sunder*, on the same side as me? I clenched my teeth and tried to focus. "What do I have to do with your plans?"

"You mean *besides* leading a score of frenzied revolutionaries in a rash and ill-planned assassination attempt at the heart of the palais?"

I gritted my teeth so hard I thought my jaw might crack.

"You were never supposed to leave the Dusklands. Did it never occur to you that whoever hid you away at the edge of the world had a good reason for doing so? Did you never read the Writ of Guardianship Dowser left with the Sisters?"

"They burned it," I whispered. Curiosity poured water over the embers of my rage, and brought with it a strange, dazed sense of inevitability. I knew there was *something*. I knew—

"Who am I?" I asked, a numb certainty breathing rainbows against my heart.

"You were *supposed* to be our secret weapon," said Sunder, his voice bitter. "You, and that hunk of rock hanging around your neck."

My hand flew to the familiar planes of the skin-warmed necklace. The bubble of anticipation exploded into a firework of nerves. "Why?"

"You're the last surviving child of the dead emperor, and besides the empress, you're the only living—if currently illegitimate—heir to the Sabourin dynasty." Sunder's voice was a kembric bell tolling in the dusk. "And that ambric necklace is a Relic of the Scion. Mirage, you alone have the power to change the face of the Amber Empire."

FORTY-FOUR

hock turned my insides liquid with heat.

"What?" I spluttered. "But I've had this since I was a child! It's the only thing my—"

Sunders eyes sparked on mine, and things began to make sense.

"Oh." My heart stuttered in my chest like some invisible force had a fist wrapped around it.

"Dowser was a junior advisor in the emperor's cabinet when Severine reached her majority," said Sunder, his voice pitched low. "Barely out of Unitas. He saw the warning signs of her rabid ambition before anyone else did, not least because he briefly shared the then-dauphine's bed."

"What?" My head jerked up. "Dowser was Severine's lover?"

"He isn't a monk, you know," said Sunder, wry. "He grew even more worried in the spans following Seneca's death."

"Who?"

"The dauphin, the frail but well-liked heir to the Amber Empire. He was poorly throughout his childhood, but the fatal illness that struck him weeks before his twentieth birthday seemed suspicious to Dowser. He expressed his concerns, but the emperor was healthy and his Council busy administrating a vast empire Sylvain had largely left in their able hands in order to pursue . . . other interests."

"His mistress," I guessed.

"*Mistresses,*" corrected Sunder. "A veritable harem of official and unofficial concubines, spread across the empire."

"My mother—?" The word was strange on my tongue, and I choked on the question before I could finish it.

"Is long dead." Sunder's eyes sliced back to the fire. "Madeleine Allard. A courtier. The Allards hailed from a charming estate in the Rose Valley. They're all dead now, purged in the same cull that severed the roots of my family tree."

Sudden regret for the family I never knew—and would never know—washed over me.

"I'm sorry," I whispered.

"There's no point in being sorry," muttered Sunder. "Regret changes nothing. Only action can undo the ravages of the past."

The fire spat sparks into the silence.

"Emperor Sylvain never legitimized any of his natural children," he continued, "but he made his affection for a great many of them obvious to the world. And to an ambitious heir, such blood ties can be unpredictable and dangerous. Severine didn't directly target her half siblings until after she dealt with her father, but she prepared for the moment in advance—making lists, identifying threats, keeping tabs on potential problems. Dowser tried to head her off. He counseled many of the emperor's mistresses to flee, to protect themselves. But few listened, and the few who did were slow to run and ill-equipped to remain in hiding for long.

"Madeleine was barely pregnant when Severine seized the throne. Dowser smuggled her away to the edge of the world, hoping she would escape Severine's notice. Madeleine arrived on the doorstep of the Sisters of the Scion in a dusty hamlet outside Piana with a squalling infant, a Writ of Guardianship carrying the Imperial Insignia, and a Relic of the Scion."

"What is it?" I leaned forward, the ambric pendant thumping against my ribs. "And why is it important?"

"I hardly know," said Sunder, scrubbing a hand across his tired eyes. "Dowser is the Scion scholar. But it's been in possession of the imperial line for tides. When wielded by the right legacy, it supposedly confers untold power, especially when paired with other Relics."

"Other Relics?" I frowned. "How many are there?"

"I don't know. Some say as many as ten. Others put the number at three or four. Some don't believe they exist at all. The Sabourins claim to possess at least one other."

"Fine," I said, trying to place all this information in order. "But if they're so all-powerful, why didn't the old emperor ever use them?"

"Maybe he did." Sunder shrugged. "Or maybe he didn't need to. Regardless, Severine was cut from different cloth. Dowser didn't want any more power falling into her greedy hands, so he sent the Relic with you. If nothing else, he hoped the symbol would inspire the Sisters to guard you with every superstitious bone in their bodies."

"A true believer yourself, I assume?"

"Some call it faith. I call it credulity," Sunder snarled. "When Meridian descends from the sky in a chariot of fire with the armies of Dominion at his back, I'll believe in the Scion."

I bit back a laugh. For once, I had to agree with him.

"So what happened?" I pressed. "Did Dowser's plan work?"

"Madeleine is long dead, and you're at Coeur d'Or instead of waiting patiently to be fetched when the time is right," snarled Sunder. "So, no. Severine's spies followed Madeleine to the Dusklands and slaughtered her on the steps of the cloister. They demanded the Sisters give you up, under threat of death. The Sisters obeyed."

Confusion muddled through the churn of horror and regret.

"They did? Then I'm not—"

"Disciples of the Scion may be pious zealots, but they are willing to risk almost anything in the service of their idol. Sabourin blood flowed through your veins, direct from Meridian's mythic line. You wore the Scion's mark around your neck. In their eyes, the choice was clear." Sunder swallowed, and looked away. "A child was handed over. A child was murdered. That child was not you."

Disgust and outrage washed over me, tinged with creeping sympathy for the hard, distant Sisters who raised me without kindness or warmth. I remembered the desperate looks on their faces when I declared my intention to leave for the Amber City, the way they burned the writ and tried to lock me in my room. In their eyes, protecting me was their sacred duty, the thing that brought them closest to the man or god they'd devoted their life to worshipping. Nothing had been too great a sacrifice to keep me safe. And even if I didn't believe in it, I could see how in their eyes, I had betrayed that faith.

"And Severine assumed she'd rid herself of the last of her blood," I supplied. It wasn't hard to guess what happened next—I lived it. "And I grew up on the edge of the darkness, never knowing who I was. Safe. Sort of. But what did Dowser intend for me? Was he ever going to rescue me from the dusk?"

"Eventually, yes," Sunder said, with frustration. "We needed the promise of another Sabourin heir to motivate reluctant dissidents. Few are willing to overthrow a tyrant without the promise of a better ruler. But we also needed to keep you hidden, and keep you safe until Severine could be deposed."

A better ruler. The full gravity of the situation hammered down on me. I wasn't merely a legacy of the empire. I was *royalty*. Except for Severine, I was the last living descendant of the Sabourin line. Even illegitimate, I was the daughter of an emperor. And that came with responsibilities. Responsibilities I could hardly comprehend. A world of hard lines and vast promise bloomed at the edge of my imagination. I shook my head, tucking away the thoughts to revisit later.

"If you've been planning this coup for tides, why haven't you let the sword drop? Why is Severine still sitting on that throne, bleeding her empire dry and culling her legacies one by one?"

Sunder's eyes grated on mine. "Do not underestimate the difficulties of launching a secret coup on a ruler with a tyrannical death grip on her security, her advisors, and her nobility. You may think felling a regime is as easy as smuggling three illiterate rebels into the empress's inner sanctum. It's not."

"We were almost there!" I bristled. "We could have succeeded."

"You think you're the first person to attempt an assassination on Severine?" Sunder's laugh was a fingernail on slate. "Not by a long shot. The empress is wily, and she has secret weapons."

"What weapons?"

"They wouldn't be much of a secret if everyone knew," Sunder said. "First: Dowser feels certain she has another Relic in her possession. She always plays her hand close to her chest, even with her closest advisors, so he isn't sure what it is or what it does. Regardless, if it makes her more powerful, then it makes her a greater and more unpredictable foe."

"Powerful at what?" I asked, thinking of Lullaby's horrified look when I asked the empress about her legacy.

"That's the second weapon," Sunder said, and there was something like disgust muddying his gaze. "Her legacy—no one knows how it manifests. No one has ever seen her use it. Not her childhood playmates, not Dowser, none of her courtiers or advisors. But she has walked away unscathed from every attempt on her life. Poison. Dristic. Magic. No one has ever managed to harm a single hair on her head."

"What about you?"

Something brittle splintered in Sunder's eyes. "I prefer to keep my *gift* as a last resort."

"You seemed more than willing to snap the necks of those rebels."

"Yes." Sunder surged to his feet. "Because you were about to march straight up to Severine and, once the assassination was inevitably foiled, announce yourself as a threat. Severine would have tracked your origins to the Temple and realized who you were. What you were wearing around your neck. Then everything Dowser and I had fought for would be ashes and dust. I consider that the definition of a *last resort*."

I jutted my chin out.

"She's already trying to trace you," muttered Sunder. "She isn't stupid. The second you walked into the Atrium she knew there was something about you. We all did. Even covered in dust, you were too powerful and beautiful and proud to be a fluke."

Heat washed over me, and it wasn't from the fire. I remembered that day in the Atrium, everyone laughing behind their fans at my common manners and dirty hair. Sunder stepping forward to sponsor me . . . for the opposing dynasty. I pushed down the old shame, trying to see the situation in a new light.

"You knew who I was," I said slowly. "When you sponsored me. How?"

"Dowser's legacy allows him to speak mind to mind," said Sunder, as if it was common knowledge. Surprise jolted me back against the seat. "He saw your unexpected arrival as a miracle and a promise. I saw it as a curse. I tried to drive you away. I tried to make the palais miserable for you. I thought if you left we could still keep you hidden, safe until we needed you. But you were too determined, too sure of yourself. And by the time I started trying to help you, it was too late. You had your own plans."

"Do the others know?" I asked. "Lullaby and the rest? Are they in on the plot? Was Thibo?"

"A few are," said Sunder carefully. "It's dangerous. Some in Dexter are sympathetic to the cause. Reaper was a great asset, especially considering his family connections. Some in Sinister too. But it's easier to deal with nobles who don't have an active presence at court. Most people are not adept at secrecy and espionage."

"So what's next?" I leaned forward. Now that I knew everything Severine had done, to me, to my friends, the family I never knew, *Sunder's* family . . . I wanted to see her ruined, her power shattered, her sick grasp on her nobility dissolved. "What can I do to help?"

Sunder drained the last of his wine and ran a harried hand through his perfect hair, leaving jagged golden strands sticking in every direction. He looked suddenly too young, too overwhelmed, and much too tired to be carrying so much weight on his shoulders. A burst of pity cooled the eagerness climbing my ribs and knocking at my heart.

"I don't know," he said. He stood abruptly. The dull glow from the window turned his hair the color of rust. "I need to think. And you need to rest. We'll all need our strength, whatever happens."

I opened my mouth to protest, but the door whispered shut and his footsteps echoed away down the hall.

I turned back toward my bed, but my eye snagged on the heavy fur Sunder had tossed over an empty chair and forgotten. I stepped closer, hating the sudden impulse to touch it, to wear it. I ran my hand over the thick ruff, sinking my fingers into the coarse black fur. I raised it to my face and breathed in the scent of Sunder, faint but unmistakable. Crisp. Sharp. Genévrier and ice. A spark of desire ignited in my belly.

I dropped the fur to the floor and dived back into the pile of blankets on my plush bed. I buried my head deep between the feather pillows and willed myself to sleep.

But much as I wished I could drift away, thoughts of treason and assassination and legacy and dynasty whirled like snowflakes caught in a stiff wind, and it was many, many long hours before I found rest.

FORTY-FIVE

I spent most of the next day pacing in my chambers and avoiding both of the de Veres.

I replayed Sunder's revelations from the previous Nocturne over and over again. Not only was I a legacy, and highborn—which I had always guessed—but I was the emperor's sole surviving natural daughter. I kept having to sit down and force myself to breathe. Sunder hadn't told me the entirety of his and Dowser's plot to overthrow Severine, but if everything went according to plan my own future might look exceedingly different from what I originally had in mind.

Empress. Amber Empire. *Empress.* Sabourin.

The words were a litany in my head. I never wanted that kind of power. All I ever wanted was a world where I belonged. A world forged in reveries and quickened with wonder, as sublime as the kaleidoscope glow bathing my soul in light. I'd fought to be part of that world, and once I'd realized it was an illusion of someone else's making, I'd fought to create my own worlds. And wasn't that what royalty—what *power*—was? Building something—creating something—from nothing more than clear-glass conviction and ephemeral power?

But what did I know about ruling?

I felt suddenly, righteously furious at Dowser. Part of me understood that he had sent me to the Dusklands as the best chance of escaping my half sister's campaign of fratricide. But couldn't he have done more to ensure I wouldn't grow up a half-literate rube from the edges of the world? Couldn't he have given me some small hint that someday, someone would come for me? That I wasn't a forgotten orphan destined for nothing but what I seized for myself?

I was staring at the spume of water feathering upward from the river gorge and feeling deeply sorry for myself when a tentative knock came at the door.

"My lady?" A servant poked her silvery head through my door. Everyone in Belsyre was pale and blond—as though the white landscape leached the color from all it touched, including its children.

"You don't have to call me that," I said, a touch unkindly. Uncertainty and anxiety had frayed my nerves to the point of snapping. "What is it?"

"His Lordship and Her Ladyship request your presence at supper, my lady," she said. "I'm to help you dress and prepare, if you please."

My mood grew forbidding as the black mountains crouching silent on the horizon. The last thing I wanted was to participate in some charade of politesse while the fate of an empire hung in the balance. But my only other option was to sit up here like a prisoner and sulk.

I honestly didn't know which was worse.

I struggled to choose a gown from the haphazard selection of dresses the staff of Belsyre had culled from Bane's wardrobe. They were all exquisite, but they were tailored for Bane's willowy frame and designed to suit her icy complexion. Jewel-bright velvets; metallic satins. None of the light, soft Dexter styles that flattered my sable hair and warm complexion.

Finally, I selected an elegant, if slightly eerie gown. A pale skirt drifted like snow, etched in lines of pewter like the bare, spreading branches of a winter forest. Leafless twigs in dristic and charcoal crept up from the wrists and the narrow waist, branching across the bodice and twining around the arms.

The girl coiled my dark hair into a twisting braid and planted tiny, glinting jewels among the tresses. She glazed my lips and smeared kohl along the curve of my lashes. Diamonds like chips of ice winked from my ears. And when I stared at myself in the burnished mirror, I felt suddenly as though I'd become a part of this cold, lonely place. I imagined walking out those lofty doors and being swallowed up by the hungry forest, a pale dauphine made of nothing more than ice and brittle wood, blood and snow, frozen water and strange desires.

I descended the looping staircase with nerves tangling in my belly.

The Suicide Twins waited at the bottom, sipping ice wine and talking. They glanced up at the sound of my footsteps, Bane very pale against the deep violet of her low-cut gown, Sunder angular and polished in black and green. He cut a small bow and offered his free arm. I took it, laying light fingers against the cool brocade. I didn't look at him, staring straight ahead with my chin high, but I felt his eyes graze my face, my neck. I was suddenly and intensely conscious of the transparent branches twisting across my chest, barely hiding the breathless rise and fall of my rib cage. I fought the flush staining my cheeks.

Dinner was an uneasy affair. We three sat at one end of the vast dining table in that echoing feast hall, barely talking. Servants served mountain hare doused in a rich sauce spiced with genévrier and sour-sweet lingonberry. Savory squash and roast vegetables. Smoked salmon with cream and dill. Cloudberries with cream.

Sunder ate quickly, his manners elegant but cursory. Bane cut her food into smaller and smaller pieces, then nibbled daintily. I was starving, but the second I piled my plate high, bile climbed my throat and I could barely eat a thing.

Finally, Bane pushed her chair away from the table.

"I'm going to bed," she announced, turning on her heel.

"Oleander—" Sunder began, but his sister was already gone. His eyes cut to mine, and for a moment I thought he was going to say something to me. Then he too rose from the table and stalked away through Belsyre.

I sat mute and uncomfortable, suppressing another blush. Irritation and impatience sliced through my shame, and I shoved back from the table and stomped after Sunder.

He wasn't hard to follow—his boots sent crisp echoes ricocheting off the cold tiles. I had a sudden, sharp memory of following him down another hall in another palais; a crimson storm and a jardin made of ice. I quelled a burble of nervous laughter.

Sunder stepped through a pair of tall glass doors onto a secluded balcony. I followed, bracing myself for a frigid bite on my nearly bare arms, but the air was only pleasantly crisp, not freezing. I glanced around the terrace. Hot water cascaded down the walls in crystal sheets before gathering in broad shallow basins at the base of the walls. Plumes of steam billowed up from the pools, heating the air above. Tiny red blossoms twined along swan-slim pillars, droplets of blood against ice.

Sunder stood in the shadow of one marble pillar, staring out across his estate. Two black-and-white mountains dipped low to the churning froth of a coursing river. The low sun peered between the peaks, sending vermeil fingers to caress the snow-draped hills.

"You call her Oleander here," I remarked when the silence grew too heavy.

"It's her name, demoiselle."

"Should I call you Aubrey?" I asked. The name felt clumsy on my cold lips.

"No. That's not who I am anymore. Maybe it never was." His eyes rose suddenly to mine, and a tangle of indecision fractured his features. "I wanted—"

He hesitated. I waited.

"I wanted to apologize. For Lullaby." His voice rasped, rough as unpolished marble. "The Nocturne of the Blood Rain Ball, after you left my jardin—"

Horror and rage flashed white-hot. I remembered her eyes swollen with tears as she limped to bed. Thibo's haunted gaze: *We are all thieves here.*

"What did you do to her?"

"I broke every one of her fingers. Twice." A drowning abyss opened in his eyes. "Severine commanded it, as punishment for your failure. I tried to dissuade her, but she was rabid with fury. She smiled as I—" He choked on the words. "But Lullaby never once screamed. She just wept silent tears. For hours."

Wrath and outrage and misery pulped my heart. I wanted to blame Sunder, to scream and push and cry, but a cold, calculating corner of my mind tallied Lullaby's torture and Sunder's guilt and my own failure to protect my friend onto the empress's ever-growing list of sins. Her debt was growing.

"Lullaby doesn't remember," Sunder added. "Reaper took the memory away. After. All she knows is she was punished, not how. But I thought you ought to know that it was me. And that if I could—if I could somehow take that pain away, take it onto myself, I would."

Reaper took the memory away. I sucked in a deep breath of pine-scented steam, feeling as though it was I who took my friends' pain onto myself, not him. That old ember of fury blazed up, but this time it was new. Different. It was hard as diamond and sharp as dristic. Polished and faceted as a ruby, it burned with a smoldering, scorching intensity. It burned like a spark that wanted to set the world on fire.

When the time was right.

"I forgive you," I finally said. I didn't think I was lying.

"Why?" Sunder's shoulders curled, and he dragged his bleak gaze back to the expanse of snow. "How can I be redeemed for causing that kind of pain?"

"I didn't say you could be redeemed," I whispered. "I said that I forgave you. I'm sorry if that's not enough."

Hot water trickled. Red flowers shuddered in the breeze. I considered leaving.

"Have you decided?" I asked, instead. "What happens next?"

"Yes," he said. "I'm sending you away."

"Oh?" My hands curled into fists. "Where?"

"Somewhere you and the Relic will be safe until we find a way to deal with Severine."

"No," I said. The ember glowed red-hot. "I'm going back to the Amber City with you."

Sunder cut his eyes to me. The blackness of his pupils seemed to swallow all the green. "Why?"

Why. I fumbled for some way to explain that ember smoldering within me. The rage, and the dread, and the steady throb of inevitability I felt whenever I thought about where I belonged. The world I'd fought for, and now felt responsible for. I took a deep breath, and tried.

"Growing up in the Dusklands, all I knew was dust, and twilight, and the desolate edge of the known world. Out there, you can never trust your eyes. Distances are strange and difficult to measure. Shadows betray. Colors are dimmer, without light."

Sunder turned his head to look back over the crags of his domain, but I knew he was still listening; his head tilted to one side, and pale strands of hair drifted in the steam-warm air.

"There were children, from the village," I continued. "Grubby little things. Just like me, I guess. The Sisters let me play with them, sometimes. One boy bullied me: jabbed me with rocks, teased me, pulled my hair. Once, things went too far. He pushed me to the ground. Punched me, kicked hard at my ribs. I remember terror and anger and humiliation all curled up inside me, whimpering like an animal that's been beaten." I paused, letting the soul-etched horror of that moment wash over me and then drift away. "That animal snapped. Something let go inside me and there were colors all around. It wasn't a thing, or a shape. It was a dream, a muddled collection of sounds and feelings and colors crushing and shifting against each other. It was vibrant, intense. Beautiful."

I opened my palms, and that dream spilled out, as vivid now as it was then. A song in color, a gossamer impression of violet clouds and silver wind and the keening feeling of being alive. Sunder's eyes widened.

"The children ran, screaming like I was a monster. And in that moment, I knew I was different. Not in degree, but in *kind*. I dreamed of a world graced with light and redolent with color, and I yearned for it. To see those brazen shades again, experience that strange joy, wield that kind of power: That's what I wanted. That's what I *deserved*."

Sunder nodded, terse, as though he understood something he hadn't a moment ago.

"I will not sit idly by while the world changes around me," I murmured. "I don't know whether my blood is a gift or a curse. And I don't relish breaking the world in order to remake it the way I see it." I took a deep breath. "But I will if I have to. Does that make me a monster?"

Sunder turned away from the ledge and stepped toward me, until he was close enough that I could have reached out and touched him. In the cavern of his frost-limned eyes I saw some sheer part of myself reflected back.

"Do you know why our gifts manifest in such different ways?" he murmured. "Pain, poison; healing, song. Illusion."

I shook my head.

"No one does. Some think it's passed parent to child, shifting and warping as blood binds to blood. But no one is born wielding magic. Our legacies only manifest after we grow and mature, experience the diversity of joy and pain life invariably brings."

I frowned. "What do you mean?"

"Oleander and I were barely older than babes when our parents were killed." Remembered pain chiseled Sunder's features. "But we both understood too well what had happened. I remember she used to sit in the greenhouse beneath the flowering oleander, our mother's favorite flower and my sister's namesake.

The flower is lovely, but poisonous in all its parts. She would sit, and weep bitter tears, plucking the blooms from their stems and crushing the petals between her little hands. And I—I would wander the woods beyond the ravine, setting traps for rabbits and foxes because I wanted them as my pets. I wanted them as my *friends*. But I didn't know how to catch them without maiming them. And even the animals I eventually caught, and tamed, and kept, were afraid of me. Because I had broken their bones, spilled their blood across the snow."

An arrow of sympathy laced with shock sang toward my heart. Sunder leaned closer.

"I believe that, instead of arising from our blood, our legacies are shaped by who we are. Our abilities rise and shape to our own inclinations. For better or for worse, I *want* to cause pain, even to the things I love."

His hand drifted toward me, slow enough that I could slap it away if I wanted to. I didn't. His fingers hovered above my collarbone. A crackle of energy passed between us.

"And me?" My voice was breathless. "If that's true, what do my illusions mean?"

"Perhaps you have deceit in your soul," whispered Sunder. His hand floated higher, raising the hairs along my neck. "Or perhaps you want to show the world something only you can see. Something lovely, and strange, and just a little bit monstrous."

"So you don't mind," I managed, "if I'm a monster?"

"No." He rocked closer, and his closeness sent a thread of desire stitching up my spine. "Because I'm a monster too."

I kissed him. It was as simple as turning my head and pressing my lips against his. For a moment, time waited. My heart stopped. His hands stilled. His lips brushed against mine, cool and soft and light as a flake of falling snow.

Time stuttered. And started again.

He deepened the kiss, his lips a promise: a covenant of the sublime. His hand found my waist and crushed me against him. Our heartbeats thundered side by side. I slid my palms up the front of his coat, finding his collar. I tugged, pulling him closer. Strands of his hair whispered against my knuckles and sent my thoughts whirling away into the dusk. He nudged me backward. My shoulders hit the edge of the pillar. I gasped.

The clouds of our breath mingled as he drew away, eyes snagging on mine. And for the first time since I'd met him, I saw Sunder utterly unmasked and unguarded. I saw the deep well of torment pooling behind eyes dark with want. I saw desolation, and desire, and an icy, endless strength.

He captured my lips with his once more. But this kiss was laced with desperation, and something else: a zinging ache that jolted the skin across my face and tightened my muscles. His hands glided down the column of my neck and left scorching trails in their wake. A high ringing pierced my ears. My palms itched. I clenched my hands into fists and shoved him away.

"No," I breathed. "Not like that."

A cold breeze off the mountains gusted between us. Sunder stared at me. He was breathing hard, and spots of hectic red stood out high on his angular cheekbones. He shuddered, and pushed the spill of white-gold hair off his furrowed brow.

"I'm sorry," he said.

And I believed him. Because I was sorry too.

"You're cold," I whispered, because he was shivering in his fine brocade, shivering like he'd break apart, shivering like he'd never be warm again.

"I'm always cold," he replied.

"We should go inside." I laughed. The sound was as hollow as my heart. "Before you catch your death."

"Death," he repeated, and turned his face toward the mountains. The low sun drenched him in blood. "I've dreamed of dying so many times. Sometimes, I can't help but think that somehow, somewhere, it must have already happened."

He straightened, turned, and smiled like an ice wolf.

"Come on." He brushed past me and into the château. "We have much planning to do if we ever hope to outsmart that lying witch and steal the throne from under her nose."

I watched him disappear back into Belsyre. Another icy wind stole the breath from my lungs. I couldn't help but feel like something else had been stolen from me too.

FORTY-SIX

We planned until Compline turned to Nocturne and a sweep of freezing fog shrouded the valley.

"To mount a successful coup," Sunder said, "we're going to need the Amber Court on our side. We don't have time to requisition the noble families from their country estates, so we'll have to rely on our peers. Sinister is ruthless and fierce, but their loyalties can be unpredictable. There are a few courtiers I've been grooming to turn against the empress. I can try to motivate them with favors or fortune."

"Most of Dexter is furious and deeply resentful about all the legacies the empress has been seizing from their ranks," I added. "I might not be able to incite them myself, but now that Thibo—"

Sunder nodded. "The Montrachets have no great love for imperial rule—they were annexed during the Conquest, same as the de Veres. From what I hear, half his clan has already been drafted for the empress's petty battles. Use his disappearance if you can."

"And Luca—"

"We are not involving that feckless ore trader!" Sunder's eyes slashed up to meet mine. "He nearly ruined all our plans. Besides, we want to replace the empress with an heir *we* control—"

"Control?" My voice was icy.

"You know what I mean." Sunder sat back against his chair. "We don't know how many militants La Discorde has in its ranks, nor how much support they have among the commoners. If we cede any part of this overthrow to Luca and his friends, we could have a revolution on our hands, instead of a clean coup with relatively few casualties. Do you want to eviscerate the Amber Empire, or just remove its head?"

"Fine," I snapped. "Maybe you're right. But we could still use them without telling them what we're doing. They could create a diversion—draw away the Skyclad Gardes while we put the rest of our plan into motion."

Sunder opened his mouth, then closed it again. He grimaced, and put his head in his hands.

"That might actually be a good idea, demoiselle," he muttered. "Discuss it with Luca when we're back in the city. But no promises."

"Agreed." I glanced up to find his eyes lingering on my face. My mouth parted, and the silent press of heightened emotions threatened to collapse the frigid wall we'd built between us since that moment on the terrace. I looked away first. "Will you speak to Dowser, or should I?"

"I will," he said. "He's not going to like any of this. He's been trying to find out for tides what Severine's legacy is, and has spent almost as long trying to find out which of her treasures is the second Relic. He's going to counsel us to wait until you're stronger, until we have more information, until we know we can win."

"Do you think he's right?"

"That depends on you." Sunder splayed his hands across the table. "For this to work, you won't be able to lead the dissident courtiers against the Skyclad Gardes to secure the palais. The nobility know me; they fear me. They may or may not be willing to follow me, but they most certainly won't follow you. Furthermore, we're going to have to separate Severine from those among her court who remain loyal. She knows how to manipulate them, how to bend them to her will. No—you're going to have to be the one to vanquish Severine. Alone."

"I know," I said, and even as the words left my mouth I realized that ever since I had discovered who I was—who my father was, and what Severine had done to my mother, my innocent siblings—I had known that I was going to have to be the one to face the empress. The ember inside me spat sparks. "I need to remind everyone—commoner and noble alike—what she did to seize power, so I can discredit her. I need to find out what her legacy is, so she can't use it against me, or the rest of the court. And I need to defeat her, in whatever way I can."

Sunder's gaze flicked with jagged awe. "And how do you plan to do that?"

I smiled. "I have a few ideas."

We spent hours planning moves, and countermoves. Attack, parry, riposte. We mapped out every player at our disposal, and tried to predict where our enemies would be, and how they would act. We planned until my head swam with so many plots and gambits that I could barely remember my own name, much less who I could and couldn't trust, and under what circumstances.

When the bells for Nocturne turned to Matin, and the fog turned to feathered blasts of downy snow, our plans were finally complete. We rose from the table in the gloom, the silence between us fragile as glass.

"Have you thought at all—" Sunder began, tentative. He cleared his throat. "You said that you would break the world, if you had to; to remake it the way you see it. What will that world look like, when you sit upon the Amber Throne?"

I opened my mouth to say I hadn't thought about it. But when I met his eyes—taut with expectation and bright with brittle hope—I realized that wasn't true. In a strange way, it was all I'd ever thought about. From the moment I learned what I was, I'd dreamed of that world. I'd crossed an empire for that world, only to realize that if I truly wanted a place to belong, I'd have to create it.

I can do better than she can.

"I don't have easy answers," I whispered. "And I know next to nothing about ruling. But when I close my eyes I dream of a world where beauty is an intention, not a pretense. Where grace reigns. Where compassion dwells. I can't promise to make this empire great again, but I can promise—I can *try*—to make it *good* again. I have to believe I'm capable of that."

"Then I have to believe it too."

Sunder reached for me, one last time. His hand brushed against mine. I flinched. He had to look away to hide the pain twisting his face into something desolate, broken, and more than a little monstrous.

FORTY-SEVEN

C oeur d'Or was so busy and full of activity that our return a week later was barely remarked upon.

The remaining members of La Discorde had been publicly executed. The sight of their gore-striped heads adorning spikes on the city gates striated my bones with cold-hot blades of fear and fury. Nausea punched holes in my stomach and bile seared my throat, but I refused to look away, forcing myself to memorize their agonized, disfigured faces.

This, I whispered to myself, *this is the price of failure.*

And when at last I turned away, I thanked the Scion that Luca's dark-curled head did not hang among them.

Carrousel was going forward as planned, preparations turning the palais into a carnival. The jardins bustled with tradespeople and artisans and artificers building grand pavilions and gazebos and magical mechanisms to transform the landscape. Trees and shrubbery swarmed with decorations: bright lanterns flapping like strange colored birds, streamers gossamer as captured cobwebs, white lights glittering like the stars of legend.

I went directly to my seamstress. I didn't have time to waste if I wanted the gown for my performance to be perfect. I tipped her handsomely to have the gown ready by the end of the week, and tipped her even better for her discretion.

Lullaby greeted me with narrowed eyes.

"Where have you been?" she demanded, and I fought the

urge to cry. I'd left her without a word, abandoning her like I'd abandoned *Thibo*—

No. Nothing I could have done would have saved Thibo. I gathered my memories of my friend into a precious bundle and stored them in the quietest corner of my mind. I'd grieved and would continue to grieve him. But the best thing I could do now was stick to the plan and make sure that murderous witch didn't steal any more of my friends.

I told Lullaby, as concisely as possible, about my time at Belsyre. About Sunder, and Bane, and Severine. Everything I knew. Everything we planned. How I hoped she'd fit into that plan.

When I was finished, Lullaby sat back against the divan. She barely looked surprised.

"I'm glad." Her mouth hardened. "I'm only sad Thibo isn't here to be a part of it. He's been talking about this for spans, he—" She broke off, and that determined mouth quivered. "He said he was in contact with a spy in Sinister, someone planning something big. He guessed it was Sunder. I always said he was insane. Shows you what I know about intrigue."

"I'm sorry. I'm sorry I was too late."

"Don't." Lullaby turned to look out the window, her gaze distant. "He used to say: *I reap what others have sown; I am the scythe they least expect.* I suppose now you—*we*—have to be that scythe."

I tamped down the flames of anger and pain and futility, glazing them along the facets of that ember smoldering beside my heart. A cinder that a single spark would reignite into an inferno of sunlight and perilous dreams, jewel-bright visions and monstrous hopes.

And when I left Lullaby with a strong embrace and a handful of instructions, I saw that fire reflected in her own water-blue eyes.

"Mirage?" she said as I turned away.

"Yes?"

"Make her pay for what she did to Thibo."

A letter. A handful of écu here, and a few kembric livres there. Whispered conversations.

I signaled Luca with our old method of red handkerchiefs in the window, and when he stalked out to meet me along the Esplanade I told him about the plan. Just enough about the plan, just enough to get him excited, like I knew it would. His smile flashed sharp as a dagger forged in the red light of our sun. His eyes didn't flicker as he agreed to involve La Discorde, whose recent loss had only strengthened their resolve. He didn't even flinch when I told him he'd have to work with Sunder.

And that's when I knew my friend—the boy with the wild curls who somersaulted from Madame Rina's convoy and snuck me crusts of bread because he knew how hungry I was—was gone forever. He'd transformed into a man I'd once glimpsed long ago by the uneven light of a guttering cook fire. A man scarred by tragedy and transformed by rage, with death in his eyes and revolution in his soul.

My disappearance with the Suicide Twins was talked about, but not in the way I would have expected. As Sunder predicted, everyone at court assumed he and I were lovers. I tried not to dwell on the various twisted and unspeakable speculations regarding the nature of our relationship. Eyes raked my back when I passed through the corridors of Coeur d'Or, but I straightened my shoulders and lengthened my stride.

Sunder was—*Sunder*. He inhaled wine and exhaled insults. We saw each other at parties and salons and concerts, and if he leaned too close to whisper something in my ear, or curled a proprietorial hand around my waist, I only smiled, and simpered, and hid the bleak, delicious flare of heat burning through my veins.

What was it he said, that day beneath the pergola? *To sell the illusion.*

Because that's all it was. Yet another illusion in my growing repertoire of fancies and delusions. A cheap facsimile of something that, for a moment, felt real. *Was* real. Wasn't it? But even now, mere days after my time at Belsyre, those moments seemed to be slipping away, like a half-remembered dream. I closed my eyes, and tried to remember, but it was like reaching for someone else's memory. A broken promise, a good dream turned bad; blood on the snow where before there were red flowers.

So I focused on the plan. I ran through it again and again, every step, every illusion, over and over. I practiced it until I dreamed it. And then I practiced again.

FORTY-EIGHT

I paced the annex with the mosaic floor, my eyes trained on the frescoed ceiling. I tried to concentrate on the Sun in his sapphire throne, the Moon flanked by her star-eyed maidens. The Scion on his chariot of flames. But the images blurred behind the film of tears prickling hot at my eyes, and all I could think of was the first time I came to this room. Thibo, laughing at my ignorance. Thibo, dancing me across a map sparkling with gems and mica. I rubbed a thumb over the locket I'd started carrying in my pocket. Thibo—

"Don't cry on my account, demoiselle." A cool voice cut through my misery.

I whirled. Sunder stood across the mosaic of the daylight world, clad in a kembric-gilded waistcoat so bright he could have been the Scion himself. For the first time in days, his entourage of Sinister lords and ladies was nowhere to be seen.

"We met here, once," Sunder mused, his tone bittersweet. His polished boots carried him across the Dusklands toward the Meteor Mountains, where my jeweled slippers nudged tiles of onyx and opal.

"I remember," I muttered. Uncertainty battled with a sour, brittle yearning. "Didn't you accuse me of pawning your money for tacky gowns?"

"Maybe." He smiled, whisper-thin. "But you accused me of defiling innocent horses."

I choked on a laugh. Mirth tinted with old embarrassment

chased away the last tatter of my sorrow. "More fool you for matching wits with me."

"A lesson I've learned time and again." His boots paused by my slippers. His dristic-edged eyes searched mine, but he didn't touch me. "And you were dancing that day, were you not? With your friend. With Thibo."

I opened my mouth to correct him, to explain that Thibo was only showing me the map. But Sunder suddenly bowed, hand out and palm up. I hesitated, staring at the long, elegant fingers, the ridge of callus where a sword hilt fit. His hand trembled in an unspoken question.

I bit my lip, and slid my hand into the curl of his palm.

A thrill sang up my arm. The world tilted on its axis as he dipped me, the brush of his hands at my waist featherlight. He swirled me across the mosaic, the tiles blurring in a circle of kembric and blue. He was deft, deliberate, stepping in time to the echoes of some forgotten music. I drifted, my feet barely touching the floor, hypnotized by the measured sway and dip of our first dance.

He eased me back into a niche between two pillars. I gasped in a breath of that sharp, clean scent of him. He closed the gap between us. I could hear the thud of his heart, too fast. His lips brushed my ear, sending a shiver dancing toward the base of my skull. My mind went smooth and hard with desire.

"Someone requires your presence," he murmured. The wall behind us clicked audibly, then swung open.

I stumbled and almost fell into the cramped, dingy room behind me. A single ambric lamp lent a fitful glow. A dark shadow loomed, light glinting off oval spectacles.

Dowser.

I set my jaw and glared at Sunder, who leaned against the wall and avoided my eyes. I'd evaded my teacher since I'd gotten back from Belsyre, because I knew what he'd say about all this. He'd tell me—

"You're not ready!" he roared, slamming his fist on the table. As my eyes adjusted to the dimness, I saw he was incandescent with rage. Angrier than I'd ever seen him. "The time isn't right!"

"What do you propose?" I snapped. Exhaustion and grief and duplicity cut my fuse short. "Wait another seventeen tides for you to leave that smoke-filled study and discover how to defeat your old lover?"

He stiffened. "You are an absolute fool if you think you can face the empress and survive."

"How would you know what I can survive?" The old resentment stirred, smooth and polished by tides of use. "You abandoned me at the edge of the world to wait patiently for a destiny that might never come. Out there they treated me like a monster, a freak. They reviled and abused me for the one thing that made me strong. But I survived. I traveled halfway across the world. I fought tooth and nail for everything I've been given. This is me fighting to create the world I want to live in. You have no right to tell me I'm not ready for that."

"*The world you want to live in?*" His voice was appalled. "By the Scion, you actually *want* this. Not just to oust the empress, but to take her place."

"I do." My skin flared hot and cold. "I will remake this world. It's my birthright."

"The birthright of the Sabourin dynasty is lust and blood and death. After everything I taught you, is that who you want to be?"

"Take me or leave me," I snarled. "I know you'll do your part regardless."

He rocked back on his heels, shocked into silence. I turned on my heel. I was tired of going around in circles. Everything had already been decided.

"When you first came," Dowser whispered. Something in his voice stopped me in my tracks. "When you first came, I thought you were like your father. Lavish, but generous. Unthinking, but brave. Selfish, but ultimately kind. But every day I see it more and more. The single-minded pursuit of a world only you desire. A world only you can see." He took a deep breath. "You're just like her."

Ice crackled the length of my spine when I realized who he meant. "You don't mean that."

"You're right: I will do my part." His voice trembled, then cracked. "But I hope you are very careful when you look your sister in the eye. You don't want to see yourself staring back."

Outrage and grief and a terrible sucking dread filled the cavern of my heart. I felt Sunder lift his eyes to my face.

"Dark seeks dark, Mirage," Dowser whispered, and his words were like a song of undoing, an elegy for a disappointed hope. "And pain seeks pain."

My gaze slashed up. Sunder's eyes crackled with ice, and again I glimpsed that unending expanse of desolation held back by pure, steely will. Cold fire and a monstrous longing crackled in the air between us.

I shoved out into the annex, gasping for breath like I'd been underwater. I stalked away without looking behind me, choking on bitterness and conviction and the glass-bright shards of soul-deep fear.

FORTY-NINE

Carrousel arrived at last.

A Matin like any other, except for the buzz of anticipation buoying Coeur d'Or. The sky was clear, strung with distant clouds of lavender and mauve. Even the sun seemed to pulsate with slow excitement.

My handmaidens helped me prepare for the day. Sunder had bribed Severine's hairdresser with an astonishing amount of livres to divulge the style the empress requested for the day, and I asked Louise to imitate the same coiffure. It took shape slowly, a complicated tower of curls and braids, elegant and bold. I did my own cosmetics, lining my eyes in heavy kohl and glossing my lips until they were ripe and plump. I took kembric leaf I bought off an artificer and spread it along the contours of my face: the edge of my hairline, the tops of my cheekbones. I dusted crushed gold powder along my collarbones, the line of my nose, and my décolletage, until I glimmered like a gilt statue in the red light filtering through the window.

Elodie cinched my corset until I was gasping for breath, and helped me into the extravagant gown. The skirt was pure kembric, a cascade of liquid satin glowing molten in the lamplight. A bodice of thick black lace twisted up over a golden underlay, clinging tightly to the contours of my chest. A black capelet hung from my shoulders, with a deep hood. I didn't want to be recognized until my big reveal in front of the entire court.

The bells for Prime rang, and the gates to the palais thundered open. I couldn't hear it, but I could feel it in my bones—the juddering rush of hundreds of feet pouring across the pavement, up the stairs, into the palais. Boots tromping across the jardins, spectators crushing the shrubbery and peering into the ponds. Voices raised in eager chatter.

This was the custom: One day per tide, on Carrousel, the gates of Coeur d'Or swung open and anyone who could afford the entrance fee was allowed to come, and admire, and take part in the rollicking merriment organized by the Amber Empress and her court. Peasant, pauper, merchant, fool. All were welcome. Carrousel was a day when anyone could imagine they were anything. A housewife could imagine she was a beautiful courtesan, gowned in expensive silks and crowned in the jewels of her patrons. A lord could imagine he was a merchant stuffing his face with sausage and beer, with no lands or legacy to plague him. The secret child of a dead emperor could pretend she wasn't about to intentionally turn the world on its head. She could pretend she was the person she used to be: nobody.

I wandered through the festivities with my face hidden beneath my hood. It was strange to see the jardins and the Esplanade and the Hall of Portraits packed with strangers. Men and women jostled for space, clad in everything from plain cotton to velvet, linen to brocade. Strange, vain, elaborate costumes. Simple rags. Masks. Stilts. An air of merriment and revelry quickened my heartbeat and tightened my fists.

Pavilions erected on the lawn offered curiosities from distant lands: baubles, trinkets, ornaments, and oddities. A fortune-teller with eyes white as snow and hair forged from dristic promised true love for the low cost of one deadly secret. A troupe of tumbling children flipped and whirled, a motley, gymnastic rainbow. Hawkers peddled spices from across the sea: the powdered horn of an incubus, said to raise your mettle in the bedroom; the liquid tails of captured sea-stallions, guaranteed to speed any journey. Vials of flaming sand enchanted by a desert *d'haka*. Liquors to make you drunk; elixirs to turn you sober once more.

Near Compline, Skyclad chevaliers paraded along the Esplanade, their prancing destriers decked in armure chevaline, spiked armor forged from dristic and steel. The chevaliers' extravagant coats and polished armor sent spears of light to pierce at watching eyes, and the plumes dancing from their helms frothed like great clouds in hues of raspberry and tangerine.

Finally, the bells for second Compline rang, and the crowd hushed. Whispers sprinted around the edges of the courtyard as the merrymakers waited. Finally, someone pointed, and the crowd cheered, clapping and waving and howling at the palais.

From a balcony halfway up the tower Severine emerged, her gown glowing like its own sun in the brilliant light shining at her back. Her kembric crown was a stylized sunburst, alternating straight and curving rays to affect a gleaming corona around her head. She waved, and smiled, elegant and benevolent, then stepped off the edge of the balcony.

The crowd gasped. Someone shrieked.

Severine didn't fall. She floated gently down, her gown billowing and belling around her. She alit like a feather, her pointed slippers delicate on the manicured lawn.

The crowd roared its pleasure, and the empress curtsied deep, her violet eyes sparking. I peered at the balcony to see which legacies had been drafted to forge this illusion, but the courtiers lurked out of sight.

"Welcome!" she called. The onlookers quieted, craning and pushing. "The wonderful Fête du Carrousel returns once more.

Sample the delights we offer you, for nothing is too grand or too decadent on this festival day! And when you are sated, follow me to the Golden Grotto, where my most talented courtiers will entertain us all with the glory of their legacies!"

She curtsied once more, and again the crowd roared its approval. She danced across the lawn toward the little wilderness and the amphitheater beyond, where the evening's performances would be held. Ladies and gentlemen frolicked in her wake, but not too close—a platoon of Skyclad Gardes shadowed her every move, a grim reminder that even on this day of celebration, the empress didn't fully trust her own people.

I let the crowd part around me, and stared up at the balcony, letting my imagination soar. Severine's entrance was just a show. I knew it, and the crowd knew it. But everyone loved a show.

At least, that's what I was hoping.

❧

Past the Weeping Pools, the trees grew closer together, their untrimmed branches shadowing the sun. A narrow pathway coiled between the boughs, shimmering globes strung along the darkened trail. Veils of flowers festooned the trees, light and color swaying between the looming shadows of crooked branches. The scents of jasmin and lavender drifted thick in the languid air.

I trailed at the back of the crowd following Severine to the Grotto. Because of the famous wager and the buzz surrounding my performance, I'd been designated to appear last. I had an hour, if not two, before I had to prepare. I wanted to see a few of the other courtiers perform—Lullaby was singing, and I had missed her last concert—but part of me wanted to linger here, to savor my last moments of relative anonymity, before chaos descended and the world burst apart with noise and color.

I glanced quickly over my shoulder, then stepped off the pathway into the shadows. I lifted my skirts, moving quietly through the clinging underbrush, until I looked back and couldn't see the path anymore. I gazed upward through the reaching branches, glimpsing a sky stained with rust and wine. A sudden breeze sent leaves rustling on the trees, and I couldn't help but think of bare branches etched in pewter on a pale floating skirt, the nip of an icy wind, the steam of someone's breath mingling with my own.

A heavy hand fell on my shoulder.

I stifled a scream and spun on my heel. A dark hooded figure loomed between the trees. I swallowed my fear, steadying myself on the trunk of a tree. He wore all black. He knew what I was wearing. He was—

The figure held out a placatory hand and brushed the hood away from his face. Dark brown skin. A glimmer of spectacles.

A wave of residual anger crashed against sweeping disappointment. He wasn't who I hoped he would be.

"Dowser." The ragged edge of resentment made my throat hoarse. "What are you doing here? Come to scold me one last time?"

"Scion's breath, Mirage." He stepped closer, lowering the hood of my capelet with wary fingers. His eyes took in the kembric leaf slicked along my skin, the shimmer of golden dust along my neck, the elaborate coiffure. "You really do look like her."

"I have to get to the Grotto." Bitterness and misery made my voice foreign.

"I know," he murmured, and stepped away. His throat bobbed

as his hands folded into their black sleeves. "You must know I never meant to say those things. And I didn't mean a word."

Something collapsed inside me. "Yes, you did."

"Some of it," he amended. "But it's hard not to be frightened of how powerful you've become. This place has changed you. Not just your legacy, but your sense of self. You came here to fight for a place in this world where you thought you belonged. Now you fight for a new world—a world you think you can create. You are formidable in so many ways, Mirage. I only hope you can remember why you really want the things you strive for."

"I—" I choked on my words, casting my eyes to the jeweled hem of my dress and fighting for composure. "I understand what you're saying. But this place hasn't changed me. It's just given me the opportunity to show the world who I really am. And I won't apologize for being who I'm not. And never was."

"I remember I once said you were ambitious, arrogant, and even a little cruel." Dowser turned his eyes to the burnt sky high above. "I wasn't far off. But I hadn't realized yet how deeply the pains of this world reverberate inside you. How they are transformed, in you, into something sublime. Transcendent. That, Mirage, is your gift."

A fragile seed burst into tenuous bloom inside me. I tried hard not to think about another Nocturne. *Perhaps you want to show the world something only you can see. Something lovely, and strange, and just a little bit monstrous.*

"I just hope you remember how much good there is in this world, although too often it is obscured behind shadow and pain." His voice cracked with all the things he would never tell me. "I hope you remember how much good there is in *you*."

"I never wanted to be good," I muttered.

"That's what makes it so special." He smiled, a clear-glass swell of pure joy. "I want you to know how much it meant to me that you cared. About me. I never—" He cut off abruptly, staring at the ground and polishing his spectacles on his sleeve. His eyes gleamed with varnish. "I never had a child, Mirage. But—"

"I know," I whispered. The words were a strip of splintered wood tearing at my throat. "I know."

He leaned down, slowly, and brushed a breath of a kiss on my temple. Hot nettles prickled my eyes as I flung my arms around his neck. When he drew back, some of my makeup had smeared on his cheek, leaving a swathe of golden stars glittering against his night-dark skin.

"Here," I said. I couldn't help but laugh as I lifted a gloved thumb to swipe away the dust. "You'll give me away."

He chuckled, but we both knew it was for show.

Something made me reach into my pocket and draw out a small velvet pouch. I placed it in Dowser's palm, and before I could change my mind, I curled his fingers around it.

"Keep it for me," I whispered. "You'll know what to do with it, if anything—if anything happens."

He nodded, grave. "Please, Mirage. Be careful. If not for your sake, then for mine."

"I promise."

He disappeared between the trees, silent as a wraith. But as I turned and faced toward the Grotto, I felt like an iron band had been unfastened from my heart, and I smiled through the film of tears turning the world soft as watercolors.

FIFTY

The Golden Grotto was riotous with light. Built into the edge of an old quarry, the amphitheater rose in sloping tiers. Hidden fountains gurgled and plashed, releasing the scents of fresh mint and spring water. Hundreds of floating lanterns mixed a cool white glow with the red burn of the sun. The crowd was raucous and merry, half-drunk and well pleased by the performances of the empress's captive legacies: a festive aria sung by a radiant Lullaby, whose dulcet tones had most of them dancing like enchanted marionettes in the aisles; a watery display by River, who floated undulating globes and sent liquid javelins lancing in great arcs; Tangle, who grew an entire brambled jardin into a spiky château, then made giant blossoms float to the heavens like colorful balloons.

And finally, my turn came.

An uneasy silence fell as I stepped out onto the stage. I was still wearing my cloak and hood, but I heard a few murmurs about my dress, so similar to the empress's outfit. I cut my eyes to the great lady herself, careful to keep my face out of the light. She perched on the top tier of the theater, voluminous skirts arrayed and sunburst crown gleaming. Courtiers fawned over her.

The lacquered ruby sleeping by my heart spat a spark.

Strains of music rose from the edge of the stage: the Meridian Suite, by a composer well known in court. The piece began slowly as I lifted my arms and surrendered to my illusion.

Night. A swathe of purest black, impenetrable save for

distant stars prickling like chips of diamond. I made the night vast, stretching from one end of the amphitheater to the other, blocking out the sun. I imagined the Midnight Dominion, and it was so.

A soft moan of appreciation rose from the crowd.

I showed them the moon, drifting pale and cold and distant across the night. And then I shifted the night into day, black bleeding slowly into red, bleeding slowly into bright, eye-stinging blue at true Prime. I'd never seen such a sky, but then, I'd never seen true night either. And in that azure sweep I put the sun, a giant globe of pulsating orange.

The crowd gasped, and clapped.

I spun the illusion, slow then fast. Dawn, day, dusk, night. Day. Night. Sun. Moon. And as I spun I subtly transformed the sun and moon into figures—people, dressed in elaborate costumes. I finished the metamorphosis, placing the figures at opposite ends of the amphitheater, facing each other across the dusk.

The crowd murmured, a touch uneasily.

They finally understood what I was doing. It was a modified version of the Meridian story, the legend we'd all heard so many times from the cradle that most of us could recite it verbatim. But I'd altered it. Instead of making the Moon a lovely woman floating in a pearly palais, I'd made her a man, clad in a fine silvery coat. He wore an elaborate plumed hat, and a mask shaped like adjoining crescents covered his face. And instead of making the Sun a man—a king in a golden château—I'd made the Sun a woman. More specifically, I'd made the Sun Severine—the illusion wore her radiant gown and elaborate hairstyle, bedecked in a sunburst circlet. The only difference: The Sun wore a kembric mask around her sparking violet eyes.

I chanced a glance at the empress, but she just swept her fan in slow circles around her smiling face.

I reenacted the legend of Meridian. The Sun chased the foppish Moon, but he rebuffed her love. Now that the story was well under way, the crowd was enjoying itself again, laughing and clapping at the charade. Finally, the Sun grew angry and sour, heartbroken that the Moon would not be hers.

The crowd grew somber. Everyone knew this part.

I made Meridian a towering Skyclad Garde. There was the flaming chariot, the weapons forged to catch and destroy the Moon. I projected a glorious, heartrending chase across the sky: a flaming star inscribing an elegant arc in the night, a long tail of sparks streaming out behind it. The Moon fled, flickering between his phases, but the dristic-clad lord was too slow. At last, the chariot approached the Moon.

The crowd held a single breath.

But my Meridian didn't fall in love in a single glance. He didn't spare the Moon. He didn't fall to earth with his weapons of destruction. My Meridian caught the Moon. His net of glittering kembric snared the dancing lord, crushing his curling hat feather and bearing him to the ground. Meridian lashed the lord to his chariot and flew him back to the Sun.

Uncertainty pulsed through the watching revelers. This was an unfamiliar twist. I dared another glance at the empress. She was no longer smiling. Her fan flicked like the tail of an irritated house cat.

I took a deep breath, and focused all my energy on the next part of the illusion.

The Sun empress stepped from her shining throne to where the Moon lord knelt at her feet. She yanked the hat off his head, spinning him to face the audience and exposing his features for all the world to see. There was cropped red-brown hair. A trim beard on a handsome—if grizzled—face. And piercing, wise eyes a shade somewhere between grey and violet: a shade darker than my own blue-grey eyes, a shade paler than the empress's stunning gaze.

It was Sylvain, the old and very dead emperor. I'd studied his portrait for hours, searing the image of my murdered father into the flesh of my brain. I faced him toward the audience long enough for the crowd to react.

An anxious laugh. A shriek of surprise. Severine rose to her feet.

The empress's fantasy doppelgänger took a dagger from her waist and plunged the blade into her father's heart. A fountain of blood spurted out, drenching the onlookers seated in the first row with phantom gore. They scattered and jumped away, even though the scarlet droplets were nothing but illusion.

Chaos erupted. The crowd surged to its feet, shouting and screaming. I thought I heard clapping, and a possible roar of approval, and a grim smile crossed my face when I turned my gaze to the empress. She was livid with fury, snarling orders at her courtiers and her Skyclad bodyguards. Three of the silver-cloaked soldats detached from the phalanx and pushed through the crowd.

Time for the final act.

I dissolved the illusion, and the Sun and the Moon and Meridian all faded like a lover's promise. There was only me, standing cloaked and gowned at the center of the stage. The crowd quieted, waiting to see what I would do. Even the Skyclad Gardes slowed their booted steps. Would I plead for my life or shout murder at the empress? Would I weep, or laugh, or rant like a madwoman?

Would it all be a strange joke, a twisted prank among bored aristos?

Behind me, the music swelled. Slowly, theatrically, I drew back my hood and let the cape fall. The crowd leaned in, confused. My hair, though a few shades darker than Severine's, was coiled in the precise manner of their empress. A sunburst circlet sat on my head. A golden mask covered my features. With one smooth gesture, I tore away the black lace overlay of my gown. The cloth whispered to the ground, exposing a gown identical to Severine's.

Silence hung thick enough to choke.

I reached into the pocket I had specially commissioned on my counterfeit dress and drew out my ambric pendant, the Relic everyone seemed so eager to possess. It glinted dully in the light, rotating gently on the end of its golden chain.

At the top of the amphitheater, Severine's violet eyes went wide with rage and greed.

I pulled off the glittering mask obscuring my features and dropped it to the ground. There was no mistaking me now—without the mask I was most assuredly not the empress. My grey-blue eyes were closer set, my skin more tanned, my lips fuller. Anyone who lived in the Amber City—a city emblazoned with banners sporting their ruler's face—would know in an instant that I wasn't the empress.

I was just announcing to the world that I ought to be.

The Grotto exploded with noise. People rushed toward and away from the stage, shouting and roaring in a maelstrom of emotion. Severine was no longer content to let her lackeys do her bidding; she hiked her voluminous skirts to her knees and marched down the tiered theater, murder in her eyes and destruction in her soul.

I was so focused on the empress striding through the humanity churning at her feet that I nearly didn't see the Skyclad soldat remove a crossbow from his back and notch a bolt. The string drew back. The trigger pulled.

A straight, true shot. The arrow flew toward my pale breast, exposed above the plunging neckline of the replica gown. The bolt pierced skin, flesh, bone. I fell backward.

And dissolved into a cloud of fantasy and imagination.

The real me stepped out of the shadows at the edge of the stage, still clad in a cape and black lace. I held up the pendant and gave it a gentle swing. The empress screamed, her eyes venomous with spite. The Skyclad Gardes drew their weapons and loped toward me.

Now, I whispered in my head. I imagined the thought winging out across the palais jardins, piercing stone and marble and amber to hit its mark. *Now, Dowser.* NOW.

A half mile away, Coeur d'Or exploded with a rumbling thrum that shook the earth and sent a cloud of fire and ash climbing toward the sky.

FIFTY-ONE

Melee.

Shouting. Screaming. Wailing. Shoving.

The Skyclad twisted to stare at the plume of smoke disfiguring the red sky, their usually impassive faces distorted with confusion and fear. Only the empress stalked forward, her eyes fixed on me and the dull glow of the Relic around my neck.

I turned on my heel and left the Grotto, heading in the opposite direction of the explosion. I counted—*one, two, three*—then glanced over my shoulder. Severine followed, hunger in her eyes and only two Skyclad at her shoulder. She must have sent the rest to the palais.

I quickly turned myself invisible as I sent a copy of myself streaking across the lawn at an angle. She was fast, and the Skyclad Gardes didn't hesitate before giving chase, cocking their crossbows and moving with practiced ease. Only the empress paused, her eyes fixed to the spot where she'd seen me standing a moment ago. She'd noticed what the Skyclad Garde had not— my illusory double wasn't wearing the Relic.

Trust Severine to notice the difference.

I winked back into view. Severine frowned and whirled to call her guards, but they were already out of earshot, chasing their false prey. I kicked off my heels and took off at a trot, brutally aware that the real me was much less graceful than my imaginary twin. I had to trust that my actual half sister was seventeen tides older, hours drunker, and more burdened by her voluminous skirts than the dress I'd had specially made for tonight.

I led her across the lawn and through the trees, cursing my heavy legs and thumping heart. I shed first my hooded cape, then the swathe of black lace differentiating my gown from Severine's. How strange we must look, if anyone were to see us: two nearly identical women in identical outfits, sprinting across the palais jardins like the world depended on it.

I choked on a breathless, bitter laugh. Maybe the world did depend on it.

I reached the Solarium with strides to spare. The empress was flagging, her long train slowing her progress. I dashed into the pavilion, darting my gaze around the arched room. I'd had Sunder's men shift the high mirrors, angling and tilting them in a design of my own concoction. I just hoped my calculations were correct.

I spared an anxious moment to catch my breath and calm the reedy thrum of my heart. Then I darted to the back of the room, slid behind a mirror, and projected myself throughout the circular room. I made two of me, four of me, eight: the angled mirrors made me sixteen, twenty-eight, fifty.

I was legion.

I waited, trembling in the corner, for Severine to arrive. And in some twisted corner of my mind, I heard Sunder's voice, tight with irony and rich with humor.

Finally, not-Sunder drawled. *Mirage earns her name.*

And even though I knew it wasn't really Sunder, even though I knew it was some crazed corner of my fearful mind playing tricks on me, the words sent a veil of calm settling over my frayed nerves.

The empress burst into the Solarium, and stopped dead. I almost laughed at the look on her face, but the laugh died on my lips when I saw her eyes narrow and murder creep back into her gaze. She stalked toward the center of the room, examining each of my replicas in turn.

I didn't skimp. A copy of the Relic hung around each doppelgänger's neck. It took all of my concentration, but each time she approached one of the illusions, I had it back away. All the others twisted and shifted in different directions, their reflections spinning in a kaleidoscope of echoing reflection and deflection.

It worked. Irritation and confusion twisted the calm mask on my sister's face, transforming her into a vengeful demon.

"Come out, you coward!" she shouted, her fluted voice loud in the cavernous space. "Are you going to hide from me all Nocturne? Or are you too afraid to face a woman twice your age, unarmed and unguarded?"

I gritted my teeth and settled deeper into my crouch, fighting the flare of pride her words ignited. I knew she was trying to bait me into fighting her on equal footing, but that wasn't going to happen. I needed to buy Dowser, Sunder, and Luca more time. And I needed to find out how Severine's legacy manifested. If we couldn't find a way to defeat her power, then all of this would be for nothing.

I nudged one of my replicas forward to turn and frown at the empress. She lifted her gold-dusted arms in a placating gesture. I spoke, and in the echoing room, it was impossible to tell where my voice came from.

"I'm frightened," said the copy. "I didn't know it would go this far. If I surrender, will you grant me mercy?"

Light sparked in the empress's lucent eyes, and she crossed to the illusion in two fast strides. Her hands lashed up, so fast I barely saw them move. One grabbed for the Relic, and the other curled into a claw latching around the illusion's throat.

The other me dissolved into mist. The copies around her shifted and turned, their reflections rotating in a disorienting rush.

Severine screamed, the inhuman sound exploding from her mouth and reverberating around the room. I gasped, clapping my hands over my ears and fighting for control. I tried to sort through what I had just witnessed. When Severine thought she had me in her reach, she went straight for the Relic. But she also reached for my throat, like she wanted to choke me. Like the Nocturne of the Blood Rain Ball, when she'd wrapped blood-tipped nails around the throat of a man I'd thought was her lover.

I wasn't big, and I didn't know how to fight. But I was nearly the same height as my half sister, and with her slender frame and slim arms, I didn't doubt I could break her hold in an instant. So her legacy was either enhanced strength, or—

What? What else?

Think, Mirage, think, I whispered to myself. *Time is running out.*

"I know who you are!" called the livid empress. She stalked through the labyrinth of mirrors and illusion, her composure untangling as her patience faded. "You're one of his brats! One of the many litters whelped on his kennel full of bitches."

I caught my lower lip between my teeth, and tried to smother the kernel of fury spitting sparks. *Not yet.*

"I should have noticed," she continued. "You look like him. You even look a little like me, if I'm feeling especially generous. But mostly, you look like her. Madeleine Allard, wasn't it? The one who *almost* got away. I say almost because she didn't, of course. Do you know, she begged to trade her life for yours, in the end? Before she bled out slowly on the steps of a cloister." She chuckled. "Isn't that ironic? Maybe if she'd gone to the nunnery first she wouldn't have gotten herself knocked up with my father's indiscriminating seed."

Something tore inside me. Flames licked at my heart.

"Yes, you look like her. The same unfocused ignorance around your close-set little eyes. The same vulgar air of entitlement, like the world owes you something. She thought she deserved special treatment because she rutted with royalty. Well, she got what she deserved. It just wasn't what she expected."

A hot tear squeezed down the ridge of my nose.

"And you," she screamed. She punched one of my illusions, haphazardly, and missed. I wished I could make the replica punch her back on my behalf. "That's what all this is about, isn't it? You think you deserve *my* throne because you were born with *his* blood in your veins. Blood means *nothing*. He thought his blood kept him safe. He sat on his throne with his merciful laws and moderate policies, and delegated the empire away to his Council while he tried to bed every girl who'd have him. He thought he deserved what he was given just because he was born to it."

"And you weren't?" The cinder pulsed hotter. My voice echoed from every direction. "You were a dauphine. An heir to an empire. Isn't that the definition of bloodline? Of entitlement?"

"I would never have sat on that throne if I hadn't earned it," Severine snarled. "I never wanted what I was born to—*second in line*. No one deserves anything. The only things worth having are the things you take."

"Don't you mean steal?" I screamed. My voice rasped hoarse, and I knew I should be more careful, but the kernel of rage had splintered into chips of ruby, singeing my veins. "You stole your brother's life. You stole your father's life. You stole the lives of countless children for no other reason than your own self-loathing. You're nothing but a thief."

Her high-pitched cackle spangled through the room.

"I'd wager more thieves wish they could brag of the bounty of an empire."

"And I suppose you'd have to be a thief," I shouted. A voice inside me kept telling me *Stop, no, it's too soon*, but I was incandescent. Too hot, too bright. "Since you have no legacy. There's no use pretending you even know how to use this Relic." I forced myself to laugh, and it was a wretched, savage sound. "You may rule an empire, but you can never steal the one thing that even the lowliest of legacies possesses: *magic*."

"You have no idea what you're talking about!" Severine screamed at the ceiling.

"You're giftless!" I continued, savage. "Not one magical bone in your body. Or perhaps it's a pathetic legacy so useless you'd be derided until the day you died! Why else hide it, unless it's so weak you can't bear anyone to know what it is?"

Severine stood quiet for a bare second, surrounded on all sides by copies of me. Then she thrust her arms outward.

The room exploded.

A hundred angled mirrors burst instantly, sending needles of glass winging into every corner of the room. I threw my arms up in time to protect my eyes, but shards of pain erupted along my bare arms, in the small of my back, the base of my neck. I sucked a sharp breath of air into paralyzed lungs, and when I lowered my stinging arms Severine was standing right over me. A long shard of mirrored glass smiled silver against her palm.

"Say hello to our brothers and sisters for me," she snarled, and slashed her makeshift dagger toward my throat.

FIFTY-TWO

Instinct pushed me out of the way and rolled me along the floor.

I felt the wind as the dagger sliced by my ear. Lines of pain flared along my waist and shoulders as scattered mirror shards cut me. I was on my feet in a moment, crouched low in the tatters of my once beautiful gown.

"No legacy?" The empress smiled. "Wrong guess."

She lifted her arms, and the piles of broken glass trembled and lifted, hovering in the air like a frozen rain of tiny daggers. I conjured up four illusions of myself, and sent them running around the room as I dashed for the door.

But Severine was smart. She sent the shards flashing through the air toward the real me, the only one who fled straight for the door. I cursed my panicked idiocy, and flattened myself to the floor.

A thousand needles whistled inches above my head. Fear was a tremulous pulse forcing me up, pushing me up by my bleeding palms, revving my flailing muscles. *Run.* I took off for the door, but the heavy slab slammed shut in my face. I pounded my bloody hands against the door. It didn't budge. I whirled, planting my stinging back against the wood.

"You have something I want," purred the empress. She stalked closer. She didn't seem to mind that her hand was slick with blood where the mirrored shard dug into her palm. Her violet eyes glued to the cabochon of ambric bouncing above my breast. "Give it willingly and perhaps I'll be merciful, in the end."

"How stupid do you think I am?" I hissed through my teeth. Every breath stung—one of my ribs must have broken.

"Very, very stupid," she said as she took one final step and grabbed at the Relic.

Her blood-slicked fingers brushed through empty air, dissolving the illusion like mist and leaving smears of red across my chest.

"Not that stupid," I croaked. I launched myself at my half sister, barreling into her with all the force of the rage and fear and pain boiling up inside me. She screamed as she fell, and we tumbled across the floor, shredding our gowns and flaying our skin. She scrabbled at me with sharp fingernails, slashing across my face. My head snapped back. I fought for a grip around her wrists, but she was stronger than she looked. She slapped my fumbling hands away and jerked her clawed hands toward my neck.

"Nothing that is mine will ever be yours," she snarled. "But know that I will steal everything you ever loved."

Her fingers encircled my neck. Her nails dug sharp grooves in my skin, and she squeezed. She was strong, viciously so. The room blurred.

Nothing but a thief.

My hands flailed at my side, even as my vision darkened. Distantly, I felt the prickle of tiny shards against my fingertips. Prick. Snick. Slide.

In the weightless, vital space between breath and blood, I heard an echo of Thibo's voice: *We are all thieves here.*

A long laceration along my hand jolted me. I blinked at the ceiling. A chunk of the central mirror remained intact, and I saw a woman in a kembric dress throttling the life out of another woman in a kembric dress. Blood-tipped nails left welts against her bare throat.

Nothing but a thief.

I thought of disappearing courtiers, of sand and blood and bramble, of Thibo's empty, staring eyes. And then I felt as though I was being lifted out of myself, my colored heartbeats separating and floating apart. Weightless, as though something warmer than air and more vital than blood was being lifted from my chest.

I am the scythe they least expect.

Thibo had stolen memories. What if—

A firework epiphany exploded in my mind. Severine wasn't trying to murder me. She was trying to *steal my legacy.*

My hand closed around a shard of glass.

Somewhere, someone dreamed of dying.

That someone wasn't me.

We are all thieves here.

I tightened my hand. Pain carved through my bones, but I bit down on the final scrap of myself left and lifted the shard. It slipped against my bloody palm.

I shoved it home.

Severine grunted, and loosened her grip. Air rushed into my lungs. Warmth spilled down the front of my dress, but it wasn't my blood.

It wasn't my blood.

Consciousness returned in a spiral of pain so agonizing and brutal that for the sparest moment I wished I had died. I rolled my sister's jerking body off me. She flopped back onto the glass-littered floor, staring at the ceiling. A long needle of broken mirror winked at me from its home deep between her ribs. Her mouth worked. She coughed, wetly, and a bubble of blood splattered down her chin.

"Scion curse you," I spat at her. "I hope our siblings are happy to see you."

FIFTY-THREE

I limped to my feet. The door swung open at my touch. Outside, the world was red and smoke-tinged, stained with distant sounds of screaming. My head spun, but I sucked in deep breaths of air until my wooden limbs moved and I didn't think I was going to collapse.

The trek back to Coeur d'Or was torment. I could barely move; every inch of me hurt, and each step sent flares of pain smashing against the back of my skull. My slashed palms dripped steady rivulets of blood onto the grass. My dress was so shredded that it hardly counted as clothing, but I wouldn't have cared even if my body didn't feel like someone had flayed me, then boiled me.

Finally, the trees cleared and the Esplanade swam into view.

What was left of the Esplanade.

A whole wing of the palais was burned away to nearly nothing. Splashes of red marked where fire still burned amid the rubble. Thick black smoke climbed away from the charred hunk of what was once expensive marble and gilt.

Luca's diversion, timed precisely to coincide with the finale of my illusory drama, and set to blast its way into the vault buried at the heart of the palais. The vault where Dowser suspected the empress's other Relic was stashed. It was the other half of our careful plan, and the signal to Lullaby and all the other sympathetic legacies to drop what they were doing and keep the Skyclad Gardes from getting to Severine, Dowser, or Luca.

Sorrow and regret and a blistering disappointment stitched

cold threads down my spine. Was this what it took, to remake a world? Was this what change looked like, in a world forged of metal and stone instead of flimsy wishes? This wasn't what I'd dreamed.

I tried to hurry my hobbling pace. I skirted the worst of the damage, ducking into an unharmed hallway and coughing against the spume of black smoke clogging my lungs. The palais churned in disarray. I heard the sounds of distant shouting. Servants and Gardes sprinted by me in the opposite direction, but I couldn't tell what was going on. How long was I gone? My clash with Severine felt like an eternity, but it could have been mere moments, or an hour. I had no idea.

Anxiety pushed through the haze of pain clouding my thoughts. Sunder was supposed to come to the Solarium when he was done rallying Sinister to his cause. Luca too. Anyone who wasn't fighting was supposed to retreat to the Solarium, in case I needed help against the empress.

No one had come.

I quickened my steps, pushing through the agony tearing me from the inside out. Hallways flashed by, marred by grim scenes of destruction. Skyclad Gardes, facedown and bloodied. Courtiers, unrecognizable beneath the curling feathers on their fine velvet hats. Smoke. Ash. Blood.

Too much blood.

I recognized the golden torches grasped in motionless hands. Dowser's chambers. I limped faster, reaching for the dark wooden door that had become so familiar to me.

"Mirage!"

The voice was distraught, thick with tears. I spun. Lullaby nearly barreled into me, a flurry of black hair and blue skin and blood. Blood on her hands. Tears cutting long trails through the soot on her cheeks.

A slab of iron sank into my stomach. Bile surged toward a throat already tightening with fear.

"Everything went wrong," she wept. "Come quickly. Sunder's hurt."

I forgot my pain and flew on my friend's heels as she dashed through the palais. She hurried me through the vast doors of the Atrium. I heard the thunder of them being barred behind us.

Entering the Atrium was like plunging into a nightmare. The cavernous chamber was thick with smoke. Sooty sunlight crept in through shattered windows; colored glass lay smashed on the floor. The cinders of burnt flowers hung like shrouds from the walls, filling my nostrils with an acrid stench.

Sunder lay halfway up the dais, prone in Bane's lap. Her shaking hand held a bloodied bandage to his ribs. Red stained his lips, and his breath rattled.

"No," I whispered. I fell to my knees beside him. My hands fluttered, useless. I grabbed one of his limp hands in my own. "No!"

"He was badly hurt," murmured Dowser, and I jumped to find him looming behind me, grave and severe. "His injuries are beyond my medical abilities. We need to find a healer at once."

"How—?" I choked on a bitter mixture of tears and blood. "What happened?"

"The explosion collapsed one of the passageways," spat Luca. He paced along a shallow tier, hands shoved deep in his pockets. He looked unhurt, but bitterness twisted his features. "Sunder's legacies were cut off from La Discorde. It was a bloodbath. The Skyclad Gardes slaughtered my men out of hand."

"What about the dissident legacies?"

"The ones that weren't killed in the blast dispersed," said Lullaby. "It was the right thing to do—in all the chaos the Gardes won't know which courtiers aren't loyal to the empress."

"And you?" I glanced up at Dowser. Dismay slowed my blood to an anxious trickle. "Did you find the other Relic?"

The older man gave his head one hard shake. He lifted my ambric necklace out of his pocket, the velvet-wrapped Relic I'd left with him for safekeeping. "This is still the only one I know of."

"Then it was all for nothing?" My voice came out high and hysterical as I took the amulet from Dowser. I squeezed Sunder's hand, hard. "Nothing happened the way it was supposed to."

"You're alive," groaned Sunder. His eyes glinted between slitted lashes. "And strong enough to crush the bones in my hand to dust. So that's something."

My hand flew to my mouth. Tears burned the back of my throat.

"Lullaby!" I called. She was at my side in an instant. "Do you know if any of the legacies still alive are healers? Vida, maybe?"

"Maybe." Her mouth flattened into a line. "But they're scattered. I don't know where anyone is."

"Please," I whispered. A tear squeezed beneath my eyelids. "Please find someone to help him."

Her eyes flickered toward the blond lord, leaking blood on the marble. I could almost hear the mental tally of Sunder's past sins as Lullaby pondered my request. Finally, she nodded.

"For you, Mirage." And she disappeared into Coeur d'Or.

"What happened to you?" Bane snapped. "I hope Severine came out worse for wear. If that's possible."

"I killed her," I whispered. The dam broke, sending a water-fall of pain and misery and ashy disenchantment gushing down my cheeks. For a long while, all I could do was cry, replaying the moment like a bad dream. Her hands digging into my neck. The shard of mirror lacerating my palm. Stab. Gush.

Finally, I tuned back in. Thunder shook the Atrium doors: the stomp of boots and the shouts of Gardes.

"We'll stay with you." Bane wept over her twin brother. "Lullaby's finding you a healer."

"Dowser and I will be fine," croaked Sunder. "Go with Mirage. She needs your help more than I do."

"What?" I jerked my head up and dashed the tears from my cheeks. "No one's leaving. The empress is dead. I'm Sylvain's daughter. I have to declare my intention to ascend the throne immediately."

"That's too dangerous," said Dowser. "The Skyclad have taken the palais. If they see you, they will kill you."

"He's right," growled Luca, still pacing like a wild animal. "Even looking like you do, that dress is too recognizable. If the empress is truly dead, the best thing we can do is retreat and regroup."

"Astonishingly," managed Sunder, "I agree with him. You need to go. Belsyre. Our militia can protect you. Wait until I send word. You're our jewel in the crown, our one shot at doing this right. We need you to stay safe."

"And I need you to stay safe!"

"Dowser is above suspicion," Sunder croaked. "As for me, even if I was seen with the dissident legacies, we're all too valuable to be butchered out of hand. And I've never met a dungeon guard who couldn't be bought with the right amount of kembric."

"But—" I leaned closer, fighting another spill of tears. "I can't leave you. Not like this."

His free hand drifted up to hover over my cheekbone, where crinkled kembric foil peeled away like burnt skin. "I'll survive," he said, and smiled. Even though his teeth were bloody and his hair was black with soot, he was beautiful. "I always do."

"We need to go," urged Luca. "*Sylvie.*"

"*That's not my name,*" I cried, fighting back anguish. A cool touch brushed against my wrist, soothing.

"Come here, demoiselle," whispered Sunder. His eyes were distant, clouded with pain. I leaned in, and he wrapped shaking fingers around the sides of my face. An ache numbed my skin and clenched my teeth, but for once I didn't care. I was wracked with so much pain already that a little more wouldn't kill me.

"I'm here," I choked out, resting my forehead against his. His eyes fluttered shut.

"I know this isn't what you wanted," he rasped. "This isn't the world you dreamed of, long ago in that pallid dusk."

I choked on a soot-stained hallucination of a perfect city, a perfect life.

"But you deserve the chance to live in that world," he said. "You deserve a chance to create it. And even if I can't be redeemed, I *know* you can be."

He struggled to sit up, propping himself onto his elbows. He leaned forward, and brushed his lips against mine.

I plummeted into the kiss. I didn't care that we both tasted of blood and desperation, or that pain needled my skin from a hundred shallow wounds. I fell like I'd never dared to fall before—through a riot of bright, fragile hopes toward a cool promise of belonging.

"My monster," he whispered against my mouth. "Show me what you dream, when you dream of new worlds."

And he cut his gaze to the hulking ambric throne sitting empty at the top of the dais.

I climbed the shallow steps with shaking footsteps. I brushed my palm against the smooth beveled surface, polished smooth and glowing from within. It hummed against my hand. The amulet between my breasts throbbed. I turned, hesitant, and sank down onto the sleek, curving throne.

Radiance painted my bones in sunlight and drowned my eyes in dusk. I roared with the prismatic pulse, sending threads of light and shadow toward the corners of the room. A covenant of colors: Dominion's black heart, warming to violet; crimson glow against pale ambric; sanded kembric and sheer towering blue; dristic and genévrier and cold white. And at its center breathed a city. A city gilded with kembric and bathed in amber light. A city sharp as a wish and dazzling as a secret. A city where I dreamed of belonging, and where that dream came true.

I smiled into the blinding promise of what might never be. I smiled, and engraved an oath upon my heart with lines of amber fire.

It might not be today, or tomorrow. I would wait a thousand tides if I had to. But I would show this world my dream. My dream of a world that was lovely, and strange . . . and just a little bit monstrous.

ACKNOWLEDGMENTS

Publishing this book is a dream come true for me. But there were times I felt like I was sleepwalking more than anything else, and if it weren't for the incredible support of so many people, I would probably have fallen to the bottom of a (metaphorical) well.

To my amazing editor, Lisa Sandell, for seeing what this book could be, instead of what it was, and easing me through that transition so smoothly that it almost felt effortless. I cannot thank you enough for your enduring faith in Mirage's world, even when it felt like mine was flagging. To Olivia Valcarce, for always knowing what I was trying to say even when the words on the page weren't quite there yet—your intuition is invaluable. And to Scholastic, for taking a chance on me, and this book I love so much.

To the entire Curtis Brown family, but especially my agent Ginger Clark: I am in awe of your humor, experience, wit, wisdom, and strength. Whether I need tough love or pep talks, you're always a speedy email away. There will never be enough wombat photos to thank you for your help in bringing this book into the world.

To my critique partner, Roshani Chokshi, for reading everything I write in record time and never failing to gently eviscerate my drafts with your genius. You are eternally gorgeous and flawlessly wise, and I would never have made it without your lengthy emails and perfect GIFs. To M. Evan Matyas, for being a roommate, friend, sounding board, commiserator in chief, and

OXFORD REFERENCE

A Concise
Dictionary of
Physics

D0166566

A Concise Dictionary of Physics

NEW EDITION

OXFORD   NEW YORK
OXFORD UNIVERSITY PRESS

Oxford University Press, Walton Street, Oxford OX2 6DP

Oxford New York Toronto
Delhi Bombay Calcutta Madras Karachi
Petaling Jaya Singapore Hong Kong Tokyo
Nairobi Dar es Salaam Cape Town
Melbourne Auckland

and associated companies in
Berlin Ibadan

Oxford is a trade mark of Oxford University Press

© *Market House Books Ltd. 1985, 1990*

First published 1985
Second edition first published as an Oxford University Press
paperback 1990
Reprinted 1991 (twice)

British Library Cataloguing in Publication Data
A Concise dictionary of physics—New ed.
1. Physics. Encyclopaedias
I. Concise science dictionary
530.03
ISBN 0-19-286111-5

Library of Congress Cataloging-in-Publication Data
A Concise dictionary of physics.—New ed.
p. cm.—(Oxford reference)
1. Physics—Dictionaries. I. Series.
530'.03—dc20 QA5.C56 1990 90-38628
ISBN 0-19-286111-5

Printed and bound in Great Britain by
Biddles Ltd, Guildford and King's Lynn

Preface

This dictionary is derived from the *Concise Science Dictionary*, first published by Oxford University Press in 1984. It consists of all the entries relating to physics in this dictionary, together with some of those entries relating to astronomy that are required for an understanding of astrophysics and many entries that relate to physical chemistry. It also includes a selection of the words used in mathematics that are relevant to physics, as well as the key words in metal science, computing, and electronics. For this second edition many new terms have been added, particularly in the fields of nuclear and particle physics, quantum theory, and solid-state physics. The more chemical aspects of physical chemistry and the chemistry itself will be found in *A Concise Dictionary of Chemistry*, which is a companion volume to this dictionary.

A Concise Dictionary of Biology contains the biophysical entries from the *Concise Science Dictionary* together with the entries relating to biology.

SI units are used throughout this book and its companion volumes.

A.I. 1990

A

ab- A prefix attached to the name of a practical electrical unit to provide a name for a unit in the *electromagnetic system of units, e.g. abampere, abcoulomb, abvolt. The prefix is an abbreviation of the word 'absolute' as this system is also known as the *absolute system. Compare* stat-. In modern practice both absolute and electrostatic units have been replaced by *SI units.

Abelian group *See* group.

aberration 1. (in optics) A defect in the image formed by a lens or curved mirror. In *chromatic aberration* the image formed by a lens (but not a mirror) has coloured fringes as a result of the different extent to which light of different colours is refracted by glass. It is corrected by using an *achromatic lens. In *spherical aberration*, the rays from the object come to a focus in slightly different positions as a result of the curvature of the lens or mirror. For a mirror receiving light strictly parallel with its axis, this can be corrected by using a parabolic surface rather than a spherical surface. Spherical aberration in lenses is minimized by making both surfaces contribute equally to the ray deviations, and can (though with reduced image brightness) be reduced by the use of diaphragms to let light pass only through the centre part of the lens. *See also* astigmatism; coma. **2.** (in astronomy) The apparent displacement in the position of a star as a result of the earth's motion round the sun. Light appears to come from a point that is slightly displaced in the direction of the earth's motion. The angular displacement $\alpha = v/c$, where v is the earth's orbital velocity and c is the speed of light.

abscissa *See* Cartesian coordinates.

absolute 1. Not dependent on or relative to anything else, e.g. *absolute zero. **2.** Denoting a temperature measured on an *absolute scale*, a scale of temperature based on absolute zero. The usual absolute scale now is that of thermodynamic *temperature; its unit, the kelvin, was formerly called the degree absolute (°A) and is the same size as the degree Celsius. In British engineering practice an absolute scale with Fahrenheit-size degrees has been used: this is the Rankine scale.

absolute expansivity *See* expansivity.

absolute humidity *See* humidity.

absolute permittivity *See* permittivity.

absolute pitch (perfect pitch) The ability of a person to identify and reproduce a note without reference to a tuned musical instrument.

absolute temperature *See* absolute; temperature.

absolute value (modulus) The square root of the sum of the squares of the real numbers in a *complex number, i.e. the absolute value of the complex number $z = x + iy$ is $|z| = \sqrt{(x^2 + y^2)}$.

absolute zero Zero of thermodynamic *temperature (0 kelvin) and the lowest temperature theoretically attainable. It is the temperature at which the kinetic energy of atoms and molecules is minimal. It is equivalent to $-273.15\,°C$ or $-459.67\,°F$. *See also* zero-point energy; cryogenics.

absorptance Symbol α. The ratio of the radiant or luminous flux absorbed by a body to the flux falling on it. Formerly called *absorptivity*, the absorptance of a *black body is by definition 1.

absorption 1. The take up of a gas by a solid or liquid, or the take up of a liquid by a solid. Absorption differs from *adsorption in that the absorbed substance permeates the bulk of the absorbing substance. **2.** The conversion of the energy of elec-

tromagnetic radiation, sound, streams of particles, etc., into other forms of energy on passing through a medium. A beam of light, for instance, passing through a medium, may lose intensity because of two effects: *scattering of light out of the beam, and absorption of photons by atoms or molecules in the medium. When a photon is absorbed, there is a transition to an excited state.

absorption coefficient *See* Lambert's laws.

absorption spectrum *See* spectrum.

absorptivity *See* absorptance.

abundance 1. The ratio of the total mass of a specified element in the earth's crust to the total mass of the earth's crust, often expressed as a percentage. For example, the abundance of aluminium in the earth's crust is about 8%. **2.** The ratio of the number of atoms of a particular isotope of an element to the total number of atoms of all the isotopes present, often expressed as a percentage. For example, the abundance of uranium−235 in natural uranium is 0.71%. This is the *natural abundance*, i.e. the abundance as found in nature before any enrichment has taken place.

a.c. *See* alternating current.

acceleration Symbol a. The rate of increase of speed or velocity. It is measured in m s^{-2}. For a body moving linearly with constant acceleration a from a speed u to a speed v,

$$a = (v - u)/t = (v^2 - u^2)/2s$$

where t is the time taken and s the distance covered.
If the acceleration is not constant it is given by $dv/dt = d^2s/dt^2$. If the motion is not linear the vector character of displacement, velocity, and acceleration must be considered.

acceleration of free fall Symbol g. The acceleration experienced by any massive object falling freely in the earth's gravitational field. Experimen-

tally this is almost constant for all positions near the earth's surface, independent of the nature of the falling body (provided air resistance is eliminated). This is taken to indicate the strict proportionality of *weight (the force causing the acceleration) and *inertial mass, on the basis of *Newton's second law of motion. There is some variation of g with latitude, because of the earth's rotation and because the earth is not completely spherical. The standard value is taken as 9.806 65 m s^{-2}. The acceleration of free fall is also called the *acceleration due to gravity*.

accelerator An apparatus for increasing the kinetic energies of charged particles, used for research in nuclear and particle physics. *See* cyclotron; linear accelerator; synchrocyclotron; synchrotron.

acceptor A substance that is added as an impurity to a *semiconductor because of its ability to accept electrons from the valence bands, causing p-type conduction by the mobile positive holes left.

accommodation The process by which the focal length of the *lens of the eye is changed so that clear images of objects at a range of distances are displayed on the retina. In man and some other mammals accommodation is achieved by reflex adjustments in the shape of the lens brought about by relaxation and contraction of muscles within the ciliary body.

accretion disc A disc-shaped rotating mass formed by gravitational attraction. *See* black hole; neutron star; white dwarf.

accumulator (secondary cell; storage battery) A type of *voltaic cell or battery that can be recharged by passing a current through it from an external d.c. supply. The charging current, which is passed in the opposite direction to that in which the cell supplies current, reverses the chemical

reactions in the cell. The common types are the *lead–acid accumulator and the *nickel–iron accumulator.

achromatic lens A lens that corrects for chromatic *aberration by using a combination of two lenses, made of different kinds of glass, such that their *dispersions neutralize each other although their *refractions do not. The aberration can be reduced further by using an *apochromatic lens*, which consists of three or more different kinds of glass.

acoustics 1. The study of sound and sound waves. **2.** The characteristics of a building, especially an auditorium, with regard to its ability to enable speech and music to be heard clearly within it. For this purpose there should be no obtrusive echoes or resonances and the reverberation time should be near the optimum for the hall. Echoes are reduced by avoiding sweeping curved surfaces that could focus the sound and by breaking up large plane surfaces or covering them with sound-absorbing materials. Resonance is avoided by avoiding simple ratios for the main dimensions of the room, so that no one wavelength of sound is a factor of more than one of them. If the reverberation time is too long, speech will sound indistinct and music will be badly articulated, with one note persisting during the next. However, if it is too short, music sounds dead. It is long in a bare room with hard walls, and can be deliberately reduced by carpets, soft furnishings and sound-absorbent ('acoustic') felt. Reverberation times tend to be reduced by the presence of an audience and this must be taken into account in the design of the building.

acoustoelectronic devices (electro-acoustic devices) Devices in which electronic signals are converted into acoustic waves. Acoustoelectronic devices are used in constructing *delay lines and also in converting digital data from computers for transmission by telephone lines.

actinic radiation Electromagnetic radiation that is capable of initiating a chemical reaction. The term is used especially of ultraviolet radiation and also to denote radiation that will affect a photographic emulsion.

actinium Symbol Ac. A silvery radioactive metallic element belonging to group IIIB of the periodic table; a.n. 89; mass number of most stable isotope 227 (half-life 21.7 years); m.p. 1050 $\pm$ 50°C; b.p. 3300°C (estimated). Actinium–227 occurs in natural uranium to an extent of about 0.715%. Actinium–228 (half-life 6.13 hours) also occurs in nature. There are 22 other artificial isotopes, all radioactive and all with very short half-lives. It has no uses and was discovered by A. Debierne in 1899.

actinium series *See* radioactive series.

actinoid contraction A smooth decrease in atomic or ionic radius with increasing proton number found in the actinoids.

actinometer Any of various instruments for measuring the intensity of electromagnetic radiation. Recent actinometers use the *photoelectric effect but earlier instruments depended either on the fluorescence produced by the radiation on a screen or on the amount of chemical change induced in some suitable substance.

action potential The change in electrical potential that occurs across a cell membrane during the passage of a nerve impulse. As an impulse travels in a wavelike manner along the axon of a nerve, it causes a localized and transient switch in electrical potential across the cell membrane from –60 mV (millivolts) to +45 mV. Nervous stimulation of a muscle fibre has a similar effect.

action spectrum A graphical plot of the efficiency of electromagnetic

3

radiation in producing a photochemical reaction against the wavelength of the radiation used. For example, the action spectrum for photosynthesis using light shows a peak in the region 670–700 nm. This corresponds to a maximum absorption in the absorption spectrum of chlorophylls in this region.

activation analysis An analytical technique that can be used to detect most elements when present in a sample in milligram quantities (or less). In *neutron activation analysis* the sample is exposed to a flux of thermal neutrons in a nuclear reactor. Some of these neutrons are captured by nuclides in the sample to form nuclides of the same atomic number but a higher mass number. These newly formed nuclides emit gamma radiation, which can be used to identify the element present by means of a gamma-ray spectrometer. Activation analysis has also been employed using charged particles, such as protons or alpha particles.

active device 1. An electronic component, such as a transistor, that is capable of amplification. **2.** An artificial *satellite that receives information and retransmits it after amplification. **3.** A radar device that emits microwave radiation and provides information about a distant body by receiving a reflection of this radiation. *Compare* passive device.

activity 1. Symbol *a*. A thermodynamic function used in place of concentration in equilibrium constants for reactions involving nonideal gases and solutions. For example, in a reaction

$$A \rightleftharpoons B + C$$

the true equilibrium constant is given by

$$K = a_B a_C / a_A$$

where a_A, a_B, and a_C are the activities of the components, which function as concentrations (or pressures) corrected for nonideal behaviour. *Activity coef-*

ficients (symbol γ) are defined for gases by $\gamma = a/p$ (where p is pressure) and for solutions by $\gamma = aX$ (where X is the mole fraction). Thus, the equilibrium constant of a gas reaction has the form

$$K_p = \gamma_B p_B \gamma_C p_C / \gamma_A p_A$$

The equilibrium constant of a reaction in solution is

$$K_c = \gamma_B X_B \gamma_C X_C / \gamma_A X_A$$

The activity coefficients thus act as correction factors for the pressures or concentrations. *See* fugacity.

2. Symbol *A*. The number of atoms of a radioactive substance that disintegrate per unit time. The *specific activity* (*a*) is the activity per unit mass of a pure radioisotope. *See* radiation units.

additive process *See* colour.

adiabatic demagnetization A technique for cooling a paramagnetic salt, such as potassium chrome alum, to a temperature near *absolute zero. The salt is placed between the poles of an electromagnet and the heat produced during magnetization is removed by liquid helium. The salt is then isolated thermally from the surroundings and the field is switched off; the salt is demagnetized adiabatically and its temperature falls. This is because the demagnetized state, being less ordered, involves more energy than the magnetized state. The extra energy can come only from the internal, or thermal, energy of the substance.

adiabatic process Any process that occurs without heat entering or leaving a system. In general, an adiabatic change involves a fall or rise in temperature of the system. For example, if a gas expands under adiabatic conditions, its temperature falls (work is done against the retreating walls of the container). The *adiabatic equation* describes the relationship between the pressure (*p*) of an ideal gas and its volume (*V*), i.e. $pV^\gamma = K$, where γ is the ratio of the principal specific

*heat capacities of the gas and K is a constant.

admittance Symbol Y. The reciprocal of *impedance. It is measured in siemens.

adsorbate A substance that is adsorbed on a surface.

adsorption The formation of a layer of gas, liquid, or solid on the surface of a solid or, less frequently, of a liquid. There are two types depending on the nature of the forces involved. In *chemisorption* a single layer of molecules, atoms, or ions is attached to the adsorbent surface by chemical bonds. In *physisorption* adsorbed molecules are held by the weaker *van der Waals' forces.

advanced gas-cooled reactor (AGR) See nuclear reactor.

aerial (antenna) The part of a radio or television system from which radio waves are transmitted into the atmosphere or space (*transmitting aerial*) or by which they are received (*receiving aerial*). A *directional* or *directive aerial* is one in which energy is transmitted or received more effectively from some directions than others, whereas an *omnidirectional aerial* transmits and receives equally well in all directions.

aerogenerator See wind power.

aerosol A colloidal dispersion of a solid or liquid in a gas. The commonly used aerosol sprays contain an inert propellant liquefied under pressure. Halogenated alkanes containing chlorine and fluorine (chlorofluorocarbons, or CFCs) have been used in aerosol cans. This use has been criticized on the grounds that these compounds persist in the atmosphere and lead to depletion of the *ozone layer.

aerospace The earth's atmosphere and the space beyond it.

AFM See atomic force microscope.

after-heat Heat produced by a nuclear reactor after it has been shut down. The after-heat is generated by radioactive substances formed in the fuel elements.

AGR Advanced gas-cooled reactor. *See* nuclear reactor.

air *See* earth's atmosphere.

albedo 1. The ratio of the radiant flux reflected by a surface to that falling on it. **2.** The probability that a neutron entering a body of material will be reflected back through the same surface as it entered.

algebraic sum The total of a set of quantities paying due regard to sign, e.g. the algebraic sum of 3 and −4 is −1.

algorithm A method of solving a problem, involving a finite series of steps. In computing practice the algorithm denotes the expression on paper of the proposed computing process (often by means of a flowchart) prior to the preparation of the program. If no algorithm is possible a *heuristic solution has to be sought.

allowed bands *See* energy bands.

alloy A material consisting of two or more metals (e.g. brass is an alloy of copper and zinc) or a metal and a nonmetal (e.g. steel is an alloy of iron and carbon, sometimes with other metals included). Alloys may be compounds, *solid solutions, or mixtures of the components.

alloy steels *See* steel.

Alnico A tradename for a series of alloys, containing iron, aluminium, nickel, cobalt, and copper, used to make permanent magnets.

alpha-iron *See* iron.

alpha particle A helium−4 nucleus emitted by a larger nucleus during the course of the type of radioactive decay known as *alpha decay*. As a helium−4 nucleus consists of two protons and two neutrons bound together as a stable entity the loss of

an alpha particle involves a decrease in *nucleon number of 4 and decrease of 2 in the *atomic number, e.g. the decay of a uranium–238 nucleus into a thorium–234 nucleus. A stream of alpha particles is known as an *alpha-ray* or *alpha-radiation*.

alternating current (a.c.) An electric current that reverses its direction with a constant *frequency (f). If a graph of the current against time has the form of a *sine wave, the current is said to be *sinusoidal*. Alternating current, unlike direct current, is therefore continuously varying and its magnitude is either given as its peak value (I_0) or its *root-mean-square value ($I_0/\sqrt{2}$ for a sinusoidal current). This r.m.s. value is more useful as it is comparable to a d.c. value in being a measure of the ability of the current to transmit power. The instantaneous value of a sinusoidal current (I) is given by $I = I_0\sin2\pi ft$. If a direct current is supplied to a circuit the only opposition it encounters is the circuit's *resistance. However, an alternating current is opposed not only by the resistance of the circuit but also by its *reactance. This reactance is caused by *capacitance and *inductance in the circuit. In a circuit consisting of a resistance (R), an inductance (L), and a capacitance (C) all in series, the reactance (X) is equal to $(2\pi fL) - (1/2\pi fC)$. The total opposition to the current, called the *impedance (Z), is then equal to the ratio of the r.m.s. applied p.d. to the r.m.s. current and is given by $\sqrt{(R^2 + X^2)}$.

alternator An *alternating-current generator consisting of a coil or coils that rotate in the magnetic field produced by one or more permanent magnets or electromagnets. The electromagnets are supplied by an independent direct-current source. The frequency of the alternating current produced depends on the speed at which the coil rotates and the number of pairs of magnetic poles. In the large alternators of power stations the electromagnets rotate inside fixed coils; many bicycle dynamos are alternators with rotating permanent magnets inside fixed coils.

altimeter A device used to measure height above sea level. It usually consists of an aneroid *barometer measuring atmospheric pressure. Aircraft are fitted with altimeters, which are set to the atmospheric pressure at a convenient level, usually sea level, before take off. The height of the aircraft can then be read off the instrument as the aircraft climbs and the pressure falls.

AM (amplitude modulation) *See* modulation.

amalgam An alloy of mercury with one or more other metals. Most metals form amalgams (iron and platinum are exceptions), which may be liquid or solid. Some contain definite intermetallic compounds, such as $NaHg_2$.

americium Symbol Am. A radioactive metallic transuranic element belonging to the actinoids; a.n. 95; mass number of most stable isotope 243 (half-life 7.95×10^3 years); r.d. 13.67 (20°C); m.p. 994 ± 4°C; b.p. 2607°C. Ten isotopes are known. The element was discovered by G. T. Seaborg and associates in 1945, who obtained it by bombarding uranium–238 with alpha particles.

ammeter An instrument that measures electric current. The main types are the *moving-coil* ammeter, the *moving-iron* ammeter, and the *thermoammeter*. The moving-coil instrument is a moving-coil *galvanometer fitted with a *shunt to reduce its sensitivity. It can only be used for d.c., but can be adapted for a.c. by using a *rectifier. In moving-iron instruments, a piece of soft iron moves in the magnetic field created when the current to be measured flows through a fixed coil. They can

be used with a.c. or d.c. but are less accurate (though more robust) than the moving-coil instruments. In thermoammeters, which can also be used with a.c. or d.c., the current is passed through a resistor, which heats up as the current passes. This is in contact with a thermocouple, which is connected to a galvanometer. This indirect system is mainly used for measuring high frequency a.c. In the *hot-wire* instrument the wire is clamped at its ends and its elongation as it is heated causes a pointer to move over a scale.

ammonia clock A form of atomic clock in which the frequency of a quartz oscillator is controlled by the vibrations of excited ammonia molecules (*see* excitation). The ammonia molecule (NH_3) consists of a pyramid with a nitrogen atom at the apex and one hydrogen atom at each corner of the triangular base. When the molecule is excited, once every 20.9 microseconds the nitrogen atom passes through the base and forms a pyramid the other side: 20.9 microseconds later it returns to its original position. This vibration back and forth has a frequency of 23 870 hertz and ammonia gas will only absorb excitation energy at exactly this frequency. By using a *crystal oscillator to feed energy to the gas and a suitable feedback mechanism, the oscillator can be locked to exactly this frequency.

amorphous Describing a solid that is not crystalline; i.e. one that has no long-range order in its lattice. Many powders that are described as 'amorphous' in fact are composed of microscopic crystals, as can be demonstrated by X-ray diffraction. Glasses are examples of true amorphous solids.

amount of substance Symbol *n*. A measure of the number of entities present in a substance. The specified entity may be an atom, molecule, ion, electron, photon, etc., or any specified group of such entities. The amount of substance of an element, for example, is proportional to the number of atoms present. For all entities, the constant of proportionality is the inverse *Avogadro constant. The SI unit of amount of substance is the *mole.

ampere Symbol A. The SI unit of electric current. The constant current that, maintained in two straight parallel infinite conductors of negligible cross section placed one metre apart in a vacuum, would produce a force between the conductors of 2×10^{-7} $N \, m^{-1}$. This definition replaced the earlier international ampere defined as the current required to deposit 0.001 118 00 gram of silver from a solution of silver nitrate in one second. The unit is named after A. M. Ampère (1775–1836).

ampere-hour A practical unit of electric charge equal to the charge flowing in one hour through a conductor passing one ampere. It is equal to 3600 coulombs.

ampere-turn The SI unit of *magnetomotive force equal to the magnetomotive force produced when a current of one ampere flows through one turn of a magnetizing coil.

amplifier A device that increases the strength of an electrical signal by drawing energy from a separate source to that of the signal. The original device used in electronic amplifiers was the *triode valve, in which the cathode–anode current is varied in accordance with the low-voltage signal applied to the valve's control grid. In the more recent *transistor, the emitter–collector current is controlled in much the same way by the signal applied to the transistor's base region. In the most modern devices the complete amplifier circuit is manufactured as a single *integrated circuit. The ratio of the output amplitude (of p.d. or current)

of an amplifier (or stage of an amplifier) to the corresponding input amplitude is called the *gain* of the amplifier.

amplitude *See* wave.

amplitude modulation (AM) *See* modulation; radio.

a.m.u. *See* atomic mass unit.

analytical geometry (coordinate geometry) A form of geometry in which points are located in a two-dimensional or three-dimensional space by means of a system of coordinates. Curves are represented by an equation for a set of such points. The geometry of figures can thus be analysed by algebraic methods. *See* Cartesian coordinates; polar coordinates.

anastigmatic lens 1. An objective lens for an optical instrument in which all *aberrations, including *astigmatism, are reduced greatly. 2. A spectacle lens designed to correct astigmatism. It has different radii of curvature in the vertical and horizontal planes.

anchor ring *See* torus.

and circuit *See* logic circuits.

anechoic Having a low degree of reverberation with little or no reflection of sound. An *anechoic* chamber is one designed for experiments in acoustics. The walls are covered with small pyramids to avoid the formation of stationary waves between facing surfaces and the whole of the interior surface is covered with an absorbent material to avoid reflections.

anemometer An instrument for measuring the speed of the wind or any other flowing fluid. The simple *vane anemometer* consists of a number of cups or blades attached to a central spindle so that the air, or other fluid, causes the spindle to rotate. The instrument is calibrated to give a wind speed directly from a dial. The instrument can be mounted to rotate

about a vertical axis and in this form it also gives an indication of the direction of the wind. A *hot-wire anemometer* consists of an electrically heated wire that is cooled by the flow of fluid passing round it. The faster the flow the lower the temperature of the wire and the lower its resistance. Thus the rate of flow can be calculated by measuring the resistance of the wire.

aneroid barometer *See* barometer.

angle modulation *See* modulation.

angle of incidence 1. The angle between a ray falling on a surface and the perpendicular (normal) to the surface at the point at which the ray strikes the surface. 2. The angle between a wavefront and a surface that it strikes.

angle of reflection 1. The angle between a ray leaving a reflecting surface and the perpendicular (normal) to the surface at the point at which the ray leaves the surface. 2. The angle between a wavefront and a surface that it leaves.

angle of refraction 1. The angle between a ray that is refracted at a surface between two different media and the perpendicular (normal) to the surface at the point of refraction. 2. The angle between a wavefront and a surface at which it has been refracted.

angstrom Symbol Å. A unit of length equal to 10^{-10} metre. It was formerly used to measure wavelengths and intermolecular distances but has now been replaced by the nanometre. 1 Å = 0.1 nanometre. The unit is named after the Swedish pioneer of spectroscopy A. J. Ångström (1814–74).

angular displacement, velocity, and acceleration *See* rotational motion.

angular frequency (pulsatance) A quantity proportional to the *frequency of a periodic phenomenon but having the dimensions of angular velocity. The angular frequency in

radians per second = frequency in hertz × 2π radians per cycle.

angular magnification (magnifying power) *See* magnification.

angular momentum Symbol L. The product of the angular velocity of a body and its *moment of inertia about the axis of rotation, i.e. $L = I\omega$.

anion A negatively charged *ion, i.e. an ion that is attracted to the *anode in *electrolysis. *Compare* cation.

anisotropic Denoting a medium in which certain physical properties are different in different directions. Wood, for instance, is an anisotropic material: its strength along the grain differs from that perpendicular to the grain. Single crystals that are not cubic are anisotropic with respect to some physical properties, such as the transmission of electromagnetic radiation. *Compare* isotropic.

annealing A form of heat treatment applied to a metal to soften it, relieve internal stresses and instabilities, and make it easier to work or machine. It consists of heating the metal to a specified temperature for a specified time, both of which depend on the metal involved, and then allowing it to cool slowly. It is applied to both ferrous and nonferrous metals and a similar process can be applied to other materials, such as glass.

annihilation The destruction of a particle and its *antiparticle as a result of a collision between them. The *annihilation radiation* produced is carried away by *photons or *mesons. For example, in a collision between an electron and a positron the energy produced is carried away by two photons, each having an energy of 0.511 MeV, which is equivalent to the rest-mass energies of the annihilated particles plus their kinetic energies. When nucleons annihilate each other the energy is carried away by mesons.

annulus The plane figure formed between two concentric circles of different radii, R and r. Its area is $\pi(R^2 - r^2)$.

anode A positive electrode. In *electrolysis anions are attracted to the anode. In an electronic vacuum tube it attracts electrons from the *cathode and it is therefore from the anode that electrons flow out of the device. In these instances the anode is made positive by external means; however in a *voltaic cell the anode is the electrode that spontaneously becomes positive and therefore attracts electrons to it from the external circuit.

anomaly An angle used to fix the position of a body, such as a planet, in an elliptical orbit. The *true anomaly* of a planet is the angle between the *perihelion, the sun, and the planet in the direction of the planet's motion. The *mean anomaly* is the angle between the perihelion, the sun, and an imaginary planet having the same period as the real planet, but assumed to be moving at constant speed.

antenna *See* aerial.

antiferromagnetism *See* magnetism.

antilogarithm *See* logarithm.

antimatter *See* antiparticle.

antinode *See* stationary wave.

antiparallel vectors Vectors directed along the same line but in opposite directions.

antiparticle A subatomic particle that has the same mass as another particle and equal but opposite values of some other property or properties. For example, the antiparticle of the electron is the positron, which has a positive charge equal in magnitude to the electron's negative charge. The antiproton has a negative charge equal to the proton's positive charge. The neutron and the antineutron have *magnetic moments opposite in sign relative to their *spins. The existence of antiparticles is predicted by relativ-

istic *quantum mechanics. When a
particle and its corresponding antiparticle collide *annihilation takes place.
Antimatter is postulated to consist of
matter made up of antiparticles. For
example, antihydrogen would consist
of an antiproton with an orbiting
positron. It appears that the universe
consists overwhelmingly of (normal)
matter, and explanations of the
absence of large amounts of antimatter have been incorporated into cosmological models that involve the use
of *grand unified theories of elementary particles.

anyon *See* quantum statistics.

aperture The effective diameter of a
lens or mirror. The ratio of the effective diameter to the focal length is
called the *relative aperture*, which is
commonly known as the aperture,
especially in photographic usage. The
reciprocal of the relative aperture is
called the *focal ratio*. The numerical
value of the focal ratio is known as
the *f-number* of a lens. For example,
a camera lens with a 40 mm focal
length and a 10 mm aperture has a
relative aperture of 0.25 and a focal
ratio of 4. Its f-number would be f/4,
often written f4.
The light-gathering power of a telescope depends on the area of the
lens, i.e. it is related to the square of
the aperture. However, the larger the
relative aperture the greater the
*aberrations. In microscopy large-
aperture objectives (corrected for
aberrations) are preferred, since they
reduce the blurring caused by *diffraction of light waves.

aperture synthesis *See* radio telescope.

aphelion The point in the orbit of a
planet, comet, or artificial satellite in
solar orbit at which it is farthest from
the sun. The earth is at aphelion on
about July 3. *Compare* perihelion.

aplanatic lens A lens that reduces
both spherical *aberration and
*coma.

apochromatic lens *See* achromatic
lens.

apocynthion The point in the orbit
around the moon of a satellite
launched from the earth that is furthest from the moon. For a satellite
launched from the moon the equivalent point is the *apolune*. *Compare*
pericynthion.

apogee The point in the orbit of the
moon, or an artificial earth satellite,
at which it is furthest from the earth.
At apogee the moon is 406 700 km
from the earth, some 42 000 km further away than at *perigee*, the nearest
point to the earth.

apolune *See* apocynthion.

apparent expansivity *See* expansivity.

Appleton layer *See* earth's atmosphere.

apsides The two points in an astronomical orbit that lie closest to (*periapsis*) and farthest from (*apoapsis*)
the centre of gravitational attraction.
The *line of apsides* is the straight line
that joins the two apsides. If the orbit
is elliptical the line of apsides is the
major axis of the ellipse.

aqueous Describing a solution in
water.

arccos, arcsin, arctan *See* inverse
functions.

Archimedes' principle The weight of
the liquid displaced by a floating
body is equal to the weight of the
body. The principle was not in fact
stated by the Greek mathematician
Archimedes (287–212 BC), though it
has some connection with his discov-
eries. The principle is often stated in
the form: when a body is (partially or
totally) immersed in a fluid, the
upthrust on the body is equal to the
weight of fluid displaced.

arc lamp *See* electric lighting.

arcosh, arsinh, artanh *See* inverse
functions.

Argand diagram *See* complex number.

argument 1. A sequence of logical propositions based on a set of premisses and leading to a conclusion. **2.** *See* complex number.

arithmetic average (arithmetic mean) *See* average.

arithmetic series (arithmetic progression) A series or progression of numbers in which there is a common difference between terms, e.g. 3, 9, 15, 21,... is an arithmetic series with a common difference of 6. The general formula for the *n*th term is $[a + (n - 1)d]$ and the sum of *n* terms is
$$n[2a + (n - 1)d]/2.$$
Compare geometric series.

armature Any moving part in an electrical machine in which a voltage is induced by a magnetic field, especially the rotating coils in an electric motor or generator and the ferromagnetic bar attracted by an electromagnet in a *relay.

associative law The mathematical law stating that the value of an expression is independent of the grouping of the numbers, symbols, or terms in the expression. The *associative law for addition* states that numbers may be added in any order, e.g. $(x + y) + z = (x + z) + y$. The *associative law for multiplication* states that numbers can be multiplied in any order, e.g. $x(yz) = (xy)z$. Subtraction and division are not associative. *Compare* commutative law; distributive law.

astatic galvanometer A sensitive form of moving-magnet *galvanometer in which any effects of the earth's magnetic field are cancelled out. Two small oppositely directed magnets are suspended at the centres of two oppositely wound coils. As its resultant moment on the magnets is zero, the earth's field has no effect and the only restoring torque on the magnets is that provided by the suspending fibre. This makes a sensitive but delicate instrument.

astatine Symbol At. A radioactive halogen element; a.n. 85; r.a.m. 211; m.p. 302°C; b.p. 377°C. It occurs naturally by radioactive decay from uranium and thorium isotopes. Astatine forms at least 20 isotopes, the most stable astatine–210 has a half-life of 8.3 hours. It can also be produced by alpha bombardment of bismuth–200. The existence of At_2 has not yet been established. The element was synthesized by nuclear bombardment in 1940 by D. R. Corson, K. R. MacKenzie, and E. Segré at the University of California.

asteroids (minor planets; planetoids) A number of small bodies that revolve around the sun between the orbits of Mars and Jupiter (in the *asteroid belt*). The size of the bodies varies from the largest, Ceres (with a diameter of about 1000 km), to objects less than 1 km in diameter. It is estimated that there are about 10 bodies with diameters in excess of 300 km and some 200 bodies with diameters over 100 km.

asthenosphere A layer of the earth's mantle (*see* earth) that underlies the lithosphere at a depth of about 70 km. The velocity of seismic waves is considerably reduced in the asthenosphere and it is thought to be a zone of partial melting. It extends to a depth of about 250 km where rocks again become solid.

astigmatism A lens defect in which when rays in one plane are in focus those in another plane are not. In lenses and mirrors it occurs with objects not on the axis and is best controlled by reducing the *aperture to restrict the use of the lens or mirror to its central portion. The eye can also suffer from astigmatism, usually when the cornea is not spherical. It is corrected by using an *anastigmatic lens.

11

astrometry The branch of astronomy concerned with the measurement of the positions of the celestial bodies on the *celestial sphere.

astronomical telescope *See* telescope.

astronomical unit (AU) The mean distance between the sun and the earth. It is equal to 149 597 870 km (499 light seconds).

astronomy The study of the universe beyond the earth's atmosphere. The main branches are *astrometry, *celestial mechanics, and *astrophysics.

astrophysics The study of the physical and chemical processes involving astronomical phenomena. Astrophysics deals with stellar structure and evolution (including the generation and transport of energy within stars), the properties of the interstellar medium and its interactions with stellar systems, and the structure and dynamics of systems of stars (such as *clusters and *galaxies), and of systems of galaxies. *See also* cosmology.

asymmetric atom *See* optical activity.

asymptote A line that a curve approaches but only touches at infinity.

asymptotic freedom The consequence of certain *gauge theories, particularly *quantum chromodynamics, that the forces between such particles as quarks become weaker at shorter distances (i.e. higher energies) and vanish as the distance between particles tends to zero. Only non-Abelian gauge theories with unbroken gauge symmetries can have asymptotic freedom (*see* group). In contrast, *quantum electrodynamics implies that the interaction between particles decreases as a result of dielectric screening; asymptotic freedom for quarks implies that antiscreening occurs. Physically, asymptotic freedom postulates that the *vacuum state for gluons is a medium that has colour paramagnetism, i.e. the vacuum antiscreen colour charges.

Asymptotic freedom explains the successes of the *parton model of point-like objects inside hadrons and enables systematic corrections to the parton model to be calculated using perturbation theory. That the interaction between quarks increases as the distance between them increases has given rise to the hypothesis of *quark confinement. It appears that if a theory requires the presence of Higgs bosons, asymptotic freedom is destroyed. Thus, *electroweak theory does not have asymptotic freedom.

asymptotic series A series formed by the expansion of a function in the form $a_0 + a_1/x + a_2/x^2 + \ldots + a_n/x^n + \ldots$, such that the error resulting from terminating the series at the term a_n/x^n tends to zero more rapidly than $1/x^n$ as x tends to infinity. An asymptotic series expansion is not necessarily a *convergent series.

atmolysis The separation of a mixture of gases by means of their different rates of diffusion. Usually, separation is effected by allowing the gases to diffuse through the walls of a porous partition or membrane.

atmosphere 1. (atm.) A unit of pressure equal to 101 325 pascals. This is equal to 760.0 mmHg. The actual *atmospheric pressure fluctuates around this value. The unit is usually used for expressing pressures well in excess of standard atmospheric pressure, e.g. in high-pressure chemical processes. **2.** *See* earth's atmosphere.

atmospheric pressure The pressure exerted by the weight of the air above it at any point on the earth's surface. At sea level the atmosphere will support a column of mercury about 760 mm high. This decreases with increasing altitude. The standard value for the atmospheric pressure at

sea level in SI units is 101 325 pascals.

atom The smallest part of an element that can exist. Atoms consist of a small dense nucleus of protons and neutrons surrounded by moving electrons. The number of electrons equals the number of protons so the overall charge is zero. The electrons may be thought of as moving in circular or elliptical orbits (*see* Bohr theory) or, more accurately, in regions of space around the nucleus (*see* orbital).

The *electronic structure* of an atom refers to the way in which the electrons are arranged about the nucleus, and in particular the *energy levels that they occupy. Each electron can be characterized by a set of four quantum numbers, as follows:

(1) The *principal quantum number n* gives the main energy level and has values 1, 2, 3, etc. (the higher the number, the further the electron from the nucleus). Traditionally, these levels, or the orbits corresponding to them, are referred to as *shells* and given letters K, L, M, etc. The K-shell is the one nearest the nucleus.

(2) The *orbital quantum number l*, which governs the angular momentum of the electron. The possible values of l are $(n - 1)$, $(n - 2)$, . . . , 1, 0. Thus, in the first shell ($n = 1$) the electrons can only have angular momentum zero ($l = 0$). In the second shell ($n = 2$), the values of l can be 1 or 0, giving rise to two *subshells* of slightly different energy. In the third shell ($n = 3$) there are three subshells, with $l = 2$, 1, or 0. The subshells are denoted by letters s ($l = 0$), p ($l = 1$), d ($l = 2$), f ($l = 3$). The orbital quantum number is sometimes called the *azimuthal quantum number*.

(3) The *magnetic quantum number m*, which governs the energies of electrons in an external magnetic field. This can take values of $+l$, $+(l - 1)$, . . . , 1, 0, -1, . . . , $-(l - 1)$, $-l$. In an s-subshell (i.e. $l = 0$) the value of m = 0. In a p-subshell ($l = 1$), m can have values +1, 0, and –1; i.e. there are three p-orbitals in the p-subshell, usually designated p_x, p_y, and p_z. Under normal circumstances, these all have the same energy level.

(4) The *spin quantum number* m_s, which gives the spin of the individual electrons and can have the values $+\frac{1}{2}$ or $-\frac{1}{2}$.

According to the *Pauli exclusion principle, no two electrons in the atom can have the same set of quantum numbers. The numbers define the *quantum state* of the electron, and explain how the electronic structures of atoms occur.

atomic bomb *See* nuclear weapons.

atomic clock An apparatus for measuring or standardizing time that is based on periodic phenomena within atoms or molecules. *See* ammonia clock; caesium clock.

atomic energy *See* nuclear energy.

atomic force microscope (AFM) A type of microscope in which a small probe, consisting of a tiny chip of diamond, is held on a spring-loaded cantilever in contact with the surface of the sample. The probe is moved slowly across the surface and the tracking force between the tip and the surface is monitored. The probe is raised and lowered so as to keep this force constant, and a profile of the surface is produced. Scanning the probe over the sample gives a computer-generated contour map of the surface. The instrument is similar to the *scanning tunnelling microscope, but uses mechanical forces rather than electrical signals. It can resolve individual molecules and, unlike the scanning tunnelling microscope, can be used with nonconducting samples, such as biological specimens.

atomic mass unit (a.m.u.) A unit of mass used to express *relative atomic masses. It is 1/12 of the mass of an atom of the isotope carbon–12 and is equal to $1.660\,33 \times 10^{-27}$ kg. This

unit superseded both the physical and chemical mass units based on oxygen–16 and is sometimes called the *unified mass unit* or the *dalton*.

atomic number (proton number) Symbol *Z*. The number of protons in the nucleus of an atom. The atomic number is equal to the number of electrons orbiting the nucleus in a neutral atom.

atomic orbital *See* orbital.

atomic pile An early form of *nuclear reactor using graphite as a *moderator.

atomic volume The relative atomic mass of an element divided by its density.

atomic weight *See* relative atomic mass.

attenuation 1. A loss of intensity suffered by sound, radiation, etc., as it passes through a medium. It may be caused by absorption or scattering. **2.** The drop in voltage or current experienced by a signal as it passes through a circuit.

atto- Symbol a. A prefix used in the metric system to denote 10^{-18}. For example, 10^{-18} second = 1 attosecond (as).

attractor The set of points in *phase space to which the representative point of a dissipative system (i.e. one with internal friction) tends as the system evolves. The attractor can be: a single point; a closed curve (a *limit cycle*), which describes a system with periodic behaviour; or a *fractal (or *strange attractor*), in which case the system exhibits *chaos.

AU *See* astronomical unit.

audibility The limits of audibility of the human ear are between about 20 hertz (a low rumble) and 20 000 hertz (a shrill whistle). With increased age the upper limit falls quite considerably.

audiofrequency A frequency that is audible to the human ear. *See* audibility.

audiometer An instrument that generates a sound of known frequency and intensity in order to measure an individual's hearing ability.

Auger effect The ejection of an electron from an atom without the emission of an X- or gamma-ray photon, as a result of the de-excitation of an excited electron within the atom. This type of transition occurs in the X-ray region of the emission spectrum. The kinetic energy of the ejected electron, called an *Auger electron*, is equal to the energy of the corresponding X-ray photon minus the binding energy of the Auger electron. The effect was discovered by Pierre Auger (1899–   ) in 1925.

aurora The luminous phenomena seen in the night sky in high latitudes, occurring most frequently near the earth's geomagnetic poles. The displays of aurora appear as coloured arcs, rays, bands, streamers, and curtains, usually green or red. The aurora is caused by the interaction of the atoms (mainly atomic oxygen) and molecules in the upper atmosphere (above about 100 km) with charged particles streaming from the sun, attracted to the auroral regions by the earth's magnetic field. The aurora is known as the *aurora borealis* (or northern lights) in the northern hemisphere and as the *aurora australis* (or southern lights) in the southern hemisphere.

austenite *See* steel.

autoclave A strong steel vessel used for carrying out chemical reactions, sterilizations, etc., at high temperature and pressure.

autoradiography An experimental technique in which a radioactive specimen is placed in contact with (or close to) a photographic plate, so as

to produce a record of the distribution of radioactivity in the specimen. The film is darkened by the ionizing radiation from radioactive parts of the sample. Autoradiography has a number of applications, particularly in the study of living tissues and cells.

avalanche A shower of ionized particles created by a single *ionization as a result of secondary ionizations caused by the original electron and ion being accelerated in an electric field. Each ionization leads to the formation of more electrons and ions, which themselves cause further ionizations. Such avalanches occur in a *Geiger counter.

average (mean) 1. The *arithmetic average* of a set of n numbers is the sum of the numbers divided by n. **2.** The *geometric average* of a set of n numbers is the nth root of their product. *See also* root-mean-square value.

Avogadro constant Symbol N_A or L. The number of atoms or molecules in one *mole of substance. It has the value $6.022\,1367(36) \times 10^{23}$. Formerly it was called *Avogadro's number*.

Avogadro's law Equal volumes of all gases contain equal numbers of molecules at the same pressure and temperature. The law, often called *Avogadro's hypothesis*, is true only for ideal gases. It was first proposed in 1811 by Count Amadeo Avogadro (1776–1856).

axion A hypothetical elementary particle postulated to explain why there is no observed CP violation (*see* CP invariance) in the strong interaction (*see* fundamental interactions). Axions have not been detected experimentally, although it has been possible to put limits on their mass and other properties from the effects that they would have on some astrophysical phenomena (e.g. the cooling of stars). It has also been suggested that they may account for some or all of the *missing matter in the universe.

axis 1. One of a set of reference lines used to locate points on a graph or in a coordinate system. *See* Cartesian coordinates; polar coordinates. **2.** A line about which a figure, curve, or body is symmetrical (*axis of symmetry*) or about which it rotates (*axis of rotation*).

azeotrope (azeotropic mixture; constant-boiling mixture) A mixture of two liquids that boils at constant composition; i.e. the composition of the vapour is the same as that of the liquid. Azeotropes occur because of deviations in Raoult's law leading to a maximum or minimum in the *boiling-point–composition diagram. When the mixture is boiled, the vapour initially has a higher proportion of one component than is present in the liquid, so the proportion of this in the liquid falls with time. Eventually, the maximum and minimum point is reached, at which the two liquids distil together without change in composition. The composition of an azeotrope depends on the pressure.

azimuth *See* polar coordinates.

azimuthal quantum number *See* atom.

B

Babbit metal Any of a group of related alloys used for making bearings. They consist of tin containing antimony (about 10%) and copper (1–2%), and often lead. The original alloy was invented in 1839 by the US inventor Isaac Babbit (1799–1862).

Babo's law The vapour pressure of a liquid is decreased when a solute is added, the amount of the decrease being proportional to the amount of solute dissolved. The law was discovered in 1847 by the German

chemist Lambert Babo (1818–99). *See also* Raoult's law.

back e.m.f. An electromotive force that opposes the main current flow in a circuit. For example, when the coils of the armature in an electric motor are rotated a back e.m.f is generated in these coils by their interaction with the field . magnet (*see* inductance). Also, in an electric cell, *polarization causes a back e.m.f. to be set up, in this case by chemical means.

background radiation Low intensity *ionizing radiation present on the surface of the earth and in the atmosphere as a result of *cosmic radiation and the presence of radioisotopes in the earth's rocks, soil, and atmosphere. The radioisotopes are either natural or the result of nuclear fallout or waste gas from power stations. Background counts must be taken into account when measuring the radiation produced by a specified source. *See also* microwave background radiation.

balance An accurate weighing device. The simple *beam balance* consists of two pans suspended from a centrally pivoted beam. Known masses are placed on one pan and the substance or body to be weighed is placed in the other. When the beam is exactly horizontal the two masses are equal. An accurate laboratory balance weighs to the nearest hundredth of a milligram. Specially designed balances can be accurate to a millionth of a milligram. More modern *substitution balances* use the substitution principle. In this calibrated weights are removed from the single lever arm to bring the single pan suspended from it into equilibrium with a fixed counter weight. The substitution balance is more accurate than the two-pan device and enables weighing to be carried out more rapidly. In automatic electronic balances, mass is determined not by mechanical deflection but by electronically controlled

compensation of an electric force. A scanner monitors the displacement of the pan support generating a current proportional to the displacement. This current flows through a coil forcing the pan support to return to its original position by means of a magnetic force. The signal generated enables the mass to be read from a digital display. The mass of the empty container can be stored in the balance's computer memory and automatically deducted from the mass of the container plus its contents. *See also* spring balance.

ballistic galvanometer A moving-coil *galvanometer designed for measuring charge by detecting a surge of current. It has a heavy coil with minimal damping. When a surge of current is passed through the coil, the initial maximum deflection (the 'throw') is proportional to the total charge that has passed.

ballistic pendulum A device used to measure the velocity of a projectile, such as a bullet. A large mass of relatively soft material is suspended from a horizontal bar and the angle through which this mass is displaced when it is struck by the projectile in flight enables the momentum and hence the velocity of the projectile to be calculated by successive application of the laws of conservation of linear momentum and of energy.

ballistics The study of the flight of projectiles, especially those that have a parabolic flight path from one point on the earth's surface to another.

Balmer series *See* hydrogen spectrum.

band spectrum *See* spectrum.

band theory *See* energy bands.

bandwidth The frequency range over which a radio signal of specified frequency spreads. For example, in a *modulation system it is the range of frequencies occupied by the modulating signal on either side of the carrier

wave. In an amplifier, it is the range of frequencies over which the power amplification falls within a specified fraction of the maximum value. In an aerial it is the range of frequencies that an aerial system can handle without mismatch.

bar A c.g.s. unit of pressure equal to 10^6 dynes per square centimetre or 10^5 pascals (approximately 750 mmHg or 0.987 atmosphere). The *millibar* (100 Pa) is commonly used in meteorology.

Barkhausen effect The magnetization of a ferromagnetic substance by an increasing magnetic field takes place in discontinuous steps rather than continuously. The effect results from the orientation of magnetic domains (*see* magnetism). It was first observed by H. Barkhausen (1881–1956) in 1919.

barn A unit of area sometimes used to measure *cross sections in nuclear interactions involving incident particles. It is equal to 10^{-28} square metre. The name comes from the phrase 'side of a barn' (something easy to hit).

barograph A meteorological instrument that records on paper variations in atmospheric pressure over a period. It often consists of an aneroid barometer operating a pen that rests lightly on a rotating drum to which the recording paper is attached.

barometer A device for measuring *atmospheric pressure. The *mercury barometer* in its simplest form consists of a glass tube about 80 cm long sealed at one end and filled with mercury. The tube is then inverted and the open end is submerged in a reservoir of mercury; the mercury column is held up by the pressure of the atmosphere acting on the surface of mercury in the reservoir. This type of device was invented by the Italian scientist Evangelista Torricelli (1608–47), who first noticed the variation in

height from day to day, and constructed a barometer in 1644.

In such a device, the force exerted by the atmosphere balanced the weight of the mercury column. If the height of the column is h and the cross-sectional area of the tube is A, then the volume of the mercury in the column is hA and its weight is $hA\rho$, where ρ is the density of mercury. The force is thus $hA\rho g$, where g is the acceleration of free fall and the pressure exerted is this force divided by the area of the tube; i.e. $h\rho g$. Note that the height of the mercury is independent of the diameter of the tube. At standard atmospheric pressure the column is 760 mm high. The pressure is then expressed as 760 mmHg (101 325 pascals).

Mercury barometers of this type, with a reservoir of mercury, are known as *cistern barometers*. A common type is the *Fortin barometer*, in which the mercury is held in a leather bag so that the level in the reservoir can be adjusted. The height is read from a scale along the side of the tube in conjunction with a vernier scale that can be moved up and down. Corrections are made for temperature.

The second main type of barometer is the *aneroid barometer*, in which the cumbersome mercury column is replaced by a metal box with a thin corrugated lid. The air is removed from the box and the lid is supported by a spring. Variations in atmospheric pressure cause the lid to move against the spring. This movement is magnified by a system of delicate levers and made to move a needle around a scale. The aneroid barometer is less accurate than the mercury type but much more robust and convenient, hence its use in *altimeters.

barycentre The *centre of mass of a system.

barye A c.g.s. unit of pressure equal to one dyne per square centimetre (0.1 pascal).

17

baryon

baryon A *hadron with half-integral spin. Nucleons comprise a subclass of baryons. According to currently accepted theory, baryons are made up of three *quarks (*antibaryons* are made up of three antiquarks) held together by gluons (*see* quantum chromodynamics). Baryons possess a quantum number, called the *baryon number*, which is +1 for baryons, −1 for antibaryons, and 0 for all other particles. Baryon number has always appeared to have been conserved experimentally, but *grand unified theories postulate interactions at very high energies that allow it not to be conserved. *See* proton decay.

base 1. (in mathematics) **a.** The number of different symbols in a number system. In the decimal system the base is 10; in *binary notation it is 2. **b.** The number that when raised to a certain power has a *logarithm equal to that power. For example if 10 is raised to the power of 3 it is equal to 1000; 3 is then the (common) logarithm of 1000 to the base 10. In natural or Napierian logarithms the base is e. To change the base from common to natural logarithms the formula used is: $\log_{10}y = \log_e y \times \log_{10}e = 0.43429\log_e y$.

2. (in electronics) *See* transistor.

base unit A unit that is defined arbitrarily rather than being defined by simple combinations of other units. For example, the ampere is a base unit in the SI system defined in terms of the force produced between two current-carrying conductors, whereas the coulomb is a *derived unit*, defined as the quantity of charge transferred by one ampere in one second.

basic-oxygen process (BOP process) A high-speed method of making high-grade steel. It originated in the *Linnz–Donnewitz* (*L–D*) *process*. Molten pig iron and scrap are charged into a tilting furnace, similar to the Bessemer furnace except that it has no tuyeres. The charge is con-verted to steel by blowing high-pressure oxygen onto the surface of the metal through a water-cooled lance. The excess heat produced enables up to 30% of scrap to be incorporated into the charge. The process has largely replaced the Bessemer and open-hearth processes.

battery A number of electric cells joined together. The common car battery, or *accumulator, usually consists of six secondary cells connected in series to give a total e.m.f. of 12 volts. A torch battery is usually a dry version of the *Leclanché primary cell, two of which are often connected in series. Batteries may also have cells connected in parallel, in which case they have the same e.m.f. as a single cell, but their capacity is increased, i.e. they will provide more total charge. The capacity of a battery is usually specified in ampere-hours, the ability to supply 1 A for 1 hr, or the equivalent.

BCS theory *See* superconductivity.

beam A group of rays moving in an organized manner. It may consist of particles (e.g. an electron beam) or of electromagnetic radiation (e.g. a radar beam).

beam balance *See* balance.

beam hole A hole through the shielding of a *nuclear reactor to enable a beam of neutrons or other particles to escape for experimental purposes.

beats A periodic increase and decrease in loudness heard when two notes of slightly different frequency are sounded at the same time. If a note of frequency n is heard at the same time as a note of frequency m, the resulting note will have a frequency of about $(n + m)/2$. However the amplitude of this note will vary from the difference to the sum of the amplitudes of the m and n notes and the frequency (called the *beat frequency*) of this variation will be (m −

18

n). The beating sound produced occurs as the waves successively reinforce and oppose each other as they move in and out of phase. *See also* interference.

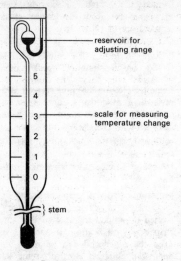

reservoir for adjusting range

scale for measuring temperature change

} stem

Beckmann thermometer

Beckmann thermometer A thermometer for measuring small changes of temperature. It consists of a mercury-in-glass thermometer with a scale covering only 5 or 6°C calibrated in hundredths of a degree. It has two mercury bulbs, the range of temperature to be measured is varied by running mercury from the upper bulb into the larger lower bulb (see illustration). It is used particularly for measuring *depression of freezing point or *elevation of boiling point of liquids when solute is added, in order to find relative molecular masses. The instrument was invented by the German chemist E. O. Beckmann (1853–1923).

becquerel Symbol Bq. The SI unit of activity (*see* radiation units). The unit is named after the discoverer of radioactivity A. H. Becquerel (1852–1908).

bel Ten *decibels.

bell metal A type of *bronze used in casting bells. It consists of 60–85% copper alloyed with tin, often with some zinc and lead included.

bending moment (about any point or section of a horizontal beam under load) The algebraic sum of the *moments of all the vertical forces to either side of that point or section.

berkelium Symbol Bk. A radioactive metallic transuranic element belonging to the actinoids; a.n. 97; mass number of the most stable isotope 247 (half-life 1.4×10^3 years); r.d. (calculated) 14. There are eight known isotopes. It was first produced by G. T. Seaborg and associates in 1949 by bombarding americium–241 with alpha particles.

Bernoulli theorem At any point in a pipe through which a fluid is flowing the sum of the pressure energy, the kinetic energy, and the potential energy of a given mass of the fluid is constant. This is equivalent to a statement of the law of the conservation of energy. The law was published in 1738 by the Swiss physicist Daniel Bernoulli (1700–82).

Bessemer process A process for converting *pig iron from a *blast furnace into *steel. The molten pig iron is loaded into a refractory-lined tilting furnace (*Bessemer converter*) at about 1250°C. Air is blown into the furnace from the base and *spiegel is added to introduce the correct amount of carbon. Impurities (especially silicon, phosphorus, and manganese) are removed by the converter lining to form a slag. Finally the furnace is tilted so that the molten steel can be poured off. In the modern VLN (very low nitrogen) version of this process, oxygen and steam are blown into the furnace in place of air to minimize the absorption of nitrogen from the air by the steel. The process is named after the British engineer Sir Henry Bessemer (1813–

98), who announced it in 1856. *See also* basic-oxygen process.

beta decay A type of weak interaction in which an unstable atomic nucleus changes into a nucleus of the same mass number but different proton number. The change involves the conversion of a neutron into a proton with the emission of an electron and an electron antineutrino ($n \rightarrow p + e^- + \bar{\nu}_e$) or of a proton into a neutron with the emission of a positron and an electron neutrino ($p \rightarrow n + e^+ + \nu_e$). An example is the decay of carbon–14:

$$^{14}_{6}C \rightarrow ^{14}_{7}N + e^- + \bar{\nu}_e$$

The electrons or positrons emitted are called *beta particles* and streams of beta particles are known as *beta radiation*.

beta-iron A nonmagnetic allotrope of iron that exists between 768°C and 900°C.

beta particle *See* beta decay.

betatron A particle *accelerator for producing high-energy electrons (up to 340 MeV) for research purposes, including the production of high-energy X-rays. The electrons are accelerated by electromagnetic induction in a doughnut-shaped (toroidal) ring from which the air has been removed. This type of accelerator was first developed by D. W. Kerst (1911–) in 1939; the largest such machine, at the University of Illinois, was completed in 1950.

Bevatron A colloquial name for the proton *synchrotron at the Berkeley campus of the University of California. It produces energies up to 6 GeV.

biaxial crystal *See* double refraction.

biconcave *See* concave.

big-bang theory The cosmological theory that all the matter and energy in the universe originated from a state of enormous density and temperature that exploded at a finite moment in the past. This theory successfully explains the *expansion of the universe; the observed *microwave background radiation, characteristic of *black-body radiation at a temperature of 3 K; and the observed abundance of helium in the universe, formed in the first 100 seconds after the explosion from deuterium at a temperature of 10^9 K. It is now generally considered to be more satisfactory than the rival *steady-state theory. The big-bang theory was first developed in 1927 by A. G. E. Lemaitre (1894–1966) and revived and revised in 1946 by George Gamow (1904–68). Several variants of it have been proposed. *See* early universe.

billion 1. (in the UK and Germany) One million million, 10^{12}. **2.** (in the USA and France) One thousand million, 10^9.

bimetallic strip A strip consisting of two metals of different *expansivity riveted or welded together so that the strip bends on heating. If one end is fixed the other end can be made to open and close an electric circuit, as in a *thermostat.

bimorph cell A device consisting of two plates of piezoelectric material, such as Rochelle salt, joined together so that one expands on the application of a potential difference and the other contracts. The cell thus bends as a result of the applied p.d. The opposite effect is also used, in which the mechanical bending of the cell is used to produce a p.d., as in the crystal microphone and some types of record-player pickups.

binary notation A number system using only two different digits, 0 and 1. Instead of units, tens, hundreds, etc., as used in the decimal system, digits in the binary notation represent units, twos, fours, eights, etc. Thus one in decimal notation is represented by 0001, two by 0010, four by 0100, and eight by 1000. Because 0 and 1 can be made to correspond to off and on conditions in an electric circuit,

the binary notation is widely used in computers.

binary stars A pair of stars revolving about a common centre of mass. In a *visual binary* the stars are far enough apart to be seen separately by an optical telescope. In an *astrometric binary* one component is too faint to be seen and its presence is inferred from the perturbations in the motion of the other. In a *spectrosopic binary* the stars cannot usually be resolved by a telescope, but the motions can be detected by different Doppler shifts in the spectrum at each side of the binary, according to whether the components are approaching or receding from the observer.

binding energy The energy equivalent to the *mass defect when nucleons bind together to form an atomic nucleus. When a nucleus is formed some energy is released by the nucleons, since they are entering a more stable lower-energy state. Therefore the energy of a nucleus consists of the energy equivalent of the mass of its individual nucleons minus the binding energy. The binding energy per nucleon plotted against the mass number provides a useful graph showing that up to a mass number of 50–60, the binding energy per nucleon increases rapidly, thereafter it falls slowly. Energy is released both by fission of heavy elements and by fusion of light elements because both processes entail a rearrangement of nuclei in the lower part of the graph to form nuclei in the higher part of the graph.

binoculars Any optical instrument designed to serve both the observer's eyes at once. *Binocular field glasses* consist of two refracting astronomical *telescopes inside each of which is a pair of prisms to increase the effective length and produce an upright image. Simpler binoculars, such as *opera glasses*, consist of two Galilean telescopes which produce upright images without prisms. Commonly, binoculars are specified by a pair of numbers, such as 10×50. The first number indicates the angular *magnification produced. The second is the diameter of the objective lens in millimetres, and indicates the amount of light gathered by the instrument. *Binocular microscopes* are used in biology and surgery to enable the observer to obtain a stereoscopic view of small objects or parts.

binocular vision The ability, found only in animals with forward-facing eyes, to produce a focused image of the same object simultaneously on the retinas of both eyes. This permits three-dimensional vision and contributes to distance judgment.

binomial theorem (binomial expansion) A rule for the expansion of a binomial expression (expression consisting of the sum of two variables raised to a given power). The general binomial expression $(x + y)^n$ expands to:

$$x^n + nx^{n-1}y + [n(n - 1)/2!]x^{n-2}y^2 + \ldots y^n.$$

bioenergetics The study of the flow and the transformations of energy that occur in living organisms. Typically, the amount of energy that an organism takes in (from food or sunlight) is measured and divided into the amount used for growth of new tissues; that lost through death, wastes, and (in plants) transpiration; and that lost to the environment as heat (through respiration).

bioluminescence The emission of light without heat (*see* luminescence) by living organisms. The phenomenon occurs in glow-worms and fireflies, bacteria and fungi, and in many deep-sea fish (among others); in animals it may serve as a means of protection (e.g. by disguising the shape of a fish) or species recognition or it may provide mating signals. The light is produced during the oxidation of a compound called *luciferin* (the

composition of which varies according to the species), the reaction being catalysed by an enzyme, *luciferase*. Bioluminescence may be continuous (e.g. in bacteria) or intermittent (e.g. in fireflies).

biophysics *See* physics.

biprism A glass prism with an obtuse angle that functions as two acute-angle prisms placed base-to-base. A double image of a single object is thus formed; the device was used by Fresnel to produce two coherent beams for interference experiments.

birefringence *See* double refraction.

bistable circuit *See* flip-flop.

bit (binary digit) Either of the digits 0 or 1 as used in the *binary notation. Bits are therefore the basic unit of information in a computer system.

Bitter pattern A microscopic pattern that forms on the surface of a ferromagnetic material that has been painted with a colloidal suspension of small iron particles. The patterns outline the boundaries of the magnetic domains (*see* magnetism). They were first observed by F. Bitter in 1931.

black body A hypothetical body that absorbs all the radiation falling on it. It thus has an *absorptance and an *emissivity of 1. While a true black body is an imaginary concept, a small hole in the wall of an enclosure at uniform temperature is the nearest approach that can be made to it in practice.

Black-body radiation is the electromagnetic radiation emitted by a black body. It extends over the whole range of wavelengths and the distribution of energy over this range has a characteristic form with a maximum at a certain wavelength. The position of the maximum depends on temperature, moving to shorter wavelengths with increasing temperature. *See* Stefan's law; Wien's displacement law.

black hole An object in space that has collapsed under its own gravitational forces to such an extent that its *escape velocity is equal to the speed of light. Black holes are believed to be formed in the gravitational collapse of massive stars at the ends of their lives (*see* stellar evolution; supernova). If the mass of an evolved stellar core is greater than the Chandrasekhar limit for neutron stars then neutron degeneracy pressure is unable to prevent contraction until the gravitational field is sufficiently strong to prevent the escape of electromagnetic radiation. The boundary of the black hole, which is known as the *event horizon*, is the surface in space at which the gravitational field reaches this critical value. Events occurring within this horizon (i.e. in the interior of the black hole) cannot be observed from outside.

The theoretical study of black holes involves the use of general *relativity. It has been shown that a black hole can be characterized uniquely by just three properties: its mass, angular momentum, and electrical charge (this is known as the no-hair theorem). Mathematical expressions have been derived for describing black holes; these are the *Schwarzschild solution* (uncharged nonrotating hole), the *Reissner–Nordstrøm solution* (charged nonrotating hole), the *Kerr solution* (uncharged rotating hole), and the *Kerr–Newman solution* (charged rotating hole).

The ultimate fate of matter inside the black hole's event horizon is as yet unknown. General relativity predicts that at the centre of the hole there is a *singularity*, a point at which the density becomes infinite and the presently understood laws of physics break down. It is possible that a successful quantum theory of gravity could resolve this problem. However, since any singularity is hidden within the event horizon, it cannot influence the outside universe, so the normal

laws of physics, including general relativity, can be used to describe processes outside the black hole.

Observational evidence of objects thought to be black holes comes from their effect on surrounding matter. Thus, if a black hole is part of a binary system with another star it will attract and capture matter from this star. The material leaving the star first forms a rotating *accretion disc* around the black hole, in which the matter becomes compressed and heated to such an extent that it emits X-rays. In the constellation Cygnus there is an X-ray source, Cygnus X-1, which consists of a supergiant star revolving around a small invisible companion with a mass of about ten times that of the sun, and therefore well above the Chandrasekhar limit. The companion is thought to be a black hole. Black holes have also been postulated as the power sources of *quasars and as possible generators of *gravitational waves.

Theoreticians have also postulated the existence of 'mini' black holes (with masses of about 10^{12} kilogram and radii about 10^{-15} metres). Such entities might have been formed shortly after the big bang when the universe was created. Quantum-mechanical effects are important for mini black holes, which emit Hawking radiation (*see* Hawking process). *See also* Schwarzschild radius.

blast furnace A furnace for smelting iron ores, such as haematite (Fe_2O_3) or magnetite (Fe_3O_4), to make *pig iron. The furnace is a tall refractory-lined cylindrical structure that is charged at the top with the dressed ore (*see* beneficiation), coke, and a flux, usually limestone. The conversion of the iron oxides to metallic iron is a reduction process in which carbon monoxide and hydrogen are the reducing agents. The overall reaction can be summarized thus:

$$Fe_3O_4 + 2CO + 2H_2 \rightarrow 3Fe +$$

$$2CO_2 + 2H_2O$$

The CO is obtained within the furnace by blasting the coke with hot air from a ring of tuyeres about two-thirds of the way down the furnace. The reaction producing the CO is:

$$2C + O_2 \rightarrow 2CO$$

In most blast furnaces hydrocarbons (oil, gas, tar, etc.) are added to the blast to provide a source of hydrogen. In the modern *direct-reduction process* the CO and H_2 may be produced separately so that the reduction process can proceed at a lower temperature. The pig iron produced by a blast furnace contains about 4% carbon and further refining is usually required to produce steel or cast iron.

body-centred cubic (b.c.c.) *See* cubic crystal.

Bohr theory The theory published in 1913 by the Danish physicist Niels Bohr (1885–1962) to explain the line spectrum of hydrogen. He assumed that a single electron of mass m travelled in a circular orbit of radius r, at a velocity v, around a positively charged nucleus. The *angular momentum of the electron would then be mvr. Bohr proposed that electrons could only occupy orbits in which this angular momentum had certain fixed values, $h/2\pi$, $2h/2\pi$, $3h/2\pi$, ... $nh/2\pi$, where h is the Planck constant. This means that the angular momentum is quantized, i.e. can only have certain values, each of which is a multiple of n. Each permitted value of n is associated with an orbit of different radius and Bohr assumed that when the atom emitted or absorbed radiation of frequency v, the electron jumped from one orbit to another; the energy emitted or absorbed by each jump is equal to hv. This theory gave good results in predicting the lines observed in the spectrum of the hydrogen atom and simple ions such as He^+, Li^{2+}, etc. The idea of quantized values of angular momentum was later explained by

the wave nature of the electron. Each orbit has to have a whole number of wavelengths around it; i.e. $n\lambda = 2\pi r$, where λ is the wavelength and n a whole number. The wavelength of a particle is given by h/mv, so $nh/mv = 2\pi r$, which leads to $mvr = nh/2\pi$. Modern atomic theory does not allow subatomic particles to be treated in the same way as large objects, and Bohr's reasoning is somewhat discredited. However, the idea of quantized angular momentum has been retained.

boiling point (b.p.) The temperature at which the saturated vapour pressure of a liquid equals the external atmospheric pressure. As a consequence, bubbles form in the liquid and the temperature remains constant until all the liquid has evaporated. As the boiling point of a liquid depends on the external atmospheric pressure, boiling points are usually quoted for standard atmospheric pressure (760 mmHg = 101 325 Pa).

boiling-point–composition diagram A graph showing how the boiling point and vapour composition of a mixture of two liquids depends on the composition of the mixture. The abscissa shows the range of compositions from 100% A at one end to 100% B at the other. The diagram has two curves: the lower one gives the boiling points (at a fixed pressure) for the different compositions. The upper one is plotted by taking the composition of vapour at each temperature on the boiling-point curve. The two curves would coincide for an ideal mixture, but generally they are different because of deviations from Raoult's law. In some cases, they may show a maximum or minimum and coincide at some intermediate composition, explaining the formation of *azeotropes.

boiling-water reactor *See* nuclear reactor.

bolometer A sensitive instrument used to measure radiant heat. The original form consists of two elements, each comprising blackened platinum strips (about 10^{-3} mm thick) arranged in series on an insulated frame to form a zigzag. The two elements are connected into the adjacent arms of a *Wheatstone bridge; one element is exposed to the radiation, the other is shielded from it. The change in the resistance of the exposed element, as detected by the bridge galvanometer, enables the heat reaching it to be calculated.

Modern semiconductor bolometers are now common, in which the platinum is replaced by a strip of semiconductor: this has a much greater (though usually negative) *temperature coefficient of resistance, and makes the system more sensitive.

Boltzmann constant Symbol k or k_B. The ratio of the universal gas constant (R) to the Avogadro constant (N_A). It may be thought of therefore as the gas constant per molecule:

$$k = R/N_A = 1.380\,658(12) \times 10^{-23}\ \mathrm{J\,K^{-1}}$$

It is named after the Austrian physicist Ludwig Boltzmann (1844–1906).

bomb calorimeter An apparatus used for measuring heats of combustion (e.g. calorific values of fuels and foods). It consists of a strong container in which the sample is sealed with excess oxygen and ignited electrically. The heat of combustion at constant volume can be calculated from the resulting rise in temperature.

Boolean algebra A form of symbolic logic, devised by George Boole (1815–64) in the middle of the 19th century, which provides a mathematical procedure for manipulating logical relationships in symbolic form. For example in Boolean algebra $a + b$ means a or b, while ab means a and b. It makes use of *set theory and is extensively used by the designers of computers to enable the bits 0 and 1,

as used in the binary notation, to relate to the logical functions the computer needs in carrying out its calculations.

Born–Haber cycle A cycle of reactions used for calculating the lattice energies of ionic crystalline solids. For a compound MX, the lattice energy is the enthalpy of the reaction

$$M^+(g) + X^-(g) \rightarrow M^+X^-(s) \; \Delta H_L$$

The standard enthalpy of formation of the ionic solid is the enthalpy of the reaction

$$M(s) + \tfrac{1}{2}X_2(g) \rightarrow M^+X^-(s) \; \Delta H_f$$

The cycle involves equating this enthalpy (which can be measured) to the sum of the enthalpies of a number of steps proceeding from the elements to the ionic solid. The steps are:

(1) Atomization of the metal:
$$M(s) \rightarrow M(g) \; \Delta H_1$$
(2) Atomization of the nonmetal:
$$\tfrac{1}{2}X_2(g) \rightarrow X(g) \; \Delta H_2$$
(3) Ionization of the metal:
$$M(g) \rightarrow M^+(g) + e \; \Delta H_3$$
This is obtained from the ionization potential.
(4) Ionization of the nonmetal:
$$X(g) + e \rightarrow X^-(g) \; \Delta H_4$$
This is the electron affinity.
(5) Formation of the ionic solids:
$$M^+(g) + X^-(g) \rightarrow M^+X^-(s) \; \Delta H_L$$
Equating the enthalpies gives:
$$\Delta H_f = \Delta H_1 + \Delta H_2 + \Delta H_3 + \Delta H_4 + \Delta H_L$$
from which ΔH_L can be found. It is named after the German physicist Max Born (1882–1970) and the chemist Fritz Haber (1868–1934).

boron counter A *counter tube containing a *boron chamber*, used for counting slow neutrons. The boron chamber is lined with boron or a boron compound or is filled with the gas boron trifluoride (BF_3). As natural boron contains about 18% of the isotope boron–10, and as this isotope absorbs neutrons with the emission of an alpha particle, the chamber can be coupled with a scaler to count the alpha particles emitted when neutrons enter the chamber.

Bose condensation (Bose–Einstein condensation) A phenomenon occurring in a macroscopic system consisting of a large number of *bosons at a sufficiently low temperature, in which a significant fraction of the particles occupy a single quantum state of lowest energy (the ground state). Bose condensation can only take place for bosons whose total number is conserved in collisions. Because of the Pauli exclusion principle, it is impossible for two or more fermions to occupy the same quantum state, and so there is no analogous condensation phenomenon for such particles. Bose condensation is of fundamental importance in explaining the phenomenon of *superfluidity.

Bose–Einstein statistics *See* quantum statistics.

boson An *elementary particle (or bound state of an elementary particle, e.g. an atomic nucleus or an atom) with integral spin; i.e. a particle that conforms to Bose–Einstein statistics (*see* quantum statistics), from which it derives its name. *Compare* fermion.

boundary layer The thin layer of fluid formed around a solid body or surface relative to which the fluid is flowing. Adhesion between the molecules of the fluid and that of the body or surface causes the molecules of the fluid closest to the solid to be stationary relative to it. The transfer of heat or mass between a solid and a fluid flowing over it is largely controlled by the nature of the boundary layer.

Bourdon gauge A pressure gauge consisting essentially of a C-shaped or spiral tube with an oval cross section. One end of the tube is connected to the fluid whose pressure is to be measured and the other end is sealed. As the pressure inside the tube is increased, the oval tube tends to become circular and this causes the

tube to straighten. The movement of the end of the tube is transferred by a simple mechanism to a needle moving round a dial or to a digital display. With suitable design, Bourdon gauges can be used for high-pressure measurement and also for low pressures.

Boyle's law The volume (V) of a given mass of gas at a constant temperature is inversely proportional to its pressure (p), i.e. pV = constant. This is true only for an *ideal gas. This law was discovered in 1662 by the Irish physicist Robert Boyle (1627–91). On the continent of Europe it is known as *Mariotte's law* after E. Mariotte (1620–84), who discovered it independently in 1676. *See also* gas laws.

Brackett series *See* hydrogen spectrum.

Bragg's law When a beam of X-rays (wavelength λ) strikes a crystal surface in which the layers of atoms or ions are separated by a distance d, the maximum intensity of the reflected ray occurs when $\sin\theta = n\lambda/2d$, where θ (known as the *Bragg angle*) is the complement of the angle of incidence and n is an integer. The law enables the structure of many crystals to be determined. It was discovered in 1912 by Sir Lawrence Bragg (1890–1971).

brass A group of alloys consisting of copper and zinc. A typical yellow brass might contain about 67% copper and 33% zinc.

breakdown The sudden passage of a current through an insulator. The voltage at which this occurs is the *breakdown voltage*.

breaking stress *See* elasticity.

breeder reactor *See* nuclear reactor.

Bremsstrahlung (German: braking radiation) The X-rays emitted when a charged particle, especially a fast electron, is rapidly slowed down, as when it passes through the electric field around an atomic nucleus. The X-rays cover a whole continuous range of wavelengths down to a minimum value, which depends on the energy of the incident particles. Bremsstrahlung are produced by a metal target when it is bombarded by electrons. *See also* X-ray spectrum.

Brewster's law The extent of the polarization of light reflected from a transparent surface is a maximum when the reflected ray is at right angles to the refracted ray. The angle of incidence (and reflection) at which this maximum polarization occurs is called the *Brewster angle* or *polarizing angle*. For this angle i_B, the condition is that $\tan i_B = n$, where n is the refractive index of the transparent medium. The law was discovered in 1811 by the British physicist David Brewster (1781–1868).

Brinell hardness A scale for measuring the hardness of metals introduced around 1900 by the Swedish metallurgist J. A. Brinell (1849–1925). A small chromium-steel ball is pressed into the surface of the metal by a load of known weight. The ratio of the mass of the load in kilograms to the area of the depression formed in square millimetres is the *Brinell number*.

Britannia metal A silvery alloy consisting of 80–90% tin, 5–15% antimony, and sometimes small percentages of copper, lead, and zinc. It is used in bearings and some domestic articles.

British thermal unit (Btu) The Imperial unit of heat, being originally the heat required to raise the temperature of 1 lb of water by 1°F. 1 Btu is now defined as 1055.06 joules.

broken symmetry A situation in which the ground state of a many-body system or *vacuum state of a relativistic *quantum field theory has a lower symmetry than the Hamiltonian or Langrangian defining the system. Examples in solid-state physics include antiferromagnetism and super-

conductivity. In particle physics, the Weinberg–Salam model (*see* electroweak theory) is an important example of a relativistic quantum field theory with broken symmetry.

A result associated with broken symmetry is *Goldstone's theorem*. This states that a relativistic quantum field theory having continuous symmetry that is broken must include the existence of massless particles called *Goldstone bosons*. In many-body theory Goldstone bosons are *collective excitations. An exception to Goldstone's theorem is provided in the case of broken *gauge theories, such as the Weinberg–Salam model, in which the Goldstone bosons become massive bosons known as *Higgs bosons. In many-body theory, long-range forces provide the analogous exception to Goldstone's theorem, with the Higgs bosons being excitations with a nonzero gap.

bronze Any of a group of alloys of copper and tin, sometimes with lead and zinc present. The amount of tin varies from 1% to 30%. The alloy is hard and easily cast and extensively used in bearings, valves, and other machine parts. Various improved bronzes are produced by adding other elements; for instance, *phosphor bronzes* contain up to 1% phosphorus. In addition certain alloys of copper and metals other than tin are called bronzes – *aluminium bronze* is a mixture of copper and aluminium. Other special bronzes include *bell metal and *gun metal.

brown dwarf An astronomical object with a mass intermediate between the mass of a planet and that of a small star. The mass of a brown dwarf is large enough to generate energy by gravitational pressure, but not large enough to sustain nuclear fusion. The masses of brown dwarfs lie between a few times the mass of Jupiter and 80 times the mass of Jupiter. Brown dwarfs are faint objects; it has been suggested that they may contribute to the *missing mass of the universe.

Brownian movement The continuous random movement of microscopic solid particles (of about 1 micrometre in diameter) when suspended in a fluid medium. First observed by the botanist Robert Brown (1773–1858) in 1827 when studying pollen particles, it was originally thought to be the manifestation of some vital force. It was later recognized to be a consequence of bombardment of the particles by the continually moving molecules of the liquid. The smaller the particles the more extensive is the motion. The effect is also visible in particles of smoke suspended in a still gas.

brush An electrical contact to a moving commutator on a motor or generator. It is made of a specially prepared form of carbon and is kept in contact with the moving part by means of a spring.

brush discharge A luminous discharge from a conductor that takes the form of luminous branching threads that penetrate into the surrounding gas. It is a form of *corona and it occurs when the electric field near the surface of the conductor exceeds a certain value but is not sufficiently high for a spark to appear.

bubble chamber A device for detecting ionizing radiation. It consists of a chamber containing a liquid, often hydrogen, kept at slightly above its boiling point at its preliminary pressure. Immediately before the passage of the ionizing particles the pressure is reduced, and the particles then act as centres for the formation of bubbles, which can be photographed to obtain a record of the particles' tracks. The device was invented in 1952 by the US physicist D. A. Glaser (1926–). *Compare* cloud chamber.

bulk modulus *See* elastic modulus.

bumping Violent boiling of a liquid caused by superheating so that bubbles form at a pressure above atmospheric pressure. It can be prevented by putting pieces of porous pot in the liquid to enable bubbles of vapour to form at the normal boiling point.

Bunsen burner A laboratory gas burner having a vertical metal tube into which the gas is led, with a hole in the side of the base of the tube to admit air. The amount of air can be regulated by a sleeve on the tube. When no air is admitted the flame is luminous and smoky. With air, it has a faintly visible hot outer part (the oxidizing part) and an inner blue cone where combustion is incomplete (the cooler reducing part of the flame). The device is named after the German chemist Robert Bunsen (1811–99), who used a similar device (without a regulating sleeve) in 1855.

Bunsen cell A *primary cell consisting of a zinc cathode immersed in dilute sulphuric acid and a carbon anode immersed in concentrated nitric acid. The electrolytes are separated by a porous pot. The cell gives an e.m.f. of about 1.9 volts.

buoyancy The upward thrust on a body immersed in a fluid. This force is equal to the weight of the fluid displaced (*see* Archimedes' principle).

byte A subdivision of a *word in a computer, it usually consists of eight *bits.

C

cadmium cell *See* Weston cell.

caesium clock An *atomic clock that depends on the energy difference between two states of the caesium–133 nucleus when it is in a magnetic field. In one type, atoms of caesium–133 are irradiated with *radio-frequency radiation, whose frequency is chosen to correspond to the energy difference between the two states. Some caesium nuclei absorb this radiation and are excited to the higher state. These atoms are deflected by a further magnetic field, which causes them to hit a detector. A signal from this detector is fed back to the radio-frequency oscillator to prevent it drifting from the resonant frequency of 9 192 631 770 hertz. In this way the device is locked to this frequency with an accuracy better than 1 part in 10^{13}. The caesium clock is used in the *SI unit definition of the second.

calculus A series of mathematical techniques developed independently by Isaac Newton (1642–1727) and Gottfried Leibniz (1646–1716). *Differential calculus* treats a continuously varying quantity as if it consisted of an infinitely large number of infinitely small changes. For example, the velocity v of a body at a particular instant can be regarded as the infinitesimal distance, written ds, that it travels in the vanishingly small time interval, dt; the instantaneous velocity v is then ds/dt, which is called the *derivative* of s with respect to t. If s is a known function of t, v at any instant can be calculated by the process of *differentiation. The differential calculus is a powerful technique for solving many problems concerned with rate processes, maxima and minima, and similar problems.

Integral calculus is the opposite technique. For example, if the velocity of a body is a known function of time, the infinitesimal distance ds travelled in the brief instant dt is given by $ds = vdt$. The measurable distance s travelled between two instants t_1 and t_2 can then be found by a process of summation, called *integration, i.e.

$$s = \int_{t_1}^{t_2} vdt$$

The technique is used for finding areas and volumes and other problems involving the summation of infinitesimals.

californium Symbol Cf. A radioactive metallic transuranic element belonging to the actinoids; a.n. 98; mass number of the most stable isotope 251 (half-life about 700 years). Nine isotopes are known; californium–252 is an intense neutron source, which makes it useful in neutron *activation analysis and potentially useful as a radiation source in medicine. The element was first produced by G. T. Seaborg and associates in 1950.

caloric theory A former theory concerning the nature of heat, which was regarded as a weightless fluid (called *caloric*). It was unable to account for the fact that friction could produce an unlimited quantity of heat and it was abandoned when Joule showed that heat is a form of energy.

calorie The quantity of heat required to raise the temperature of 1 gram of water by 1°C (1 K). The calorie, a c.g.s. unit, is now largely replaced by the *joule, an *SI unit. 1 calorie = 4.186 8 joules.

Calorie (kilogram calorie; kilocalorie) 1000 calories. This unit is still in limited use in estimating the energy value of foods, but is obsolescent.

calorific value The heat per unit mass produced by complete combustion of a given substance. Calorific values are used to express the energy values of fuels; usually these are expressed in megajoules per kilogram ($MJ\,kg^{-1}$). They are also used to measure the energy content of foodstuffs; i.e. the energy produced when the food is oxidized in the body. The units used in this context are kilojoules per gram ($kJ\,g^{-1}$), although Calories (kilocalories) are often still used in nontechnical contexts. Calorific values are measured using a *bomb calorimeter.

calorimeter Any of various devices used to measure thermal properties such as *calorific value, *specific heat capacity, *specific latent heat, etc. *See* bomb calorimeter.

calx A metal oxide formed by heating an ore in air.

camera 1. An optical device for obtaining still photographs or for exposing cinematic film. It consists of a light-proof box with a lens at one end and a plate or film at the other. To make an exposure the shutter is opened and an image of the object to be photographed is formed on the light-sensitive film. The length of the exposure is determined by the intensity of light available, the film speed, and the *aperture of the lens. In the simpler cameras the shutter speed and aperture are controlled manually, but in automatic cameras the iris over the lens or the shutter is adjusted on the basis of information provided by a built-in *exposure meter. In ciné cameras the shutter automatically opens as the film comes to rest behind the lens for each frame; the film passes through the camera so that a set number (commonly 16, 18, or 24) of frames are exposed every second. **2.** The part of a television system that converts optical images into electronic signals. It consists of a lens system, which focuses the image to be televised on the photosensitive mosaic of the camera tube, causing localized discharge of those of its elements that are illuminated. This mosaic is scanned from behind by an electron beam so that the beam current is varied as it passes over areas of light and shade. The signal so picked up by the scanning beam is preamplified in the camera and passed to the transmitter with sound and synchronization signals. In *colour television three separate camera tubes are used, one for each *primary colour.

Canada balsam

Canada balsam A yellow-tinted resin used for mounting specimens in optical microscopy. It has similar optical properties to glass.

canal rays Streams of positive ions produced in a *discharge tube by boring holes (canals) in the cathode. The positive ions attracted to the cathode pass through the holes and emerge on the other side as positive rays.

candela Symbol Cd. The *SI unit of luminous intensity equal to the luminous intensity in a given direction of a source that emits monochromatic radiation of frequency 540×10^{12} Hz and has a radiant intensity in that direction of 1/683 watt per steradian.

candle power Luminous intensity as formerly expressed in terms of the international candle but now expressed in candela.

capacitance The property of a conductor or system of conductors that describes its ability to store electric charge. The capacitance (C) is given by Q/V, where Q is stored charge on one conductor and V the potential difference between the two conductors (or between a single conductor and earth); it is measured in farads.
An isolated sphere has a capacitance of $4\pi\varepsilon r$, where r is the radius and ε the *permittivity of the medium surrounding it. Capacitance is more commonly applied to systems of conductors (or semiconductors) separated by insulators (*see* capacitor).

capacitor An arrangement of conductors separated by an insulator (dielectric) used to store charge or introduce *reactance into an alternating-current circuit. The earliest form was the *Leyden jar. Capacitors used as circuit elements have two conducting plates separated by the dielectric. The dielectric may be air, paper impregnated with oil or wax, plastic film, or ceramic. The simplest form has two parallel rectangular conducting plates (area A) separated by a dielectric (thickness d, permittivity ε). The capacitance of such a capacitor is $A\varepsilon/d$. *Electrolytic capacitors* are devices in which the dielectric is formed by electrolysis; for example, it may be an oxide film on one of the electrodes. In these the electrolysis commonly continues during the charging process and is reversed during discharge.

capacitor microphone A microphone consisting of a *capacitor with a steady voltage applied across its parallel plates. One plate is fixed, the other is a thin diaphragm that is moved by the pressure of the sound waves. The movements of the diaphragm cause a variation in the spacing and therefore in the *capacitance of the device. This variation in capacitance is, in turn, reflected in a similar variation in the charge carried by each plate. The consequent current to and from one plate is carried by a resistor, the varying potential difference across which constitutes the device's output signal. It was formerly known as a *condenser microphone*.

capillarity *See* surface tension.

capillary A tube of small diameter, such as the narrowest type of blood vessel in the vertebrate circulatory system.

capture Any of various processes in which a system of particles absorbs an extra particle. There are several examples in atomic and nuclear physics. For instance, a positive ion may capture an electron to give a neutral atom or molecule. Similarly, a neutral atom or molecule capturing an electron becomes a negative ion. An atomic nucleus may capture a neutron to produce a different (often unstable) nucleus. Another type of nuclear capture is the process in which the nucleus of an atom absorbs an electron from the innermost orbit (the K shell) to transform into a different nucleus. In this process (called *K capture*) the atom is left in an

excited state and generally decays by emission of an X-ray photon.

Radiative capture is any such process in which the capture results in an excited state that decays by emission of photons. A common example is neutron capture to yield an excited nucleus, which decays by emission of a gamma ray.

carat 1. A measure of fineness (purity) of gold. Pure gold is described as 24-carat gold. 14-carat gold contains 14 parts in 24 of gold, the remainder usually being copper. **2.** A unit of mass equal to 0.200 gram, used to measure the masses of diamonds and other gemstones.

carbon cycle A series of nuclear reactions in which four hydrogen nuclei combine to form a helium nucleus with the liberation of energy, two positrons, and two neutrinos. The process is believed to be the source of energy in many stars and to take place in six stages. In this series carbon–12 acts as if it were a catalyst, being reformed at the end of the series:

$$^{12}_{6}C + ^{1}_{1}H \rightarrow ^{13}_{7}N + \gamma$$
$$^{13}_{7}N \rightarrow ^{13}_{6}C + e^{+} + \nu_{e}$$
$$^{13}_{6}C + ^{1}_{1}H \rightarrow ^{14}_{7}N + \gamma$$
$$^{14}_{7}N + ^{1}_{1}H \rightarrow ^{15}_{8}O + \gamma$$
$$^{15}_{8}O \rightarrow ^{15}_{7}N + e^{+} + \nu_{e}$$
$$^{15}_{7}N + ^{1}_{1}H \rightarrow ^{12}_{6}C + ^{4}_{2}He.$$

See stellar evolution.

carbon dating (radiocarbon dating) A method of estimating the ages of archaeological specimens of biological origin. As a result of *cosmic radiation a small number of atmospheric nitrogen nuclei are continuously being transformed by neutron bombardment into radioactive nuclei of carbon–14:

$$^{14}_{7}N + n \rightarrow ^{14}_{6}C + p$$

Some of these radiocarbon atoms find their way into living trees and other plants in the form of carbon dioxide, as a result of *photosynthesis. When the tree is cut down photosynthesis stops and the ratio of radiocarbon atoms to stable carbon atoms begins

to fall as the radiocarbon decays. The ratio $^{14}C/^{12}C$ in the specimen can be measured and enables the time that has elapsed since the tree was cut down to be calculated. The method has been shown to give consistent results for specimens up to some 40 000 years old, though its accuracy depends upon assumptions concerning the past intensity of the cosmic radiation. The technique was developed by Willard F. Libby (1908–80) and his coworkers in 1946–47.

carbon fibres Fibres of carbon in which the carbon has an oriented crystal structure. Carbon fibres are made by heating textile fibres and are used in strong composite materials for use at high temperatures.

Carnot cycle The most efficient cycle of operations for a reversible *heat engine. Published in 1824 by the French physicist N. L. S. Carnot (1746–1832), it consists of four operations on the working substance in the engine (see illustration):

a. Isothermal expansion at thermodynamic temperature T_1 with heat Q_1 taken in.

b. Adiabatic expansion with a fall of temperature to T_2.

c. Isothermal compression at temperature T_2 with heat Q_2 given out.

d. Adiabatic compression with a rise of temperature back to T_1.

According to the *Carnot principle*, the efficiency of any reversible heat

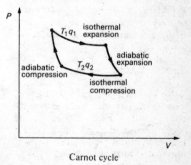

Carnot cycle

engine depends only on the temperature range through which it works, rather than the properties of the working substances. In any reversible engine, the efficiency (η) is the ratio of the work done (W) to the heat input (Q_1), i.e. $\eta = W/Q_1$. As, according to the first law of *thermodynamics, $W = Q_1 - Q_2$, it follows that $\eta = (Q_1 - Q_2)/Q_1$. For the Kelvin temperature scale, $Q_1/Q_2 = T_1/T_2$ and $\eta = (T_1 - T_2)/T_1$. For maximum efficiency T_1 should be as high as possible and T_2 as low as possible.

carrier 1. *See* carrier wave. **2.** *See* charge carrier.

carrier gas The gas that carries the sample in *gas chromatography.

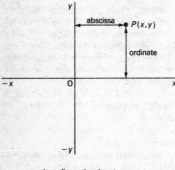

two-dimensional system

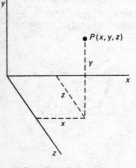

three-dimensional system

Cartesian coordinates

carrier wave An electromagnetic wave of specified frequency and amplitude that is emitted by a radio transmitter in order to carry information. The information is superimposed onto the carrier by making small changes in either its amplitude or its frequency (*see* modulation).

Cartesian coordinates A system used in analytical geometry to locate a point P, with reference to two or three *axes* (see graphs). In a two-dimensional system the vertical axis is the y-axis and the horizontal axis is the x-axis. The point at which the axes intersect each other is called the *origin*, O. Values of $y < 0$ fall on the y-axis below the origin, values of $x < 0$ fall on the x-axis to the left of the origin. Any point P is located by its perpendicular distances from the two axes. The distance from the x-axis is called the *ordinate*; the distance from the y-axis is the *abscissa*. The position is indicated numerically by enclosing the values of the abscissa and the ordinate in parentheses and separating the two by means of a comma, e.g. (x,y). In three dimensions the system can be used to locate a point with reference to a third, z-axis. It is named after René Descartes (1596–1650).

cascade liquefier An apparatus for liquefying a gas of low *critical temperature. Another gas, already below its critical temperature, is liquified and evaporated at a reduced pressure in order to cool the first gas to below its critical temperature. In practice a series of steps is often used, each step enabling the critical temperature of the next gas to be reached.

cascade process Any process that takes place in a number of steps, usually because the single step is too inefficient to produce the desired result. For example, in various uranium-enrichment processes the separation of the desired isotope is only poorly achieved in a single stage; to

achieve better separation the process has to be repeated a number of times, in a series, with the enriched fraction of one stage being fed to the succeeding stage for further enrichment. Another example of cascade process is that operating in a *cascade liquefier.

case hardening The hardening of the surface layer of steel, used for tools and certain mechanical components. The commonest method is to carburize the surface layer by heating the metal in a hydrocarbon or by dipping the red hot metal into molten sodium cyanide. Diffusion of nitrogen into the surface layer to form nitrides is also used.

Cassegrainian telescope *See* telescope.

cast iron A group of iron alloys containing 1.8 to 4.5% of carbon. It is usually cast into specific shapes ready for machining, heat treatment, or assembly. It is sometimes produced direct from the *blast furnace or it may be made from remelted *pig iron.

catenary A curve formed when a chain or rope of uniform density hangs from two fixed points. If the lowest point on the curve passes through the origin, the equation is $y = c(\cosh x/c)$, where c is the distance between the x-axis and the directrix.

cathetometer A telescope or microscope fitted with crosswires in the eyepiece and mounted so that it can slide along a graduated scale. Cathetometers are used for accurate measurement of lengths without mechanical contact. The microscope type is often called a *travelling microscope*.

cathode A negative electrode. In *electrolysis cations are attracted to the cathode. In vacuum electronic devices electrons are emitted by the cathode and flow to the *anode. It is therefore from the cathode that electrons flow into these devices. However, in a primary or secondary cell the cathode is the electrode that spontaneously becomes negative during discharge, and from which therefore electrons emerge.

cathode-ray oscilloscope (CRO) An instrument based on the *cathode-ray tube that provides a visual image of electrical signals. The horizontal deflection is usually provided by an internal time base, which causes the beam to sweep across the screen at a specified rate. The signal to be investigated is fed to the vertical deflection plates after amplification. Thus the beam traces a graph of the signal against time.

cathode rays Streams of electrons emitted at the cathode in an evacuated tube containing a cathode and an anode. They were first observed in gas *discharge tubes operated at low pressure. Under suitable conditions electrons produced by secondary emission at the cathode are accelerated down the tube to the anode. In such devices as the *cathode-ray tube the electrons are produced by *thermionic emission from a hot cathode in a vacuum.

cathode-ray tube (CRT) The device that provides the viewing screen in the television tube, the radar viewer, and the *cathode-ray oscilloscope. The cathode-ray tube consists of an evacuated tube containing a heated cathode and two or more ring-shaped

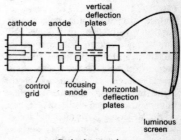

Cathode-ray tube

33

cathodic protection

anodes through which the cathode rays can pass so that they strike the enlarged end of the tube (see illustration). This end of the tube is coated with fluorescent material so that it provides a screen. Any point on the screen that is struck by the cathode ray becomes luminous. A *control grid between the cathode and the anode enables the intensity of the beam to be varied, thus controlling the brightness of the illumination on the screen. The assembly of cathode, control grid, and anode is called the *electron gun. The beam emerging from the electron gun is focused and deflected by means of plates providing an electric field or coils providing a magnetic field. This enables the beam to be focused to a small point of light and deflected to produce the illusion of an illuminated line as this point sweeps across the tube.

The television tube is a form of cathode-ray tube in which the beam is made to scan the screen 625 times to form a frame, with 25 new frames being produced every second. (These are the figures for standard television tubes in the UK). Each frame creates a picture by variations in the intensity of the beam as it forms each line.

cathodic protection *See* sacrificial protection.

cation A positively charged ion, i.e. an ion that is attracted to the cathode in *electrolysis. *Compare* anion.

cationic dye *See* dyes.

caustic (in optics) The curve or surface formed by the reflection of parallel rays of light in a large-aperture concave mirror. The apex of the caustic lies at the principal focus of the mirror. Such a curve can sometimes be seen on the surface of the liquid in a cup as a result of reflection by the curved walls of the cup. A similar curve is formed by a convex lens with spherical surfaces refracting parallel rays of light.

cavitation The formation of gas- or vapour-filled cavities in liquids in motion when the pressure is reduced to a critical value while the ambient temperature remains constant. If the velocity of the flowing liquid exceeds a certain value, the pressure can be reduced to such an extent that *Bernoulli's theorem breaks down. It is at this point that cavitation occurs, causing a restriction on the speed at which hydraulic machinery can be run without noise, vibration, erosion of metal parts, or loss of efficiency.

cavity resonator *See* resonant cavity.

celestial equator *See* equator.

celestial mechanics The study of the motions of and forces between the celestial bodies. It is based on *Newton's laws of motion and *Newton's law of gravitation. Refinements based on the general theory of *relativity are also included in the study, although the differences between the two theories are only important in a few cases.

celestial sphere The imaginary sphere of infinite radius within which celestial bodies appear to lie. The earth, and the observer, are visualized as being at the centre of the sphere and the sphere as rotating once every sidereal *day (see illustration). The sphere is used to describe the position of celestial bodies with respect to the earth.

cell 1. A system in which two electrodes are in contact with an electrolyte. The electrodes are metal or carbon plates or rods or, in some cases, liquid metals (e.g. mercury). In an *electrolytic cell a current from an outside source is passed through the electrolyte to produce chemical change (*see* electrolysis). In a *voltaic cell, spontaneous reactions between the electrodes and electrolyte(s) produce a potential difference between the two electrodes.

Voltaic cells can be regarded as made up of two *half cells, each composed

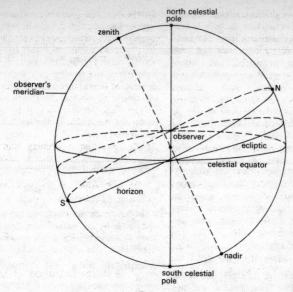

north celestial
pole

zenith

observer's
meridian

N

observer

ecliptic

celestial equator

horizon

S

nadir

south celestial
pole

Celestial sphere

of an electrode in contact with an electrolyte. For instance, a zinc rod dipped in zinc sulphate solution is a $Zn|Zn^{2+}$ half cell. In such a system zinc atoms dissolve as zinc ions, leaving a negative charge on the electrode

$$Zn(s) \rightarrow Zn^{2+}(aq) + 2e$$

The solution of zinc continues until the charge build-up is sufficient to prevent further ionization. There is then a potential difference between the zinc rod and its solution. This cannot be measured directly, since measurement would involve making contact with the electrolyte, thereby introducing another half cell (*see* electrode potential). A rod of copper in copper sulphate solution comprises another half cell. In this case the spontaneous reaction is one in which copper ions in solution take electrons from the electrode and are deposited on the electrode as copper atoms. In this case, the copper acquires a positive charge.

The two half cells can be connected by using a porous pot for the liquid junction (as in the *Daniell cell) or by using a salt bridge. The resulting cell can then supply current if the electrodes are connected through an external circuit. The cell is written

$$Zn(s)|Zn^{2+}(aq)|Cu^{2+}(aq)|Cu$$
$$E = 1.10\text{ V}$$

Here, E is the e.m.f. of the cell equal to the potential of the right-hand electrode minus that of the left-hand electrode for zero current. Note that 'right' and 'left' refer to the cell as written. Thus, the cell could be written

$$Cu(s)|Cu^{2+}(aq)|Zn^{2+}(aq)|Zn(s)$$
$$E = -1.10\text{ V}$$

The overall reaction for the cell is

$$Zn(s) + Cu^{2+}(aq) \rightarrow Cu(s) +$$
$$Zn^{2+}(aq)$$

This is the direction in which the cell reaction occurs for a positive e.m.f. The cell above is a simple example of a *chemical cell*; i.e. one in which the e.m.f. is produced by a chemical dif-

35

ference. *Concentration cells* are cells in which the e.m.f. is caused by a difference of concentration. This may be a difference in concentration of the electrolyte in the two half cells. Alternatively, it may be an electrode concentration difference (e.g. different concentrations of metal in an amalgam, or different pressures of gas in two gas electrodes). Cells are also classified into cells *without transport* (having a single electrolyte) and *with transport* (having a liquid junction across which ions are transferred). Various types of voltaic cell exist, used as sources of current, standards of potential, and experimental set-ups for studying electrochemical reactions.

2. *See* photoelectric cell.

3. *See* solar cell.

4. *See* Kerr effect (for Kerr cell).

Celsius scale A *temperature scale in which the fixed points are the temperatures at standard pressure of ice in equilibrium with water (0°C) and water in equilibrium with steam (100°C). The scale, between these two temperatures, is divided in 100 degrees. The degree Celsius (°C) is equal in magnitude to the *kelvin. This scale was formerly known as the *centigrade scale*; the name was officially changed in 1948 to avoid confusion with a hundredth part of a grade. It is named after the Swedish astronomer Anders Celsius (1701–44), who devised the inverted form of this scale (ice point 100°, steam point 0°) in 1742.

cementation Any metallurgical process in which the surface of a metal is impregnated by some other substance, especially an obsolete process for making steel by heating bars of wrought iron to red heat for several days in a bed of charcoal. *See also* case hardening.

cementite *See* steel.

centi- Symbol c. A prefix used in the metric system to denote one hun-

dredth. For example, 0.01 metre = 1 centimetre (cm).

centigrade scale *See* Celsius scale.

central processing unit (CPU) *See* computer.

centre of curvature The centre of the sphere of which a *lens surface or curved *mirror forms a part. The *radius of curvature* is the radius of this sphere.

centre of gravity *See* centre of mass.

centre of mass The point at which the whole mass of a body may be considered to be concentrated. This is the same as the *centre of gravity*, the point at which the whole weight of a body may be considered to act, if the body is situated in a uniform gravitational field.

centrifugal force *See* centripetal force.

centrifugal pump *See* pump.

centrifuge A device in which solid or liquid particles of different densities are separated by rotating them in a tube in a horizontal circle. The denser particles tend to move along the length of the tube to a greater radius of rotation, displacing the lighter particles to the other end.

centripetal force A force acting on a body causing it to move in a circular path. If the mass of the body is m, its constant speed v, and the radius of the circle r, the magnitude of the force is mv^2/r and it is directed towards the centre of the circle. Even though the body is moving with a constant speed v, its velocity is changing, because its direction is constantly changing. There is therefore an acceleration v^2/r towards the centre of the circle. For example, when an object is tied to a string and swung in a horizontal circle there is a tension in the string equal to mv^2/r. If the string breaks, this restraining force disappears and the object will move off in a straight line along the

tangent to the circle in which it was previously moving.

In the case of a satellite (mass m) orbiting the earth (mass M), the centripetal force holding the satellite in orbit is the *gravitational force, GmM/d^2, where G is the gravitational constant and d is the height of the satellite above the centre of the earth. Therefore $GmM/d^2 = mv^2/d$. This equation enables the height of the orbit to be calculated for a given orbital velocity.

Another way of looking at this situation, which was once popular, is to assume that the centripetal force is balanced by an equal and opposite force, acting away from the centre of the circle, called the *centrifugal force*. One could then say that the satellite stays in orbit when the centrifugal force balances the gravitational force. This is, however, a confusing argument because the centrifugal force is fictitious – it does not exist. The gravitational force is not balanced by the centrifugal force: it *is* the centripetal force.

Another example is that of a car rounding a bend. To an observer in the car, a tennis ball lying on the back shelf will roll across the shelf as if it was acted on by an outward centrifugal force. However, to an observer outside the car it can be seen that the ball, because of its almost frictionless contact with the car, is continuing in its straight line motion, uninfluenced by the centripetal force. Occasionally the concept of a centrifugal force can be useful, as long as it is recognized as a fictitious force. A true centrifugal force is exerted, as a *reaction, by the rotating object on whatever is providing its centripetal force.

centroid The point within an area or volume at which the centre of mass would be if the surface or body had a uniform density. For a symmetrical area or volume it coincides with the centre of mass. For a nonsymmetrical area or volume it has to be found by integration.

Cerenkov counter (Cerenkov detector) A type of *counter for detecting and counting high-energy charged particles. The particles pass through a liquid and the light emitted as *Cerenkov radiation is registered by a *photomultiplier tube.

Cerenkov radiation Electromagnetic radiation, usually bluish light, emitted by a beam of high-energy charged particles passing through a transparent medium at a speed greater than the speed of light in that medium. It was discovered in 1934 by the Russian physicist Pavel Cerenkov (1904–). The effect is similar to that of a *sonic boom when an object moves faster than the speed of sound; in this case the radiation is a shock wave set up in the electromagnetic field. Cerenkov radiation is used in the *Cerenkov counter.

cermet A composite material consisting of a ceramic in combination with a sintered metal, used when a high resistance to temperature, corrosion, and abrasion is needed.

CERN (Conseil Européen pour la Recherche Nucléaire) The European Organization for Nuclear Research, which is situated close to Geneva in Switzerland and is supported by a number of European nations. It runs the *Super Proton Synchrotron* (SPS), which has a 7-kilometre underground tunnel enabling protons to be accelerated to 400 GeV, and the *Large Electron-Positron Collider* (LEP), in which 50 GeV electron and positron beams are collided.

cetane number A number that provides a measure of the ignition characteristics of a Diesel fuel when it is burnt in a standard Diesel engine. It is the percentage of cetane (hexadecane) in a mixture of cetane and 1-methylnaphthalene that has the same ignition characteristics as the

fuel being tested. *Compare* octane number.

c.g.s. units A system of *units based on the centimetre, gram, and second. Derived from the metric system, it was badly adapted to use with thermal quantities (based on the inconsistently defined *calorie) and with electrical quantities (in which two systems, based respectively on unit permittivity and unit permeability of free space, were used). For many scientific purposes c.g.s. units have now been replaced by *SI units.

chain reaction A reaction that is self-sustaining as a result of the products of one step initiating a subsequent step.

In nuclear chain reactions the succession depends on production and capture of neutrons. Thus, one nucleus of the isotope uranium–235 can disintegrate with the production of two or three neutrons, which cause similar fission of adjacent nuclei. These in turn produce more neutrons. If the total amount of material exceeds a *critical mass, the chain reaction may cause an explosion.

Chemical chain reactions usually involve free radicals as intermediates. An example is the reaction of chlorine with hydrogen initiated by ultraviolet radiation. A chlorine molecule is first split into atoms:

$$Cl_2 \rightarrow Cl\cdot + Cl\cdot$$

These react with hydrogen as follows

$$Cl\cdot + H_2 \rightarrow HCl + H\cdot$$
$$H\cdot + Cl_2 \rightarrow HCl + Cl\cdot \text{ etc.}$$

Combustion and explosion reactions involve similar free-radical chain reactions.

Chandrasekhar limit The maximum possible mass of a star that is prevented from collapsing under its own gravity by the *degeneracy pressure of either electrons (a *white dwarf) or neutrons (a *neutron star). For white dwarfs the *Chandrasekhar mass* is about 1.4 times the mass of the sun. For neutron stars its value is less precisely known because of uncertainties regarding the equation of state of neutron matter, but it is generally taken to be in the range of 1.5 to 3 (and almost certainly no more than 5) times the mass of the sun.

change of phase (change of state) A change of matter in one physical *phase (solid, liquid, or gas) into another. The change is invariably accompanied by the evolution or absorption of energy, even if it takes place at constant temperature (*see* latent heat).

channel 1. The region between the source and the drain in a field-effect *transistor. The conductivity of the channel is controlled by the voltage applied to the gate. **2.** A path, or a specified frequency band, along which signals, information, or data flow.

chaos Unpredictable and seemingly random behaviour occurring in a system that should be governed by deterministic laws. There are many cases of chaos in physics: examples are the turbulent flow of liquids, planetary dynamics, and oscillations in electrical circuits. In other branches of science examples are oscillatory reactions in chemistry (in which the concentration of a component periodically rises and falls) and the unpredictability of the weather in meteorology. In such systems, the equations that describe the way the system changes with time are nonlinear and involve several variables. Consequently, they are very sensitive to the initial conditions, and a very small initial difference may make an enormous change to the future state of the system. This is exemplified by the *butterfly effect* in meteorology. It has been suggested that the dynamical equations governing the weather are so sensitive to the initial data that whether or not a butterfly flaps its wings in one part of the world may make the difference between a tor-

nado occurring or not occurring in some other part of the world. *See also* attractor; fractal.

characteristic *See* logarithm.

charge A property of some *elementary particles that gives rise to an interaction between them and consequently to the host of material phenomena described as electrical. Charge occurs in nature in two forms, conventionally described as *positive* and *negative* in order to distinguish between the two kinds of interaction between particles. Two particles that have similar charges (both negative or both positive) interact by repelling each other; two particles that have dissimilar charges (one positive, one negative) interact by attracting each other. The size of the interaction is determined by *Coulomb's law.

The natural unit of negative charge is the charge on an *electron, which is equal but opposite in effect to the positive charge on the proton. Large-scale matter that consists of equal numbers of electrons and protons is electrically neutral. If there is an excess of electrons the body is negatively charged; an excess of protons results in a positive charge. A flow of charged particles, especially a flow of electrons, constitutes an electric current. Charge is measured in coulombs, the charge on an electron being 1.602×10^{-19} coulombs.

charge carrier The entity that transports electric charge in an electric current. The nature of the carrier depends on the type of conductor: in metals, the charge carriers are electrons; in *semiconductors the carriers are electrons (*n*-type) or positive *holes (*p*-type); in gases the carriers are positive ions and electrons; in electrolytes they are positive and negative ions.

charge conjugation Symbol C. A property of elementary particles that determines the difference between a particle and its *antiparticle. The property is not restricted to electrically charged particles (i.e. it applies to neutral particles such as the neutron). *See* CP invariance.

charge density 1. The electric charge per unit volume of a medium or body (*volume charge density*). 2. The electric charge per unit surface area of a body (*surface charge density*).

Charles' law The volume of a fixed mass of gas at constant pressure expands by a constant fraction of its volume at 0°C for each Celsius degree or kelvin its temperature is raised. For any *ideal gas the fraction is approximately 1/273. This can be expressed by the equation $V = V_0(1 + t/273)$, where V_0 is the volume at 0°C and V is its volume at t°C. This is equivalent to the statement that the volume of a fixed mass of gas at constant pressure is proportional to its thermodynamic temperature, $V = kT$, where k is a constant. The law resulted from experiments begun around 1787 by the French scientist J. A. C. Charles (1746–1823) but was properly established only by the more accurate results published in 1802 by the French scientist Joseph Gay-Lussac (1778–1850). Thus the law is also known as *Gay-Lussac's law*. An equation similar to that given above applies to pressures for ideal gases: $p = p_0(1 + t/273)$, a relationship known as *Charles' law of pressures*. *See also* gas laws.

charm A property of certain *elementary particles that is expressed as a *quantum number and is used in the quark model. It was originally suggested to account for the unusually long lifetime of the *psi particle. In this theory the three original quark–antiquark pairs were supplemented by a fourth pair – the charmed quark and its antiquark. The psi particle itself is a meson having zero charm as it consists of the charmed pair. However, charmed *hadrons do exist; they are said to

possess *naked charm*. Charm is thought to be conserved in strong and electromagnetic interactions.

chemical cell *See* cell.

chemical dating An absolute *dating technique that depends on measuring the chemical composition of a specimen. Chemical dating can be used when the specimen is known to undergo slow chemical change at a known rate. For instance, phosphate in buried bones is slowly replaced by fluoride ions from the ground water. Measurement of the proportion of fluorine present gives a rough estimate of the time that the bones have been in the ground. Another, more accurate, method depends on the fact that amino acids in living organisms are L-optical isomers. After death, these racemize and the age of bones can be estimated by measuring the relative amounts of D- and L-amino acids present.

chemical potential Symbol: μ. For a given component in a mixture, the coefficient $\partial G/\partial n$, where G is the Gibbs free energy and n the amount of substance of the component. The chemical potential is the change in Gibbs free energy with respect to change in amount of the component, with pressure, temperature, and amounts of other components being constant. Components are in equilibrium if their chemical potentials are equal.

chemiluminescence *See* luminescence.

chemisorption *See* adsorption.

chip *See* silicon chip.

chirality The property of existing in left- and right-handed structural forms. *See* optical activity.

Chiron A minor planet discovered in 1977. It has an orbit of 50.68 years that, unlike other known minor planets, lies almost entirely outside that of Saturn. Its diameter is uncertain, but appears to be of the order of 300 km.

choke A coil of wire with high inductance and low resistance. It is used in radio circuits to impede the passage of audio-frequency or radio-frequency currents or to smooth the output of a rectifying circuit.

cholesteric crystal *See* liquid crystal.

chromatic aberration *See* aberration.

chromaticity An objective description of the colour quality of a visual stimulus that does not depend on its luminance but which, together with its luminance, completely specifies the colour. The colour quality is defined in terms of *chromaticity coordinates*, x, y, and z, where

$$x = X/(X + Y + Z)$$
$$y = Y/(X + Y + Z)$$
$$\text{and } z = Z/(X + Y + Z)$$

X, Y, and Z are the *tristimulus values* of a light, i.e. they are the amounts of three reference stimuli needed to match exactly the light under consideration in a trichromatic system.

chromium steel Any of a group of *stainless steels containing 8–25% of chromium. A typical chromium steel might contain 18% of chromium, 8% of nickel, and 0.15% of carbon. Chromium steels are highly resistant to corrosion and are used for cutlery, chemical plant, ball bearings, etc.

chromosphere The layer of the *sun's atmosphere immediately above the *photosphere. The chromosphere is normally only visible when the photosphere is totally eclipsed by the moon. The chromosphere is about 10 000 kilometres thick and the temperature in it rises from 4000 K, where it merges with the photosphere, to about 50 000 K, where it reaches the transition region below the *corona.

circle A closed curve every point on which is a fixed distance (the *radius*) from a point (the *centre*) within the

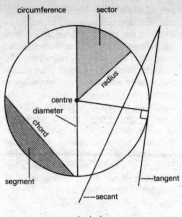

circumference   sector

radius

centre
diameter

chord

segment

tangent

secant

A circle

curve (see illustration). The *diameter* is a line that joins two points on the *circumference* and passes through the centre: the diameter is twice the radius (*r*). The circumference of a circle is equal to $2\pi r$; the area is πr^2, where π is a constant with the value 3.141 592. In analytical geometry the equation of a circle, centred at the origin, is $x^2 + y^2 = r^2$.

circular measure A method of measuring angles by treating them as the angle formed by a sector of a circle at the circle's centre. The unit of measure is the *radian*, the angle subtended at the centre of a circle by an arc of equal length to the radius. Since an arc of length *r* subtends an angle of 1 radian, the whole circumference, length $2\pi r$, will subtend an angle of $2\pi r/r = 2\pi$ radians. Thus, $360° = 2\pi$ radians; 1 radian = 57.296°.

circular polarization *See* polarization of light.

cladding 1. A thin coating of an expensive metal rolled on to a cheaper one. 2. A thin covering of a metal around a fuel element in a nuclear reactor to prevent corrosion of the fuel elements by the coolant.

Clark cell A type of *voltaic cell consisting of an anode made of zinc amalgam and a cathode of mercury both immersed in a saturated solution of zinc sulphate. The Clark cell was formerly used as a standard of e.m.f.; the e.m.f. at 15°C is 1.4345 volts. It is named after the British scientist Hosiah Clark (*d.* 1898).

classical physics Theoretical physics up to approximately the end of the 19th century, before the concepts of *quantum theory (1900) and special *relativity (1905). Classical physics relied largely on Newton's mechanics and James Clerk Maxwell's theory of electromagnetism. It may still be applied with high precision to large-scale phenomena involving no very rapid relative motion.

Claude process A process for liquefying air on a commercial basis. Air under pressure is used as the working substance in a piston engine, where it does external work and cools adiabatically. This cool air is fed to a counter-current *heat exchanger, where it reduces the temperature of the next intake of high-pressure air. The same air is re-compressed and used again, and after several cycles eventually liquefies. The process was perfected in 1902 by the French scientist Georges Claude (1870–1960).

close packing The packing of spheres so as to occupy the minimum amount of space. In a single plane, each sphere is surrounded by six close neighbours in a hexagonal arrangement. The spheres in the second plane fit into depressions in the first layer, and so on. Each sphere has 12 other touching spheres. There are two types of close packing. In *hexagonal close packing* the spheres in the third layer are directly over those in the first, etc., and the arrangement of planes is ABAB . . . . In *cubic close packing* the spheres in the third layer occupy a different set of depressions than those in the first. The arrange-

ment is ABCABC .... *See also* cubic crystal.

cloud chamber A device for making visible the paths of particles of *ionizing radiation. The *Wilson (expansion) cloud chamber* consists of a container containing air and ethanol vapour, which is cooled suddenly by adiabatic expansion, causing the vapour to become supersaturated. The excess moisture in the vapour is then deposited in drops on the tracks of ions created by the passage of the ionizing radiation. The resulting row of droplets can be photographed. If the original moving particle was being deflected by electric or magnetic fields, the extent of the deflection provides information on its mass and charge. This device was invented in 1911 by C. T. R. Wilson (1869–1961). A simpler version of this apparatus is the *diffusion cloud chamber*, developed by Cowan, Needels, and Nielsen in 1950, in which supersaturation is achieved by placing a row of felt strips soaked in a suitable alcohol at the top of the chamber. The lower part of the chamber is cooled by solid carbon dioxide. The vapour continuously diffuses downwards, and that in the centre (where it becomes supersaturated) is almost continuously sensitive to the presence of ions created by the radiation.

Clusius column A device for separating isotopes by *thermal diffusion. One form consists of a vertical column some 30 metres high with a heated electric wire running along its axis. The lighter isotopes in a gaseous mixture of isotopes diffuse faster than the heavier isotopes. Heated by the axial wire, and assisted by natural convection, the lighter atoms are carried to the top of the column, where a fraction rich in lighter isotopes can be removed for further enrichment.

cluster *See* galaxy cluster; star cluster.

coagulation The process in which colloidal particles come together to form larger masses. Coagulation can be brought about by adding ions to neutralize the charges stabilizing the colloid. Ions with a high charge are particularly effective (e.g. alum, containing Al^{3+}, is used in styptics to coagulate blood). Another example of ionic coagulation is in the formation of river deltas, which occurs when colloidal silt particles in rivers are coagulated by ions in sea water. Heating is another way of coagulating certain colloids (e.g. boiling an egg coagulates the albumin).

coaxial cable A cable consisting of a central conductor surrounded by an insulator, which is in turn contained in an earthed sheath of another conductor. The central conductor and the outer conductor are coaxial (i.e. have the same axis). They are used to transmit high-frequency signals as they produce no external fields and are not influenced by them.

cobalt steel Any of a group of *alloy steels containing 5–12% of cobalt, 14–20% of tungsten, usually with 4% of chromium and 1–2% of vanadium. They are very hard but somewhat brittle. Their main use is in high-speed tools.

Cockcroft–Walton generator The first proton accelerator; a simple *linear accelerator producing a potential difference of some 800 kV (d.c.) from a circuit of rectifiers and capacitors fed by a lower (a.c.) voltage. The experimenters, Sir John Cockcroft (1897–1967) and E. T. S. Walton (1903–), used this device in 1932 to achieve the first artificially induced nuclear reaction by bombarding lithium with protons to produce helium:

$$\text{}_1^1H + \text{}_3^7Li = \text{}_2^4He + \text{}_2^4He$$

coefficient 1. (in mathematics) A number or other known factor by which a variable quantity is multiplied, e.g. in $ax^2 + bx + c = 0$, a is the coefficient of x^2 and b is the coef-

ficient of *x*. **2.** (in physics) A measure of a specified property of a particular substance under specified conditions, e.g. the coefficient of *friction of a substance.

coefficient of expansion See expansivity.

coefficient of friction See friction.

coelostat A device that enables light from the same area of the sky to be continuously reflected into the field of view of an astronomical telescope or other instrument. It consists of a plane mirror driven by a clockwork or electrical mechanism so that it rotates from east to west to compensate for the apparent west-to-east rotation of the *celestial sphere.

coercive force (coercivity) The magnetizing force necessary to reduce the flux density in a magnetic material to zero. See hysteresis.

coherent radiation Electromagnetic radiation in which two or more sets of waves have a constant phase relationship, i.e. with peaks and troughs always similarly spaced.

coherent units A system of *units of measurement in which derived units are obtained by multiplying or dividing base units without the use of numerical factors. *SI units form a coherent system; for example the unit of force is the newton, which is equal to 1 kilogram metre per second squared $(kg\,m\,s^{-2})$, the kilogram, metre, and second all being base units of the system.

coincidence circuit An electronic logic device that gives an output only if two input signals are fed to it simultaneously or within a specified time of each other. A *coincidence counter* is an electronic counter incorporating such a device.

cold emission The emission of electrons by a solid without the use of high temperature (thermal emission), either as a result of field emission

(*see* field-emission microscope) or *secondary emission.

cold fusion See nuclear fusion.

collective excitation A quantized mode in a many-body system, occurring because of cooperative motion of the whole system as a result of interactions between particles. *Plasmons and *phonons in solids are examples of collective excitations. Collective excitations obey Bose–Einstein statistics (*see* quantum statistics).

collector See transistor.

colligative properties Properties that depend on the concentration of particles (molecules, ions, etc.) present in a solution, and not on the nature of the particles. Examples of colligative properties are osmotic pressure (*see* osmosis), *lowering of vapour pressure, *depression of freezing point, and *elevation of boiling point.

collimator 1. Any device for producing a parallel beam of radiation. A common arrangement used for light consists of a convex achromatic lens fitted to one end of a tube with an adjustable slit at the other end, the slit being at the principal focus of the lens. Light rays entering the slit leave the lens as a parallel beam. Collimators for particle beams and other types of electromagnetic radiation utilize a system of slits or apertures. **2.** A small fixed telescope attached to a large astronomical telescope to assist in lining up the large one onto the desired celestial body.

collision density The number of collisions that occur in unit volume in unit time when a given neutron flux passes through matter.

colloids Colloids were originally defined by Thomas Graham in 1861 as substances, such as starch or gelatin, which will not diffuse through a membrane. He distinguished them from *crystalloids* (e.g. inorganic salts), which would pass through membranes. Later it was recognized that

cologarithm

colloids were distinguished from true solutions by the presence of particles that were too small to be observed with a normal microscope yet were much larger than normal molecules. Colloids are now regarded as systems in which there are two or more phases, with one (the *dispersed phase*) distributed in the other (the *continuous phase*). Moreover, at least one of the phases has small dimensions (in the range 10^{-9}–10^{-6} m). Colloids are classified in various ways.

Sols are dispersions of small solid particles in a liquid. The particles may be macromolecules or may be clusters of small molecules. *Lyophobic sols* are those in which there is no affinity between the dispersed phase and the liquid. An example is silver chloride dispersed in water. In such colloids the solid particles have a surface charge, which tends to stop them coming together. Lyophobic sols are inherently unstable and in time the particles aggregate and form a precipitate. *Lyophilic sols*, on the other hand, are more like true solutions in which the solute molecules are large and have an affinity for the solvent. Starch in water is an example of such a system. *Association colloids* are systems in which the dispersed phase consists of clusters of molecules that have lyophobic and lyophilic parts. Soap in water is an association colloid (*see* micelle).

Emulsions are colloidal systems in which the dispersed and continuous phases are both liquids, e.g. oil-in-water or water-in-oil. Such systems require an emulsifying agent to stabilize the dispersed particles.

Gels are colloids in which both dispersed and continuous phases have a three-dimensional network throughout the material, so that it forms a jelly-like mass. Gelatin is a common example. One component may sometimes be removed (e.g. by heating) to leave a rigid gel (e.g. silica gel).

Other types of colloid include *aerosols (dispersions of liquid or solid particles in a gas, as in a mist or smoke) and foams (dispersions of gases in liquids or solids).

cologarithm The logarithm of the reciprocal of a number.

colorimeter Any instrument for comparing or reproducing colours. Monochromatic colorimeters match a *colour with a mixture of monochromatic and white lights. Trichromatic colorimeters use a mixture of three *primary colours.

colour The sensation produced when light of different wavelengths falls on the human eye. Although the visible spectrum covers a continuously varying range of colours from red to violet it is usually split into seven colours (the *visible spectrum*) with the following approximate wavelength ranges:

red 740–620 nm
orange 620–585 nm
yellow 585–575 nm
green 575–500 nm
blue 500–445 nm
indigo 445–425 nm
violet 425–390 nm

A mixture of all these colours in the proportions encountered in daylight gives white light; other colours are produced by varying the proportions or omitting components.

A coloured light has three attributes: its *hue*, depending on its wavelength; its *saturation*, depending on the degree to which it departs from white light; and its *luminosity. Coloured objects that owe their colour to pigments or dyes absorb some components of white light and reflect the rest. For example, a red book seen in white light absorbs all the components except the red, which it reflects. This is called a *subtractive process* as the final colour is that remaining after absorption of the rest. This is the basis of the process used in *colour photography. Combining

coloured lights, on the other hand, is an *additive process* and this is the method used in *colour television. *See also* primary colours.

colour charge *See* elementary particles.

colour photography Any of various methods of forming coloured images on film or paper by photographic means. One common process is a subtractive reversal system that utilizes a film with three layers of light-sensitive emulsion, one responding to each of the three *primary colours. On development a black image is formed where the scene is blue. The white areas are dyed yellow, the *complementary colour of blue, and the blackened areas are bleached clean. A yellow filter between this emulsion layer and the next keeps blue light from the second emulsion, which is green-sensitive. This is dyed magenta where no green light has fallen. The final emulsion is red-sensitive and is given a cyan (blue-green) image on the negative after dying. When white light shines through the three dye layers the cyan dye subtracts red where it does not occur in the scene, the magenta subtracts green, and the yellow subtracts blue. The light projected by the negative therefore reconstructs the original scene either as a transparency or for use with printing paper.

colour television A television system in which the camera filters the light from the scene into the three *primary-colour components, red, blue, and green, which are detected by separate camera tubes. The separate information so obtained relating to the colour of the image is combined with the sound and synchronization signals and transmitted using one of three systems, the American, British, or French. At the receiver, the signal is split again into red, blue, and green components, each being fed to a separate *electron gun in the cath-ode-ray tube of the receiver. By an additive process (*see* colour) the picture is reconstituted by the beam from each gun activating a set of phosphor dots of that colour on the screen.

colour temperature The temperature of a non-black body as indicated by the temperature of a black body having approximately the same spectral distribution.

coma 1. A nebulous cloud of gas and dust that surrounds the nucleus of a *comet. **2.** An *aberration of a lens or mirror in which the image of a point lying off the axis has a comet-shaped appearance.

combinations *See* permutations and combinations.

combustion A chemical reaction in which a substance reacts rapidly with oxygen with the production of heat and light. Such reactions are often free-radical chain reactions. *See also* flame.

comet A small body that travels around the sun in an eccentric orbit. *Short-period comets* have orbital periods of less than 150 years. The others have very long periods, some exceeding 100 000 years. Typical comets have three components: the *nucleus* of ice and dust, the *coma of gas and dust, and the *comet tail*, which only appears when the comet is near the sun (it, too, consists of gas and dust). The nuclei of most comets are thought to be 'dirty snowballs' about one kilometre in diameter, although the solar system has a few comets with nuclei exceeding 10 km in diameter. The coma may be 10^4–10^5 km in diameter, and the tail can be 10^7 km in length. *See also* Halley's comet.

common logarithm *See* logarithm.

communication satellite An unmanned artificial satellite sent by rocket into a geostationary orbit (*see* synchronous orbit) around the earth to enable television broadcasts and

telephone communications to be made between points on the earth's surface that could not otherwise communicate by radio owing to the earth's curvature. Modulated *microwaves are transmitted to the satellite, which amplifies them and retransmits them at a different frequency to the receiving station. The satellites are powered by *solar cells. Three or more satellites in equatorial orbits can provide a world-wide communications linkage. The satellites are placed well above the *ionosphere and therefore the carrier waves used have to be in the microwave region of the spectrum in order to pass through the ionosphere.

commutative law The mathematical law stating that the value of an expression is independent of the order of combination of the numbers, symbols, or terms in the expression. The *commutative law* for addition applies if $x + y = y + x$. The commutative law of multiplication applies if $x \times y = y \times x$. Subtraction and division are not commutative. *Compare* associative law; distributive law.

commutator The part of the armature of an electrical motor or generator through which connections are made to external circuits. It consists of a cylindrical assembly of insulated copper conductors, each of which is connected to one point in the armature winding. Spring-loaded carbon brushes are positioned around the commutator to carry the current to or from it.

compass A small magnet pivoted at its central point to revolve in a horizontal plane. In the earth's magnetic field the magnet (called the compass needle) aligns itself so that its north-seeking end points to the earth's magnetic north pole. A scale (called a compass card) is placed below the needle for use in navigation. In some navigation compasses the entire card is pivoted, indicating direction by a fixed mark on the casing. Such compasses are often filled with alcohol to provide damping. Magnetic compasses suffer from being affected by magnetic metals in their vicinity and to a large extent they have been replaced by *gyrocompasses.

complementarity The concept that a single model may not be adequate to explain all the observations made of atomic or subatomic systems in different experiments. For example, *electron diffraction is best explained by assuming that the electron is a wave (*see* de Broglie wavelength), whereas the *photoelectric effect is described by assuming that it is a particle. The idea of two different but complementary concepts to treat quantum phenomena was first put forward by the Danish physicist Niels Bohr (1855–1962) in 1927. *See also* light.

complementary colours A pair of coloured lights of specific hue (*see* colour) that produce the sensation of white when mixed in appropriate intensities. There is an infinite number of such pairs, an example (with wavelengths) is orange (608 nm) and blue (490 nm).

complex number A number that has a real part, x, and an imaginary part, iy, where $i = \sqrt{-1}$ and x and y are real (x can also equal 0). The complex number therefore has the form $x + iy$, which can also be written in the polar form $r\cos\theta + ir\sin\theta$, where

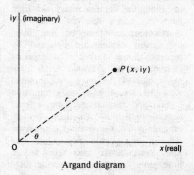

Argand diagram

r is the *modulus* and θ is the *argument* (or *amplitude*). A complex number can be represented on an *Argand diagram*, devised by J. R. Argand (1768–1822), in which the horizontal axis represents the real part of the number and the vertical axis the imaginary part (see illustration). In the polar form the modulus is the line joining the origin to the point representing the complex number and the argument is the angle between the modulus and the *x*-axis.

component vectors Two or more vectors that produce the same effect as a given vector; the vectors that combine to produce the effect of a resultant vector. A component vector in a given direction is the projection of the given vector (V) along that direction, i.e. $V\cos\theta$, where θ is the angle between the given vector and the direction.

compound microscope *See* microscope.

compressibility The reciprocal of bulk modulus (*see* elastic modulus). The compressibility (k) is given by $-V^{-1}dV/dp$, where dV/dp is the rate of change of volume (V) with pressure.

compression ratio The ratio of the total volume enclosed in the cylinder of an *internal-combustion engine at the beginning of the compression stroke to the volume enclosed at the end of the compression stroke. For petrol engines the compression ratio is 8.5–9:1, with a recent tendency to the lower end of the range in order to make use of unleaded petrols. For Diesel engines the compression ratio is in the range 12–18:1.

Compton effect The reduction in the energy of high-energy (X-ray or gamma-ray) photons when they are scattered by free electrons, which thereby gain energy. The phenomenon, first observed in 1923 by the US physicist A. H. Compton (1892–1902), occurs when the photon

collides with an electron; some of the photon's energy is transferred to the electron and consequently the photon loses energy $h(v_1 - v_2)$, where h is the *Planck constant and v_1 and v_2 are the frequencies before and after collision. As $v_1 > v_2$, the wavelength of the radiation increases after the collision. This type of inelastic scattering is known as *Compton scattering* and is similar to the *Raman effect. *See also* inverse Compton effect.

Compton wavelength The length scale below which a particle's quantum-mechanical properties become evident in relativistic *quantum mechanics. For a particle of rest mass m the Compton wavelength is $\hbar/mc$, where $\hbar$ is the rationalized Planck constant and c is the speed of light. The Compton wavelength is so named because of its occurrence in the theory of the *Compton effect, where its value for the electron is 3.8616×10^{-13} m. The Compton wavelength is sometimes defined as h/mc, with h being the Planck constant, in which case the electron value is 2.4263×10^{-12} m.

computer An electronic device that processes information according to a set of instructions, called the *program*. The most versatile type of computer is the *digital computer*, in which the input is in the form of characters, represented within the machine in *binary notation. The three basic components of a digital computer are the peripheral input and output devices, the memory, and the *central processing unit* (CPU). The input usually consists of a keyboard, tape drive, or a punched-card or tape reader. The output is usually a printer providing information on paper, a tape drive that provides it on magnetic tape, or a visual-display unit (VDU) providing it on a cathode-ray screen. The memory consists of one or more storage devices, such as magnetic disks, on which both

data and programs are stored. The CPU controls the whole system and performs arithmetical and logical operations on the data. Computers range in size from the *microprocessor* with a few thousand logic elements, to the large *mainframe computer* with millions of logic circuits.

The *analog computer* is used in scientific experiments, industrial control, etc. In this type of device the input and output are continuously varying quantities, such as a voltage, rather than the discrete digits of the more commercially useful digital device. *Hybrid computers* combine the properties of both digital and analog devices. Input is usually in analog form, but processing is carried out digitally in a CPU.

Computer *hardware* consists of the actual electronic or mechanical devices used in the system; the *software* consists of the programs and data.

concave Curving inwards. A *concave mirror* is one in which the reflecting surface is formed from the interior surface of a sphere or paraboloid. A *concave lens* has at least one face formed from the interior surface of a sphere. A *biconcave lens* has both faces concave and is therefore thinnest at its centre. The *plano-concave lens* has one plane face and one concave face. The *concavo-convex lens* (also called a *meniscus*) has one concave face and one *convex face. See lens.

concavo-convex *See* concave.

concentration cell *See* cell.

conchoidal fracture Fracture of a solid in which the surface of the material is curved and marked by concentric rings. It occurs particularly in amorphous materials.

condensation The change of a vapour or gas into a liquid. The change of phase is accompanied by the evolution of heat (*see* latent heat).

condensation pump *See* diffusion pump.

condensed-matter physics *See* solid-state physics.

condenser 1. A mirror or set of lenses used in optical instruments, such as a microscope or film projector, to concentrate the light diverging from a compact source. A common form consists of two plano-convex lenses with the plane faces pointing outwards. **2.** A device used to cool a vapour to cause it to condense to a liquid. In a steam engine the condenser acts as a reservoir that collects the part of the steam's internal energy that has not been used in doing work on the piston. The cooling water passed through the condenser is warmed and is used as fresh feedwater for the boiler. **3.** *See* capacitor.

condenser microphone *See* capacitor microphone.

conductance The reciprocal of electrical resistance in a direct-current circuit. The ratio of the resistance to the square of the *impedance in an alternating-current circuit. The SI unit is the siemens, formerly called the mho or reciprocal ohm.

conduction 1. (thermal conduction) The transmission of heat through a substance from a region of high temperature to a region of lower temperature. In gases and most liquids, the energy is transmitted mainly by collisions between atoms and molecules with those possessing lower kinetic energy. In solid and liquid metals, heat conduction is predominantly by migration of fast-moving electrons, followed by collisions between these electrons and ions. In solid insulators the absence of *free electrons restricts heat transfer to the vibrations of atoms and molecules within crystal lattices. *See* conductivity. **2. (electrical conduction)** The passage of electric charge through a substance under the influence of an elec-

tric field. *See also* charge carrier; energy bands.

conduction band *See* energy bands.

conductivity 1. (thermal conductivity) A measure of the ability of a substance to conduct heat. For a block of material of cross section A, the energy transferred per unit time E/t, between faces a distance, l, apart is given by $E/t = \lambda A(T_2 - T_1)/l$, where λ is the conductivity and T_2 and T_1 are the temperatures of the faces. This equation assumes that the opposite faces are parallel and that there is no heat loss through the sides of the block. The SI unit is therefore $J\,s^{-1}\,m^{-1}\,K^{-1}$. **2. (electrical conductivity)** The reciprocal of the *resistivity of a material. It is measured in siemens per metre in SI units. When a fluid is involved the electrolytic conductivity is given by the ratio of the current density to the electric field strength.

conductivity water *See* distilled water.

conductor 1. A substance that has a high thermal *conductivity. Metals are good conductors on account of the high concentration of *free electrons they contain. Energy is transmitted through a metal predominantly by means of collisions between electrons and ions. Most nonmetals are poor conductors (good *thermal insulators*) because there are relatively few free electrons. **2.** A substance that has a high electrical conductivity. Again conduction results from the movement of free electrons. *See* energy bands.

cone 1. (in optics) A type of light-sensitive receptor cell, found in the *retinas of all diurnal vertebrates. Cones are specialized to transmit information about colour and they function best in bright light. They are not evenly distributed on the retina, being concentrated in the fovea and absent on the margin of the retina. *Compare* rod. **2.** (in mathematics) A solid figure generated by a line (the

generator) joining a point on the perimeter of a closed plane curve (the *directrix*) to a point (the *vertex*) outside this plane, as the line moves round the directrix. If the directrix is a circle, the figure is a *circular cone* standing on a circular *base*. If the line joining the vertex to the centre of the base (the *axis*) is perpendicular to the base the figure is a *right circular cone*, which has a volume $\pi r^2 h/3$, where r is the radius of the base and h is the height of the vertex above the base. If the axis of the cone is not perpendicular to the base, the figure is an *oblique cone*. In general, the volume of any cone is one third of its base area multiplied by the perpendicular distance of the vertex from the base.

configuration 1. The arrangement of atoms or groups in a molecule. **2.** The arrangement of electrons in atomic *orbitals in an atom.

configuration space The n-dimensional space with coordinates $(q_1, q_2, \ldots, q_n)$ associated with a system that has n *degrees of freedom, where the values q describe the degrees of freedom. For example, in a gas of N atoms each atom has three positional coordinates, so the configuration space is $3N$-dimensional. If the particles also have internal degrees of freedom, such as those caused by vibration and rotation in a molecule, then these must be included in the configuration space, which is consequently of a higher dimension. *See also* phase space.

confinement *See* quantum chromodynamics; quark confinement.

conic A figure formed by the intersection of a plane and a *cone. If the intersecting plane is perpendicular to the axis of a right circular cone, the figure formed is a *circle. If the intersecting plane is inclined to the axis at an angle in excess of half the apex angle of the cone it is an *ellipse. If the plane is parallel to the sloping side of the cone, the figure is a

*parabola. If the plane cuts both halves of the cone a *hyperbola is formed.

A conic can be defined as a plane curve in which for all points on the curve the ratio of the distance from a fixed point (the *focus*) to the perpendicular distance from a straight line (the *directrix*) is a constant called the *eccentricity e*. For a parabola $e = 1$, for an ellipse $e < 1$, and for a hyperbola $e > 1$.

conjugate points Two points in the vicinity of a *lens or *mirror such that a bright object placed at one will form an image at the other.

conjunction The alignment of two celestial bodies within the solar system so that they have the same longitude as seen from the earth. A planet that orbits between the sun and the earth (Venus and Mercury) is in *superior conjunction* when it is in line with the sun and the earth but on the opposite side of the sun to the earth. It is in *inferior conjunction* when it lies between the earth and the sun. Conjunction may also occur between two planets or a moon and a planet.

conservation law A law stating that the total magnitude of a certain physical property of a system, such as its mass, energy, or charge, remains unchanged even though there may be exchanges of that property between components of the system. For example, imagine a table with a bottle of salt solution (NaCl), a bottle of silver nitrate solution ($AgNO_3$), and a beaker standing on it. The mass of this table and its contents will not change even when some of the contents of the bottles are poured into the beaker. As a result of the reaction between the chemicals two new substances (silver chloride and sodium nitrate) will appear in the beaker: $NaCl + AgNO_3 \rightarrow AgCl + NaNO_3$, but the total mass of the table and its contents will not change. This *conservation of mass* is a law of wide and general applicability, which is true for the universe as a whole, provided that the universe can be considered a closed system (nothing escaping from it, nothing being added to it). According to Einstein's mass–energy relationship, every quantity of energy (E) has a mass (m), which is given by E/c^2, where c is the speed of light. Therefore if mass is conserved, the law of *conservation of energy* must be of equally wide application. The laws of *conservation* of *linear momentum* and *angular momentum* also are believed to be universally true.

Because no way is known of either creating or destroying electric charge, the law of *conservation of charge* is also a law of universal application. Other quantities are also conserved in reactions between elementary particles.

conservative field A field of force in which the work done in moving a body from one point to another is independent of the path taken. The force required to move the body between these points in a conservative field is called a *conservative force*.

consolute temperature The temperature at which two partially miscible liquids become fully miscible as the temperature is increased.

constant 1. A component of a relationship between variables that does not change its value, e.g. in $y = ax + b$, b is a constant. **2.** A fixed value that has to be added to an indefinite integral. Known as the *constant of integration*, it depends on the limits between which the integration has been performed. **3.** *See* fundamental constants.

constantan An alloy having an electrical resistance that varies only very slightly with temperature (over a limited range around normal room temperatures). It consists of copper (50–60%) and nickel (40–50%) and is used in resistance wire, thermocouples, etc.

constant-boiling mixture *See* azeotrope.

contact potential difference The potential difference that occurs between two electrically connected metals or between the base regions of two semiconductors. If two metals with work functions ϕ_1 and ϕ_2 are brought into contact, their Fermi levels will coincide. If $\phi_1 > \phi_2$ the first metal will acquire a positive surface charge with respect to the other at the area of contact. As a result, a contact potential difference occurs between the two metals or semiconductors.

containment 1. The prevention of the escape of radioactive materials from a *nuclear reactor. **2.** The process of preventing the plasma in a *thermonuclear reactor from touching the walls of the vessel by means of magnetic fields.

continuous function A function $f(x)$ is continuous at $x = a$ if the limit of $f(x)$ as x approaches a is $f(a)$. A function that does not satisfy this condition is said to be a *discontinuous function*.

continuous phase *See* colloid.

continuous spectrum *See* spectrum.

continuous wave A wave that is transmitted continuously rather than in pulses.

continuum A system of axes that form a *frame of reference. The three dimensions of space and the dimension of time together can be taken to form a four-dimensional continuum; this was suggested by Minkowski in connection with special *relativity.

control grid A wire-mesh electrode placed between the cathode and anode in a *thermionic valve or a *cathode-ray tube to control the flow of electrons from one to the other. A fluctuating potential signal fed to the control grid produces at the anode a current signal with similar but amplified fluctuations. It thus forms the

basis of the electronic valve amplifier. In a cathode-ray tube the grid controls the intensity of the electron beam and hence the brightness of the image on the screen.

control rod One of a number of rods of a material, such as boron or cadmium, that absorbs neutrons. Control rods can be moved into or out of the core of a *nuclear reactor to control the rate of the reaction taking place within it.

convection A process by which heat is transferred from one part of a fluid to another by movement of the fluid itself. In *natural convection* the movement occurs as a result of gravity; the hot part of the fluid expands, becomes less dense, and is displaced by the colder denser part of the fluid as this drops below it. This is the process that occurs in most domestic hot-water systems between the boiler and the hot-water cylinder. A natural convection current is set up transferring the hot water from the boiler up to the cylinder (always placed above the boiler) so that the cold water from the cylinder can move down into the boiler to be heated. In some modern systems, where small-bore pipes are used or it is inconvenient to place the cylinder above the boiler, the circulation between boiler and hot-water cylinder relies upon a pump. This is an example of *forced convection*, where hot fluid is transferred from one region to another by a pump or fan.

conventional current A 19th-century convention, still in use, that treats any electrical current as a flow of positive charge from a region of positive potential to one of negative potential. The real motion, however, in the case of electrons flowing through a metal conductor, is in the opposite direction, from negative to positive. In semiconductors *hole conduction is in the direction of the con-

ventional current; electron conduction is in the opposite direction.

convergent series A series $a_1 + a_2 + \ldots + a_i + \ldots$, for which a partial sum $S_n = a_1 + a_2 + \ldots + a_n$ tends to a finite (or zero) limit as n tends to infinity. This limit is the *sum* of the series. For example, the series $1 + 1/2 + 1/3 + 1/4 + \ldots$ (with the general term a_i equal to $(1/2)^{i-1}$) tends to the limit 2. A series that is not convergent is said to be a *divergent series*. In such a series the partial sum tends to plus or minus infinity or may oscillate. For example, the series $1 + 1/2 + 1/3 + 1/4 + \ldots$ (with a_i equal to $1/i$) is divergent. As can be seen from this latter example, a series may be divergent even if the individual terms a_i tend to zero as i tends to infinity.

converging lens or mirror A lens or mirror that can refract or reflect a parallel beam of light so that it converges at a point (the principal focus). Such a mirror is concave; a converging lens is thicker at its centre than at its edges (i.e. it is biconvex, plano-convex, or convexo-concave). *Compare* diverging lens or mirror.

conversion electron *See* internal conversion.

converter 1. An electrical machine for converting alternating current into direct current, or less frequently, vice versa. **2.** The reaction vessel in the *Bessemer process or some similar steel-making process. **3.** A computer device for converting information coded in one form into some other form.

converter reactor A *nuclear reactor that converts fertile material (e.g. thorium–232) into *fissile material (e.g. uranium–233). A converter reactor can also be used to produce electrical power.

convex Curving outwards. A *convex mirror* is one in which the reflecting surface is formed from the exterior surface of a sphere or paraboloid. A *convex lens* has at least one face formed from the exterior surface of a sphere. A *biconvex lens* has both faces convex and is therefore thickest at its centre. The *plano-convex lens* has one plane face and one convex face. The *convexo-concave lens* (also called a *meniscus*) has one convex face and one *concave face. *See* lens.

coolant A fluid used to remove heat from a system by *convection (usually forced), either to control the temperature or to extract energy. In a water-cooled car engine the coolant is water (or water and antifreeze), which is pumped around the engine and cooled in the radiator. In a *nuclear reactor the coolant is used to transfer the heat of the reaction from the core to a heat exchanger or to the steam-raising plant. In gas-cooled reactors the coolant is usually carbon dioxide. Pressurized water or boiling water is used as both coolant and *moderator in several types of reactor. In fast reactors, liquid sodium is used as the coolant.

Cooper pairs *See* superconductivity.

coordinate *See* Cartesian coordinates; polar coordinates.

coordinate geometry *See* analytical geometry.

coordination number The number of groups, molecules, atoms, or ions surrounding a given atom or ion in a complex or crystal. For instance, in a square-planar complex the central ion has a coordination number of four. In a close-packed crystal (*see* close packing) the coordination number is twelve.

Copernican astronomy The system of astronomy that was proposed by the Polish canon Nicolaus Copernicus (1473–1543) in his book *De revolutionibus orbium coelestium*, which was published in the month of his death and first seen by him on his deathbed. It used some elements of *Ptol-

emaic astronomy, but rejected the notion, then current, that the earth was a stationary body at the centre of the universe. Instead, Copernicus proposed the apparently unlikely concept that the sun was at the centre of the universe and that the earth was hurtling through space in a circular orbit about it. Galileo's attempts, some 70 years later, to convince the Catholic church that in spite of scriptural authority to the contrary, the Copernican system was correct, resulted in *De revolutionibus* being placed on the Index of forbidden books, where it remained until 1835.

core 1. A rod or frame of magnetic material that increases the inductance of a coil through which it passes. Cores are used in transformers, electromagnets, and the rotors and stators of electrical machines. It may consist of laminated metal, ferrite, or compressed ferromagnetic particles in a matrix of an insulating binder (*dust core*). **2.** The inner part of a *nuclear reactor in which the nuclear reaction takes place. **3.** The devices that make up the memory in certain types of computer. **4.** The central region of a star or planet.

Coriolis force A fictitious force sometimes used to simplify calculations involving rotating systems, such as the movement of air, water, and projectiles over the surface of the rotating earth. The concept was first used in 1835 by Gaspard de Coriolis (1792–1843), a French physicist. The daily rotation of the earth means that in 24 hours a point on its equator moves a distance of some 40 000 kilometres, giving it a tangential velocity of about 1670 kilometres per hour. A point at the latitude of, say, Rome, travels a shorter distance in the same time and therefore has a lower tangential velocity – about 1340 km/hr. Air over the equator has the full tangential velocity of 1670 km/hr and as it travels north,

say, it will retain this velocity; to an observer outside the earth this would be clear. However, to an observer in Rome it appears to be moving eastwards, because the earth at that point is moving eastwards more slowly than the air. The Coriolis force (which is quite fictitious) is the force that a naive observer thinks is needed to push the air eastwards.

corona 1. The outer part of the sun's atmosphere. Its two main components are the K-corona (or inner corona), with a temperature of about 2×10^6 K at a height of some 75 000 km, and the F-corona (or outer corona), which is considerably cooler and extends for several million kilometres into space. **2.** A glowing region of the air surrounding a conductor when the potential gradient near it exceeds a critical value. It is caused by ionization of the air and may be accompanied by hissing sounds. *Corona discharge* (or *point discharge*) occurs at sharp points where the surface charge density is high by the attraction, charging, and consequent repulsion of air molecules.

corpuscular theory *See* light.

corrosion Chemical or electrochemical attack on the surface of a metal. *See also* electrolytic corrosion; rusting.

cosine rule In any triangle, with sides of length a, b, and c, $c^2 = a^2 + b^2 - 2ab\cos\theta$, where θ is the angle between sides a and b.

cosmic radiation High-energy particles that fall on the earth from space. *Primary cosmic rays* consist of nuclei of the most abundant elements, with *protons (hydrogen nuclei) forming by far the highest proportion; electrons, positrons, neutrinos, and gamma-ray photons are also present. The particle energies range from 10^{-11} J to 10 J (10^8 to 10^{20} eV) and as they enter the earth's atmosphere they collide with oxygen and nitrogen nuclei producing *secondary cosmic*

rays. The secondary rays consist of elementary particles and gamma-ray photons. A single high-energy primary particle can produce a large *shower* of secondary particles. The sources of the primary radiation are not all known, although the sun is believed to be the principal source of particles with energies up to about 10^{10} eV. It is believed that all particles with energies of less than 10^{18} eV originate within the Galaxy.

cosmic string *See* string.

cosmology The study of the nature, origin, and evolution of the universe. Various theories concerning the origin and evolution of the universe exist. *See* big-bang theory; steady-state theory.

Cottrell precipitator An electrostatic precipitator used to remove dust particles from industrial waste gases, by attracting them to charged grids or wires.

coudé system *See* telescope.

coulomb Symbol C. The *SI unit of electric charge. It is equal to the charge transferred by a current of one ampere in one second. The unit is named after Charles de Coulomb (1736–1806), a French physicist.

Coulomb's law The force (sometimes called the *Coulomb force*) between two charged particles, regarded as point charges Q_1 and Q_2 a distance d apart, is proportional to the product of the charges and inversely proportional to the square of the distance between them. The law is now usually stated in the form $F = Q_1Q_2/4\pi\varepsilon d^2$, where ε is the absolute *permittivity of the intervening medium. $\varepsilon = \varepsilon_r\varepsilon_0$, where ε_r is the relative permittivity (the dielectric constant) and ε_0 is the electric constant. The electric field surrounding a point charge is called the *Coulomb field* and the scattering of charged particles by the Coulomb field surrounding an atomic nucleus is called *Coulomb scattering*. The law

was first published by Charles de Coulomb in 1785.

counter Any device for detecting and counting objects or events, often incident charged particles or photons. The latter devices usually work by allowing the particle to cause ionization, which creates a current or voltage pulse. The pulses are then counted electronically. *See* Cerenkov counter; crystal counter; Geiger counter; proportional counter; scintillation counter; semiconductor counter; spark counter. These names are often applied merely to the actual detectors; the ancillary counting mechanism is then called a *scaler.

couple Two equal and opposite parallel forces applied to the same body that do not act in the same line. The forces create a torque, the *moment of which is equal to the product of the force and the perpendicular distance between them.

CP invariance The symmetry generated by the combined operation of changing *charge conjugation (C) and *parity (P). *CP violation* occurs in weak interactions in kaon decay. *See also* CPT theorem; time reversal.

CPT theorem The theorem that the combined operation of changing *charge conjugation C, *parity P, and *time reversal T, denoted *CPT*, is a fundamental *symmetry of relativistic *quantum field theory. No violation of the CPT theorem is known experimentally. When C, P, and T (or any two of them) are violated, the principles of relativistic quantum field theory are not affected; however, violation of *CPT invariance* would drastically alter the fundamentals of relativistic quantum field theory. It is not known whether *superstrings or *supermembranes obey versions of the CPT theorem.

creep The continuous deformation of a solid material, usually a metal, under a constant stress that is well below its *yield point. It usually only

occurs at high temperatures and the creep characteristics of any material destined to be used under conditions of high stress at high temperatures must be investigated.

critical angle *See* total internal reflection.

critical damping *See* damping.

critical mass The minimum mass of fissile material that will sustain a nuclear *chain reaction. For example, when a nucleus of uranium–235 disintegrates two or three neutrons are released in the process, each of which is capable of causing another nucleus to disintegrate, so creating a chain reaction. However, in a mass of U–235 less than the critical mass, too many neutrons escape from the surface of the material for the chain reaction to proceed. In the atom bomb, therefore, two or more subcritical masses have to be brought together to make a mass in excess of the critical mass before the bomb will explode.

critical pressure The pressure of a fluid in its *critical state; i.e. when it is at its critical temperature and critical volume.

critical reaction A nuclear *chain reaction in which, on average, one transformation causes exactly one other transformation so that the chain reaction is self-sustaining. If the average number of transformations caused by one transformation falls below one, the reaction is *subcritical* and the chain reaction ceases; if it exceeds one the reaction is *supercritical* and proceeds explosively.

critical state The state of a fluid in which the liquid and gas phases both have the same density. The fluid is then at its *critical temperature, *critical pressure, and *critical volume.

critical temperature 1. The temperature above which a gas cannot be liquefied by an increase of pressure. *See*

also critical state. **2.** *See* transition temperature.

critical volume The volume of a fixed mass of a fluid in its *critical state; i.e. when it is at its critical temperature and critical pressure. The *critical specific volume* is its volume per unit mass in this state: in the past this has often been called the critical volume.

CRO *See* cathode-ray oscilloscope.

cross product *See* vector product.

cross section 1. A plane surface formed by cutting a solid, especially by cutting at right angles to its longest axis. **2.** The area of such a surface. **3.** A measure of the probability that a collision will occur between a beam of radiation and a particular particle, expressed as the effective area presented by the particle in that particular process. It is measured in square metres or *barns.

crucible A dish or other vessel in which substances can be heated to a high temperature.

cryogenic pump A *vacuum pump in which pressure is reduced by condensing gases on surfaces maintained at about 20 K by means of liquid hydrogen or at 4 K by means of liquid helium. Pressures down to 10^{-8} mmHg (10^{-6} Pa) can be maintained; if they are used in conjunction with a *diffusion pump, pressures as low as 10^{-15} mmHg (10^{-13} Pa) can be reached.

cryogenics The study of very low temperatures and the techniques for producing them. Objects are most simply cooled by placing them in a bath containing liquefied gas maintained at a constant pressure. In general, a liquefied gas can provide a constant bath temperature from its triple point to its critical temperature and the bath temperature can be varied by changing the pressure above the liquid. The lowest practical temperature for a liquid bath is 0.3 K.

Refrigerators (*see* refrigeration) consist essentially of devices operating on a repeated cycle, in which a low-temperature reservoir is a continuously replenished liquid bath. Above 1 K they work by compressing and expanding suitable gases. Below this temperature liquids or solids are used and by *adiabatic demagnetization it is possible to reach 10^{-6} K.

cryohydrate A eutectic mixture of ice and some other substance (e.g. an ionic salt) obtained by freezing a solution.

cryometer A thermometer designed to measure low temperatures. *Thermocouples can be used down to about 1 K and *resistance thermometers can be used at 0.01 K. Below this magnetic thermometers (0.001 K) and nuclear-resonance thermometers (3×10^{-7} K) are required.

cryoscopic constant *See* depression of freezing point.

cryostat A vessel enabling a sample to be maintained at a very low temperature. The *Dewar flask is the most satisfactory vessel for controlling heat leaking in by radiation, conduction, or convection. Cryostats usually consist of two or more Dewar flasks nesting in each other. For example, a liquid nitrogen bath is often used to cool a Dewar flask containing a liquid helium bath.

cryotron A switch that relies on *superconductivity. It consists of a coil of wire of one superconducting material surrounding a straight wire of another superconducting material; both are immersed in a liquid-helium bath. A current passed through the coil creates a magnetic field, which alters the superconducting properties of the central wire, switching its resistance from zero to a finite value. Cryotron switches can be made very small and take very little current.

crystal A solid with a regular polyhedral shape. All crystals of the same substance grow so that they have the same angles between their faces. However, they may not have the same external appearance because different faces can grow at different rates, depending on the conditions. The external form of the crystal is referred to as the *crystal habit*. The atoms, ions, or molecules forming the crystal have a regular arrangement and this is the *crystal structure*.

crystal counter A type of solid-state *counter in which a potential difference is applied across a crystal; when the crystal is struck by an elementary particle or photon, the electron–ion pairs created cause a transient increase in conductivity. The resulting current pulses are counted electronically.

crystal habit *See* crystal.

crystal lattice The regular pattern of atoms, ions, or molecules in a crystalline substance. A crystal lattice can be regarded as produced by repeated translations of a *unit cell* of the lattice. *See also* crystal system.

crystallography The study of crystal form and structure. *See also* X-ray crystallography.

crystalloids *See* colloids.

crystal microphone A microphone in which the sound waves fall on a plate of Rochelle salt or similar material with piezoelectric properties, the variation in pressure being converted into a varying electric field by the *piezoelectric effect. Crystal microphones have strong high-frequency response and are nondirectional; they are now rarely used except when their cheapness is important.

crystal oscillator An oscillator of precisely determined frequency in which a piezoelectric crystal is used to produce the oscillation in a tuned circuit or is coupled to a tuned circuit to control its frequency. An alternating electric field applied to

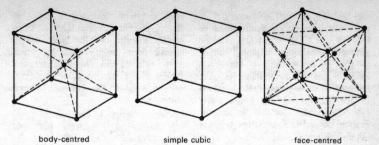

body-centred   simple cubic   face-centred

Cubic crystal structures

two metallic films sputtered onto the parallel faces of a crystal, usually of quartz, causes it to vibrate at its natural frequency; this frequency can be in the kilohertz or megahertz range, depending on how the crystal is cut. The mechanical vibrations in turn create an alternating electric field across the crystal that does not suffer from frequency drift. The device is widely used in *quartz clocks and watches.

crystal pick-up A pick-up in a record player in which the mechanical vibrations produced by undulations in the record groove are transmitted to a piezoelectric crystal, which produces a varying electric field of the same frequency as the sound. This signal is amplified and fed to loudspeakers in order to recreate the sound.

crystal structure *See* crystal.

crystal system A method of classifying crystalline substances on the basis of their unit cell. There are seven crystal systems. If the cell is a parallelopiped with sides a, b, and c and if α is the angle between b and c, β the angle between a and c, and γ the angle between a and b, the systems are:

(1) *cubic* $a=b=c$ and $\alpha=\beta=\gamma=90°$
(2) *tetragonal* $a=b\neq c$ and $\alpha=\beta=\gamma=90°$
(3) *rhombic* (or *orthorhombic*) $a\neq b\neq c$ and $\alpha=\beta=\gamma=90°$

(4) *hexagonal* $a=b\neq c$ and $\alpha=\beta=\gamma=90°$
(5) *trigonal* $a=b\neq c$ and $\alpha=\beta=\gamma\neq90°$
(6) *monoclinic* $a\neq b\neq c$ and $\alpha=\gamma=90°\neq\beta$
(7) *triclinic* $a=b=c$ and $\alpha\neq\beta\neq\gamma$

CT scanner (computerized tomography scanner) *See* tomography.

cubic crystal A crystal in which the unit cell is a cube (*see* crystal system). There are three possible packings for cubic crystals: *simple cubic*, *face-centred cubic*, and *body-centred cubic*. See illustration.

cubic equation An equation in which the highest power of the variable is three. It has the general form $ax^3 + bx^2 + cx + d = 0$ and, in general, is satisfied by three values of x.

cubic expansivity *See* expansivity.

curie The former unit of *activity (*see* radiation units). It is named after the Polish-born French physicist Marie Curie (1867–1934).

Curie point (Curie temperature) The temperature at which a ferromagnetic substance loses its ferromagnetism and becomes only paramagnetic. For iron the Curie point is 760°C and for nickel 356°C.

Curie's law The susceptibility (χ) of a paramagnetic substance is proportional to the thermodynamic tempera-

ture (*T*), i.e. $\chi = C/T$, where *C* is the Curie constant. A modification of this law, the *Curie–Weiss law*, is more generally applicable. It states that $\chi = C/(T - \theta)$, where θ is the Weiss constant, a characteristic of the material. The law was first proposed by the French physicist Pierre Curie (1859–1906) and modified by another French physicist, Pierre-Ernest Weiss (1865–1940).

curium Symbol Cm. A radioactive metallic transuranic element belonging to the actinoids; a.n. 96; mass number of the most stable isotope 247 (half-life 1.64×10^7 years); r.d. (calculated) 13.51; m.p. $1340 \pm 40°C$. There are nine known isotopes. The element was first identified by G. T. Seaborg and associates in 1944 and first produced by L. B. Werner and I. Perlman in 1947 by bombarding americium–241 with neutrons.

curl (rot) The *vector product of the *gradient operator with a vector. For a vector *u* that has components u_1, u_2, and u_3 in the *x*, *y*, and *z* directions (with respective unit vectors *i*, *j*, and *k*), and is a function of *x*, *y*, and *z*, the curl is given by:

$$\text{curl}\,u = \nabla \times u$$
$$= (\partial u_3/\partial y - \partial u_2/\partial z)i +$$
$$(\partial u_1/\partial z - \partial u_3/\partial x)j +$$
$$(\partial u_2/\partial x - \partial u_1/\partial y)k.$$

See also divergence.

current Symbol *I*. A flow of electric charge through a conductor. The current at a particular cross section is the rate of flow of charge. The charge may be carried by electrons, ions, or positive holes (*see* charge carrier). The unit of current is the ampere. *See also* conventional current.

current balance An instrument used to measure a current absolutely, on the basis of the definition of the ampere. An accurate form consists of a beam balance with similar coils attached to the ends of the balance arms. Fixed coils are situated above and below these two coils. The six coils are then connected in series so that a current passing through them creates a torque on the beam, which is restored to the horizontal by means of a rider. From the position and weight of the rider, and the geometry of the system, the current can be calculated.

current density 1. The current flowing through a conductor per unit cross-sectional area, measured in amperes per square metre. **2.** The current flowing through an electrolyte per unit area of electrode.

cusp A point at which two arcs of a curve intersect.

cycle A regularly repeated set of changes to a system that brings back all its parameters to their original values once in every set of changes. The duration of one cycle is called its *period and the rate of repetition of cycle, called the *frequency, is measured in *hertz. *See* simple harmonic motion.

cycloid The curve traced by a point on the circumference of a circle as it rolls without slipping along a straight line. The length of the arc formed by one revolution of the circle is 8*r*, where *r* is the radius of the circle. The horizontal distance between cusps is $2\pi r$.

cyclotron A cyclic particle *accelerator in which charged particles fed into the centre of the device are accelerated in an outward spiral path inside two hollow D-shaped conductors placed to form a split circle. A magnetic field is applied at right-angles to the plane of the dees and an alternating potential difference is applied between them. The frequency of the alternating p.d. is arranged so that the particles are accelerated each time they reach the evacuated gap between the dees. The magnetic field makes them follow curved paths. After several thousand revolutions inside the dees the particles reach the perimeter of the dees, where a deflect-

ing field directs them onto the target. In this device protons can achieve an energy of 10^{-12} J (10 MeV). The first working cyclotron was produced in 1931 by the US physicist E. O. Lawrence (1901–58). *See also* synchrocyclotron.

cylindrical polar coordinates *See* polar coordinates.

D

dalton *See* atomic mass unit.

Dalton's atomic theory A theory of chemical combination, first stated by the British chemist John Dalton (1766–1844) in 1803. It involves the following postulates:
(1) Elements consist of indivisible small particles (atoms).
(2) All atoms of the same element are identical; different elements have different types of atom.
(3) Atoms can neither be created nor destroyed.
(4) 'Compound elements' (i.e. compounds) are formed when atoms of different elements join in simple ratios to form 'compound atoms' (i.e. molecules).
Dalton also proposed symbols for atoms of different elements (later replaced by the present notation using letters).

Dalton's law The total pressure of a mixture of gases or vapours is equal to the sum of the partial pressures of its components, i.e. the sum of the pressures that each component would exert if it were present alone and occupied the same volume as the mixture of gases. Strictly speaking, the principle is true only for ideal gases.

damping A decrease in the amplitude of an oscillation as a result of energy being drained from the oscillating system to overcome frictional or other resistive forces. For example, a pendulum soon comes to rest unless it is supplied with energy from an outside source; in a pendulum clock, energy is supplied through an *escapement from a wound spring or a falling mass to compensate for the energy lost through friction. Damping is introduced intentionally in measuring instruments of various kinds to overcome the problem of taking a reading from an oscillating needle. A measuring instrument is said to be *critically damped* if the system just fails to oscillate and the system comes to rest in the shortest possible time. If it is *underdamped* it will oscillate repeatedly before coming to rest; if it is *overdamped* it will not oscillate but it will take longer to come to rest than it would if it was critically damped. An instrument, such as a galvanometer, that is critically damped is often called a *deadbeat* instrument.

dark matter *See* missing mass.

database A large collection of information that has been coded and stored in a computer in such a way that it can be extracted under a number of different category headings.

dating techniques Methods of estimating the true age of rocks, palaeontological specimens, archaeological sites, etc. *Relative dating techniques* date specimens in relation to one another; for example, stratigraphy is used to establish the succession of fossils. *Absolute* (or *chronometric*) *techniques* give an absolute estimate of the age and fall into two main groups. The first depends on the existence of something that develops at a seasonally varying rate, as in dendrochronology and varve dating. The other uses some measurable change that occurs at a known rate, as in *chemical dating, radioactive (or radiometric) dating (see carbon dating; fission-track dating; potassium–argon dating; rubidium–strontium dating; uranium–lead dating), and *thermoluminescence.

daughter 1. A nuclide produced by radioactive *decay of some other nuclide (the *parent*). **2.** An ion or free radical produced by dissociation or reaction of some other (*parent*) ion or radical.

day The time taken for the earth to complete one revolution on its axis. The *solar day* is the interval between two successive returns of the sun to the *meridian. The *mean solar day* of 24 hours is the average value of the solar day for one year. The *sidereal day* is measured with respect to the fixed stars and is 4.09 minutes shorter than the mean solar day as a result of the imposition of the earth's orbital motion on its rotational motion.

d.c. *See* direct current.

deadbeat *See* damping.

de Broglie wavelength The wavelength of the wave associated with a moving particle. The wavelength (λ) is given by $\lambda = h/mv$, where h is the Planck constant, m is the mass of the particle, and v its velocity. The *de Broglie wave* was first suggested by the French physicist Louis de Broglie (1892–1987) in 1924 on the grounds that electromagnetic waves can be treated as particles (*photons) and one could therefore expect particles to behave in some circumstances like waves (*see* complementarity). The subsequent observation of *electron diffraction substantiated this argument and the de Broglie wave became the basis of *wave mechanics.

debye A unit of electric *dipole moment in the electrostatic system, used to express dipole moments of molecules. It is the dipole moment produced by two charges of opposite sign, each of 1 statcoulomb and placed 10^{-18} cm apart, and has the value $3.335\,64 \times 10^{-30}$ coulomb metre.

Debye–Hückel theory A theory to explain the nonideal behaviour of electrolytes, published in 1923 by Peter Debye (1884–1966) and Erich Hückel (1896–). It assumes that electrolytes in solution are fully dissociated and that nonideal behaviour arises because of electrostatic interactions between the ions. The theory shows how to calculate the extra free energy per ion resulting from such interactions, and consequently the activity coefficient. It gives a good description of nonideal electrolyte behaviour for very dilute solutions, but cannot be used for more concentrated electrolytes.

deca- Symbol da. A prefix used in the metric system to denote ten times. For example, 10 coulombs = 1 decacoulomb (daC).

decay The spontaneous transformation of one radioactive nuclide into a daughter nuclide, which may be radioactive or may not, with the emission of one or more particles or photons. The decay of N_0 nuclides to give N nuclides after time t is given by $N = N_0\exp(-\gamma t)$, where γ is called the *decay constant* or the *disintegration constant*. The reciprocal of the decay constant is the *mean life*. The time required for half the original nuclides to decay (i.e. $N = \frac{1}{2}N_0$) is called the *half-life* of the nuclide. The same terms are applied to elementary particles that spontaneously transform into other particles. For example, a free neutron decays into a proton and an electron (*see* beta decay). *See also* alpha particle.

deci- Symbol d. A prefix used in the metric system to denote one tenth. For example, 0.1 coulomb = 1 decicoulomb (dC).

decibel A unit used to compare two power levels, usually applied to sound or electrical signals. Although the decibel is one tenth of a *bel*, it is the decibel, not the bel, that is invariably used. Two power levels P and P_0 differ by n decibels when $n = 10\log_{10}P/P_0$. If P is the level of sound intensity

to be measured, P_0 is a reference level, usually the intensity of a note of the same frequency at the threshold of audibility.

The logarithmic scale is convenient as human audibility has a range of 1 (just audible) to 10^{12} (just causing pain) and one decibel, representing an increase of some 26%, is about the smallest change the ear can detect.

decimal system A number system based on the number 10; the number system in common use. All rational numbers can be written as a *finite decimal* (e.g. $\frac{1}{4}$ = 0.25) or a *repeating decimal* (e.g. 5/27 = 0.185 185 185 . . .). An *irrational number can be written to any number of decimal places, but can never be given exactly (e.g. $\sqrt{3}$ = 1.732 050 8 . . .).

declination 1. The angle between the magnetic meridian and the geographic meridian at a point on the surface of the earth. *See* geomagnetism. **2.** The angular distance of a celestial body north (positive) or south (negative) of the celestial *equator.

deconfinement temperature *See* quark confinement.

defect 1. A discontinuity in a crystal lattice. A *point defect* consists either of a missing atom or ion creating a *vacancy* in the lattice (a vacancy is sometimes called a *Schottky defect*) or an extra atom or ion between two normal lattice points creating an *interstitial*. A *Frenkel defect* consists of a vacancy in which the missing atom or ion has moved to an interstitial position. If more than one adjacent point defect occurs in a crystal there may be a slip along a surface causing a *line defect* (or *dislocation*). Defects are caused by strain or, in some cases, by irradiation. All crystalline solids contain an equilibrium number of point defects above absolute zero; this number increases with temperature. The existence of defects in crystals is important in the con-

ducting properties of *semiconductors. **2.** *See* mass defect.

definite integral *See* integration.

degaussing The process of neutralizing the magnetization in an object that has inadvertently become magnetized. For example, ferromagnetic components of TV sets may become magnetized and misdirect the electron beams. A degaussing coil is often provided and fed with a diminishing alternating current each time the set is switched on. Ships can be degaussed by surrounding them with current-carrying cables that set up an equal and opposite field. This prevents the ships from detonating magnetic mines. Degaussing is used to protect scientific and other electronic devices from strong magnetic fields; usually a system of coils is designed to neutralize such fields over the important region or the equipment is surrounded by a shield of suitable alloy (e.g. Mumetal).

degeneracy pressure The pressure in a *degenerate gas of fermions caused by the Pauli exclusion principle and the Heisenberg uncertainty principle. Because of the exclusion principle, fermions at a high density, with small interparticle spacing, must have different momenta; from the uncertainty principle, the momentum difference must be inversely proportional to the spacing. Consequently, in a high-density gas (small spacing) the particles have high relative momenta, which leads to a degeneracy pressure much greater than the thermal pressure. *White dwarfs and *neutron stars are supported against collapse under their own gravitational fields by the degeneracy pressure of electrons and neutrons, respectively.

degenerate gas A gas in which, because of high density, the particle concentration is so high that the *Maxwell–Boltzmann distribution does not apply and the behaviour of the gas is governed by *quantum sta-

tistics. Examples of degenerate gases are the conduction electrons in a metal, the electrons in a *white dwarf, and the neutrons in a *neutron star. *See also* degeneracy pressure.

degenerate level An *energy level of a quantum-mechanical system that corresponds to more than one *quantum state.

degenerate semiconductor A heavily doped *semiconductor in which the *Fermi level is located in either the valence band or the conduction band (*see* energy levels) causing the material to behave as a metal.

degenerate states *Quantum states of a system that have the same energy.

degree 1. A unit of plane angle equal to 1/360th of a complete revolution. **2.** A division on a *temperature scale. **3.** The power to which a variable is raised. If one expression contains several variables the overall degree of the expression is the sum of the powers. For example, the expression $p^2q^3r^4$ has a degree of 9 overall (it is a second-degree expression in p). The degree of a polynomial is the degree of the variable with the highest power, e.g. $ax^5 + bx^4 + c$ has a degree of 5. **4.** The highest power to which the derivative of the highest order is raised in a *differential equation. For example, $(d^2y/dx^2)^3 + dy/dx = c$ is a differential equation of the third degree (but second order).

degrees of freedom 1. The number of independent parameters required to specify the configuration of a system. This concept is applied in the *kinetic theory to specify the number of independent ways in which an atom or molecule can take up energy. There are however various sets of parameters that may be chosen, and the details of the consequent theory vary with the choice. For example, in a monatomic gas each atom may be

allotted three degrees of freedom, corresponding to the three coordinates in space required to specify its position. The mean energy per atom for each degree of freedom is the same, according to the principle of the *equipartition of energy, and is equal to $kT/2$ for each degree of freedom (where k is the *Boltzmann constant and T is the thermodynamic temperature). Thus for a monatomic gas the total molar energy is $3LkT/2$, where L is the Avogadro constant (the number of atoms per mole). As $k = R/L$, where R is the molar gas constant, the total molar energy is $3RT/2$.

In a diatomic gas the two atoms require six coordinates between them, giving six degrees of freedom. Commonly these are interpreted as six independent ways of storing energy: on this basis the molecule has three degrees of freedom for different directions of *translational motion, and in addition there are two degrees of freedom for rotation of the molecular axis and one vibrational degree of freedom along the bond between the atoms. The rotational degrees of freedom each contribute their share, $kT/2$, to the total energy; similarly the vibrational degree of freedom has an equal share of kinetic energy and must on average have as much potential energy (*see* simple harmonic motion). The total energy per molecule for a diatomic gas is therefore $3kT/2$ (for translational energy of the whole molecule) plus $2kT/2$ (for rotational energy of each atom) plus $2kT/2$ (for vibrational energy), i.e. a total of $7kT/2$.

2. The least number of independent variables required to define the state of a system in the *phase rule. In this sense a gas has two degrees of freedom (e.g. temperature and pressure).

dekatron A neon-filled tube with a central anode surrounded by ten cathodes and associated transfer electrodes. As voltage pulses are received

by the tube a glow discharge moves from one set of electrodes to the next, enabling the device to be used as a visual counting tube in the decimal system. The tube can also be used for switching.

delayed neutrons The small proportion of neutrons that are emitted with a measurable time delay in a nuclear fission process. *Compare* prompt neutrons.

delay line A component in an electronic circuit that is introduced to provide a specified delay in transmitting the signal. Coaxial cable or inductor-capacitor networks can be used to provide a short delay but for longer delays an *acoustic delay line* is required. In this device the signal is converted by the *piezoelectric effect into an acoustic wave, which is passed through a liquid or solid medium, before reconversion to an electronic signal.

deliquescence The absorption of water from the atmosphere by a hygroscopic solid to such an extent that a concentrated solution of the solid eventually forms.

delta-iron *See* iron.

demagnetization The removal of the ferromagnetic properties of a body by disordering the domain structure (*see* magnetism). One method of achieving this is to insert the body within a coil through which an alternating current is flowing; as the magnitude of the current is reduced to zero, the domains are left with no predominant direction of magnetization.

demodulation The process of extracting the information from a modulated carrier wave (*see* modulation; radio). The device used is called a *demodulator* or a *detector*.

denature To add another isotope to a fissile material to make it unsuitable for use in a nuclear weapon.

densitometer An instrument used to measure the *photographic density of

an image on a film or photographic print. Densitometers work by letting the specimen transmit or reflect a beam of light and monitoring the transmitted or reflected intensity. They originally consisted of visual *photometers but most instruments are now photoelectric. The simplest transmission densitometer consists of a light source, a photosensitive cell, and a microammeter: the density is measured in terms of the meter readings with and without the sample in place. They have a variety of uses, including detecting the sound track on a cinematic film, measuring intensities in spectrographic records, and checking photographic prints.

density 1. The mass of a substance per unit of volume. In *SI units it is measured in $kg\,m^{-3}$. *See also* relative density; vapour density. **2.** *See* charge density. **3.** *See* photographic density.

depleted Denoting a material that contains less of a particular isotope than it normally contains, especially a residue from a nuclear reactor or isotope-separation plant containing fewer fissile atoms than natural uranium.

depletion layer A region in a *semiconductor that has a lower-than-usual number of mobile charge carriers. A depletion layer forms at the interface between two dissimilar regions of conductivity (e.g. a p–n junction). *See* semiconductor diode.

depolarization The prevention of *polarization in a *primary cell. For example, manganese(IV) oxide (the *depolarizer*) is placed around the positive electrode of a *Leclanché cell to oxidize the hydrogen released at this electrode.

depression of freezing point The reduction in the freezing point of a pure liquid when another substance is dissolved in it. It is a *colligative property – i.e. the lowering of the freezing point is proportional to the number of dissolved particles (molecules or ions), and does not

depend on their nature. It is given by $\Delta t = K_f C_m$, where C_m is the molar concentration of dissolved solute and K_f is a constant (the *cryoscopic constant*) for the solvent used. Measurements of freezing-point depression (using a Beckmann thermometer) can be used for finding relative molecular masses of unknown substances.

depth of field The range of distance in front of and behind an object that is being focused by an optical instrument, such as a microscope or camera, within which other objects will be in focus. The *depth of focus* is the amount by which the distance between the camera and the film can be changed without upsetting the sharpness of the image.

derivative *See* differentiation; calculus.

derived unit *See* base unit.

desorption The removal of adsorbed atoms, molecules, or ions from a surface.

detector 1. *See* demodulation. **2.** *See* counter.

deuterated compound A compound in which some or all of the hydrogen-1 atoms have been replaced by deuterium atoms.

deuterium (heavy hydrogen) Symbol D. The isotope of hydrogen that has a mass number 2 (r.a.m. 2.0144). Its nucleus contains one proton and one neutron. The abundance of deuterium in natural hydrogen is about 0.015%. It is present in water as the oxide HDO (*see also* heavy water), from which it is usually obtained by electrolysis or fractional distillation. Its chemical behaviour is almost identical to hydrogen although deuterium compounds tend to react rather more slowly than the corresponding hydrogen compounds. Its physical properties are slightly different from those of hydrogen, e.g. b.p. 23.6 K (hydrogen 20.4 K).

deuterium oxide *See* heavy water.

deuteron A nucleus of a deuterium atom, consisting of a proton and a neutron bound together.

deviation 1. (angle of deviation) The angle formed between a ray of light falling on a surface or transparent body and the ray leaving it. **2.** The difference between one of an observed set of values and the true value, usually represented by the mean of all the observed values. The *mean deviation* is the mean of all the individual deviations of the set. *See* standard deviation.

dew *See* precipitation.

Dewar flask A vessel for storing hot or cold liquids so that they maintain their temperature independently of the surroundings. Heat transfer to the surroundings is reduced to a minimum: the walls of the vessel consist of two thin layers of glass (or, in large vessels, steel) separated by a vacuum to reduce conduction and convection; the inner surface of a glass vessel is silvered to reduce radiation; and the vessel is stoppered to prevent evaporation. It was devised around 1872 by the British physicist Sir James Dewar (1842–1923) and is also known by its first trade name *Thermos flask*. *See also* cryostat.

dew point The temperature at which the water vapour in the air is saturated. As the temperature falls the dew point is the point at which the vapour begins to condense as droplets of water.

dew-point hygrometer *See* hygrometer.

dextrorotatory Denoting a compound that rotates the plane of polarization of plane-polarized light to the right (clockwise as observed by someone facing the oncoming radiation). *See* optical activity.

***d*-form** *See* optical activity.

diamagnetism *See* magnetism.

diamond The hardest known mineral (with a hardness of 10 on Mohs'

scale). It is an allotropic form of pure carbon that has crystallized in the cubic system, usually as octahedra or cubes, under great pressure. Diamond crystals may be colourless and transparent or yellow, brown, or black. They are highly prized as gemstones but also have extensive uses in industry, mainly for cutting and grinding tools. Industrial diamonds are increasingly being produced synthetically.

diaphragm An opaque disc with a circular aperture at its centre. Diaphragms of different sizes are used to control the total light flux passing through an optical system or to reduce aberration by restricting the light passing through a system to the central portion. An *iris diaphragm* consists of a number of overlapping crescent-shaped discs arranged so that the central aperture can be continuously varied in diameter.

diastereoisomers Stereoisomers that are not identical and yet not mirror images. For instance, the *d*-form of tartaric acid and the meso form constitute a pair of diastereoisomers. *See* optical activity.

dichroism The property of some crystals, such as tourmaline, of selectively absorbing light vibrations in one plane while allowing light vibrations at right angles to this plane to pass through. Polaroid is a synthetic dichroic material. *See* polarization.

dielectric A nonconductor of electric charge in which an applied electric field causes a *displacement of charge but not a flow of charge. Electrons within the atoms of a dielectric are, on average, displaced by an applied field with respect to the nucleus, giving rise to a dipole that has an electric moment in the direction of the field. The resulting stress within the dielectric is known as the *electric polarization* (P) and is defined by $P = D - E\varepsilon_0$, where D is the displacement, E is the electric field strength, and ε_0 is the electric constant.

The *dielectric constant* is now called the relative *permittivity. The *dielectric strength* is the maximum potential gradient that can be applied to a material without causing it to break down. It is usually expressed in volts per millimetre. *See also* capacitor.

dielectric constant *See* permittivity.

dielectric heating The heating of a dielectric material, such as a plastic, by applying a radio-frequency electric field to it. The most common method is to treat the material as the dielectric between the plates of a capacitor. The heat produced is proportional to $V^2 f A \phi / t$, where V is the applied potential difference, f its frequency, A is the area of the dielectric, t its thickness, and ϕ is the loss factor of the material (related to its *permittivity).

Diesel engine *See* internal-combustion engine.

differential calculus *See* calculus.

differential equation An equation in which a derivative of y with respect to x appears as well as the variables x and y. The *order* of a differential equation is the order of its highest derivative. The *degree* of the equation is the highest power present of the highest order derivative. There are many types of differential equation, each having its own method of solution. The simplest type has separable variables, enabling each side of the equation to be integrated separately.

differentiation The process of finding the *derivative* of a function in differential *calculus. If $y = f(x)$, the derivative of y, written dy/dx or $f'(x)$, is equal to the limit as $\Delta x \to 0$ of $[f(x + \Delta x) - f(x)]/\Delta x$. In general, if $y = x^n$, then $dy/dx = nx^{n-1}$. On a graph of $y = f(x)$, the derivative dy/dx is the gradient of the tangent to the curve at the point x.

diffraction The spreading or bending of waves as they pass through an aperture or round the edge of a bar-

rier. The diffracted waves subsequently interfere with each other (*see* interference) producing regions of reinforcement and weakening. First noticed as occurring with light by Francesco Grimaldi (1618–63), the phenomenon gave considerable support to the wave theory of light. Diffraction also occurs with streams of particles. *See also* Fresnel diffraction; Fraunhofer diffraction; electron diffraction.

diffraction grating A device for producing spectra by diffraction and interference. The usual grating consists of a glass or speculum-metal sheet with a very large number of equidistant parallel lines ruled on it (usually of the order of 1000 per mm). Diffracted light after transmission through the glass or reflection by the speculum produces maxima of illumination (spectral lines) according to the equation $m\lambda = d(\sin i + \sin\theta)$, where d is the distance between grating lines, λ is the wavelength of the light, i is the angle of incidence, θ the direction of the diffracted maximum, and m is the 'order' of the spectral line. Reflection gratings are also used to produce spectra in the ultraviolet region of the electromagnetic spectrum.

diffusion 1. The process by which different substances mix as a result of the random motions of their component atoms, molecules, and ions. In gases, all the components are perfectly miscible with each other and mixing ultimately becomes nearly uniform, though slightly affected by gravity (*see also* Graham's law). The diffusion of a solute through a solvent to produce a solution of uniform concentration is slower, but otherwise very similar to the process of gaseous diffusion. In solids, however, diffusion occurs very slowly at normal temperatures. **2.** The scattering of a beam of light by reflection at a rough surface or by transmission through a translu-cent (rather than transparent) medium, such as frosted glass. **3.** The passage of elementary particles through matter when there is a high probability of scattering and a low probability of capture.

diffusion cloud chamber *See* cloud chamber.

diffusion pump (condensation pump) A *vacuum pump in which oil or mercury vapour is diffused through a jet, which entrains the gas molecules from the container in which the pressure is to be reduced. The diffused vapour and entrained gas molecules are condensed on the cooled walls of the pump. Pressures down to 10^{-7} Pa can be reached by sophisticated forms of the diffusion pump.

digit A symbol used to represent a single number. For example, the number 479 consists of three digits.

digital computer *See* computer.

digital display A method of indicating a reading of a measuring instrument, clock, etc., in which the appropriate numbers are generated on a fixed display unit by the varying parameter being measured rather than fixed numbers on a scale being indicated by a moving pointer or hand. *See* digitron; light-emitting diode; liquid-crystal display.

digital recording A method of recording or transmitting sound in which the sound itself is not transmitted or recorded. Instead the pressure in the sound wave is sampled at least 30 000 times per second and the successive values represented by numbers, which are then transmitted or recorded. Afterwards they are restored to analogue form in the receiver or player. This method is used for very high fidelity recordings as no distortion or interference occurs during transmission or in the recording process.

digitron An electronic gas-discharge tube that provides a *digital display in calculators, counters, etc. It usually has 10 cold cathodes shaped into the form of the digits 0–9. The cathode selected receives a voltage pulse causing a glow discharge to illuminate the digit. It has now largely been superseded by *light-emitting diodes and *liquid-crystal displays.

dihedral (**dihedron**) An angle formed by the intersection of two planes (e.g. two faces of a polyhedron). The *dihedral angle* is the angle formed by taking a point on the line of intersection and drawing two lines from this point, one in each plane, perpendicular to the line of intersection.

dilatancy *See* Newtonian fluid.

dilation (*or* **dilatation**) 1. An increase in volume. 2. *See* time dilation.

dilatometer A device for measuring the cubic *expansivities of liquids. It consists of a bulb of known volume joined to a graduated capillary tube, which is closed at the top to prevent evaporation. A known mass of liquid is introduced into the device, which is submerged in a bath maintained at different temperatures t_1 and t_2. The two volumes corresponding to these temperatures, V_1 and V_2, are read off the calibrated stem. The value of the cubic expansivity (γ) is then given by

$$\gamma = (V_2 - V_1)/V_1(t_2 - t_1).$$

dimensional analysis A method of checking an equation or a solution to a problem by analysing the dimensions in which it is expressed. It is also useful for establishing the form, but not the numerical coefficients, of an empirical relationship. If the two sides of an equation do not have the same dimensions, the equation is wrong. If they do have the same dimensions, the equation may still be wrong, but the error is likely to be in the arithmetic rather than the method of solution.

dimensions The product or quotient of the basic physical quantities, raised to the appropriate powers, in a derived physical quantity. The basic physical quantities of a mechanical system are usually taken to be mass (M), length (L), and time (T). Using these dimensions, the derived physical quantity velocity will have the dimensions L/T and acceleration will have the dimensions L/T^2. As force is the product of a mass and an acceleration (*see* Newton's law of motion), force has the dimensions MLT^{-2}. In electrical work in *SI units, current, I, can be regarded as dimensionally independent and the dimensions of other electrical units can be found from standard relationships. Charge, for example, is measured as the product of current and time. It therefore has the dimension IT. Potential difference is given by the relationship $P = VI$, where P is power. As power is force × distance ÷ time ($MLT^{-2} \times L \times T^{-1} = ML^2T^{-3}$), voltage V is given by $V = ML^2T^{-3}I^{-1}$.

diode An electronic device with two electrodes. In the obsolescent *thermionic diode* a heated cathode emits electrons, which flow across the intervening vacuum to the anode when a positive potential is applied to it. The device permits flow of current in one direction only as a negative potential applied to the anode repels the electrons. This property of diodes was made use of in the first thermionic radios, in which the diode was used to demodulate the transmitted signal (*see* modulation). In the *semiconductor diode*, a *p–n* junction performs a similar function. The forward current increases with increasing potential difference whereas reverse current is very small indeed. *See* semiconductor; transistor.

dioptre A unit for expressing the power of a lens or mirror equal to the reciprocal of its focal length in metres. Thus a lens with a focal

length of 0.5 metre has a power of $1/0.5 = 2$ dioptres. The power of a converging lens is usually taken to be positive and that of a diverging lens negative. Because the power of a lens is a measure of its ability to cause a beam to converge, the dioptre is now sometimes called the radian per metre.

dip *See* geomagnetism.

dipole 1. Two equal and opposite charges that are separated by a distance. The *dipole moment* is the product of either charge and the distance between them. Some molecules behave as dipoles and measurement of the dipole moments can often provide information regarding the configuration of the molecule. 2. An aerial commonly used for frequencies below 30 megahertz. It consists of a horizontal rod, fed or tapped at its centre. It may be half a wavelength or a full wavelength long.

direct current (d.c.) An electric current in which the net flow of charge is in one direction only. *Compare* alternating current.

direct-current motor *See* electric motor.

direct motion 1. The apparent motion of a planet from west to east as seen from the earth against the background of the stars. 2. The anticlockwise rotation of a planet, as seen from its north pole. *Compare* retrograde motion.

directrix 1. A plane curve defining the base of a *cone. 2. A straight line from which the distance to any point on a *conic is in a constant ratio to the distance from that point to the focus.

discharge 1. The conversion of the chemical energy stored in a *secondary cell into electrical energy. 2. The release of electric charge from a capacitor in an external circuit. 3. The passage of charge carriers through a gas at low pressure in a

discharge tube. A potential difference applied between cathode and anode creates an electric field that accelerates any free electrons and ions to their appropriate electrodes. Collisions between electrons and gas molecules create more ions. Collisions also produce excited ions and molecules (*see* excitation), which decay with emission of light in certain parts of the tube.

discontinuous function *See* continuous function.

disintegration Any process in which an atomic nucleus breaks up spontaneously into two or more fragments in a radioactive decay process or breaks up as a result of a collision with a high-energy particle or nuclear fragment.

disintegration constant *See* decay.

dislocation *See* defect.

disperse phase *See* colloids.

dispersion The splitting up of a ray of light of mixed wavelengths by refraction into its components. Dispersion occurs because the *deviation for each wavelength is different on account of the different speeds at which waves of different wavelengths pass through the refracting medium. If a ray of white light strikes one face of a prism and passes out of another face, the white light will be split into its components and the full visible spectrum will be formed. The *dispersive power* of a prism (or other medium) for white light is defined by
$$(n_b - n_r)/(n_y - 1),$$
where n_b, n_r, and n_y are the *refractive indexes for blue, red, and yellow light respectively. The term is sometimes applied to the separation of wavelengths produced by a *diffraction grating.

dispersion forces *See* van der Waals' force.

dispersive power *See* dispersion.

displacement (electric flux density) Symbol D. The ratio of the charge displaced in a medium subjected to

an electric field and the area of an imagined plane perpendicular to the potential gradient.

distortion The extent to which a system fails to reproduce the characteristics of its input in its output. It is most commonly applied to electronic amplifiers and to optical systems. *See* aberration.

distributive law The mathematical law stating that one operation is independent of being carried out before or after another operation. For example, multiplication is distributive with respect to addition and subtraction, i.e. $x(y + z) = xy + xz$. *Compare* associative law; commutative law.

diurnal Daily; denoting an event that happens once every 24 hours.

divergence (div) The *scalar product of the *gradient operator ∇ with a vector. For a vector u that has components u_1, u_2, and u_3 in the x, y, and z directions, and is a function of x, y, and z, the divergence is given by:
$$\text{div}u = \nabla.u$$
$$= \partial u_1/\partial x + \partial u_2/\partial y + \partial u_3/\partial z.$$
The divergence of a vector at a given point represents the flux of the vector per unit volume in the neighbourhood of that point. *See also* curl; Laplace equation.

divergent series *See* convergent series.

diverging lens or mirror A lens or mirror that can refract or reflect a parallel beam of light into a diverging beam. A diverging lens is predominantly concave; a diverging mirror is convex. *Compare* converging lens or mirror.

dl-form *See* optical activity; racemic mixture.

D-lines Two close lines in the yellow region of the visible spectrum of sodium, having wavelengths 589.0 and 589.6 nm. As they are prominent and easily recognized they are used as a standard in spectroscopy.

domain *See* magnetism.

donor *See* semiconductor.

doping *See* semiconductor.

Doppler effect The apparent change in the observed frequency of a wave as a result of relative motion between the source and the observer. For example, the sound made by a low-flying aircraft as it approaches appears to fall in pitch as it passes and flies away. In fact, the frequency of the aircraft engine remains constant but as it is approaching more sound waves per second impinge on the ear and as it recedes fewer sound waves per second impinge on the ear. The apparent frequency, F, is given by
$$F = f(c - u_o)/(c - u_s),$$
where f is the true frequency, c is the speed of sound, and u_o and u_s are the speeds of the observer and the source, respectively.

Although the example of sound is most commonly experienced, the effect was suggested by Christian Johann Doppler (1803–53), an Austrian physicist, as an attempt to explain the coloration of stars. In fact the Doppler effect cannot be observed visually in relation to the stars, although the effect does occur with electromagnetic radiation and the *red shift of light from receding stars can be observed spectroscopically. The Doppler effect is also used in radar to distinguish between stationary and moving targets and to provide information regarding the speed of moving targets by measuring the frequency shift between the emitted and reflected radiation.

For electromagnetic radiation, the speed of light, c, features in the calculation and as there is no fixed medium to provide a frame of reference, relativity has to be taken into account, so that
$$F = f\sqrt{[(1 - v/c)/(1 + v/c)]},$$
where v is the speed at which source and observer are moving apart. If v^2/c^2 is small compared to 1, i.e. if

d-orbital

the speed of separation is small compared to the speed of light, this equation simplifies to

$$F = f(1 - v/c).$$

d-orbital *See* orbital.

dose A measure of the extent to which matter has been exposed to *ionizing radiation. The *absorbed dose* is the energy per unit mass absorbed by matter as a result of such exposure. The SI unit is the gray, although it is often measured in rads (1 rad = 0.01 gray; *see* radiation units). The *maximum permissible dose* is the recommended upper limit of absorbed dose that a person or organ should receive in a specified period according to the International Commission on Radiological Protection. *See also* linear energy transfer.

dosimeter Any device used to measure absorbed *dose of ionizing radiation. Methods used include the *ionization chamber, photographic film, or the rate at which certain chemical reactions occur in the presence of ionizing radiation.

dot product *See* scalar product.

double refraction The property, possessed by certain crystals (notably calcite), of forming two refracted rays from a single incident ray. The *ordinary ray* obeys the normal laws of refraction. The other refracted ray, called the *extraordinary ray*, follows different laws. The light in the ordinary ray is polarized at right angles to the light in the extraordinary ray. Along an *optic axis the ordinary and extraordinary rays travel with the same speed. Some crystals, such as calcite, quartz, and tourmaline, have only one optic axis; they are *uniaxial crystals*. Others, such as mica and selenite, have two optic axes; they are *biaxial crystals*. The phenomenon is also known as *birefringence* and the double-refracting crystal as a *birefringent crystal*. *See also* polarization.

doublet 1. A pair of optical lenses of different shapes and made of different materials used together so that the chromatic aberration produced by one is largely cancelled by the reverse aberration of the other. **2.** A pair of associated lines in certain spectra, e.g. the two lines that make up the sodium D line.

drain *See* transistor.

dry cell A primary or secondary cell in which the electrolytes are in the form of a paste. Many torch, radio, and calculator batteries are *Leclanché cells in which the electrolyte is an ammonium chloride paste and the container is the negative zinc electrode (with an outer plastic wrapping).

dry ice Solid carbon dioxide used as a refrigerant. It is convenient because it sublimes at −78°C (195 K) at standard pressure rather than melting.

ductility The ability of certain metals, such as copper, to retain their strength when their shape is changed, especially the ability of such metals to be drawn into a thin wire without cracking or breaking.

Dulong and Petit's law For a solid element the product of the relative atomic mass and the specific heat capacity is a constant equal to about $25 \text{ J mol}^{-1} \text{ K}^{-1}$. Formulated in these terms in 1819 by the French scientists Pierre Dulong (1785–1838) and A. T. Petit (1791–1820), the law in modern terms states: the molar heat capacity of a solid element is approximately equal to $3R$, where R is the *gas constant. The law is only approximate but applies with fair accuracy at normal temperatures to elements with a simple crystal structure.

dust core *See* core.

dwarf star A star, such as the sun, that lies on the main sequence in a *Hertzsprung–Russell diagram. *See also* white dwarf.

dynamic equilibrium *See* equilibrium.

dynamics The branch of mechanics concerned with the motion of bodies under the action of forces. Time intervals, distances, and masses are regarded as fundamental and bodies are assumed to possess *inertia. Bodies in motion have an attribute called *momentum (*see* Newton's laws of motion), which can only be changed by the application of a force. *Compare* kinetics; statics.

dynamo An electric *generator, especially one designed to provide *direct current. Alternating-current generators can be called dynamos but are more often called alternators.

dynamo action The generation of electrical current and magnetic field by the motion of an electrically conducting fluid. It is generally believed that the magnetic fields of the earth and the sun are produced by dynamo action in the molten iron–nickel core of the earth and in the plasma of the solar interior.

dynamometer 1. An instrument used to measure a force, often a spring balance. **2.** A device used to measure the output power of an engine or motor. **3.** (**current dynamometer**) A variety of *current balance, for measuring electric current.

dyne The unit of force in the *c.g.s. system; the force required to give a mass of one gram an acceleration of 1 cm s^{-2}. 1 dyne = 10^{-5} newton.

dystectic mixture A mixture of substances that has a constant maximum melting point.

E

e The irrational number defined as the limit as n tends to infinity of $(1 + 1/n)^n$. It has the value $2.718\,28\ldots$. It is used as the base of natural *logarithms and occurs in the *exponential function, e^x.

early universe The study of *cosmology at the time very soon after the *big bang. Theories of the early universe have led to a mutually beneficial interaction between cosmology and the theory of *elementary particles, particularly *grand unified theories.

Because there were very high temperatures in the early universe many of the *broken symmetries in *gauge theories become unbroken symmetries at these temperatures. As the universe cools after the big bang there is thought to be a sequence of transitions to broken symmetry states.

Combining cosmology with grand unified theories helps to explain why the observed universe appears to consist of matter with no *antimatter. This means that one has a nonzero *baryon number for the universe. This solution relies on the fact that there were nonequilibrium conditions in the early universe due to its rapid expansion after the big bang.

An important idea in the theory of the early universe is that of *inflation* – the idea that the nature of the *vacuum state gave rise, after the big bang, to an exponential expansion of the universe. The hypothesis of the *inflationary universe* solves several long-standing problems in cosmology, such as the flatness and homogeneity of the universe.

earth The planet that orbits the sun between the planets Venus and Mars at a mean distance from the sun of $149\,600\,000$ km. It has a mass of about 5.976×10^{24} kg and an equatorial diameter of $12\,756$ km. The earth consists of three layers: the gaseous atmosphere (*see* earth's atmosphere), the liquid hydrosphere, and the solid lithosphere. The solid part of the earth also consists of three layers: the *crust* with a mean thickness of about 32 km under the land and 10 km

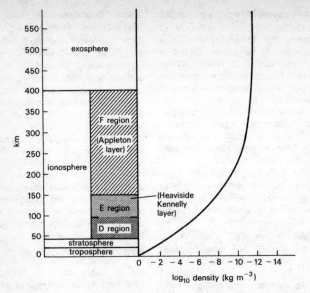

Earth's atmosphere

under the seas; the *mantle*, which extends some 2900 km below the crust; and the *core*, part of which is believed to be liquid. The crust has a relative density of about 3 and consists largely of sedimentary rocks overlaying igneous rocks. The composition of the crust is: oxygen 47%, silicon 28%, aluminium 8%, iron 4.5%, calcium 3.5%, sodium and potassium 2.5% each, and magnesium 2.2%. Hydrogen, carbon, phosphorus, and sulphur are all present to an extent of less than 1%. The mantle reaches a relative density of about 5.5 at its maximum depth and is believed to consist mainly of silicate rocks. The core is believed to have a maximum relative density of 13 and a maximum temperature of 6400 K. *See also* geomagnetism.

earthquake A sudden movement or fracturing within the earth's lithosphere, followed by the series of shocks generated by this movement. This may range from a mild tremor

to a large-scale earth movement causing extensive damage over a wide area. The point at which the earthquake originates is known as the *seismic focus*; the point on the earth's surface directly above this is the *epicentre* (or *hypocentre*). Earthquakes result from a build-up of stresses within the rocks until they are strained to the point beyond which they will fracture. They occur in narrow continuous belts of activity, which correspond with the junction of lithospheric plates, including the circum-Pacific belt, the Alpine–Himalayan belt, and the mid-ocean ridges. The scale of the shock of an earthquake is known as the magnitude; the most commonly used scale for comparing the magnitude of earthquakes is the logarithmic *Richter scale (8.9 is the highest recorded magnitude on the scale).

earth's atmosphere The gas that surrounds the earth. The composition of dry air at sea level is: nitrogen

78.08%, oxygen 20.95%, argon 0.93%, carbon dioxide 0.03%, neon 0.0018%, helium 0.0005%, krypton 0.0001%, and xenon 0.00001%. In addition to water vapour, air in some localities contains sulphur compounds, hydrogen peroxide, hydrocarbons, and dust particles.

The lowest level of the atmosphere, in which most of the weather occurs, is called the *troposphere*. Its thickness varies from about 7 km at the poles to 28 km at the equator and in this layer temperature falls with increasing height. The next layer is the *stratosphere*, which goes up to about 50 km. Here the temperature remains approximately constant. Above this is the *ionosphere*, which extends to about 1000 km, with the temperature rising and the composition changing substantially. At about 100 km and above most of the oxygen has dissociated into atoms; at above 150 km the percentage of nitrogen has dropped to nil. In the ionosphere the gases are ionized by the absorption of solar radiation. This enables radio transmissions to be made round the curved surface of the earth as the ionized gas acts as a reflector for certain wavelengths. The ionosphere is divided into three layers. The D-layer (50–90 km) contains a low concentration of free electrons and reflects low-frequency radio waves. The E-layer (90–150 km) is also called the *Heaviside layer* or *Heaviside–Kennelly layer* as its existence was predicted independently by Oliver Heaviside (1850–1925) and Arthur E. Kennelly (1861–1939). This layer reflects medium-frequency waves. The F-layer (150–1000 km) is also called the *Appleton layer* after its discoverer Sir Edward Appleton (1892–1965). It has the highest concentration of free electrons and is the most useful for radio transmission. Wavelengths between 8 mm and 20 m are not reflected by the ionosphere but escape into space. Therefore television transmissions, which utilize this range, require artificial *satellites for reflection (or reception, amplification, and retransmission). From about 400 km, the outermost region of the atmosphere is also called the *exosphere*. See illustration.

earthshine Sunlight reflected from the surface of the earth. An observer in space may see nearby objects dimly illuminated by earthshine, as things on earth may be illuminated by moonlight. Under certain conditions near new moon the dark disc of the moon can be seen faintly illuminated by earthshine – a phenomenon called 'the old moon in the new moon's arms'.

earth's magnetic field *See* geomagnetism.

ebullioscopic constant *See* elevation of boiling point.

eccentricity *See* conic.

ECG *See* electrocardiogram.

echelon A form of *interferometer consisting of a stack of glass plates arranged stepwise with a constant offset. It gives a high resolution and is used in spectroscopy to study hyperfine line structure. In the *transmission echelon* the plates are made equal in optical thickness to introduce a constant delay between adjacent parts of the wavefront. The *reflecting echelon* has the exposed steps metallized and acts like an exaggerated *diffraction grating.

echo The reflection of a wave by a surface or object so that a weaker version of it is detected shortly after the original. The delay between the two is an indication of the distance of the reflecting surface. An *echo sounder* is an apparatus for determining the depth of water under a ship. The ship sends out a sound wave and measures the time taken for the echo to return after reflection by the sea bottom. *Sonar* (*sound navigation ranging*) is a technique for locating underwater objects by a similar

echolocation

method. Echoes also occur with radio waves; reflection of waves causes an echo in radio transmission and ghosts in television pictures. *See also* radar.

echolocation 1. *See* radar; echo. **2.** A method used by some animals (such as bats, dolphins, and certain birds) to detect objects in the dark. The animal emits a series of high-pitched sounds that echo back from the object and are detected by the ear or some other sensory receptor. From the direction of the echo and from the time between emission and reception of the sounds the object is located, often very accurately.

eclipse The total (*total eclipse*) or partial (*partial eclipse*) obscuring of light from a celestial body as it passes behind or through the shadow of another body. A *lunar eclipse* occurs when the sun, earth, and moon are in a straight line and the shadow of the earth falls on the moon. A *solar eclipse* occurs when the

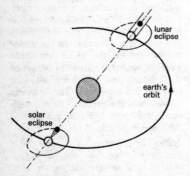

Solar and lunar eclipses

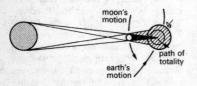

Moon's shadow in solar eclipse

shadow of the moon falls on the earth. See illustrations.

ecliptic The *great circle in which the plane of the earth's orbit round the sun intersects the *celestial sphere. It is thus the sun's apparent annual path across the sky.

eddy current A current induced in a conductor situated in a changing magnetic field or moving in a fixed one. Any imagined circuit within the conductor will change its magnetic flux linkage, and the consequent induced e.m.f. will drive current around the circuit. In a substantial block of metal the resistance will be small and the current therefore large. Eddy currents occur in the cores of transformers and other electrical machines and represent a loss of useful energy (the *eddy-current loss*). To reduce this loss to a minimum metal cores are made of insulated sheets of metal, the resistance between these laminations reducing the current. In high-frequency circuits *ferrite cores can be used. Eddy currents in a moving conductor interact with the magnetic field producing them to retard the motion of the conductor. This enables some electrical instruments (moving-coil type) to utilize eddy currents to create damping. Eddy currents are also used in *induction heating.

Edison cell *See* nickel–iron accumulator.

EEG *See* electroencephalogram.

effective temperature *See* luminosity.

effective value *See* root-mean-square value.

efficiency A measure of the performance of a machine, engine, etc., being the ratio of the energy or power it delivers to the energy or power fed to it. In general, the efficiency of a machine varies with the conditions under which it operates and there is usually a load at which

it operates with the highest efficiency. The *thermal efficiency* of a heat engine is the ratio of the work done by the engine to the heat supplied by the fuel. For a *reversible heat engine this efficiency is equal to $(T_1 - T_2)/T_1$, where T_1 is the thermodynamic temperature at which all the heat is taken up and T_2 is the thermodynamic temperature at which it is given out (*see* Carnot cycle). For real engines it is always less than this.

effusion The flow of a gas through a small aperture. The relative rates at which gases effuse, under the same conditions, is approximately inversely proportional to the square roots of their densities.

eigenfunction An allowed *wave function of a system in quantum mechanics. The associated energies are *eigenvalues*.

Einstein equation 1. The mass–energy relationship announced by Einstein in 1905 in the form $E = mc^2$, where E is a quantity of energy, m its mass, and c is the speed of light. It presents the concept that energy possesses mass. *See also* relativity. **2.** The relationship $E_{max} = hf - W$, where E_{max} is the maximum kinetic energy of electrons emitted in the photoemissive effect, h is the Planck constant, f the frequency of the incident radiation, and W the *work function of the emitter. This is also written $E_{max} = hf - \phi e$, where e is the electronic charge and ϕ a potential difference, also called the work function. (Sometimes W and ϕ are distinguished as *work function energy* and *work function potential*.) The equation can also be applied to photoemission from gases, when it has the form: $E = hf - I$, where I is the ionization potential of the gas.

einsteinium Symbol Es. A radioactive metallic transuranic element belonging to the actinoids; a.n. 99; mass number of the most stable isotope 254 (half-life 270 days). Eleven isotopes are known. The element was first identified by A. Ghiorso and associates in debris from the first hydrogen bomb explosion in 1952. Microgram quantities of the element did not become available until 1961.

Einstein shift *See* redshift.

elastance The reciprocal of *capacitance. It is measured in $farad^{-1}$ (sometimes called a 'daraf').

elastic collision A collision in which the total kinetic energy of the colliding bodies after collision is equal to their total kinetic energy before collision. Elastic collisions occur only if there is no conversion of kinetic energy into other forms, as in the collision of atoms. In the case of macroscopic bodies this will not be the case as some of the energy will become heat. In a collision between polyatomic molecules, some kinetic energy may be converted into vibrational and rotational energy of the molecules, but otherwise molecular collisions appear to be elastic.

elasticity The property of certain materials that enables them to return to their original dimensions after an applied *stress has been removed. In general, if a stress is applied to a wire, the *strain will increase in proportion (*see OA* on the illustration) until a certain point called the *limit of proportionality* is reached. This is in accordance with *Hooke's law. Thereafter there is at first a slight increase in strain with increased load until a

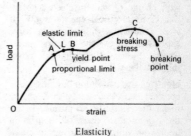

Elasticity

point L is reached. This is the *elastic limit*; up to this point the deformation of the specimen is elastic, i.e. when the stress is removed the specimen returns to its original length. Beyond the point L there is permanent deformation when the stress is removed, i.e. the material has ceased to be *elastic* and has become *plastic*. In the plastic stages individual materials vary somewhat; in general, however, at a point B there is a sudden increase in strain with further increases of stress – this is the *yield point*. Beyond the point C, the *breaking stress*, the wire will snap (which occurs at point D).

elastic modulus The ratio of the *stress applied to a body to the *strain produced. The *Young modulus of elasticity*, named after the British physicist Thomas Young (1773–1829), refers to longitudinal stress and strain. The *bulk modulus* is the ratio of the pressure on a body to its fractional decrease in volume. The *shear* (or *rigidity*) *modulus* is the tangential force per unit area divided by the angular deformation in radians.

electret A permanently electrified substance or body that has opposite charges at its extremities. They resemble permanent magnets in many ways. An electret can be made by cooling certain waxes in a strong electric field.

electrical energy A form of energy related to the position of an electric charge in an electric field. For a body with charge Q and an electric potential V, its electrical energy is QV. If V is a potential difference, the same expression gives the energy transformed when the charge moves through the p.d.

electric arc A luminous discharge between two electrodes. The discharge raises the electrodes to incandescence, the resulting thermal ionization largely providing the carriers to maintain the high current between the electrodes.

electric-arc furnace A furnace used in melting metals to make alloys, especially in steel manufacture, in which the heat source is an electric arc. In the direct-arc furnace, such as the Héroult furnace, an arc is formed between the metal and an electrode. In the indirect-arc furnace, such as the Stassano furnace, the arc is formed between two electrodes and the heat is radiated onto the metal.

electric bell A device in which an electromagnetically operated hammer strikes a bell (see illustration). Pressing the bell-push closes a circuit, causing current to flow from a battery or mains step-down transformer through an electromagnet. The electromagnet attracts a piece of soft iron attached to the hammer, which strikes the bell and at the same time breaks the circuit. The hammer springs back into its original position again, closing the circuit and causing the magnet to attract the soft iron. This pro-

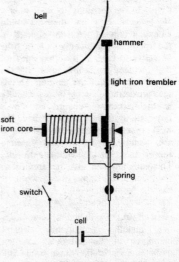

Electric bell

cess continues until the bell-push is released.

electric charge *See* charge.

electric constant *See* permittivity.

electric current *See* current.

electric displacement (electric flux density) Symbol D. The charge per unit area that would be displaced across a layer of conductor placed across an *electric field. This describes also the charge density on an extended surface that could be causing the field.

electric field A region in which an electric charge experiences a force usually because of a distribution of other charges. The *electric field strength* or *electric intensity* (E) at any point in an electric field is defined as the force per unit charge experienced by a small charge placed at that point. This is equivalent to a potential gradient along the field and is measured in volts per metre. The strength of the field can alternatively be described by its *electric displacement D. The ratio D/E for measurements in a vacuum is the electric constant ε_0. In a substance the observed potential gradient is reduced by electron movement so that D/E appears to increase: the new ratio (ε) is called the *permittivity of the substance. An electric field can be created by an isolated electric charge, in which case the field strength at a distance r from a point charge Q is given by $E = Q/4\pi r^2 \varepsilon$, where ε is the permittivity of the intervening medium (*see* Coulomb's law). An electric field can also be created by a changing magnetic field.

electric flux Symbol Ψ. In an *electric field, the product of the electric flux density and the relevant area. *See* electric displacement.

electric flux density *See* electric displacement.

electricity Any effect resulting from the existence of stationary or moving electric charges.

electric lighting Illumination provided by electric currents. The devices used are the *arc lamp*, the *light bulb* (incandescent filament lamp), and the *fluorescent tube*. In the arc lamp, which is no longer used as a general means of illumination, an electric current flows through a gap between two carbon electrodes, between which a high potential difference is maintained. The current is carried by electrons and ions in the vapour produced by the electrodes and a mechanism is required to bring the electrodes closer together as they are vaporized. The device produces a strong white light but has many practical disadvantages. However, arcs enclosed in an inert gas (usually xenon) are increasingly used for such purposes as cinema projectors. The common light bulb is a glass bulb containing a tungsten filament and usually an inert gas. The passage of an electric current through the filament heats it to a white heat. Inert gas is used in the bulb to minimize blackening of the glass by evaporation of tungsten. In the fluorescent tube a glass tube containing mercury vapour (or some other gas) at a low pressure has its inner surface coated with a fluorescent substance. A discharge is created within the tube between two electrodes. Electrons emitted by the cathode collide with gas atoms or molecules and raise them to an excited state (*see* excitation). When they fall back to the *ground state they emit photons of ultraviolet radiation, which is converted to visible light by the coating of phosphor on the inner walls of the tube. In some lamps, such as the *sodium-vapour and *mercury-vapour lamps used in street lighting, no fluorescent substance is used, the light being emitted directly by the excited

atoms of sodium or mercury. Vapour lights are more efficient than filament lights as less of the energy is converted into heat.

electric motor A machine for converting electrical energy into mechanical energy. They are quiet, clean, and have a high efficiency (75–95%). They work on the principle that a current passing through a coil within a magnetic field will experience forces that can be used to rotate the coil. In the *induction motor*, alternating current is fed to a stationary coil (the *stator*), which both creates the magnetic field and induces a current in the rotating coil (*rotor*), which it surrounds. The advantage of this kind of motor is that current does not have to be fed through a commutator to a moving part. In the *synchronous motor*, alternating current fed to the stator produces a magnetic field that rotates and locks with the field of the rotor, in this case an independent magnet, causing the rotor to rotate at the same speed as the stator field rotates. The rotor is either a permanent magnet or an electromagnet fed by a direct current through slip rings. In the *universal motor*, current is fed to the stator and, through a commutator, to the rotor. In the series-wound motor the two are in series; in the shunt-wound motor they are in parallel. These motors can be used with either a.c. or d.c. but some small motors use a permanent magnet as the stator and require d.c. for the rotor (via the commutator). *See also* linear motor.

electric polarization *See* dielectric.

electric potential Symbol V. The energy required to bring unit electric charge from infinity to the point in an electric field at which the potential is being specified. The unit of electric potential is the volt. The *potential difference (p.d.)* between two points in an electric field or circuit is the difference in the values of the electric potentials at the two points, i.e. it is the work done in moving unit charge from one point to the other.

electric power The rate of expending energy or doing work in an electrical system. For a direct-current circuit, it is given by the product of the current passing through a system and the potential difference across it. In alternating-current circuits, the power is given by $VI\cos\phi$, where V and I are the RMS values and ϕ is the *phase angle. $\cos\phi$ is called the *power factor* of the circuit.

electric spark The transient passage of an electric current through a gas between two points of high opposite potential, with the emission of light and sound. *Lightning consists of a spark between a cloud and earth or between two oppositely charged parts of the same cloud.

electric susceptibility *See* susceptibility.

electrocardiogram (ECG) A tracing or graph of the electrical activity of the heart. Recordings are made from electrodes fastened over the heart and usually on both arms and a leg. Changes in the normal pattern of an ECG may indicate heart irregularities or disease.

electrochemical cell *See* cell.

electrochemical equivalent Symbol z. The mass of a given element liberated from a solution of its ions in electrolysis by one coulomb of charge. *See* Faraday's laws (of electrolysis).

electrochemical series *See* electromotive series.

electrochemistry The study of chemical properties and reactions involving ions in solution, including electrolysis and electric cells.

electrochromatography *See* electrophoresis.

electrode A conductor that emits or collects electrons in a cell, thermionic valve, semiconductor device, etc. The

anode is the positive electrode and the *cathode* is the negative electrode.

electrodeposition The process of depositing one metal on another by electrolysis, as in *electroforming and *electroplating.

electrode potential The potential difference produced between the electrode and the solution in a *half cell. It is not possible to measure this directly since any measurement involves completing the circuit with the electrolyte, thereby introducing another half cell. *Standard electrode potentials* $E^{\ominus}$ are defined by measuring the potential relative to a standard *hydrogen half cell using 1.0 molar solution at 25°C. The convention is to designate the cell so that the oxidized form is written first. For example,

$$Pt(s)|H_2(g)H^+(aq)|Zn^{2+}(aq)|Zn(s)$$

The e.m.f. of this cell is –0.76 volt (i.e. the zinc electrode is negative). Thus the standard electrode potential of the $Zn^{2+}|Zn$ half cell is –0.76 V. Electrode potentials are also called *reduction potentials*. *See also* electromotive series.

electrodialysis A method of obtaining pure water from water containing a salt, as in desalination. The water to be purified is fed into a cell containing two electrodes. Between the electrodes is placed an array of semipermeable membranes alternately semipermeable to positive ions and negative ions. The ions tend to segregate between alternate pairs of membranes, leaving pure water in the other gaps between membranes. In this way, the feed water is separated into two streams: one of pure water and the other of more concentrated solution.

electrodynamics The study of electric charges in motion, the forces created by electric and magnetic fields, and the relationship between them. *Compare* electrostatics.

electroencephalogram (EEG) A tracing or graph of the electrical activity of the brain. Electrodes taped to the scalp record electrical waves from different parts of the brain. The pattern of an EEG reflects an individual's level of consciousness and can be used to detect such disorders as epilepsy, tumours, or brain damage.

electroforming A method of forming intricate metal articles or parts by *electrodeposition of the metal on a removable conductive mould.

electroluminescence *See* luminescence.

electrolysis The production of a chemical reaction by passing an electric current through an electrolyte. In electrolysis, positive ions migrate to the cathode and negative ions to the anode.

electrolyte A liquid that conducts electricity as a result of the presence of positive or negative ions. Electrolytes are molten ionic compounds or solutions containing ions, i.e. solutions of ionic salts or of compounds that ionize in solution. Liquid metals, in which the conduction is by free electrons, are not usually regarded as electrolytes.

electrolytic capacitor *See* capacitor.

electrolytic cell A cell in which electrolysis occurs; i.e. one in which current is passed through the electrolyte from an external source.

electrolytic corrosion Corrosion that occurs through an electrochemical reaction.

electrolytic gas The highly explosive gas formed by the electrolysis of water. It consists of two parts hydrogen and one part oxygen by volume.

electrolytic rectifier A *rectifier consisting of two dissimilar electrodes immersed in an electrolyte. By suitable choice of electrodes and electrolyte the cell can be made to pass current easily in one direction but hardly at all in the other. Examples include

a lead–aluminium cell with ammonium phosphate(V) electrolyte and a tantalum–lead cell with sulphuric acid as the electrolyte.

electrolytic refining The purification of metals by electrolysis. It is commonly applied to copper. A large piece of impure copper is used as the anode with a thin strip of pure copper as the cathode. Copper(II) sulphate solution is the electrolyte. Copper dissolves at the anode: Cu → Cu^{2+} + 2e, and is deposited at the cathode. The net result is transfer of pure copper from anode to cathode. Gold and silver in the impure copper form a so-called *anode sludge* at the bottom of the cell, which is recovered.

electrolytic separation A method of separating isotopes by exploiting the different rates at which they are released in electrolysis. It was formerly used for separating deuterium and hydrogen. On electrolysis of water, hydrogen is formed at the cathode more readily than deuterium, thus the water becomes enriched with deuterium oxide.

electromagnet A magnet consisting of a soft ferromagnetic core with a coil of insulated wire wound round it. When a current flows through the wire the core becomes magnetized; when the current ceases to flow the core loses its magnetization. Electromagnets are used in switches, solenoids, electric bells, metal-lifting cranes, and many other applications.

electromagnetic induction The production of an electromotive force in a conductor when there is a change of magnetic flux linkage with the conductor or when there is relative motion of the conductor across a magnetic field. The magnitude of the e.m.f. is proportional (and in modern systems of units equal) to the rate of change of the flux linkage or the rate of cutting flux $d\Phi/dt$; the sense of the induced e.m.f. is such that any induced current will oppose the change causing the induction, i.e. E = $-d\Phi/dt$. *See* Faraday's laws; Lenz's law; Neumann's law; inductance.

electromagnetic interaction *See* fundamental interactions.

electromagnetic pump A pump used for moving liquid metals, such as the liquid-sodium coolant in a fast nuclear reactor. The liquid is passed through a flattened pipe over two electrodes between which a direct current flows. A magnetic field at right angles to the current causes a force to be created directly on the liquid, along the axis of the tube. The pump has no moving parts and is therefore safe and trouble free.

electromagnetic radiation Energy resulting from the acceleration of electric charge and the associated electric fields and magnetic fields. The energy can be regarded as waves propagated through space (requiring no supporting medium) involving oscillating electric and magnetic fields at right angles to each other and to the direction of propagation. In a vacuum the waves travel with a constant speed (the speed of light) of 2.9979×10^8 metres per second; if material is present they are slower. Alternatively, the energy can be regarded as a stream of *photons travelling at the speed of light, each photon having an energy hc/λ, where h is the Planck constant, c is the speed of light, and λ is the wavelength of the associated wave. A fusion of these apparently conflicting concepts is possible using the methods of *quantum mechanics or *wave mechanics. The characteristics of the radiation depend on its wavelength. *See* electromagnetic spectrum.

electromagnetic spectrum The range of wavelengths over which *electromagnetic radiation extends. The longest waves (10^5–10^{-3} metres) are radio waves, the next longest (10^{-3}–10^{-6} m) are infrared waves, then

comes the narrow band (4–7×10^{-7} m) of visible light, followed by ultraviolet waves (10^{-7}–10^{-9} m), X-rays (10^{-9}–10^{-11} m), and gamma rays (10^{-11}–10^{-14} m).

electromagnetic units (e.m.u.) A system of electrical units formerly used in the *c.g.s. system. The e.m.u. of electric current is the *abampere* (all e.m.u. have the prefix *ab-* attached to the names of practical units). The abampere is the current that, flowing in an arc of a circle (1 centimetre in diameter), exerts a force of 1 dyne on unit magnetic pole at the centre of the circle. In e.m.u. the magnetic constant is of unit magnitude. The system has now been replaced by *SI units for most purposes. *Compare* electrostatic units; Gaussian units; Heaviside–Lorentz units.

electromagnetic wave *See* electromagnetic radiation; wave.

electrometallurgy The uses of electrical processes in the separation of metals from their ores, the refining of metals, or the forming or plating of metals.

electrometer A measuring instrument for determining a voltage difference without drawing an appreciable current from the source. Originally electrostatic instruments based on the electroscope, they are now usually based on operational amplifiers, solid-state devices with high input impedances. Electrometers are also used to measure low currents (nanoamperes), by passing the current through a high resistance.

electromotive force (e.m.f.) The greatest potential difference that can be generated by a particular source of electric current. In practice this may be observable only when the source is not supplying current, because of its *internal resistance.

electromotive series (electrochemical series) A series of chemical elements arranged in order of their *electrode potentials. The hydrogen electrode ($H^+ + e \rightarrow \frac{1}{2}H_2$) is taken as having zero electrode potential. Elements that have a greater tendency than hydrogen to lose electrons to their solution are taken as *electropositive*; those that gain electrons from their solution are below hydrogen in the series and are called *electronegative*. The series shows the order in which metals replace one another from their salts; electropositive metals will replace hydrogen from acids. The chief metals and hydrogen, placed in order in the series, are: potassium, calcium, sodium, magnesium, aluminium, zinc, cadmium, iron, nickel, tin, lead, hydrogen, copper, mercury, silver, platinum, gold.

electron An *elementary particle, classed as a *lepton, with a rest mass (symbol m_e) of $9.109\,3897(54) \times 10^{-31}$ kg and a negative charge of $1.602\,177\,33(49) \times 10^{-19}$ coulomb. Electrons are present in all atoms in groupings called shells around the nucleus; when they are detached from the atom they are called *free electrons*. The antiparticle of the electron is the *positron*.

electron affinity Symbol A. The energy change occurring when an atom or molecule gains an electron to form a negative ion. For an atom or molecule X, it is the energy released for the electron-attachment reaction

$$X(g) + e \rightarrow X^-(g)$$

Often this is measured in electronvolts. Alternatively, the molar enthalpy change, ΔH, can be used.

electron biprism An arrangement of fields that splits a beam of electrons or other charged particles in an analogous way to an optical biprism.

electron capture 1. The formation of a negative ion by an atom or molecule when it acquires an extra free electron. **2.** A radioactive transformation in which a nucleus acquires an electron from an inner orbit of the atom, thereby transforming, initially,

electron diffraction

into a nucleus with the same mass number but an atomic number one less than that of the original nucleus (capture of the electron transforms a proton into a neutron). This type of capture is accompanied by emission of an X-ray photon as the vacancy in the inner orbit is filled by an outer electron.

electron diffraction *Diffraction of a beam of electrons by atoms or molecules. The fact that electrons can be diffracted in a similar way to light and X-rays shows that particles can act as waves (*see* de Broglie wavelength). An electron (mass m, charge e) accelerated through a potential difference V acquires a kinetic energy $mv^2/2 = eV$, where v is the velocity of the electron. The (nonrelativistic) momentum (p) of the electron is $\sqrt{(2eVm)}$. The de Broglie wavelength (λ) of an electron is given by h/p, where h is the Planck constant, thus $\lambda = h/\sqrt{(2eVm)}$. For an accelerating voltage of 3600 V, the wavelength of the electron beam is 0.02 nanometre, some 3×10^4 times shorter than visible radiation.

Electrons then, like X-rays, show diffraction effects with molecules and crystals in which the interatomic spacing is comparable to the wavelength of the beam. They have the advantage that their wavelength can be set by adjusting the voltage. Unlike X-rays they have very low penetrating power. The first observation of electron diffraction was by George Thomson (1892–1975) in 1927, in an experiment in which he passed a beam of electrons in a vacuum through a very thin gold foil onto a photographic plate. Concentric circles were produced by diffraction of electrons by the lattice. The same year Clinton J. Davisson (1881–1958) and Lester Germer (1896–1971) performed a classic experiment in which they obtained diffraction patterns by glancing an electron beam off the surface of a nickel crystal. Both experiments were important verifications of de Broglie's theory and the new quantum theory.

Electron diffraction, because of the low penetration, cannot easily be used to investigate crystal structure. It is, however, employed to measure bond lengths and angles of molecules in gases. Moreover, it is extensively used in the study of solid surfaces and absorption. The main techniques are low-energy electron diffraction (*LEED*) in which the electron beam is reflected onto a fluorescent screen, and high-energy electron diffraction (*HEED*) used either with reflection or transmission in investigating thin films.

electronegative Describing elements that tend to gain electrons and form negative ions. The halogens are typical electronegative elements. For example, in hydrogen chloride, the chlorine atom is more electronegative than the hydrogen and the molecule is polar, with negative charge on the chlorine atom. There are various ways of assigning values for the *electronegativity* of an element. *Mulliken electronegativities* are calculated from $E = (I + A)/2$, where I is ionization potential and A is electron affinity. More commonly, *Pauling electronegativities* are used. These are based on bond dissociation energies using a scale in which fluorine, the most electronegative element, has a value 4. Some other values on this scale are B 2, C 2.5, N 3.0, O 3.5, Si 1.8, P 2.1, S 2.5, Cl 3.0, Br 2.8.

electron gun A device used in *cathode-ray tubes (including television tubes), electron microscopes, etc., to produce a steady narrow beam of electrons. It usually consists of a heated cathode, control grid, and two or more annular anodes inserted in an evacuated tube. The electrons emitted by the cathode are attracted to the final anode, through which

they pass. The intensity of the beam is regulated by the control grid and potential differences between the anodes create electric fields that focus the diverging electrons into a narrow beam.

electronics The study and design of control, communication, and computing devices that rely on the movement of electrons in circuits containing semiconductors, thermionic valves, resistors, capacitors, and inductors.

electron lens A device used to focus an electron beam. It is analogous to an optical lens but instead of using a refracting material, such as glass, it uses a coil or coils to produce a magnetic field or an arrangement of electrodes between which an electric field is created. Electron lenses are used in *electron microscopes and *cathode-ray tubes.

electron microscope A form of microscope that uses a beam of electrons instead of a beam of light (as in the optical microscope) to form a large image of a very small object. In optical microscopes the resolution is limited by the wavelength of the light. High-energy electrons, however, can be associated with a considerably shorter wavelength than light; for example, electrons accelerated to an energy of 10^5 electronvolts have a wavelength of 0.004 nanometre (*see* de Broglie wavelength) enabling a resolution of 0.2–0.5 nm to be achieved. The *transmission electron microscope* (see illustration) has an electron beam, sharply focused by *electron lenses, passing through a very thin metallized specimen (less than 50 nanometres thick) onto a fluorescent screen, where a visual image is formed. This image can be photographed. The *scanning electron microscope* can be used with thicker specimens and forms a perspective image, although the resolution and magnification are lower. In this type of instrument a beam of primary electrons scans the specimen and those that are reflected, together with any secondary electrons emitted, are collected. This current is used to modulate a separate electron beam in a TV monitor, which scans the screen at the same frequency, consequently building up a picture of the specimen. The resolution is limited to about 10–20 nm.

electron optics The study of the use of *electron lenses in the *electron microscope, *cathode-ray tubes, and other similar devices. The focusing of beams of positive or negative ions also relies on these methods.

electron probe microanalysis (EPM) A method of analysing a very small quantity of a substance (as little as 10^{-13} gram). The method consists of directing a very finely focused beam of electrons on to the sample to produce the characteristic X-ray spectrum of the elements present. It can be used quantitatively for elements with atomic numbers in excess of 11.

electron-spin resonance (ESR) A spectroscopic method of locating elec-

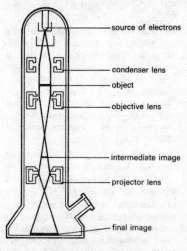

source of electrons

condenser lens

object

objective lens

intermediate image

projector lens

final image

Principle of transmission electron microscope

trons within the molecules of a paramagnetic substance (*see* magnetism) in order to provide information regarding its bonds and structure. The spin of an unpaired electron is associated with a *magnetic moment that is able to align itself in one of two ways with an applied external magnetic field. These two alignments correspond to different *energy levels, with a statistical probability, at normal temperatures, that there will be slightly more in the lower state than in the higher. By applying microwave radiation to the sample a transition to the higher state can be achieved. The precise energy difference between the two states of an electron depends on the surrounding electrons in the atom or molecule. In this way the position of unpaired electrons can be investigated. The technique is used particularly in studying free radicals and paramagnetic substances such as inorganic complexes. *See also* nuclear magnetic resonance.

electronvolt Symbol eV. A unit of energy equal to the work done on an electron in moving it through a potential difference of one volt. It is used as a measure of particle energies although it is not an *SI unit. 1 eV = 1.602×10^{-19} joule.

electrophoresis (cataphoresis) A technique for the analysis and separation of colloids, based on the movement of charged colloidal particles in an electric field. There are various experimental methods. In one the sample is placed in a U-tube and a buffer solution added to each arm, so that there are sharp boundaries between buffer and sample. An electrode is placed in each arm, a voltage applied, and the motion of the boundaries under the influence of the field is observed. The rate of migration of the particles depends on the field, the charge on the particles, and on other factors, such as the size and shape of the particles. More simply,

electrophoresis can be carried out using an adsorbent, such as a strip of filter paper, soaked in a buffer with two electrodes making contact. The sample is placed between the electrodes and a voltage applied. Different components of the mixture migrate at different rates, so the sample separates into zones. The components can be identified by the rate at which they move. This technique has also been known as *electrochromatography*.

Electrophoresis is used extensively in studying mixtures of proteins, nucleic acids, carbohydrates, enzymes, etc. In clinical medicine it is used for determining the protein content of body fluids.

electrophorus An early form of *electrostatic generator. It consists of a flat dielectric plate and a metal plate with an insulated handle. The dielectric plate is charged by friction and the metal plate is placed on it and momentarily earthed, which leaves the metal plate with an induced charge of opposite polarity to that of the dielectric plate. The process can be repeated until all of the original charge has leaked away.

electroplating A method of plating one metal with another by *electrodeposition. The articles to be plated are made the cathode of an electrolytic cell and a rod or bar of the plating metal is made the anode. Electroplating is used for covering metal with a decorative, more expensive, or corrosion-resistant layer of another metal.

electropositive Describing elements that tend to lose electrons and form positive ions. The alkali metals are typical electropositive elements.

electroscope A device for detecting electric charge and for identifying its polarity. In the *gold-leaf electroscope* two rectangular gold leaves are attached to the end of a conducting rod held in an insulated frame. When

a charge is applied to a plate attached to the other end of the conducting rod, the leaves move apart owing to the mutual repulsion of the like charges they have received.

electrostatic field The *electric field that surrounds a stationary charged body.

electrostatic generator A device used to build up electric charge to an extreme potential usually for experimental purposes. The *electrophorus and the *Wimshurst machine were early examples; a more usual device now is the *Van de Graaff generator.

electrostatic precipitation A method of removing solid and liquid particles from suspension in a gas. The gas is exposed to an electric field so that the particles are attracted to and deposited on a suitably placed electrode. Electrostatic precipitation is widely used to remove dust and other pollutants from waste gases and from air. *See also* Cottrell precipitator.

electrostatics The study of electric charges at rest, the forces between them (*see* Coulomb's law), and the electric fields associated with them. *Compare* electrodynamics.

electrostatic units (e.s.u.) A system of electrical units in the *c.g.s. system. The e.s.u. of electric charge is the *statcoulomb* (all e.s.u. have the prefix *stat-* attached to the names of practical units). The statcoulomb is the quantity of electric charge that will repel an equal quantity 1 centimetre distant with a force of 1 dyne. In e.s.u. the electric constant is of unit magnitude. The system has now been replaced for most purposes by *SI units. *Compare* electromagnetic units; Gaussian units; Heaviside–Lorentz units.

electrostriction A change in the dimensions of a body as a result of reorientation of its molecules when it is placed in an electric field. If the field is not homogeneous the body

will tend to move; if its relative permittivity is higher than that of its surroundings it will tend to move into a region of higher field strength. *Compare* magnetostriction.

electroweak theory A *gauge theory (sometimes called *quantum flavourdynamics*, or *QFD*) that gives a unified description of the electromagnetic and weak interactions (*see* fundamental interactions). A successful electroweak theory was proposed in 1967 by Steven Weinberg and Abdul Salam, known as the *Weinberg–Salam model* or *WS model*. Because similar ideas were put forward by Sheldon Glashow, it is sometimes known as the *Glashow–Weinberg–Salam model* or *GWS model*. In this electroweak theory the gauge group is non-Abelian and the gauge symmetry is a *broken symmetry. The electroweak interaction is mediated by photons and by intermediate vector bosons, called the *W boson and the *Z boson. The observation of these particles in 1983/84, with their predicted energies, was a major success of the theory. The theory successfully accounts for existing data for electroweak processes and also predicts the existence of a heavy particle with spin 0, the *Higgs boson.

electrum 1. An alloy of gold and silver containing 55–88% of gold. **2.** A *German silver alloy containing 52% copper, 26% nickel, and 22% zinc.

elementary particles The fundamental constituents of all the matter in the universe. Until the discovery of the electron by J. J. Thomson in 1897, it was assumed that atoms were the fundamental constituents of matter. This discovery, and Rutherford's discovery of the atomic nucleus and the proton in 1911, made it apparent that atoms were not themselves elementary, in the sense that they have an internal structure. Chadwick's discovery of the neutron in 1932 completed the atomic model based on an

elementary particles

atomic nucleus consisting of protons and neutrons surrounded by sufficient electrons to balance the nuclear charge. It did not, however, explain the great stability of the nucleus, which clearly could not be held together by an electromagnetic interaction, as the neutron has no electric charge. In 1935 Yukawa suggested that the *exchange forces* that held them together involved short-lived particles, called *mesons*, which jumped from proton to neutron and back again. This concept led to the discovery of strong interactions, and weak interactions, bringing the total of *fundamental interactions to four. It also led to the discovery of some 200 short-lived 'elementary' particles, some of which were clearly more elementary than others. In the current classification two main classes of particles are recognized: *leptons (electron, muon, neutrinos, tau particle), which interact either by the electromagnetic interaction or the weak interaction and have no apparent internal structure; and *hadrons (nucleons, pions, etc.), which interact by the strong interaction and have a complex internal structure.

Hadron structure is currently based on Murray Gell-Mann's concept of the *quark*, introduced in 1964. In this model, hadrons are divided into *baryons* (which decay into protons) and *mesons* (which decay into leptons and photons). Baryons consist of three quarks and mesons consist of two quarks (a quark and antiquark). In the quark theory, therefore, the only truly elementary particles are leptons and quarks. Unlike electrons and protons, which have exactly equal but opposite charges, quarks have charges that are fractions of the electronic charge ($+2/3$ or $-1/3$ of the electronic charge). Quarks occur in six *flavours* (no connection with taste): up (u; $+2/3$ charge), down (d; $-1/3$), charmed (c; $+2/3$), strange (s; $-1/3$), top (t; $+2/3$), and bottom (b; $-1/3$).

The evidence for the existence of top is not totally established. The proton, being a baryon, consists of three quarks uud ($2/3 + 2/3 - 1/3 = 1$) and the neutron consists of udd ($2/3 - 1/3 - 1/3 = 0$). For each flavour there are equivalent antiquarks (ū, đ, etc.), which have opposite values of electric charge (ū $= -2/3$, etc.).

In order to avoid conflict with the *Pauli exclusion principle it has proved necessary to add the concept of *colour charge* to the six flavours. Each flavour of quark occurs in the three primary colours red, green, and blue; each antiquark has the complementary anticolours cyan, magenta, and yellow. There are therefore a total of 18 quarks and 18 antiquarks. The rules of combination to form hadrons are that the combinations of colours should always give white, either by mixing three primary colours to make baryons or by mixing one primary colour with its complementary anticolour to make mesons. The use of the word 'colour' in this context implies an analogy to visual colours, not that the particles are coloured. The theory governing these combinations is modelled on quantum electrodynamics and is called *quantum chromodynamics.

The strong interaction between quarks is visualized as occurring by the exchange of eight types of chargeless particles, with no rest mass, called *gluons* (because they glue the quarks together). Although gluons, like the photons that perform an analogous function between leptons, have no electrical charge, they do have a colour charge. Each gluon carries one colour and one anticolour. There are nine colour–anticolour pairs but one is excluded as it is equivalent to white. In an interaction a quark can change its colour, but all colour changes are accompanied by the emission of a gluon. This gluon is then absorbed by another quark, whose colour changes to compensate

for the original change. For example, if a red quark changes to green it emits a gluon bearing the colours red + antigreen. When this is absorbed by a green quark the green of the quark and the antigreen of the gluon annihilate each other leaving the second quark with the colour red, acquired from the gluon. The net change is nil, because as a result of the interaction there is still one green quark and one red quark. All hadrons therefore remain white, even though quark colours move from point to point. The strong force can be envisaged as the system of interactions needed to maintain this condition.

The whole elaborate quark theory is now well established by circumstantial evidence, but as neither quarks nor gluons have ever been identified in experiments the theory does not claim to have been directly verified. Individual quarks would have the curious property of being much more massive than the hadrons they usually form (because of the enormous potential energy they would have when separated) and some theorists believe it is in consequence fundamentally impossible for them to exist in isolation. However some experimenters have reported results consistent with the presence of the fractional charges that unattached quarks would have. *See also* grand unified theory; superstring theory; supersymmetry.

elements of an orbit Six parameters that can be used to define the path of a celestial body. The shape of the orbit is defined by its eccentricity (*see* conic) and semimajor axis. The orientation of the orbit is specified by the *inclination of the orbital plane to the reference plane (usually the *ecliptic) and by the longitude of the ascending *node (the angular distance from the vernal equinox to the ascending node). The position of the body in its orbit is defined by its

eccentric *anomaly and the position as a function of time is calculated from the time of periapsis passage (*see* apsides).

elevation of boiling point An increase in the boiling point of a liquid when a solid is dissolved in it. The elevation is proportional to the number of particles dissolved (molecules or ions) and is given by $\Delta t = k_B C$, where C is the molal concentration of solute. The constant k_B is the *ebullioscopic constant* of the solvent and if this is known, the molecular weight of the solute can be calculated from the measured value of Δt. The elevation is measured by a Beckmann thermometer. *See also* colligative property.

Elinvar Trade name for a nickel–chromium steel containing about 36% nickel, 12% chromium, and smaller proportions of tungsten and manganese. Its elasticity does not vary with temperature and it is therefore used to make hairsprings for watches.

ellipse A *conic formed by the intersection of a plane with a right circular cone, so that the plane is inclined to the axis of the cone at an angle in excess of half the apex angle of the cone. The ellipse has two vertices, which are joined by a line called the *major axis*. The centre of the ellipse falls on this line, midway between the vertices. The *minor axis* is the line perpendicular to the major axis that passes through the centre and joins two points on the ellipse. The *foci* of

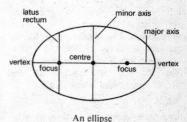

An ellipse

ellipsoid

an ellipse are two points on the major axis so placed that for any point on the ellipse the sum of the distances from that point to each focus is constant. (See illustration.) The area of an ellipse is πab, where a and b are half the major and minor axes, respectively. For an ellipse centred at the origin, the equation in Cartesian coordinates is $x^2/a^2 + y^2/b^2 = 1$. The foci are at $(ea, 0)$ and $(-ea, 0)$, where e is the eccentricity. Each of the two chords of the ellipse passing through a focus and parallel to the minor axis is called a *latus rectum* and has a length equal to $2b^2/a$.

ellipsoid A solid body formed when an *ellipse is rotated about an axis. If it is rotated about its major axis it is a *prolate ellipsoid*; if it is rotated about its minor axis it is an *oblate ellipsoid*. For an ellipsoid centred at the origin the equation in Cartesian coordinates is:
$$x^2/a^2 + y^2/b^2 + z^2/c^2 = 1.$$

elliptical galaxy See galaxy.

elliptical polarization See polarization of light.

eluate See elution.

eluent See elution.

elution The process of removing an adsorbed material (*adsorbate*) from an adsorbent by washing it in a liquid (*eluent*). The solution consisting of the adsorbate dissolved in the eluent is the *eluate*.

elutriation The process of suspending finely divided particles in an upward flowing stream of air or water to wash and separate them into sized fractions.

emanation The former name for the gas radon, of which there are three isotopes: Rn–222 (radium emanation), Rn–220 (thoron emanation), and Rn–219 (actinium emanation).

e.m.f. See electromotive force.

emission spectrum See spectrum.

emissivity Symbol ε. The ratio of the power per unit area radiated by a surface to that radiated by a *black body at the same temperature. A black body therefore has an emissivity of 1 and a perfect reflector has an emissivity of 0. The emissivity of a surface is equal to its *absorptance.

emittance See exitance.

emitter See transistor.

empirical Denoting a result that is obtained by experiment or observation rather than from theory.

empirical formula See formula.

emulsion A *colloid in which small particles of one liquid are dispersed in another liquid. Usually emulsions involve a dispersion of water in an oil or a dispersion of oil in water, and are stabilized by an *emulsifier*. Commonly emulsifiers are substances, such as detergents, that have lyophobic and lyophilic parts in their molecules.

enantiomers See optical activity.

enantiomorphism See optical activity.

endoergic Denoting a nuclear process that absorbs energy. *Compare* exoergic.

endothermic Denoting a chemical reaction that takes heat from its surroundings. *Compare* exothermic.

energy A measure of a system's ability to do work. Like work itself, it is measured in joules. Energy is conveniently classified into two forms: *potential energy* is the energy stored in a body or system as a consequence of its position, shape, or state (this includes gravitational energy, electrical energy, nuclear energy, and chemical energy); *kinetic energy* is energy of motion and is usually defined as the work that will be done by the body possessing the energy when it is brought to rest. For a body of mass m having a speed v, the kinetic energy is $mv^2/2$ (classical) or $(m - m_0)c^2$ (relativistic). The rota-

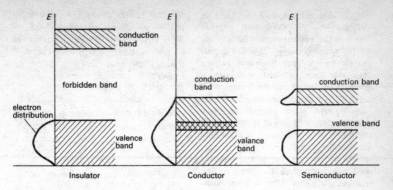

Energy bands

tional kinetic energy of a body having an angular velocity ω is $I\omega^2/2$, where I is its moment of inertia.

The *internal energy of a body is the sum of the potential energy and the kinetic energy of its component atoms and molecules.

energy band A range of energies that electrons can have in a solid. In a single atom, electrons exist in discrete *energy levels. In a crystal, in which large numbers of atoms are held closely together in a lattice, electrons are influenced by a number of adjacent nuclei and the sharply defined levels of the atoms become bands of allowed energy (see illustration); this approach to energy levels in solids is often known as the *band theory*. Each band represents a large number of allowed quantum states. Between the bands are *forbidden bands*. The outermost electrons of the atoms (i.e. the ones responsible for chemical bonding) form the *valence band* of the solid. This is the band, of those occupied, that has the highest energy.

The band structure of solids accounts for their electrical properties. In order to move through the solid, the electrons have to change from one quantum state to another. This can only occur if there are empty quantum states with the same energy. In gen-

eral, if the valence band is full, electrons cannot change to new quantum states in the same band. For conduction to occur, the electrons have to be in an unfilled band – the *conduction band*. Metals are good conductors either because the valence band and the conduction band are only half-filled or because the conduction band overlaps with the valence band; in either case vacant states are available. In insulators the conduction band and valence band are separated by a wide forbidden band and electrons do not have enough energy to 'jump' from one to the other.

In intrinsic *semiconductors the forbidden gap is narrow and, at normal temperatures, electrons at the top of the valence band can move by thermal agitation into the conduction band (at absolute zero, a semiconductor would act as an insulator). Doped semiconductors have extra bands in the forbidden gap.

energy level A definite fixed energy that a system described by *quantum mechanics, such as a molecule, atom, electron, or nucleus, can have. In an atom, for example, the atom has a fixed energy corresponding to the *orbitals in which its electrons move around the nucleus. The atom can accept a quantum of energy to become an excited atom (*see* excita-

tion) if that extra energy will raise an electron to a permitted orbital. Between the *ground state*, which is the lowest possible energy level for a particular system, and the first excited state there are no permissible energy levels. According to the *quantum theory, only certain energy levels are possible. An atom passes from one energy level to the next without passing through fractions of that energy transition. These levels are usually described by the energies associated with the individual electrons in the atoms, which are always lower than an arbitrary level for a free electron. The energy levels of molecules also involve quantized vibrational and rotational motion.

engine Any device for converting some forms of energy by mechanical work. *See* heat engine; Carnot cycle; internal-combustion engine; steam engine.

enrichment The process of increasing the abundance of a specified isotope in a mixture of isotopes. It is usually applied to an increase in the proportion of U–235, or the addition of Pu–239 to natural uranium for use in a nuclear reactor or weapon.

enthalpy Symbol H. A thermodynamic property of a system defined by $H = U + pV$, where H is the enthalpy, U is the internal energy of the system, p its pressure, and V its volume. In a chemical reaction carried out in the atmosphere the pressure remains constant and the enthalpy of reaction, ΔH, is equal to $\Delta U + p\Delta V$. For an exothermic reaction ΔH is taken to be negative.

entropy Symbol S. A measure of the unavailability of a system's energy to do work; in a closed system an increase in entropy is accompanied by a decrease in energy availability. When a system undergoes a reversible change the entropy (S) changes by an amount equal to the energy (Q) transferred to the system by heat divided by the thermodynamic temperature (T) at which this occurs, i.e. $\Delta S = \Delta Q/T$. However, all real processes are to a certain extent irreversible changes and in any closed system an irreversible change is always accompanied by an increase in entropy.

In a wider sense entropy can be interpreted as a measure of disorder; the higher the entropy the greater the disorder. As any real change to a closed system tends towards higher entropy, and therefore higher disorder, it follows that the entropy of the universe (if it can be considered a closed system) is increasing and its available energy is decreasing (*see* heat death of the universe). This increase in the entropy of the universe is one way of stating the second law of *thermodynamics.

ephemeris A tabulation showing the calculated future positions of the sun, moon, and planets, together with other useful information for astronomers and navigators. It is published at regular intervals.

ephemeris time (ET) A time system that has a constant uniform rate as opposed to other systems that depend on the earth's rate of rotation, which has inherent irregularities. It is reckoned from an instant in 1900 (Jan 0d 12h) when the sun's mean longitude was $279.696\,677\,8°$. The unit by which ephemeris time is measured is the tropical year, which contains $31\,556\,925.9747$ *ephemeris seconds*. This fundamental definition of the *second was replaced in 1964 by the caesium second of atomic time.

epicentre The point on the surface of the earth directly above the focus of an earthquake or directly above or below a nuclear explosion.

epicycle A small circle whose centre rolls around the circumference of a larger fixed circle. The curve traced out by a point on the epicycle is called an *epicycloid*.

epidiascope An optical instrument used by lecturers, etc., for projecting an enlarged image of either a translucent object (such as a slide or transparency) or an opaque object (such as a diagram or printed page) onto a screen.

epitaxy (epitaxial growth) Growth of a layer of one substance on a single crystal of another, such that the crystal structure in the layer is the same as that in the substrate. It is used in making semiconductor devices.

epithermal neutron A neutron with an energy in excess of that associated with a thermal neutron (*see* moderator) but less than that of a *fast neutron, i.e. a neutron having an energy in the range 0.1 to 100 eV.

EPM *See* electron probe microanalysis.

equation of motion (kinematic equation) Any of four equations that apply to bodies moving linearly with uniform acceleration (*a*). The equations, which relate distance covered (*s*) to the time taken (*t*), are:

$$v = u + at$$
$$s = (u + v)t/2$$
$$s = ut + at^2/2$$
$$v^2 = u^2 + 2as$$

where *u* is the initial velocity of the body and *v* is its final velocity.

equation of state An equation that relates the pressure *p*, volume *V*, and thermodynamic temperature *T* of an amount of substance *n*. The simplest is the ideal *gas law:

$$pV = nRT,$$

where *R* is the universal gas constant. Applying only to ideal gases, this equation takes no account of the volume occupied by the gas molecules (according to this law if the pressure is infinitely great the volume becomes zero), nor does it take into account any forces between molecules. A more accurate equation of state would therefore be

$$(p + k)(V - nb) = nRT,$$

where *k* is a factor that reflects the decreased pressure on the walls of the container as a result of the attractive forces between particles, and *nb* is the volume occupied by the particles themselves when the pressure is infinitely high. In the *van der Waals equation of state*, proposed by the Dutch physicist J. D. van der Waals (1837–1923),

$$k = n^2a/V^2,$$

where *a* is a constant. This equation more accurately reflects the behaviour of real gases; several others have done better but are more complicated.

equation of time The length of time that must be added to the mean solar time, as shown on a clock, to give the apparent solar time, as shown by a sundial. The amount varies during the year, being a minimum of –14.2 minutes in February and a maximum of + 16.4 minutes in October. It is zero on four days (April 15/16, June 14/15, Sept. 1/2, Dec. 25/26). The difference arises as a result of two factors: the eccentricity of the earth's orbit and the inclination of the ecliptic to the celestial equator.

equator 1. The great circle around the earth that lies in a plane perpendicular to the earth's axis. It is equidistant from the two geographical poles. **2.** The *magnetic equator* is a line of zero magnetic dip (*see* geomagnetism) that is close to the geographical equator but lies north of it in Africa and south of it in America. **3.** The *celestial equator* is the circle formed on the *celestial sphere by the extension of the earth's equatorial plane.

equilibrium A state in which a system has its energy distributed in the statistically most probable manner; a state of a system in which forces, influences, reactions, etc., balance each other out so that there is no net change.

A body is in *static equilibrium* if the resultants of all forces and all couples acting on it are both zero; it may be at rest and will certainly not be accelerated. Such a body at rest is in *stable equilibrium* if after a slight displacement it returns to its original position – for a body whose weight is the only downward force this will be the case if the vertical line through its centre of gravity always passes through its base. If a slight displacement causes the body to move to a new position, then the body is in *unstable equilibrium.*

A body is said to be in *thermal equilibrium* if no net heat exchange is taking place within it or between it and its surroundings. A system is in chemical equilibrium when a reaction and its reverse are proceeding at equal rates. These are examples of *dynamic equilibrium*, in which activity in one sense or direction is in aggregate balanced by comparable reverse activity.

equinox 1. Either of the two points on the *celestial sphere at which the *ecliptic intersects the celestial equator. The sun appears to cross the celestial equator from south to north at the *vernal equinox* and from north to south at the *autumnal equinox.* **2.** Either of the two instants at which the centre of the sun appears to cross the celestial equator. In the northern hemisphere the vernal equinox occurs on or about March 21 and the autumnal equinox on or about Sept. 23. In the southern hemisphere the dates are reversed. *See* precession of the equinoxes.

equipartition of energy The theory, proposed by Ludwig Boltzmann (1844–1906) and given some theoretical support by James Clerk Maxwell (1831–79), that the energy of gas molecules in a large sample under thermal *equilibrium is equally divided among their available *degrees of freedom, the average energy for each degree of freedom being $kT/2$, where k is the *Boltzmann constant and T is the thermodynamic temperature. The proposition is not generally true if *quantum considerations are important, but is frequently a good approximation.

erecting prism A glass prism used in optical instruments to convert an inverted image into an erect image, as in prismatic binoculars.

erg A unit of work or energy used in the c.g.s. system and defined as the work done by a force of 1 dyne when it acts through a distance of 1 centimetre. 1 erg = 10^{-7} joule.

ergonomics The study of the engineering aspects of the relationship between workers and their working environment.

Esaki diode *See* tunnel diode.

ESCA *See* photoelectron spectroscopy.

escapement A device in a clock or watch that controls the transmission of power from the spring or falling weight to the hands. It is usually based on a balance wheel or pendulum. It thus allows energy to enter the mechanism in order to move the hands round the face, overcome friction in the gear trains, and maintain the balance wheel or pendulum in continuous motion.

escape velocity The minimum speed needed by a space vehicle, rocket, etc., to escape from the gravitational field of the earth, moon, or other celestial body. The gravitational force between a rocket of mass m and a celestial body of mass M and radius r is MmG/r^2 (*see* Newton's law of gravitation). Therefore the gravitational potential energy of the rocket with respect to its possible position very far from the celestial body on which it is resting can be shown to be $-GmM/r$, assuming (by convention) that the potential energy is zero

at an infinite distance from the celestial body. If the rocket is to escape from the gravitational field it must have a kinetic energy that exceeds this potential energy, i.e. the kinetic energy $mv^2/2$ must be greater than MmG/r, or $v > \sqrt{(2MG/r)}$. This is the value of the escape velocity. Inserting numerical values for the earth and moon into this relationship gives an escape velocity from the earth of 11 200 m s^{-1} and from the moon of 2370 m s^{-1}.

ESR *See* electron-spin resonance.

ether (aether) A hypothetical medium once believed to be necessary to support the propagation of electromagnetic radiation. It is now regarded as unnecessary and in modern theory electromagnetic radiation can be propagated through empty space. The existence of the ether was first called into question as a result of the *Michelson–Morley experiment.

eudiometer An apparatus for measuring changes in volume of gases during chemical reactions. A simple example is a graduated glass tube sealed at one end and inverted in mercury. Wires passing into the tube allow the gas mixture to be sparked to initiate the reaction between gases in the tube.

eutectic mixture A solid solution consisting of two or more substances and having the lowest freezing point of any possible mixture of these components. The minimum freezing point for a set of components is called the *eutectic point*. Low melting-point alloys are usually eutectic mixtures.

evaporation The change of state of a liquid into a vapour at a temperature below the boiling point of the liquid. Evaporation occurs at the surface of a liquid, some of those molecules with the highest kinetic energies escaping into the gas phase. The result is a fall in the average kinetic energy of the molecules of the liquid and consequently a fall in its temperature.

even–even nucleus An atomic nucleus containing an even number of protons and an even number of neutrons.

even–odd nucleus An atomic nucleus containing an even number of protons and an odd number of neutrons.

event horizon *See* black hole.

evolute The locus of the centres of curvature of all the points on a given curve (called the *involute*).

exa- Symbol E. A prefix used in the metric system to denote 10^{18} times. For example, 10^{18} metres = 1 exametre (Em).

excess electron An electron in a *semiconductor that is not required in the bonding system of the crystal lattice and has been donated by an impurity atom. It is available for conduction (*excess conduction*).

exchange force 1. A force resulting from the continued interchange of particles in a manner that bonds their hosts together. Examples are the covalent bond involving electrons, and the strong interaction (*see* fundamental interactions) in which mesons are exchanged between nucleons or gluons are exchanged between quarks (*see* elementary particles). **2.** *See* magnetism.

excitation 1. A process in which a nucleus, electron, atom, ion, or molecule acquires energy that raises it to a quantum state (*excited state*) higher than that of its *ground state. The difference between the energy in the ground state and that in the excited state is called the *excitation energy*. *See* collective excitation; energy level; quasiparticle. **2.** The process of applying current to the winding of an electromagnet, as in an electric motor. **3.** The process of applying a signal to the base of a transistor or the control electrode of a thermionic valve.

exciton An electron–hole pair in a crystal that is bound in a manner analogous to the electron and proton of a hydrogen atom. It behaves like an atomic excitation that passes from one atom to another and may be long-lived. Exciton behaviour in *semiconductors is important.

exclusion principle *See* Pauli exclusion principle.

exitance Symbol M. The radiant or luminous flux emitted per unit area of a surface. The *radiant exitance* (M_e) is measured in watts per square metre (W m^{-2}), while the *luminous exitance* (M_v) is measured in lumens per square metre (lm m^{-2}). Exitance was formerly called *emittance*.

exoergic Denoting a nuclear process that gives out energy. *Compare* endoergic.

exosphere *See* earth's atmosphere.

exothermic Denoting a chemical reaction that releases heat into its surroundings. *Compare* endothermic.

expansion The writing of a function or quantity as a *series of terms. The series may be finite or infinite. *See* binomial theorem; Taylor series.

expansion of the universe The hypothesis, based on the evidence of the *redshift, that the distance between the galaxies is continuously increasing. The original theory, which was proposed in 1929 by Edwin Hubble (1889–1953), assumes that the galaxies are flying apart as a consequence of the big bang with which the universe originated. Several variants have since been proposed. *See also* big-bang theory; Hubble constant.

expansivity (thermal expansion) 1. *Linear expansivity* is the fractional increase in length of a specimen of a solid, per unit rise in temperature. If a specimen increases in length from l_1 to l_2 when its temperature is raised $\theta°$, then the expansivity (α) is given by:

$$l_2 = l_1(1 + \alpha\theta).$$

This relationship assumes that α is independent of temperature. This is not, in general, the case and a more accurate relationship is:

$$l_2 = l_1(1 + a\theta + b\theta^2 + c\theta^3 \ldots),$$

where a, b, and c are constants. **2.** *Superficial expansivity* is the fractional increase in area of a solid surface caused by unit rise in temperature, i.e.

$$A_2 = A_1(1 + \beta\theta),$$

where β is the superficial expansivity. To a good approximation $\beta = 2\alpha$. **3.** *Volume expansivity* is the fractional increase in volume of a solid, liquid, or gas per unit rise in temperature, i.e.

$$V_2 = V_1(1 + \gamma\theta),$$

where γ is the cubic expansivity and $\gamma = 3\alpha$. For liquids, the expansivity observed directly is called the *apparent expansivity* as the container will also have expanded with the rise in temperature. The *absolute expansivity* is the apparent expansivity plus the volume expansivity of the container. For the expansion of gases, *see* Charles' Law.

exponent A number or symbol that indicates the power to which another number or expression is raised. For example, $(x + y)^n$ indicates that the expression $(x + y)$ is raised to the nth power; n is the exponent. Any number or expression in which the exponent is zero is equal to 1, i.e. $x^0 = 1$.

exponential A function that varies as the power of another quantity. If $y = a^x$, y varies exponentially with x. The function e^x, also written as exp (x), is called the *exponential function* (*see* e). It is equal to the sum of the *exponential series*, i.e.

$$e^x = 1 + x + x^2/2! + x^3/3! + \ldots + x^n/n! + \ldots$$

exponential growth A form of population growth in which the rate of growth is related to the number of

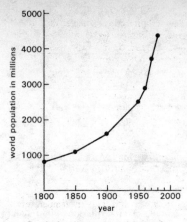

Graph showing exponential growth of the human population

individuals present. Increase is slow when numbers are low but rises sharply as numbers increase. If population number is plotted against time on a graph a characteristic J-shaped curve results (see graph). In animal and plant populations, such factors as overcrowding, lack of nutrients, and disease limit population increase beyond a certain point and the J-shaped exponential curve tails off giving an S-shaped (sigmoid) curve.

exposure meter A photocell that operates a meter to indicate the correct exposure for a specified film in photography. It enables the correct shutter speed and aperture to be chosen for any photographic circumstances. Some cameras have a built-in exposure meter that automatically sets the aperture according to the amount of light available and the chosen shutter speed.

extensometer Any device for measuring the extension of a specimen of a material under longitudinal stress. A common method is to make the specimen form part of a capacitor, the capacitance of which will change with a change in the specimen's dimensions.

extinction coefficient A measure of the extent by which the intensity of a beam of light is reduced by passing through a distance d of a solution having a molar concentration c of the dissolved substance. If the intensity of the light is reduced from I_1 to I_2, the extinction coefficient is $[\log(I_1/I_2)]/cd$.

extraction 1. The process of obtaining a metal from its ore. **2.** The separation of a component from a mixture by selective solubility.

extraordinary ray *See* double refraction.

extremely high frequency (EHF) A radio frequency between 30 000 megahertz and 300 gigahertz.

extrinsic semiconductor *See* semiconductor.

eye The organ of sight (see illustration). They normally occur in pairs, are nearly spherical, and filled with fluid. Light is refracted by the *cornea through the pupil in the *iris and onto the *lens, which focuses images onto the retina. These images are received by light-sensitive cells in the retina (*see* cone; rod), which transmit impulses to the brain via the optic nerve.

eyepiece (ocular) The lens or system of lenses in an optical instrument that is nearest to the eye. It usually produces a magnified image of the previous image formed by the instrument.

F

Fabry–Pérot interferometer A type of *interferometer in which monochromatic light is passed through a pair of parallel half-silvered glass plates producing circular interference fringes. One of the glass plates is adjustable, enabling the separation of the plates to be varied. The wavelength of the light can be determined

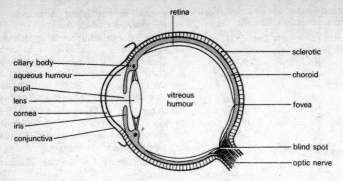

Structure of the vertebrate eye

by observing the fringes while adjusting the separation. This type of instrument is used in spectroscopy.

face-centred cubic (f.c.c.) *See* cubic crystal.

factorial The product of a given number and all the whole numbers below it. It is usually writen $n!$, e.g. factorial 4 = 4! = 4 × 3 × 2 × 1 = 24. Factorial 0 is defined as 1.

Fahrenheit scale A temperature scale in which (by modern definition) the temperature of boiling water is taken as 212 degrees and the temperature of melting ice as 32 degrees. It was invented in 1714 by the German scientist G. D. Fahrenheit (1686–1736), who set the zero at the lowest temperature he knew how to obtain in the laboratory (by mixing ice and common salt) and took his own body temperature as 96°F. The scale is no longer in scientific use. To convert to the *Celsius scale the formula is $C = 5(F - 32)/9$.

fall-out (*or* **radioactive fall-out**) Radioactive particles deposited from the atmosphere either from a nuclear explosion or from a nuclear accident. *Local fall-out*, within 250 km of an explosion, falls within a few hours of the explosion. *Tropospheric fall-out* consists of fine particles deposited all round the earth in the approximate latitude of the explosion within about one week. *Stratospheric fall-out* may fall anywhere on earth over a period of years. The most dangerous radioactive isotopes in fall-out are the fission fragments iodine–131 and strontium–90. Both can be taken up by grazing animals and passed on to human populations in milk, milk products, and meat. Iodine–131 accumulates in the thyroid gland and strontium–90 accumulates in bones.

farad Symbol F. The SI unit of capacitance, being the capacitance of a capacitor that, if charged with one coulomb, has a potential difference of one volt between its plates. 1 F = 1 C V^{-1}. The farad itself is too large for most applications; the practical unit is the microfarad (10^{-6} F). The unit is named after Michael Faraday (1791–1867).

Faraday cage An earthed screen made of metal wire that surrounds an electric device in order to shield it from external electrical fields.

Faraday constant Symbol F. The electric charge carried by one mole of electrons or singly ionized ions, i.e. the product of the *Avogadro constant and the charge on an electron (disregarding sign). It has the value 9.648 5309(29) × 10^4 coulombs per mole. This number of coulombs is

sometimes treated as a unit of electric charge called the *faraday*.

Faraday effect The rotation of the plane of polarization of electromagnetic radiation on passing through an isotropic medium exposed to a magnetic field. The angle of rotation is proportional to Bl, where l is the length of the path of the radiation in the medium and B is the magnetic flux density.

Faraday's laws Two laws describing electrolysis:
(1) The amount of chemical change during electrolysis is proportional to the charge passed.
(2) The charge required to deposit or liberate a mass m is given by $Q = Fmz/M$, where F is the Faraday constant, z the charge of the ion, and M the relative ionic mass.
These are the modern forms of the laws. Originally, they were stated by Faraday in a different form:
(1) The amount of chemical change produced is proportional to the quantity of electricity passed.
(2) The amount of chemical change produced in different substances by a fixed quantity of electricity is proportional to the electrochemical equivalent of the substance.

Faraday's laws of electromagnetic induction (1) An e.m.f. is induced in a conductor when the magnetic field surrounding it changes. (2) The magnitude of the e.m.f. is proportional to the rate of change of the field. (3) The sense of the induced e.m.f. depends on the direction of the rate of change of the field.

fast neutron A neutron resulting from nuclear fission that has an energy in excess of 0.1 MeV (1.6 × 10^{-14} J), having lost little of its energy by collision. In some contexts *fast fission* is defined as fission brought about by fast neutrons, i.e. neutrons having energies in excess of 1.5 MeV (2.4 × 10^{-13} J), the fission threshold

of uranium–238. *See also* nuclear reactor; slow neutron.

fast reactor *See* nuclear reactor.

fatigue *See* metal fatigue.

f.c.c. Face-centred cubic. *See* cubic crystal.

feedback The use of part of the output of a system to control its performance. In *positive feedback*, the output is used to enhance the input; an example is an electronic oscillator, or the howl produced by a loudspeaker that is placed too close to a microphone in the same circuit. A small random noise picked up by the microphone is amplified and reproduced by the loudspeaker. The microphone now picks it up again; it is further amplified, and fed from the speaker to microphone once again. This continues until the system is overloaded. In *negative feedback*, the output is used to reduce the input. In electronic amplifiers, stability is achieved, and distortion reduced, by using a system in which the input is decremented in proportion as the output increases. A similar negative feedback is used in *governors that reduce the fuel supply to an engine as its speed increases.

femto- Symbol f. A prefix used in the metric system to denote 10^{-15}. For example, 10^{-15} second = 1 femtosecond (fs).

Fermat's principle The path taken by a ray of light between any two points in a system is always the path that takes the least time. This principle leads to the law of the rectilinear propagation of light and the laws of reflection and refraction. It was discovered by the French mathematician, Pierre de Fermat (1601–65).

fermi A unit of length formerly used in nuclear physics. It is equal to 10^{-15} metre. In SI units this is equal to 1 femtometre (fm). It was named after the Italian-born US physicist Enrico Fermi (1901–54).

Fermi–Dirac statistics *See* quantum statistics.

Fermi level The energy in a solid at which the average number of particles per quantum state is $\frac{1}{2}$; i.e. one half of the quantum states are occupied. The Fermi level in conductors lies in the conduction band (*see* energy bands), in insulators and semiconductors it falls in the gap between the conduction band and the valence band.

fermion An *elementary particle (or bound state of an elementary particle, e.g. an atomic nucleus or an atom) with half-integral spin; i.e. a particle that conforms to Fermi–Dirac statistics (*see* quantum statistics). *Compare* boson.

fermium Symbol Fm. A radioactive metallic transuranic element belonging to the actinoids; a.n. 100; mass number of the most stable isotope 257 (half-life 10 days). Ten isotopes are known. The element was first identified by A. Ghiorso and associates in debris from the first hydrogen-bomb explosion in 1952.

ferrimagnetism *See* magnetism.

ferrite 1. A member of a class of mixed oxides $MO.Fe_2O_3$, where M is a metal such as cobalt, manganese, nickel, or zinc. The ferrites are ceramic materials that show either ferrimagnetism or ferromagnetism, but are not electrical conductors. For this reason they are used in high-frequency circuits as magnetic cores. **2.** *See* steel.

ferroalloys Alloys of iron with other elements made by smelting mixtures of iron ore and the metal ore; e.g. ferrochromium, ferrovanadium, ferromanganese, ferrosilicon, etc. They are used in making alloy *steels.

ferroelectric materials Ceramic dielectrics, such as Rochelle salt and barium titanate, that have a domain structure making them analogous to ferromagnetic materials (*see* magnetism). They exhibit hysteresis and usually the *piezoelectric effect.

ferromagnetism *See* magnetism.

fertile material A nuclide that can absorb a neutron to form a *fissile material. Uranium–238, for example, absorbs a neutron to form uranium–239, which decays to plutonium–239. This is the type of conversion that occurs in a breeder reactor (*see* nuclear reactor).

FET *See* transistor.

Feynman diagram *See* quantum electrodynamics.

fibre optics *See* optical fibres.

field A region in which a body experiences a *force as the result of the presence of some other body or bodies. A field is thus a method of representing the way in which bodies are able to influence each other. For example, a body that has mass is surrounded by a region in which another body that has mass experiences a force tending to draw the two bodies together. This is the gravitational field (*see* Newton's law of gravitation). The other three *fundamental interactions can also be represented by means of fields of force. However in the case of the *magnetic field and *electric field that together create the electromagnetic interaction, the force can vary in direction according to the character of the field. For example, in the field surrounding a negatively charged body, a positively charged body will experience a force of attraction, while another negatively charged body is repelled.

The strength of any field can be described as the ratio of the force experienced by a small appropriate specimen to the relevant property of that specimen, e.g. force/mass for the gravitational field. *See also* quantum field theory.

field coil The coil in an electrical machine that produces the magnetic field.

field-effect transistor (FET) *See* transistor.

field-emission microscope A type of electron microscope in which a high negative voltage is applied to a metal tip placed in an evacuated vessel some distance from a glass screen with a fluorescent coating. The tip produces electrons by *field emission*, i.e. the emission of electrons from an unheated sharp metal part as a result of a high electric field. The emitted electrons form an enlarged pattern on the fluorescent screen, related to the individual exposed planes of atoms. As the resolution of the instrument is limited by the vibrations of the metal atoms, it is helpful to cool the tip in liquid helium. Although the individual atoms forming the point are not displayed, individual adsorbed atoms of other substances can be, and their activity is observable.

field-ionization microscope (field-ion microscope) A type of electron microscope that is similar in principle to the *field-emission microscope, except that a high positive voltage is applied to the metal tip, which is surrounded by low-pressure gas (usually helium) rather than a vacuum. The image is formed in this case by *field ionization*: ionization at the surface of an unheated solid as a result of a strong electric field creating positive ions by electron transfer from surrounding atoms or molecules. The image is formed by ions striking the fluorescent screen. Individual atoms on the surface of the tip can be resolved and, in certain cases, adsorbed atoms may be detected.

field lens The lens in the compound eye-piece of an optical instrument that is furthest from the eye. Its function is to increase the field of view by refracting towards the main eye lens rays that would otherwise miss it.

field magnet The magnet that provides the magnetic field in an electrical machine. In some small dynamos and motors it is a permanent magnet but in most machines it is an electromagnet.

file A collection of data stored in a computer. It may consist of program instructions or numerical, textual, or graphical information. It usually consists of a set of similar or related records.

film badge A lapel badge containing masked photographic film worn by personnel who could be exposed to ionizing radiation. The film is developed to indicate the extent that the wearer has been exposed to harmful radiation.

filter 1. A device placed in the path of a beam of radiation to alter its frequency distribution. For example, a plane pigmented piece of glass may be placed over a camera lens to alter the relative intensity of the component wavelengths of the beam entering the camera. **2.** A device for separating solid particles from a fluid.

filter pump A simple laboratory vacuum pump in which air is removed from a system by a jet of water forced through a narrow nozzle. The lowest pressure possible is the vapour pressure of water.

filtrate The clear liquid obtained by filtration.

filtration The process of separating solid particles using a filter. In vacuum filtration, the liquid is drawn through the filter by a vacuum pump.

finder A small low-powered astronomical telescope, with a wide field of view, that is fixed to a large astronomical telescope so that the large telescope can be pointed in the correct direction to observe a particular celestial body.

fine structure Closely spaced optical spectral lines arising from *transitions between energy levels that are split by the vibrational or rotational motion of a molecule or by electron spin. They are visible only at high

resolution. *Hyperfine structure*, visible only at very high resolution, results from the influence of the atomic nucleus on the allowed energy levels of the atom.

finite series *See* series.

fissile material A nuclide of an element that undergoes nuclear fission, either spontaneously or when irradiated by neutrons. Fissile nuclides, such as uranium–235 and plutonium–239, are used in *nuclear reactors and nuclear weapons. *Compare* fertile material.

fission *See* nuclear fission.

fission products *See* nuclear fission.

fission-track dating A method of estimating the age of glass and other mineral objects by observing the tracks made in them by the fission fragments of the uranium nuclei that they contain. By irradiating the objects with neutrons to induce fission and comparing the density and number of the tracks before and after irradiation it is possible to estimate the time that has elapsed since the object solidified.

Fitzgerald contraction *See* Lorentz–Fitzgerald contraction.

fixed point A temperature that can be accurately reproduced to enable it to be used as the basis of a *temperature scale.

fixed star One of very many heavenly bodies that does not appear to alter its position on the *celestial sphere. They were so called to distinguish them from the planets, which were once known as *wandering stars*. The discovery of the *proper motion of stars in the 18th century established that stars are not fixed in the sky although, because of their immense distances from the solar system, they may appear to be so.

Fizeau's method A method of measuring the speed of light, invented by the French physicist Armand Fizeau (1819–96) in 1849. A cogwheel rotating at high speed enables a series of flashes to be transmitted to a distant mirror. The light reflected back to the cogwheel is observed and the speed of light calculated from the rates of rotation of the wheel required to produce an eclipse of the returning light.

flame A hot luminous mixture of gases undergoing combustion. The chemical reactions in a flame are mainly free-radical chain reactions and the light comes from fluorescence of excited molecules or ions or from incandescence of small solid particles (e.g. carbon).

flash photolysis A technique for studying free-radical reactions in gases. The apparatus used typically consists of a long glass or quartz tube holding the gas, with a lamp outside the tube suitable for producing an intense flash of light. This dissociates molecules in the sample creating free radicals, which can be detected spectroscopically by a beam of light passed down the axis of the tube. It is possible to focus the spectrometer on an absorption line for a particular product and measure its change in intensity with time using an oscilloscope. In this way the kinetics of very fast free-radical gas reactions can be studied.

flash point The temperature at which the vapour above a volatile liquid forms a combustible mixture with air. At the flash point the application of a naked flame gives a momentary flash rather than sustained combustion, for which the temperature is too low.

flavour *See* elementary particles.

Fleming's rules Rules to assist in remembering the relative directions of the field, current, and force in electrical machines. The left hand refers to motors, the right hand to generators. If the forefinger, second finger, and thumb of the left hand are extended at right angles to each other, the forefinger indicates the direction of the field, the second finger the direction

of the current, and the thumb the direction of the force. If the right hand is used the digits indicate these directions in a generator. The mnemonic was invented by Sir John Ambrose Fleming (1849–1945).

flip-flop (bistable circuit) An electronic circuit that has two stable states. It is switched from one stable state to the other by means of a triggering pulse. They are extensively used as *logic circuits in computers.

floppy disk A flexible plastic disk with a magnetic coating encased in a stiff envelope. It is used to store information in a small computer system. See magnetic disk.

fluidics The use of jets of fluid in pipes to perform many of the control functions usually performed by electronic devices. Being about one million times slower than electronic devices, fluidic systems are useful where delay lines are required. They are also less sensitive to high temperatures, strong magnetic fields, and ionizing radiation than electronic devices.

fluidization A technique used in some industrial processes in which solid particles suspended in a stream of gas are treated as if they were in the liquid state. Fluidization is useful for transporting powders, such as coal dust. *Fluidized beds*, in which solid particles are suspended in an upward stream, are extensively used in the chemical industry, particularly in catalytic reactions where the powdered catalyst has a high surface area.

fluid mechanics The study of fluids at rest and in motion. *Fluid statics* is concerned with the pressures and forces exerted on liquids and gases at rest. *Hydrostatics is specifically concerned with the behaviour of liquids at rest. In *fluid dynamics* the forces exerted on fluids, and the motion that results from these forces, are examined. It can be divided into

*hydrodynamics: the motion of liquids (not only water); and aerodynamics: the motion of gases.
Fluid dynamics is an important science used to solve many of the problems arising in aeronautical, chemical, mechanical, and civil engineering. It also enables many natural phenomena, such as the flight of birds, the swimming of fish, and the development of weather conditions, to be studied scientifically.

fluorescence See luminescence.

fluorescent light See electric lighting.

flux 1. See luminous flux. 2. See magnetic flux. 3. See electric flux. 4. The number of particles flowing per unit area of cross section in a beam of particles.

flux density 1. See magnetic flux density. 2. See electric flux density.

fluxmeter An instrument used to measure *magnetic flux. It is used in conjunction with a coil (the *search coil*) and resembles a moving-coil galvanometer except that there are no restoring springs. A change in the magnetic flux induces a momentary current in the search coil and in the coil of the meter, which turns in proportion and stays in the deflected position. This type of instrument has been largely superseded by a type using the Hall probe (*see* Hall effect).

FM (frequency modulation) See modulation.

f-number See aperture.

focal length The distance between the *optical centre of a lens or pole of a spherical mirror and its *principal focus.

focal point See focus.

focal ratio See aperture.

focus 1. (in optics) Any point in an optical system through or towards which rays of light are converged. It is sometimes called the *focal point* and sometimes loosely used to mean

*principal focus or (particularly by photographers) *focal length. **2.** (in mathematics) *See* conic; ellipse.

foot The unit of length in *f.p.s units. It is equal to one-third of a yard and is now therefore defined as 0.3048 metre. Several units based on the foot were formerly used in science, including the units of work, the *foot-pound-force* and the *foot-poundal*, and the illumination units, the *foot-candle* and the *foot-lambert*. These have all been replaced by SI units.

forbidden band *See* energy bands.

force Symbol F. The agency that tends to change the momentum of a massive body, defined as being proportional to the rate of increase of momentum. For a body of mass m travelling at a velocity v, the momentum is mv. In any coherent system of units the force is therefore given by $F = \mathrm{d}(mv)/\mathrm{d}t$. If the mass is constant $F = m\mathrm{d}v/\mathrm{d}t = ma$, where a is the acceleration (*see* Newton's laws of motion). The SI unit of force is the newton. Forces occur always in equal and opposite action–reaction pairs between bodies, though it is often convenient to think of one body being in a force *field.

forced convection *See* convection.

force ratio (mechanical advantage) The ratio of the output force (load) of a machine to the input force (effort).

formula 1. (in chemistry) A way of representing a chemical compound using symbols for the atoms present. Subscripts are used for the numbers of atoms. The *molecular formula* simply gives the types and numbers of atoms present. For example, the molecular formula of ethanoic acid is $C_2H_4O_2$. The *empirical formula* gives the atoms in their simplest ratio; for ethanoic acid it is CH_2O. The *structural formula* gives an indication of the way the atoms are arranged. Commonly, this is done by dividing the formula into groups; ethanoic acid can be written $CH_3.CO.OH$ (or more usually simply CH_3COOH). Structural formulae can also show the arrangement of atoms or groups in space. **2.** (in mathematics and physics) A rule or law expressed in algebraic symbols.

Fortin barometer *See* barometer.

fossil fuel Coal, oil, and natural gas, the fuels used by man as a source of energy. They are formed from the remains of living organisms and all have a high carbon or hydrogen content. Their value as fuels relies on the exothermic oxidation of carbon to form carbon dioxide ($C + O_2 \rightarrow CO_2$) and the oxidation of hydrogen to form water ($H_2 + \frac{1}{2}O_2 \rightarrow H_2O$).

Foucault pendulum A simple pendulum in which a heavy bob attached to a long wire is free to swing in any direction. As a result of the earth's rotation, the plane of the pendulum's swing slowly turns (at the poles of the earth it makes one complete revolution in 24 hours). It was devised by the French physicist Jean Bernard Léon Foucault (1819–68) in 1851, when it was used to demonstrate the earth's rotation.

Fourier series An expansion of a periodic function as a series of trigonometric functions. Thus,
$$f(x) = a_0 + (a_1\cos x + b_1\sin x) + (a_2\cos 2x + b_2\sin 2x) + \ldots,$$
where a_0, a_1, b_1, b_2, etc., are constants, called *Fourier coefficients*. The series was first formulated by J. B. J. Fourier (1768–1830) and is used in harmonic analysis (*Fourier analysis*) to determine the harmonic components of a complex wave.

fourth dimension *See* space–time.

f.p.s. units The British system of units based on the foot, pound, and second. It has now been replaced for all scientific purposes by SI units.

fractal A curve or surface generated by a process involving successive sub-

division. For example, a *snowflake curve* can be produced by starting with an equilateral triangle and dividing each side into three segments. The middle segments are then replaced by two equal segments, which would form the sides of a smaller equilateral triangle. This gives a 12-sided star-shaped figure. The next stage is to subdivide each of the sides of this figure in the same way, and so on. The result is a developing figure that resembles a snowflake. In the limit, this figure has 'fractional dimension' – i.e. a dimension between that of a line (1) and a surface (2); the dimension of the snowflake curve is 1.26. The study of this type of 'self-similar' figure is used in certain branches of physics – for example, crystal growth. Fractals are also important in *chaos theory.

frame of reference A set of axes, taken as being for practical purposes at rest, that enables the position of a point (or body) in space to be defined at any instant of time. In a four-dimensional continuum (*see* space–time) a frame of reference consists of a set of four coordinate axes, three spatial and one of time.

Frasch process A method of obtaining sulphur from underground deposits using a tube consisting of three concentric pipes. Superheated steam is passed down the outer pipe to melt the sulphur, which is forced up through the middle pipe by compressed air fed through the inner tube. The steam in the outer casing keeps the sulphur molten in the pipe.

Fraunhofer diffraction A form of *diffraction in which the light source and the receiving screen are in effect at infinite distances from the diffracting object, so that the wave fronts can be treated as planar rather than spherical. In practice it involves parallel beams of light. It can be regarded as an extreme case of *Fresnel diffraction but is of more practical use in explaining single and multiple slit patterns. It was studied by the German optician Joseph von Fraunhofer (1787–1826).

Fraunhofer lines Dark lines in the solar spectrum that result from the absorption by elements in the solar chromosphere of some of the wavelengths of the visible radiation emitted by the hot interior of the sun.

free electron *See* electron.

free energy A measure of a system's ability to do work. The *Gibbs free energy* (or *Gibbs function*), G, is defined by $G = H - TS$, where G is the energy liberated or absorbed in a reversible process at constant pressure and constant temperature (T), H is the *enthalpy and S the *entropy of the system. Changes in Gibbs free energy, ΔG, are useful in indicating the conditions under which a chemical reaction will occur. If ΔG is positive the reaction will only occur if energy is supplied to force it away from the equilibrium position (i.e. when $\Delta G = 0$). If ΔG is negative the reaction will proceed spontaneously to equilibrium.

The *Helmholtz free energy* (or *Helmholtz function*), F, is defined by $F = U - TS$, where U is the *internal energy. For a reversible isothermal process, ΔF represents the useful work available.

free fall Motion resulting from a gravitational field that is unimpeded by a medium that would provide a frictional retarding force or buoyancy. In the earth's gravitational field, free fall takes place at a constant acceleration, known as the *acceleration of free fall.

free space A region in which there is no matter and no electromagnetic or gravitational fields. It has a temperature of absolute zero, unit refractive index, and the speed of light is its maximum value. The electric constant (*see* permittivity) and the magnetic

freeze drying

constant (*see* permeability) are defined for free space.

freeze drying A process used in dehydrating food, blood plasma, and other heat-sensitive substances. The product is deep-frozen and the ice trapped in it is removed by reducing the pressure and causing it to sublime. The water vapour is then removed, leaving an undamaged dry product.

freezing mixture A mixture of components that produces a low temperature. For example, a mixture of ice and sodium chloride gives a temperature of –20°C.

Frenkel defect *See* defect.

frequency Symbol f. The rate of repetition of a regular event. The number of cycles of a wave, or some other oscillation or vibration, per second is expressed in *hertz (cycles per second). The frequency (f) of a wave motion is given by $f = c/\lambda$, where c is the velocity of propagation and λ is the wavelength. The frequency associated with a quantum of electromagnetic energy is given by $f = E/h$, where E is the quantum's energy and h is the Planck constant.

frequency modulation (FM) *See* modulation; radio.

fresnel A unit of frequency equal to 10^{12} hertz. In SI units this is equal to 1 terahertz (THz). It was named after the French physicist A. J. Fresnel (1788–1827).

Fresnel diffraction A form of *diffraction in which the light source or the receiving screen, or both, are at finite distances from the diffracting object, so that the wavefronts are not plane, as in *Fraunhofer diffraction. It was studied by A. J. Fresnel (1788–1827).

Fresnel lens A lens with one face cut into a series of steps. It enables a relatively light and robust lens of short focal length though poor optical quality to be used in projectors (as condenser lenses), searchlights, spotlights, car headlights, and lighthouses. Such lenses have been made fine enough to serve as magnifiers for reading small print.

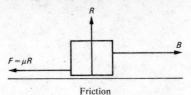

Friction

friction The force that resists the motion of one surface relative to another with which it is in contact. For a body resting on a horizontal surface there is a normal contact force, R, between the body and surface, acting perpendicularly to the surface. If a horizontal force B is applied to the body with the intention of moving it to the right, there will be an equal horizontal friction force, F, to the left, resisting the motion (see illustration). If B is increased until the body just moves, the value of F will also increase until it reaches the *limiting frictional force* (F_L), which is the maximum value of F. F_L is then equal to $\mu_s R$, where μ_s is the *coefficient of static friction*, the value of which depends on the nature of the surfaces. Once the body is moving with constant velocity, the value of F falls to a value F_k, which is equal to $\mu_k R$, where μ_k is the *coefficient of kinetic friction*. Both μ_s and μ_k are independent of the surface area of the body unless this is very small and μ_k is almost independent of the relative velocity of the body and surface. The cause of friction is that surfaces, however smooth they may look to the eye, on the microscopic scale have many humps and crests. Therefore the actual area of contact is very small indeed, and the consequent very high pressure leads to local pressure welding of the surfaces. During motion the welds are broken and

remade continually. *See also* rolling friction.

froth flotation A method of separating mixtures of solids, used industrially for separating ores from the unwanted gangue. The mixture is ground to a powder and water and a frothing agent added. Air is blown through the water. With a suitable frothing agent, the bubbles adhere only to particles of ore and carry them to the surface, leaving the gangue particles at the bottom.

frustum A solid figure produced when two parallel planes cut a larger solid or when one plane parallel to the base cuts it.

fuel A substance that is oxidized or otherwise changed in a furnace or heat engine to release useful heat or energy. For this purpose wood, vegetable oil, and animal products have largely been replaced by *fossil fuels since the 18th century.

The limited supply of fossil fuels and the expense of extracting them from the earth has encouraged the development of nuclear fuels to produce electricity (*see* nuclear energy).

fuel cell A cell in which the chemical energy of a fuel is converted directly into electrical energy. The simplest fuel cell is one in which hydrogen is oxidized to form water over porous sintered nickel electrodes. A supply of gaseous hydrogen is fed to a compartment containing the porous cathode and a supply of oxygen is fed to a compartment containing the porous anode; the electrodes are separated by a third compartment containing a hot alkaline electrolyte, such as potassium hydroxide. The electrodes are porous to enable the gases to react with the electrolyte, with the nickel in the electrodes acting as a catalyst. At the cathode the hydrogen reacts with the hydroxide ions in the electrolyte to form water, with the release of two electrons per hydrogen molecule:

$$H_2 + 2OH^- \rightarrow 2H_2O + 2e^-$$

At the anode, the oxygen reacts with the water, taking up electrons, to form hydroxide ions:

$$\frac{1}{2}O_2 + H_2O + 2e^- \rightarrow 2OH^-$$

The electrons flow from the cathode to the anode through an external circuit as an electric current. The device is a more efficient converter of electric energy than a heat engine, but it is bulky and requires a continuous supply of gaseous fuels. Their use to power electric vehicles is being actively explored.

fuel element *See* nuclear reactor.

fugacity Symbol f. A thermodynamic function used in place of partial pressure in reactions involving real gases and mixtures. For a component of a mixture, it is defined by $d(\ln f) = d\mu/RT$, where μ is the chemical potential. It has the same units as pressure and the fugacity of a gas is equal to the pressure if the gas is ideal. The fugacity of a liquid or solid is the fugacity of the vapour with which it is in equilibrium. The ratio of the fugacity to the fugacity in some standard state is the *activity. For a gas, the standard state is chosen to be the state at which the fugacity is 1. The activity then equals the fugacity.

full-wave rectifier *See* rectifier.

function Any operation or procedure that relates one variable to one or more other variables. If y is a function of x, written $y = f(x)$, a change in x produces a change in y, and if x is known, y can be determined. x is known as the *independent variable* and y is the *dependent variable*.

fundamental *See* harmonic.

fundamental constants (universal constants) Those parameters that do not change throughout the universe. The charge on an electron, the speed of light in free space, the Planck constant, the gravitational constant, the electric constant, and the magnetic

constant are all thought to be examples.

fundamental interactions The four different types of interaction that can occur between bodies. These interactions can take place even when the bodies are not in physical contact and together they account for all the observed forces that occur in the universe. While the unification of these four types of interaction into one model, theory, or set of equations has long been the aim of physicists, this has not yet been achieved, although progress has been made in the unification of the electromagnetic and weak interactions. *See also* elementary particles; gauge theory; standard model; unified-field theory.

The *gravitational interaction*, some 10^{40} times weaker than the electromagnetic interaction, is the weakest of all. The force that it generates acts between all bodies that have mass and the force is always attractive. The interaction can be visualized in terms of a classical *field of force in which the strength of the force falls off with the square of the distance between the interacting bodies (*see* Newton's law of gravitation). The hypothetical gravitational quantum, the *graviton*, is also a useful concept in some contexts. On the atomic scale the gravitational force is negligibly weak, but on the cosmological scale, where masses are enormous, it is immensely important in holding the components of the universe together. Because gravitational interactions are long-ranged, there is a well-defined macroscopic theory in general relativity. At present, there is no satisfactory quantum theory of gravitational interaction. It is possible that *superstring theory may give a consistent quantum theory of gravity as well as unifying gravity with the other fundamental interactions.

The *weak interaction*, some 10^{10} times weaker than the electromagnetic inter-action, occurs between *leptons and in the decay of hadrons. It is responsible for the *beta decay of particles and nuclei. In the current model, the weak interaction is visualized as a force mediated by the exchange of virtual particles, called intermediate vector bosons. The weak interactions are described by *electroweak theory, which unifies them with the electromagnetic interactions.

The *electromagnetic interaction* is responsible for the forces that control atomic structure, chemical reactions, and all electromagnetic phenomena. It accounts for the forces between charged particles, but unlike the gravitational interaction, can be either attractive or repulsive. Some neutral particles decay by electromagnetic interaction. The interaction is either visualized as a classical field of force (*see* Coulomb's law) or as an exchange of virtual *photons. As with gravitational interactions, the fact that electromagnetic interactions are long-ranged means that they have a well-defined classical theory given by *Maxwell's equations. The quantum theory of electromagnetic interactions is described by *quantum electro-dynamics, which is a simple form of gauge theory.

The *strong interaction*, some 10^2 times stronger than the electromagnetic interaction, functions only between *hadrons and is responsible for the force between nucleons that gives the atomic nucleus its great stability. It operates at very short range inside the nucleus (as little as 10^{-15} metre) and is visualized as an exchange of virtual mesons. The strong interactions are described by a gauge theory called *quantum chromodynamics.

fundamental units A set of independently defined *units of measurement that forms the basis of a system of units. Such a set requires three mechanical units (usually of length, mass, and time) and, in some sys-

tems, one electrical unit; it has also been found convenient to treat certain other quantities as fundamental, even though they are not strictly independent. In the metric system the centimetre–gram–second (c.g.s.) system was replaced by the metre–kilogram–second (m.k.s.) system; the latter has now been adapted to provide the basis for *SI units. In British Imperial units the foot–pound–second (f.p.s.) system was formerly used.

fuse A length of wire made of a metal alloy of low melting point that is designed to melt at a specified current loading in order to protect an electrical device or circuit from overloading. The wire is often enclosed in a small glass or ceramic cartridge with metal ends.

fusible alloys Alloys that melt at low temperature (around 100°C). They have a number of uses, including constant-temperature baths, pipe bending, and automatic sprinklers to provide a spray of water to prevent fires from spreading. Fusible alloys are usually *eutectic mixtures of bismuth, lead, tin, and cadmium. Wood's metal and Lipowitz's alloy are examples of alloys that melt at about 70°C.

fusion 1. Melting. **2.** *See* nuclear fusion.

fusion reactor *See* thermonuclear reactor.

G

gain *See* amplifier.

galaxy A vast collection of stars, dust, and gas held together by the gravitational attraction between its components. Galaxies are usually classified as elliptical, spiral, or irregular in shape. *Elliptical galaxies* appear like ellipsoidal clouds of stars, with very little internal structure apart from (in some cases) a denser nucleus. *Spiral galaxies* are flat disc-shaped collections of stars with prominent spiral arms. *Irregular galaxies* have no apparent structure or shape.

The sun belongs to a spiral galaxy known as the *Galaxy* (with a capital G) or the *Milky Way System*. There are some 10^{11} stars in the system, which is about 30 000 parsecs across with a maximum thickness at the centre of about 4000 parsecs. The sun is about 10 000 parsecs from the centre of the Galaxy.

The galaxies are separated from each other by enormous distances, the nearest large galaxy to our own (the Andromeda galaxy) being about 6.7 $\times$ 10^5 parsecs away.

galaxy cluster A group of *galaxies containing many hundreds of members extending over a radius of up to a few megaparsecs (there also exist small groups of galaxies, such as the *Local Group, with a few tens of members). The richest and most regular clusters, such as the *Coma cluster*, with thousands of members, are gravitationally bound systems; it is not certain whether other less regular and less concentrated clusters are also bound. As well as galaxies, the clusters contain hot *intracluster gas*, at temperatures between 10^7 and 10^8 K; this can be detected by its X-ray emission. On a scale larger than clusters there are also *superclusters*, with extents of the order of a hundred megaparsecs, containing about a hundred galaxies. It is not known whether superclusters are gravitationally bound. *See also* missing mass.

Galilean telescope *See* telescope.

Galilean transformations A set of equations for transforming the position and motion parameters from a frame of reference with origin at O and coordinates (x,y,z) to a frame

origin at O' and coordinates at (x',y',z'). They are:

$$x' = x - vt$$
$$y' = y$$
$$z' = z$$
$$t' = t$$

The equations conform to Newtonian mechanics. *Compare* Lorentz transformations.

gallon 1. (or Imperial gallon) The volume occupied by exactly ten pounds of distilled water of density 0.998 859 gram per millilitre in air of density 0.001 217 gram per millilitre. 1 gallon = 4.546 09 litres (cubic decimetres). **2.** A unit of volume in the US Customary system equal to 0.832 68 Imperial gallon, i.e. 3.785 44 litres.

galvanic cell *See* voltaic cell.

galvanized iron Iron or steel that has been coated with a layer of zinc to protect it from corrosion. Corrugated mild-steel sheets for roofing and mild-steel sheets for dustbins, etc., are usually galvanized by dipping them in molten zinc. The formation of a brittle zinc–iron alloy is prevented by the addition of small quantities of aluminium or magnesium. Wire is often galvanized by a cold electrolytic process as no alloy forms in this process. Galvanizing is an effective method of protecting steel because even if the surface is scratched, the zinc still protects the underlying metal. *See* sacrificial protection.

galvanometer An instrument for detecting and measuring small electric currents. In the moving-coil instrument a pivoted coil of fine insulated copper wire surrounds a fixed soft-iron core between the poles of a permanent magnet. The interaction between the field of the permanent magnet and the sides of the coil, produced when a current flows through it, causes a torque on the coil. The moving coil carries either a pointer or a mirror that deflects a light beam when it moves; the extent of the deflection is a measure of the strength of the current. The galvanometer can be converted into an *ammeter or a *voltmeter. Digital electronic instruments are increasingly replacing the moving-coil type. *See also* ballistic galvanometer.

gamma-iron *See* iron.

gamma radiation Electromagnetic radiation emitted by excited atomic nuclei during the process of passing to a lower excitation state. Gamma radiation ranges in energy from about 10^{-15} to 10^{-10} joule (10 keV to 10 MeV) corresponding to a wavelength range of about 10^{-10} to 10^{-14} metre. A common source of gamma radiation is cobalt–60:

$$^{60}_{27}Co \xrightarrow{\beta} \, ^{60}_{28}Ni \xrightarrow{\gamma} \, ^{60}_{28}Ni$$

The de-excitation of nickel–60 is accompanied by the emission of gamma-ray photons having energies 1.17 MeV and 1.33 MeV.

gas A state of matter in which the matter concerned occupies the whole of its container irrespective of its quantity. In an *ideal gas, which obeys the *gas laws exactly, the molecules themselves would have a negligible volume and negligible forces between them, and collisions between molecules would be perfectly elastic. In practice, however, the behaviour of real gases deviates from the gas laws because their molecules occupy a finite volume, there are small forces between molecules, and in polyatomic gases collisions are to a certain extent inelastic (*see* equation of state).

gas constant (universal molar gas constant) Symbol R. The constant that appears in the *universal gas equation* (*see* gas laws). It has the value 8.314 510(70) $J K^{-1} mol^{-1}$.

gas-cooled reactor *See* nuclear reactor.

gas equation *See* gas laws.

gas laws Laws relating the temperature, pressure, and volume of an

*ideal gas. *Boyle's law states that the pressure (p) of a specimen is inversely proportional to the volume (V) at constant temperature (pV = constant). The modern equivalent of *Charles' law states that the volume is directly proportional to the thermodynamic temperature (T) at constant pressure (V/T = constant); originally this law stated the constant expansivity of a gas kept at constant pressure. The pressure law states that the pressure is directly proportional to the thermodynamic temperature for a specimen kept at constant volume. The three laws can be combined in the *universal gas equation*, $pV = nRT$, where n is the amount of gas in the specimen and R is the *gas constant. The gas laws were first established experimentally for real gases, although they are obeyed by real gases to only a limited extent; they are obeyed best at high temperatures and low pressures. *See also* equation of state.

gas thermometer A device for measuring temperature in which the working fluid is a gas. It provides the most accurate method of measuring temperatures in the range 2.5 to 1337 K. Using a fixed mass of gas a *constant-volume thermometer* measures the pressure of a fixed volume of gas at relevant temperatures, usually by means of a mercury *manometer and a *barometer.

gas turbine An internal-combustion engine in which the products of combustion of a fuel burnt in compressed air are expanded through a turbine. Atmospheric air is compressed by a rotary compressor driven by the turbine, fed into a combustion chamber, and mixed with the fuel (kerosene, natural gas, etc.); the expanding gases drive the turbine and power is taken from the unit by means of rotation of the turbine shaft (as in locomotives) or thrust from a jet (as in aircraft).

gate 1. An electronic circuit with a single output and one or more inputs; the output is a function of the input or inputs. In the *transmission gate* the output waveform is a replica of a selected input during a specific interval. In the *switching gate* a constant output is obtained for a specified combination of inputs. These gates are the basic components of digital computers. *See* logic circuits. **2.** The electrode in a field-effect *transistor that controls the current through the channel.

gauge theory Any of a number of *quantum field theories put forward to explain fundamental interactions. A gauge theory involves a symmetry *group for the fields and potentials (the *gauge group*). In the case of electrodynamics, the group is Abelian whereas the gauge theories for strong and weak interactions use non-Abelian groups. Non-Abelian gauge theories are known as *Yang–Mills theories*. This difference explains why *quantum electrodynamics is a much simpler theory than *quantum chromodynamics, which describes the strong interactions, and *electroweak theory, which is the unified theory of the weak and electromagnetic interactions. In the case of quantum gravity, the gauge group is even more complicated than the gauge groups for either the strong or weak interactions.

In gauge theories the interactions between particles can be explained by the exchange of particles (intermediate vector bosons, or *gauge bosons*), such as gluons, photons, and W and Z bosons. The *graviton has been postulated as a particle exchanged in the gravitational interaction.

gauss Symbol G. The c.g.s. unit of magnetic flux density. It is equal to 10^{-4} tesla.

Gaussian units A system of units for electric and magnetic quantities based upon c.g.s. electrostatic and electromagnetic units. Although

Gauss' law

replaced by *SI units in most branches of science, they are, like Heaviside–Lorentz units, still used in relativity theory and in particle physics. In Gaussian units, the electric and magnetic constants are both equal to unity.

Gauss' law The total electric flux normal to a closed surface in an electric field is proportional to the algebraic sum of the electric charges within the surface. A similar law applies to surfaces drawn in a magnetic field and the law can be generalized for any vector field through a closed surface. It was first stated by Karl Gauss (1777–1855).

gaussmeter A *magnetometer, especially one calibrated in gauss.

Gay Lussac's law 1. When gases combine chemically the volumes of the reactants and the volume of the product, if it is gaseous, bear simple relationships to each other when measured under the same conditions of temperature and pressure. The law was first stated in 1808 by J. L. Gay Lussac (1778–1850) and led to *Avogadro's law. **2.** See Charles' law.

Gegenschein (German: counterglow) A faint elliptical patch of light visible on a moonless night on the ecliptic at a point 180° from the position of the sun. It is caused by the reflection of sunlight by meteoric particles (see also zodiacal light).

Geiger counter (Geiger–Müller counter) A device used to detect and measure *ionizing radiation. It consists of a tube containing a low-pressure gas (usually a mixture of methane with argon or neon) and a cylindrical hollow cathode through the centre of which runs a fine-wire anode. A potential difference of about 1000 volts is maintained between the electrodes. An ionizing particle or photon passing through a window into the tube will cause an ion to be produced and the high p.d. will accelerate it towards its appropriate electrode, causing an avalanche of further ionizations by collision. The consequent current pulses can be counted in electronic circuits or simply amplified to work a small loudspeaker in the instrument. It was first devised in 1908 by Hans Geiger (1882–1947). Geiger and W. Müller produced an improved design in 1928.

Geissler tube An early form of gas-discharge tube designed to demonstrate the luminous effects of an electric discharge passing through a low-pressure gas between two electrodes. Modified forms are used in spectroscopy as a source of light. It was invented in 1858 by Heinrich Geissler (1814–79).

gel A lyophilic *colloid that has coagulated to a rigid or jelly-like solid. In a gel, the disperse medium has formed a loosely-held network of linked molecules through the dispersion medium. Examples of gels are silica gel and gelatin.

general theory of relativity See relativity.

generation time The average time that elapses between the creation of a neutron by fission in a nuclear reactor and a fission produced by that neutron.

generator Any machine that converts mechanical power into electrical power. Electromagnetic generators are the main source of electricity and may be driven by steam turbines, water turbines, internal-combustion engines, windmills, or by some moving part of any other machine. In power stations, generators produce alternating current and are often called *alternators*.

geocentric universe A view of the universe in which the earth is regarded as being at its centre. Galileo finally established that the earth revolves round the sun (not the other way round, as the church believed); during the 20th century it

has become clear from advances in observational astronomy that the earth is no more than one of nine planets orbiting the sun, which is one of countless millions of similar stars, many of which undoubtedly possess planetary bodies on which life could have evolved.

geodesic (geodesic line) The shortest distance between two points on a curved surface.

geodesy The science concerned with surveying and mapping the earth's surface to determine, for example, its exact size, shape, and gravitational field. The information supplied by geodesy in the form of locations, distances, directions, elevations, and gravity information is of use in civil engineering, navigation, geophysics, and geography.

geomagnetism The science concerned with the earth's magnetic field. If a bar magnet is suspended at any point on the earth's surface so that it can move freely in all planes, the north-seeking end of the magnet (N-pole) will point in a broadly northerly direction. The angle (D) between the horizontal direction in which it points and the geographic meridian at that point is called the *magnetic declination*. This is taken to be positive to the east of geographic north and negative to the west. The needle will not, however, be horizontal except on the *magnetic equator*. In all other positions it will make an angle (I) with the horizontal, called the *inclination* (or *magnetic dip*). At the *magnetic poles* I = 90° (+90° at the N-pole, –90° at the S-pole) and the needle will be vertical. The positions of the poles, which vary with time, were in the 1970s approximately 76.1°N, 100°W (N) and 65.8°S, 139°E (S). The vector intensity F of the geomagnetic field is specified by I, D, and F, where F is the local magnetic intensity of the field measured in gauss or tesla (1 gauss = 10^{-4} tesla). F, I, and

D, together with the horizontal and vertical components of F, and its north and east components, are called the *magnetic elements*. The value of F varies from about 0.2 gauss to 0.6 gauss, in general being higher in the region of the poles than at the equator, but values vary irregularly over the earth's surface with no correlation with surface features. There is also a slow unpredictable change in the local values of the magnetic elements called the *secular magnetic variation*. For example, in London between 1576 and 1800 D changed from +11° to –24° and I varied between 74° and 67°. The study of *palaeomagnetism has extended knowledge of the secular magnetic variation into the geological past and it is clear that the direction of the geomagnetic field has reversed several times. The source of the field and the cause of the variations are not known with any certainty but the source is believed to be associated with *dynamo action in the earth's liquid core.

geometrical optics See optics.

geometric average See average.

geometric series A series of numbers or terms in which the ratio of any term to the subsequent term is constant. For example, 1, 4, 16, 64, 256, ... has a *common ratio* of 4. In general, a geometric series can be written:

$$a + ar + ar^2 \ldots + ar^{n-1}$$

and the sum of n terms is:

$$a(r^n - 1)/(r - 1).$$

geometrized units A system of units, used principally in general relativity, in which all quantities that have dimensions involving length, mass, and time are given dimensions of a power of length only. This is equivalent to setting the gravitational constant and the speed of light both equal to unity. *See also* Gaussian units; Heaviside–Lorentz units; natural units; Planck units.

geophysics The branch of science in which the principles of mathematics and physics are applied to the study of the earth's crust and interior. It includes the study of earthquake waves, geomagnetism, gravitational fields, and electrical conductivity using precise quantitative principles. In applied geophysics the techniques are applied to the discovery and location of economic minerals (e.g. petroleum). Meteorology and physical oceanography can also be considered as geophysical sciences.

geostationary orbit *See* synchronous orbit.

geosynchronous orbit *See* synchronous orbit.

geothermal energy Heat within the earth's interior that is a potential source of energy. Volcanoes, geysers, hot springs, and fumaroles are all sources of geothermal energy. The main areas of the world in which these energy sources are used to generate power include Larderello (Italy), Wairakei (New Zealand), Geysers (California, USA), and Reykjavik (Iceland). High-temperature porous rock also occurs in the top few kilometres of the earth's crust. Thermal energy from these reservoirs can be tapped by drilling into them and extracting their thermal energy by conduction to a fluid. The hot fluid can then be used for direct heating or to raise steam to drive a turbogenerator.

German silver (nickel silver) An alloy of copper, zinc, and nickel, often in the proportions 5:2:2. It resembles silver in appearance and is used in cheap jewellery and cutlery and as a base for silver-plated wire. *See also* electrum.

getter A substance with a strong affinity for specified other substances. A getter may be used to remove the last traces of a gas when achieving a high vacuum. It may also be used to remove impurities from semiconductors.

GeV Gigaelectronvolt, i.e. 10^9 eV. In the USA this is often written BeV, billion-electronvolt.

giant star A very large star that is highly luminous. Lying above the main sequence on a *Hertzsprung–Russell diagram, giant stars represent a late stage in *stellar evolution. *See also* red giant; supergiant.

gibbous *See* phases of the moon.

Gibbs free energy (Gibbs function) *See* free energy. It is named after the US chemist J. W. Gibbs (1839–1903).

giga- Symbol G. A prefix used in the metric system to denote one thousand million times. For example, 10^9 joules = 1 gigajoule (GJ).

gilbert Symbol Gb. The c.g.s. unit of *magnetomotive force equal to $10/4\pi$ (= 0.795 77) ampere-turn. It is named after the English physician William Gilbert (1544–1603).

gimbal A type of mount for an instrument (such as a *gyroscope or compass) in which the instrument is free to rotate about two perpendicular axes.

Giorgi units *See* m.k.s. units.

Glashow–Weinberg–Salam model (GWS model) *See* electroweak theory.

glass fibres Melted glass drawn into thin fibres some 0.005 mm–0.01 mm in diameter. The fibres may be spun into threads and woven into fabrics, which are then impregnated with resins to give a material that is both strong and corrosion resistant for use in car bodies and boat building.

globular cluster *See* star cluster.

glove box A metal box that has gloves fitted to ports in its walls. It is used to manipulate mildly radioactive materials and in laboratory techniques in which an inert, sterile, dry, or

dust-free atmosphere has to be maintained.

glow discharge An electrical discharge that passes through a gas at low pressure and causes the gas to become luminous. The glow is produced by the decay of excited atoms and molecules.

glueball A hypothetical state consisting of two or more gluons, having no overall colour. There is, as yet, no conclusive evidence for the existence of glueballs.

gluino *See* supersymmetry.

gluon *See* elementary particles.

Goldstone's theorem The theorem in relativistic quantum field theory that if there is an exact continuous symmetry of the *Hamiltonian or *Langrangian defining the system, and this is not a symmetry of the *vacuum state (i.e. there is *broken symmetry), then there must be at least one spin-zero massless particle called a *Goldstone boson*. In the quantum theory of many-body systems Goldstone bosons are *collective excitations. An important exception to Goldstone's theorem is provided in *gauge theories with the Higgs mechanism, whereby the Goldstone bosons gain mass and become *Higgs bosons.

governor A device that maintains a motor or engine at a constant speed despite variations in the load, using the principle of negative feedback. A common method uses a set of flying balls that reduce the fuel intake as the speed increases. The balls, attached by flexible steel strips to a collar capable of moving vertically up and down a rotating shaft, move outwards as the speed increases. The collar rises as the balls fly out and is coupled to a lever that controls the fuel intake.

grad *See* gradient operator.

gradient 1. The slope of a line. In Cartesian coordinates, a straight line

$y = mx + c$, has a gradient m. For a curve, $y = f(x)$, the gradient at a point is the derivative dy/dx at that point, i.e. the slope of the tangent to the curve at that point. **2.** *See* gradient operator.

gradient operator (grad) The *operator

$$\nabla = i\,\partial/\partial x + j\,\partial/\partial y + k\,\partial/\partial z,$$

where i, j, and k are unit vectors in the x, y, and z directions. Given a scalar function f and a unit vector n, the *scalar product $n.\nabla f$ is the rate of change of f in the direction of n. *See also* curl; divergence.

Graham's law The rates at which gases diffuse is inversely proportional to the square roots of their densities. This principle is made use of in the diffusion method of separating isotopes. The law was formulated in 1829 by Thomas Graham (1805–69).

gram Symbol g. One thousandth of a kilogram. The gram is the fundamental unit of mass in *c.g.s. units and was formerly used in such units as the *gram-atom*, *gram-molecule*, and *gram-equivalent*, which have now been replaced by the *mole.

grand unified theory (GUT) A theory that attempts to combine the strong, weak, and electromagnetic interactions into a single *gauge theory with a single symmetry group. There are a number of different theories, most of which postulate that the interactions merge at high energies into a single interaction (the *standard model emerges from the GUT as a result of *broken symmetry). The energy above which the interactions are the same is around 10^{15} GeV, which is much higher than those obtainable with existing accelerators.

One prediction of GUTs is the occurrence of *proton decay. Some also predict that the neutrino has nonzero mass. There is no conclusive evidence for either at the moment. *See also* superstring theory.

graph A diagram that illustrates the relationship between two variables. It usually consists of two perpendicular axes, calibrated in the units of the variables and crossing at a point called the *origin*. Points are plotted in the spaces between the axes and the points are joined to form a curve. *See also* Cartesian coordinates; polar coordinates.

graphite-modulated reactor *See* nuclear reactor.

graticule (in optics) A network of fine wires or a scale in the eyepiece of a telescope or microscope or on the stage of a microscope for measuring purposes.

grating *See* diffraction grating.

gravitation *See* Newton's law of gravitation.

gravitational constant Symbol G. The constant that appears in *Newton's law of gravitation; it has the value $6.672\,59(85) \times 10^{-11}$ N m^2 kg^{-2}. G is usually regarded as a universal constant although, in some models of the universe, it is proposed that it decreases with time as the universe expands.

gravitational field The region of space surrounding a body that has the property of *mass. In this region any other body that has mass will experience a force of attraction. The ratio of the force to the mass of the second body is the *gravitational field strength*.

gravitational interaction *See* fundamental interactions.

gravitational mass *See* mass.

gravitational shift *See* redshift.

gravitational waves Waves propagated through a *gravitational field. The prediction that an accelerating mass will radiate gravitational waves (and lose energy) comes from the general theory of *relativity. Many attempts have been made to detect waves from space directly using large metal detectors. The theory suggests that a pulse of gravitational radiation (as from a supernova explosion or *black hole) causes the detector to vibrate, and the disturbance is detected by a transducer. The interaction is very weak and extreme care is required to avoid external disturbances and the effects of thermal noise in the detecting system. So far, no accepted direct observations have been made. However, indirect evidence of gravitational waves has come from observations of a pulsar in a binary system with another star.

graviton A hypothetical particle or quantum of energy exchanged in a gravitational interaction (*see* fundamental interactions). Such a particle has not been observed but is postulated to make the gravitational interaction consistent with quantum mechanics. It would be expected to travel at the speed of light and have zero rest mass and charge, and spin 2.

gravity The phenomenon associated with the gravitational force acting on any object that has mass and is situated within the earth's *gravitational field. The weight of a body (*see* mass) is equal to the force of gravity acting on the body. According to Newton's second law of motion $F = ma$, where F is the force producing an acceleration a on a body of mass m. The weight of a body is therefore equal to the product of its mass and the acceleration due to gravity (g), which is now called the *acceleration of free fall. By combining the second law of motion with *Newton's law of gravitation ($F = GM_1M_2/d^2$) it follows that: $g = GM/d^2$, where G is the *gravitational constant, M is the mass of the earth, and d is the distance of the body from the centre of the earth. For a body on the earth's surface $g = 9.806\,65$ m s^{-2}.

A force of gravity also exists on other planets, moons, etc., but because it

depends on the mass of the planet and its diameter, the strength of the force is not the same as it is on earth. If F_e is the force acting on a given mass on earth, the force F_p acting on the same mass on another planet will be given by:

$$F_p = F_e d_e^2 M_p / M_e d_p^2,$$

where M_p and d_p are the mass and diameter of the planet, respectively. Substituting values of M_p and d_p for the moon shows that the force of gravity on the moon is only 1/6 of the value on earth.

gray Symbol Gy. The derived SI unit of absorbed *dose of ionizing radiation (*see* radiation units). It is named after the British radiobiologist L. H. Gray (1905–65).

great circle Any circle on a sphere formed by a plane that passes through the centre of the sphere. The equator and the meridians of longitude are all great circles on the earth's surface.

greenhouse effect **1.** The effect within a greenhouse in which solar radiation mainly in the visible range of the spectrum passes through the glass roof and walls and is absorbed by the floor, earth, and contents, which re-emit the energy as infrared radiation. Because the infrared radiation cannot escape through the glass, the temperature inside the greenhouse rises. **2.** A similar effect in which the earth's atmosphere behaves like the greenhouse and the surface of the earth absorbs most of the solar radiation, re-emitting it as infrared radiation. This is absorbed by carbon dioxide, water, and ozone in the atmosphere as well as by clouds and reradiated back to earth. At night this absorption prevents the temperature falling rapidly after a hot day, especially in regions with a high atmospheric water content.

Gregorian telescope *See* telescope.

grid **1.** (in electricity) The system of overhead wires or underground cables by which electrical power is distributed from power stations to users. The grid is at a high voltage, up to 750 kV in some countries. **2.** (in electronics) *See* control grid.

ground state The lowest stable energy state of a system, such as a molecule, atom, or nucleus. *See* energy level.

ground wave A radio wave that travels in approximately a straight line between points on the earth's surface. For transmission over longer distances sky waves have to be involved. *See* radio transmission.

group A set of elements A, B, C, etc., for which there exists a law of composition, referred to as 'multiplication'. Any two elements can be combined to give a 'product' AB.
(1) Every product of two elements is an element of the set.
(2) The operation is associative, i.e. $A(BC) = (AB)C$.
(3) The set has an element I, called the *identity element*, such that $IA = AI = A$ for all A in the set.
(4) Each element of the set has an *inverse* A^{-1} belonging to the set such that $AA^{-1} = A^{-1}A = I$.
Although the law of combination is called 'multiplication' this does not necessarily have its usual meaning. For example, the set of integers forms a group if the law of composition is addition.

Two elements A, B of a group *commute* if $AB = BA$. If all the elements of a group commute with each other the group is said to be *Abelian*. If this is not the case the group is said to be *non-Abelian*. The distinction between Abelian and non-Abelian groups is of fundamental importance in *gauge theories.

The interest of group theory in physics is in analysing symmetry. *Discrete groups* have a finite number of elements, such as the symmetries involved in rotations and reflections of molecules, which give rise to *point*

groups. Continuous groups have an infinite number of elements where the elements are continuous. An example of a continuous group is the set of rotations about a fixed axis. The *rotation group* thus formed underlies the *quantum theory of *angular momentum, which has many applications to *atoms and *nuclei. More abstract and more general continuous groups describe fundamental interactions by gauge theories.

gun metal A type of bronze usually containing 88–90% copper, 8–10% tin, and 2–4% zinc. Formerly used for cannons, it is still used for bearings and other parts that require high resistance to wear and corrosion.

GUT *See* grand unified theory.

GWS model Glashow–Weinberg–Salam model. *See* electroweak theory.

gyrocompass A *gyroscope that is driven continuously so that it can be used as a nonmagnetic compass. When the earth rotates the gyroscope experiences no torque if its spin axis is parallel to the earth's axis; if these axes are not parallel, however, the gyroscope experiences a sequence of restoring torques that tend to make it align itself with the earth's axis. The gyrocompass is therefore an accurate north-seeking device that is uninfluenced by metallic or magnetic objects and it is also more consistent than the magnetic compass. It is therefore widely used on ships, aircraft, missiles, etc.

gyromagnetic ratio Symbol γ. The ratio of the angular momentum of an atomic system to its magnetic moment. The inverse of the gyromagnetic ratio is called the *magnetomechanical ratio*.

gyroscope A disc with a heavy rim mounted in a double *gimbal so that its axis can adopt any orientation in space. When the disc is set spinning the whole contrivance has two useful properties: (1) Gyroscopic inertia, i.e. the direction of the axis of spin resists change so that if the gimbals are turned the spinning disc maintains the same orientation in space. This property forms the basis of the *gyrocompass and other navigational devices. (2) Precession, i.e. when a gyroscope is subjected to a torque that tends to alter the direction of its axis, the gyroscope turns about an axis at right angles both to the axis about which the torque was applied and to its main axis of spin. This is a consequence of the need to conserve *angular momentum.

In the gyrostabilizer for stabilizing a ship, aircraft, or platform, three gyroscopes are kept spinning about mutually perpendicular axes so that any torque tending to alter the orientation of the whole device affects one of the gyroscopes and thereby activates a servomechanism that restores the original orientation.

H

habit *See* crystal habit.

hadron Any of a class of subatomic particles that interact by the strong interaction (*see* fundamental interactions). The class includes protons, neutrons, and pions. Hadrons are believed to have an internal structure and to consist of quarks; they are therefore not truly elementary. Hadrons are either *baryons, which decay into protons and are believed to consist of three quarks, or *mesons, which decay into *leptons and photons or into proton pairs and are believed to consist of a quark and an antiquark. *See* elementary particles.

half cell An electrode in contact with a solution of ions, forming part of a *cell. Various types of half cell exist,

the simplest consisting of a metal electrode immersed in a solution of metal ions. Gas half cells have a gold or platinum plate in a solution with gas bubbled over the metal plate. The commonest is the *hydrogen half cell. Half cells can also be formed by a metal in contact with an insoluble salt or oxide and a solution. The calomel half cell is an example of this. Half cells are commonly referred to as *electrodes*.

half-life *See* decay.

half-thickness The thickness of a specified material that reduces the intensity of a beam of radiation to half its original value.

half-wave plate *See* retardation plate.

half-wave rectifier *See* rectifier.

half-width Half the width of a spectrum line (or in some cases the full width) measured at half its height.

Hall effect The production of an e.m.f. within a conductor or semiconductor through which a current is flowing when there is a strong transverse magnetic field. The potential difference develops at right angles to both the current and the field. It is caused by the deflection of charge carriers by the field and was first discovered by Edwin Hall (1855–1938). The strength of the electric field E_H produced is given by the relationship $E_H = R_H jB$, where j is the current density, B is the magnetic flux density, and R_H is a constant called the *Hall coefficient*. The value of R_H can be shown to be $1/ne$, where n is the number of charge carriers per unit volume and e is the electronic charge. The effect is used to investigate the nature of charge carriers in metals and semiconductors, in the *Hall probe* for the measurement of magnetic fields, and in magnetically operated switching devices. *See also* quantum Hall effect.

Halley's comet A bright *comet with a period of 76 years. Its last visit was in 1986. The comet moves around the sun in the opposite direction to the planets. Its orbit was first calculated in 1705 by Edmund Halley (1656–1742), after whom it is named.

halo A luminous ring that sometimes can be observed around the sun or the moon. It is caused by diffraction of their light by particles in the earth's atmosphere; the radius of the ring is inversely proportional to the predominant particle radius.

Hamiltonian Symbol H. A function used to express the energy of a system in terms of its momentum and positional coordinates. In simple cases this is the sum of its kinetic and potential energies. In *Hamiltonian equations*, the usual equations used in mechanics (based on forces) are replaced by equations expressed in terms of momenta. These concepts, often called *Hamiltonian mechanics*, were formulated by Sir William Rowan Hamilton (1805–65).

hard ferromagnetic materials *See* soft iron.

hard radiation Ionizing radiation of high penetrating power, usually gamma rays or short-wavelength X-rays. *Compare* soft radiation.

hardware *See* computer.

harmonic An oscillation having a frequency that is a simple multiple of a *fundamental* sinusoidal oscillation. The fundamental frequency of a

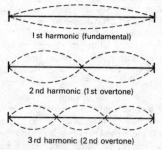

1st harmonic (fundamental)

2nd harmonic (1st overtone)

3rd harmonic (2nd overtone)

Harmonics

sinusoidal oscillation is usually called the *first harmonic*. The *second harmonic* has a frequency twice that of the fundamental and so on (see illustration). A taut string or column of air, as in a violin or organ, will sound upper harmonics at the same time as the fundamental sounds. This is because the string or column of air divides itself into sections, each section then vibrating as if it were a whole. The upper harmonics are also called *overtones*, but the second harmonic is the first overtone, and so on. Musicians, however, often regard harmonic and overtone as synonymous, not counting the fundamental as a harmonic.

harmonic motion *See* simple harmonic motion.

harmonic series (harmonic progression) A series or progression in which the reciprocals of the terms have a constant difference between them, e.g. $1 + 1/2 + 1/3 + 1/4 \ldots + 1/n$.

Harvard classification *See* spectral class.

Hawking process Emission of particles by a *black hole as a result of qantum-mechanical effects. It was discovered by Stephen Hawking (1942–). The gravitational field of the black hole causes production of particle–antiparticle pairs in the vicinity of the event horizon (the process is analogous to that of pair production). One member of each pair (either the particle or the antiparticle) falls into the black hole, while the other escapes. To an external observer, it appears that the black hole is emitting radiation (*Hawking radiation*). Furthermore, it turns out that the energy of the particles that fall in is negative and exactly balances the (positive) energy of the escaping particles. This negative energy reduces the mass of the black hole and the net result of the process

is that the emitted particle flux appears to carry off the black-hole mass. It can be shown that the black hole radiates like a *black body, with the energy distribution of the particles obeying *Planck's radiation law for a temperature that is inversely proportional to the mass of the hole. For a black hole of the mass of the sun, this temperature turns out to be only about 10^{-7} K, so the process is negligible. However, for a 'mini' black hole, such as might be formed in the early universe, with a mass of order 10^{12} kg (and a radius of order 10^{-15} m), the temperature would be of order 10^{11} K and the hole would radiate copiously (at a rate of about 6×10^9 W) a flux of gamma rays, neutrinos, and electron–positron pairs. (The observed levels of cosmic gamma rays put strong constraints on the number of such 'mini' black holes, suggesting that there are too few of them to solve the *missing-mass problem.)

health physics The branch of medical physics concerned with the protection of medical, scientific, and industrial workers from the hazards of ionizing radiation and other dangers associated with atomic physics. Establishing the maximum permissible *dose of radiation, the disposal of radioactive waste, and the shielding of dangerous equipment are the principal activities in this field.

heat The process of energy transfer from one body or system to another as a result of a difference in temperature. The energy in the body or system before or after transfer is also sometimes called heat but this leads to confusion, especially in thermodynamics.

A body in equilibrium with its surroundings contains energy (the kinetic and potential energies of its atoms and molecules) but this is called *internal energy*, U, rather than heat. When such a body changes its temperature

or phase there is a change in internal energy, ΔU, which (according to the first law of *thermodynamics) is given by $\Delta U = Q - W$, where Q is the heat absorbed by the body from the surroundings and W is the work done simultaneously on the surroundings. To use the word 'heat' for both U and Q is clearly confusing. Note also that certain physical quantities are described as *heat of atomization, *heat of combustion, etc. What is usually used is a standard molar *enthalpy change for the process under consideration. The units are $kJ\,mol^{-1}$; a negative value indicates that energy is liberated. *See also* heat capacity; heat transfer; latent heat.

heat balance 1. A balance sheet showing all the heat inputs to a system (such as a chemical process, furnace, etc.) and all the heat outputs. **2.** The equilibrium that exists on the average between the radiation received from the sun by the earth and its atmosphere and that reradiated or reflected by the earth and the atmosphere. In general, the regions of the earth nearer the equator than about 35°N or S receive more energy from the sun than they are able to reradiate, whereas those regions polewards of 35°N or S receive less energy than they lose. The excess of heat received by the low latitudes is carried to the higher latitudes by atmospheric and oceanic circulations.

heat capacity (thermal capacity) The ratio of the heat supplied to an object or specimen to its consequent rise in temperature. The *specific heat capacity* is the ratio of the heat supplied to unit mass of a substance to its consequent rise in temperature. The *molar heat capacity* is the ratio of the heat supplied to unit amount of a substance to its consequent rise in temperature. In practice, heat capacity (C) is measured in joules per kelvin, specific heat capacity (c) in

$J\,K^{-1}\,kg^{-1}$, and molar heat capacity (C_m) in $J\,K^{-1}\,mol^{-1}$. For a gas, the values of c and C_m are commonly given either at *constant volume*, when only its *internal energy is increased, or at *constant pressure*, which requires a greater input of heat as the gas is allowed to expand and do work against the surroundings. The symbols for the specific and molar heat capacities at constant volume are c_v and C_v, respectively; those for the specific and molar heat capacities at constant pressure are c_p and C_p.

heat death of the universe The condition of the universe when *entropy is maximized and all large-scale samples of matter are at a uniform temperature. In this condition no energy is available for doing work and the universe is finally unwound. The condition was predicted by Rudolph Clausius (1822–88), the German physicist, who introduced the concept of entropy. Clausius's dictum that "the energy of the universe is constant, its entropy tends to a maximum" is a statement of the first two laws of thermodynamics. These laws apply in this sense only to closed systems and, for the predicted heat death to occur, the universe must be a closed system.

heat engine A device for converting heat into work. The heat is derived from the combustion of a fuel. In an *internal-combustion engine the fuel is burnt inside the engine, whereas in a *steam engine or steam turbine, examples of external-combustion engines, the fuel is used to raise steam outside the engine and then some of the steam's internal energy is used to do work inside the engine. Engines usually work on cycles of operation, the most efficient of which would be the *Carnot cycle. This cannot be realized in practice, but the *Rankine cycle is approximated by some engines.

heat exchanger A device for transferring heat from one fluid to another without permitting the two fluids to contact each other. A simple industrial heat exchanger consists of a bundle of parallel tubes, through which one fluid flows, enclosed in a container, through which the other fluid flows in the opposite direction (a *counter-current heat exchanger*).

heat of atomization The energy required to dissociate one mole of a given substance into atoms. *See* heat.

heat of combustion The energy liberated when one mole of a given substance is completely oxidized. *See* heat.

heat of formation The energy liberated or absorbed when one mole of a compound is formed from its constituent elements.

heat of neutralization The energy liberated in neutralizing one mole of an acid or base.

heat of reaction The energy liberated or absorbed as a result of the complete chemical reaction of molar amounts of the reactants.

heat of solution The energy liberated or absorbed when one mole of a given substance is completely dissolved in a large volume of solvent (strictly, to infinite dilution).

heat pump A device for transferring heat from a low temperature source to a high temperature region by doing work. It is essentially a refrigerator with a different emphasis. The working fluid is at one stage a vapour, which is compressed by a pump adiabatically so that its temperature rises. It is then passed to the radiator, where heat is given out to the surroundings (the space to be heated) and the fluid condenses to a liquid. It is then expanded into an evaporator where it takes up heat from its surroundings and becomes a vapour again. The cycle is completed by returning the vapour to the compressor. Heat pumps are sometimes adapted to be used as dual-purpose space-heating-in-winter and air-conditioning-in-summer devices.

heat radiation (radiant heat) Energy in the form of electromagnetic waves emitted by a solid, liquid, or gas as a result of its temperature. It can be transmitted through space; if there is a material medium this is not warmed by the radiation except to the extent that it is absorbed. Although it covers the whole electromagnetic spectrum, the highest proportion of this radiation lies in the infrared portion of the spectrum at normal temperatures. *See* black body; Planck's radiation law; Stefan's law; Wien's displacement law.

heat shield A specially prepared surface that prevents a spacecraft or capsule from overheating as it re-enters the earth's atmosphere. The surface is coated with a plastic impregnated with quartz fibres, which is heated by friction with air molecules as the craft enters the atmosphere, causing the outer layer to vaporize. In this way about 80% of the energy is reradiated and the craft is safeguarded from an excessive rise in temperature.

heat transfer The transfer of energy from one body or system to another as a result of a difference in temperature. The heat is transferred by *conduction (see also conductivity), *convection, and radiation (see heat radiation).

Heaviside–Kennelly layer *See* earth's atmosphere.

Heaviside–Lorentz units A system of units for electric and magnetic quantities based upon c.g.s. electrostatic and electromagnetic units. They are the rationalized forms of *Gaussian units and, like the latter, are widely used in particle physics and relativity in preference to the *SI units now employed for general purposes in physics.

heavy-fermion system A substance in which the electrons have a very high effective mass; i.e. they act as if they had masses several hundred times the normal mass of the electron. An example of a heavy-fermion system is the cerium–copper–silicon compound $CeCuSi_2$. The high-effective-mass electrons are f-electrons in narrow energy bands associated with strong many-body effects. Substances containing such electrons have unusual thermodynamic, magnetic, and superconducting properties, which are still not completely understood. The *superconductivity of such materials has a more complicated mechanism than that for metals described by the BCS theory, since the Cooper pairs are formed from *quasiparticles with very-high-effective masses rather than from electrons.

heavy hydrogen *See* deuterium.

heavy water (deuterium oxide) Water in which hydrogen atoms, ^1H, are replaced by the heavier isotope deuterium, ^2H (symbol D). It is a colourless liquid, which forms hexagonal crystals on freezing. Its physical properties differ from those of 'normal' water; r.d. 1.105; m.p. 3.8°C; b.p. 101.4°C. Deuterium oxide, D_2O, occurs to a small extent (about 0.003% by weight) in natural water, from which it can be separated by fractional distillation or by electrolysis. It is useful in the nuclear industry because of its ability to reduce the energies of fast neutrons to thermal energies (*see* moderator) and because its absorption cross-section is lower than that of hydrogen and consequently it does not appreciably reduce the neutron flux. Water also contains the compound HDO.

hecto- Symbol h. A prefix used in the metric system to denote 100 times. For example, 100 coulombs = 1 hectocoulomb (hC).

Heisenberg uncertainty principle *See* uncertainty principle.

heliocentric universe A view of the universe in which the sun is taken to be at its centre. The model was first proposed by Aristarchus of Samos (310–230 BC) but dropped in favour of the *geocentric system proposed by Ptolemy (*c.* 90–168 AD). Copernicus (1473–1543) revived an essentially heliocentric view, which was upheld by Galileo (1564–1642) against strong opposition from the church on the grounds that if the earth was not at the centre of the universe man's position in it was diminished. In the modern view the sun is at the centre of the *solar system, but the solar system is one of an enormous number of stars in the Galaxy, which is itself one of an enormous number of *galaxies.

Helmholtz free energy *See* free energy.

henry Symbol H. The *SI unit of inductance equal to the inductance of a closed circuit in which an e.m.f. of one volt is produced when the electric current in the circuit varies uniformly at a rate of one ampere per second. It is named after Joseph Henry (1797–1878), a US physicist.

Henry's law At a constant temperature the mass of gas dissolved in a liquid at equilibrium is proportional to the partial pressure of the gas. The law, discovered in 1801 by the British chemist and physician William Henry (1775–1836), is a special case of the partition law. It applies only to gases that do not react with the solvent.

hertz Symbol Hz. The *SI unit of frequency equal to one cycle per second. It is named after Heinrich Hertz (1857–94), a German physicist.

Hertzsprung–Russell diagram (H–R diagram) A graphical representation of the absolute magnitude of stars (usually along the y-axis) plotted against the spectral class or colour index (x-axis): see illustration. The y-axis then represents the energy output of the star and the x-axis its

Hess's law

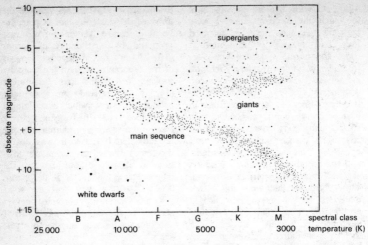

Hertzsprung–Russell diagram

surface temperature. The majority of stars on such a diagram fall on a band running from the top left to the bottom right of the graph. These are called *main-sequence stars* (the sun falls into this class). The few stars falling in the lower left portion are called *white dwarfs. The *giants fall in a cluster above the main sequence and the *supergiants are above them. The diagram, which was first devised in 1911 by Ejnar Hertzsprung (1873–1969) and in 1913 by H. N. Russell (1897–1957), forms the basis of the theory of *stellar evolution.

Hess's law If reactants can be converted into products by a series of reactions, the sum of the heats of these reactions (with due regard to their sign) is equal to the heat of reaction for direct conversion from reactants to products. More generally, the overall energy change in going from reactants to products does not depend on the route taken. The law can be used to obtain thermodynamic data that cannot be measured directly. For example, the heat of for-

mation of ethane can be found by considering the reaction:

$$2C(s) + 3H_2(g) + 3\tfrac{1}{2}O_2(g) \rightarrow 2CO_2(g) + 3H_2O(l)$$

The heat of this reaction is $2\Delta H_C + 3\Delta H_H$, where ΔH_C and ΔH_H are the heats of combustion of carbon and hydrogen respectively, which can be measured. By Hess's law, this is equal to the sum of the energies for two stages:

$$2C(s) + 3H_2(g) \rightarrow C_2H_6(g)$$

(the heat of formation of ethane, ΔH_f) and

$$C_2H_6(g) + 3\tfrac{1}{2}O_2 \rightarrow 2CO_2(g) + 3H_2O(l)$$

(the heat of combustion of ethane, ΔH_E). As ΔH_E can be measured and as

$$\Delta H_f + \Delta H_E = 2\Delta H_c + 3\Delta H_H$$

ΔH_f can be found. Another example is the use of the *Born–Haber cycle to obtain lattice energies. The law was first put forward in 1840 by the Russian chemist Germain Henri Hess (1802–50). It is sometimes called the *law of constant heat summation* and is a consequence of the law of conservation of energy.

heterodyne Denoting a device or method of radio reception in which *beats are produced by superimposing a locally generated radio wave on an incoming wave. In the *superheterodyne receiver the intermediate frequency is amplified and demodulated. In the *heterodyne wavemeter*, a variable-frequency local oscillator is adjusted to give a predetermined beat frequency with the incoming wave, enabling the frequency of the incoming wave to be determined.

heuristic Denoting a method of solving a problem for which no *algorithm exists. It involves trial and error, as in *iteration.

Heusler alloys Ferromagnetic alloys containing no ferromagnetic elements. The original alloys contained copper, manganese, and tin and were first made by Conrad Heusler (19th century mining engineer).

hidden matter *See* missing mass.

Higgs boson A spin-zero particle with a nonzero mass, predicted by Peter Higgs (1929–) to exist in certain *gauge theories, in particular in *electroweak theory (the Weinberg–Salam model). The Higgs boson has not yet been found but it is thought likely that it will be found by larger *accelerators in the next few years, especially since other associated features of the theory, including W and Z bosons, have been found. *See also* Goldstone's theorem.

high frequency (HF) A radio frequency in the range 3–30 megahertz; i.e. having a wavelength in the range 10–100 metres.

high-speed steel A steel that will remain hard at dull red heat and can therefore be used in cutting tools for high-speed lathes. It usually contains 12–22% tungsten, up to 5% chromium, and 0.4–0.7% carbon. It may also contain small amounts of vanadium, molybdenum, and other metals.

high-temperature superconductivity *See* superconductivity.

high tension (HT) A high potential difference, usually of one of several hundred volts or more. However, batteries supplying the anode circuits of radio devices using valves are usually called *high-tension batteries*, even when they supply a lower potential difference.

hole A vacant electron position in the lattice structure of a solid that behaves like a mobile positive *charge carrier with a negative *rest energy. *See* semiconductor.

holography A method of recording and displaying a three-dimensional image of an object, usually using *coherent radiation from a *laser and photographic plates (see illustration). The light from a laser is divided so that some of it (the reference beam) falls directly on a photographic plate. The other part illuminates the object, which reflects it back onto the photographic plate. The two beams form interference patterns on the plate, which when developed is called the *hologram*. To reproduce the image of the object, the hologram is illuminated by coherent light, ideally the original reference beam. The hologram produces two sets of diffracted waves; one set forms a virtual image

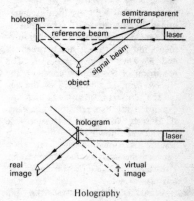

Holography

coinciding with the original object position and the other forms a real image on the other side of the plate. Both are three-dimensional. The method was invented by Dennis Gabor (1900–79) in 1948. More recent techniques can produce holograms visible in white light.

Hooke's law The *stress applied to any solid is proportional to the *strain it produces within the elastic limit for that solid. The ratio of longitudinal stress to strain is equal to the Young modulus of elasticity (*see* elastic modulus). The law was first stated by the English scientist Robert Hooke (1635–1703) in the form "Ut tensio, sic vis."

horsepower (hp) An imperial unit of power originally defined as 550 foot-pound force per second; it is equal to 745.7 watts.

hot-wire instrument An electrical measuring instrument (basically an ammeter) in which the current to be measured is passed through a thin wire and causes its temperature to rise. The temperature rise, which is proportional to the square of the current, is measured by the expansion of the wire. Such instruments can be used for either direct current or alternating current.

Hubble constant The rate at which the velocity of recession of the galaxies increases with distance as determined by the *redshift. The value is not agreed upon but current measurements indicate that it lies between 49 and 95 $km\,s^{-1}$ per megaparsec. The reciprocal of the Hubble constant, the *Hubble time*, is a measure of the age of the universe, assuming that the expansion rate has remained constant. If, as seems likely, the expansion rate has slowed down with time as a result of gravitational attraction between the galaxies, the Hubble time gives an upper limit to the age of the universe of some 2×10^{10} years. The constant is named after the US astronomer Edwin Hubble (1889–1953).

hue *See* colour.

humidity The concentration of water vapour in the atmosphere. The *absolute humidity* is the mass of water vapour per unit volume of air, usually expressed in $kg\,m^{-3}$. A useful measure is the *relative humidity*, the ratio, expressed as a percentage, of the moisture in the air to the moisture it would contain if it were saturated at the same temperature and pressure. The *specific humidity* is also sometimes used: this is the mass of water vapour in the atmosphere per unit mass of air.

Huygens' construction (Huygens' principle) Every point on a wavefront may itself be regarded as a source of secondary waves. Thus, if the position of a wavefront at any instant is known, a simple construction enables its position to be drawn at any subsequent time. The construction was first used by Christian Huygens (1629–95).

hydraulic press A device in which a force (F_1) applied to a small piston (A_1) creates a pressure (p), which is transmitted through a fluid to a larger piston (A_2), where it gives rise to a larger force (F_2): see illustration. This depends on Pascal's principle that the pressure applied anywhere in an enclosed fluid is transmitted equally in all directions. The principle of the

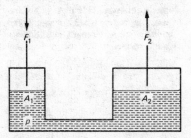

Hydraulic press

hydraulic press is widely used in jacks, vehicle brakes, presses, and earth-moving machinery, usually with oil as the working fluid.

hydraulics The study of water or other fluids at rest or in motion, particularly with respect to their engineering uses. The study is based on the principles of *hydrostatics and *hydrodynamics.

hydrodynamics The study of the motion of incompressible fluids and the interaction of such fluids with their boundaries.

hydroelectric power Electric power generated by a flow of water. A natural waterfall provides a source of energy, in the form of falling water, which can be used to drive a water *turbine. This turbine can be coupled to a generator to provide electrical energy. Hydroelectric generators can be arranged to work in reverse so that during periods of low power demand current can be fed to the generator, which acts as a motor. This motor drives the turbine, which then acts as a pump. The pump then raises water to an elevated reservoir so that it can be used to provide extra power at peak-load periods.

hydrogen bomb *See* nuclear weapons.

hydrogen electrode *See* hydrogen half cell.

hydrogen half cell (hydrogen electrode) A type of half cell in which a metal foil is immersed in a solution of hydrogen ions and hydrogen gas is bubbled over the foil. The standard hydrogen electrode, used in measuring standard *electrode potentials, uses a platinum foil with a 1.0 M solution of hydrogen ions, the gas at 1 atmosphere pressure, and a temperature of 25°C. It is written Pt(s)|H$_2$(g), H$^+$ (aq), the effective reaction being H$_2$ $\rightarrow$ 2H$^+$ + 2e.

hydrogen ion *See* pH.

hydrogen spectrum The atomic spectrum of hydrogen is characterized by lines corresponding to radiation quanta of sharply defined energy. A graph of the frequencies at which these lines occur against the ordinal number that characterizes their position in the series of lines, produces a smooth curve indicating that they obey a formal law. In 1885 J. J. Balmer (1825–98) discovered the law having the form:

$$1/\lambda = R(1/n_1^2 + 1/n_2^2)$$

This law gives the so-called *Balmer series* of lines in the visible spectrum in which $n_1 = 2$ and $n_2 = 3,4,5\ldots$, λ is the wavelength associated with the lines, and R is the *Rydberg constant.

In the *Lyman series*, discovered by Theodore Lyman (1874–1954), $n_1 = 1$ and the lines fall in the ultraviolet. The Lyman series is the strongest feature of the solar spectrum as observed by rockets and satellites above the earth's atmosphere. In the *Paschen series*, discovered by F. Paschen (1865–1947), $n_1 = 3$ and the lines occur in the far infrared. The *Brackett series* also occurs in the far infrared, with $n_1 = 4$.

hydrometer An instrument for measuring the density or relative density of liquids. It usually consists of a glass tube with a long bulb at one end. The bulb is weighted so that the device floats vertically in the liquid, the relative density being read off its calibrated stem by the depth of immersion.

hydrostatics The study of liquids at rest, with special reference to storage tanks, dams, bulkheads, and hydraulic machinery.

hygrometer An instrument for measuring *humidity in the atmosphere. The mechanical type uses an organic material, such as human hair, which expands and contracts with changes in atmospheric humidity. The expansion and contraction is used to oper-

ate a needle. In the electric type, the change in resistance of a hygroscopic substance is used as an indication of humidity. In *dew-point hygrometers* a polished surface is reduced in temperature until water vapour from the atmosphere forms on it. The temperature of this dew point enables the relative humidity of the atmosphere to be calculated. In the *wet-and-dry bulb hygrometer*, two thermometers are mounted side by side, the bulb of one being surrounded by moistened muslin. The thermometer with the wet bulb will register a lower temperature than that with a dry bulb owing to the cooling effect of the evaporating water. The temperature difference enables the relative humidity to be calculated. Only the dew-point hygrometer can be operated as an absolute instrument; all the others must ultimately be calibrated against this.

hyper- A prefix denoting over, above, high; e.g. hypersonic.

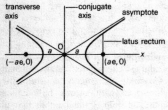

A hyperbola

hyperbola A *conic with eccentricity $e > 1$. It has two branches (see graph). For a hyperbola centred at the origin, the *transverse axis* runs along the x-axis between the vertices and has length $2a$. The *conjugate axis* runs along the y-axis and has length $2b$. There are two *foci* on the x-axis at $(ae, 0)$ and $(-ae, 0)$. The *latus rectum*, the chords through the foci perpendicular to the transverse axis, have length $2b^2/a$. The equation of the hyperbola is:

$$x^2/a^2 - y^2/b^2 = 1,$$

and the asymptotes are $y = \pm bx/a$.

hyperbolic functions A set of functions; *sinh*, *cosh*, and *tanh*, that have similar properties to *trigonometric functions but are related to the hyperbola in the manner that trigonometric functions are related to the circle. The hyperbolic sine (sinh) of the angle x is defined by:

$$\sinh x = \tfrac{1}{2}(e^x - e^{-x}).$$

Similarly,

$$\cosh x = \tfrac{1}{2}(e^x + e^{-x})$$
$$\tanh x = (e^x - e^{-x})/(e^x + e^{-x})$$

Hyperbolic secant (sech), cosecant (cosech), and cotangent (coth) are the reciprocals of cosh, sinh, and tanh, respectively.

hypercharge A quantized property of *baryons (see elementary particles) that provides a formal method of accounting for the nonoccurrence of certain expected decays by means of the strong interaction (see fundamental interactions). Hypercharge is in some respects analogous to electric charge but it is not conserved in weak interactions. Nucleons have a hypercharge of $+1$, and the *pion has a value of 0. Quarks would be expected to have fractional hypercharges.

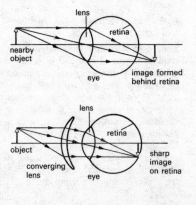

Hypermetropia

hyperfine structure *See* fine structure.

hypermetropia (hyperopia) Longsightedness. A vision defect in which the lens of the eye is unable to accommodate sufficiently to throw the image of near objects onto the retina. It is caused usually by shortness of the eyeball rather than any fault in the lens system. The subject requires spectacles with converging lenses to bring the image from behind the retina back on to its surface. See illustration.

hyperon A shortlived *elementary particle; it is classified as a *baryon and has a nonzero *strangeness.

hypersonic Denoting a velocity in excess of Mach 5 (*see* Mach number). *Hypersonic flight* is flight at hypersonic speeds in the earth's atmosphere.

hypertonic solution A solution that has a higher osmotic pressure than some other solution.

hypo- A prefix denoting under, below, low; e.g. hypotonic.

hypotonic solution A solution that has a lower osmotic pressure than some other solution.

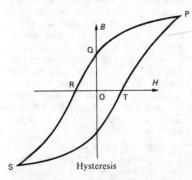

Hysteresis

hypsometer A device for calibrating thermometers at the boiling point of water. As the boiling point depends on the atmospheric pressure, which in turn depends on the height above sea

level, the apparatus can be used to measure height above sea level.

hysteresis A phenomenon in which two physical quantities are related in a manner that depends on whether one is increasing or decreasing in relation to the other.

The repeated measurement of *stress against *strain, with the stress first increasing and then decreasing, will produce for some specimens a graph that has the shape of a closed loop. This is known as a *hysteresis cycle*. The most familiar hysteresis cycle, however, is produced by plotting the magnetic flux density (B) within a ferromagnetic material against the applied magnetic field strength (H).

If the material is initially unmagnetized at O it will reach saturation at P as H is increased. As the field is reduced and again increased the loop PQRSTP is formed (see graph). The area of this loop is proportional to the energy loss (*hysteresis loss*) occurring during the cycle. The value of B equal to OQ is called the *remanance* (or retentivity) and is the magnetic flux density remaining in the material after the saturating field has been reduced to zero. This is a measure of the tendency of the magnetic domain patterns (*see* magnetism) to remain distorted even after the distorting field has been removed. The value of H equal to OR is called the *coercive force* (or coercivity) and is the field strength required to reduce the remaining flux density to zero. It is a measure of the difficulty of restoring the symmetry of the domain patterns.

I

ice point The temperature at which there is equilibrium between ice and water at standard atmospheric pressure (i.e. the freezing or melting point under standard conditions). It was

used as a fixed point (0°) on the Celsius scale, but the kelvin and the International Practical Temperature Scale are based on the *triple point of water.

iconoscope A form of television camera tube (*see* camera) in which the beam of light from the scene is focused on to a thin mica plate. One side of the plate is faced with a thin metallic electrode, the other side being coated with a mosaic of small globules of a photoemissive material. The light beam falling on the mosaic causes photoemission of electrons, creating a pattern of positive charges in what is effectively an array of tiny capacitors. A high-velocity electron beam scans the mosaic, discharging each capacitor in turn through the metallic electrode. The resulting current is fed to amplification circuits, the current from a particular section of the mosaic depending on the illumination it has received. In this way the optical information in the light beam is converted into an electrical signal.

ideal crystal A single crystal with a perfectly regular lattice that contains no impurities, imperfections, or other defects.

ideal gas (perfect gas) A hypothetical gas that obeys the *gas laws exactly. An ideal gas would consist of molecules that occupy negligible space and have negligible forces between them. All collisions made between molecules and the walls of the container or between molecules and other molecules would be perfectly elastic, because the molecules would have no means of storing energy except as translational kinetic energy.

ideal solution *See* Raoult's law.

identity Symbol ≡. A statement of equality that applies for all values of the unknown quantity. For example, $5y \equiv 2y + 3y$.

ignition temperature 1. The temperature to which a substance must be heated before it will burn in air. **2.** The temperature to which a *plasma has to be raised in order that nuclear fusion will occur.

illuminance (illumination) Symbol E. The energy in the form of visible radiation reaching a surface per unit area in unit time; i.e. the luminous flux per unit time. It is measured in *lux (lumens per square metre).

image A representation of a physical object formed by a lens, mirror, or other optical instrument. If the rays of light actually pass through the image, it is called a *real image*. If a screen is placed in the plane of a real image it will generally become visible. If the image is seen at a point from which the rays appear to come to the observer, but do not actually do so, the image is called a *virtual image*. No image will be formed on a screen placed at this point. Images may be *upright* or *inverted* and they may be *magnified* or *diminished*.

image converter An electronic device in which an image formed by invisible radiation (usually gamma rays, X-rays, ultraviolet, or infrared) is converted into a visible image. Commonly the invisible radiation is focused on to a photocathode, which emits electrons when it is illuminated. These electrons fall on a fluorescent anode screen, after acceleration and focusing by a system of electron lenses. The fluorescent screen produces a visible image. The device is used in fluoroscopes, infrared telescopes, ultraviolet microscopes, and other devices.

imaginary number A number that is a multiple of $\sqrt{-1}$, which is denoted by i; for example $\sqrt{-3} = i\sqrt{3}$. *See also* complex number.

immersion objective An optical microscope objective in which the front surface of the lens is immersed in a liquid on the cover glass of the

microscope specimen slide. Cedar-wood oil or sugar solution is frequently used. It has the same refractive index as the glass of the slide, so that the object is effectively immersed in it. The presence of the liquid increases the effective aperture of the objective, thus increasing the resolution.

impedance Symbol Z. The quantity that measures the opposition of a circuit to the passage of a current and therefore determines the amplitude of the current. In a d.c. circuit this is the resistance (R) alone. In an a.c. circuit, however, the *reactance (X) also has to be taken into account, according to the equation: $Z^2 = R^2 + X^2$, where Z is the impedance. The *complex impedance* is given by $Z = R + iX$, where $i = \sqrt{-1}$. The real part of the complex impedance, the resistance, represents the loss of power according to *Joule's law. The ratio of the imaginary part, the reactance, to the real part is an indication of the difference in phase between the voltage and the current.

Imperial units The British system of units based on the pound and the yard. The former f.p.s. system was used in engineering and was loosely based on Imperial units; for all scientific purposes *SI units are now used. Imperial units are also being replaced for general purposes by metric units.

implosion An inward collapse of a vessel, especially as a result of evacuation.

impulse Symbol J. The product of a force F and the time t for which it acts. If the force is variable, the impulse is the integral of Fdt from t_0 to t_1. The impulse of a force acting for a given time interval is equal to the change in momentum produced over that interval, i.e. $J = m(v_1 - v_0)$, assuming that the mass (m) remains constant while the velocity changes from v_0 to v_1.

incandescence The emission of light by a substance as a result of raising it to a high temperature. An *incandescent lamp* is one in which light is emitted by an electrically heated filament. *See* electric lighting.

inclination 1. *See* geomagnetism. **2.** The angle between the orbital plane of a planet, satellite, or comet and the plane of the earth's *ecliptic.

indefinite integral *See* integration.

indeterminacy *See* uncertainty principle.

inductance The property of an electric circuit or component that causes an e.m.f. to be generated in it as a result of a change in the current flowing through the circuit (*self inductance*) or of a change in the current flowing through a neighbouring circuit with which it is magnetically linked (*mutual inductance*). In both cases the changing current is associated with a changing magnetic field, the linkage with which in turn induces the e.m.f. In the case of self inductance, L, the e.m.f., E, generated is given by $E = -L.dI/dt$, where I is the instantaneous current and the minus sign indicates that the e.m.f. induced is in opposition to the change of current. In the case of mutual inductance, M, the e.m.f., E_1, induced in one circuit is given by $E_1 = -M.dI_2/dt$, where I_2 is the instantaneous current in the other circuit.

induction A change in the state of a body produced by a field. *See* electromagnetic induction; inductance.

induction coil A type of *transformer used to produce a high-voltage alternating current or pulses of high-voltage current from a low-voltage direct-current source. The induction coil is widely used in spark-ignition *internal-combustion engines to produce the spark in the sparking plugs. In such an engine the battery is connected to the primary winding of the coil through a circuit-breaking device

driven by the engine and the e.m.f. generated in the secondary winding of the coil is led to the sparking plugs through the distributor. The primary coil consists of relatively few turns, whereas the secondary consists of many turns of fine wire.

induction heating The heating of an electrically conducting material by *eddy currents induced by a varying electromagnetic field. Induction heating may be an undesirable effect leading to power loss in transformers and other electrical devices. It is, however, useful for melting, forging, rolling, and heat-treating metals, as well as for welding, brazing, and soldering. The material to be heated is inserted into a coil through which an alternating current flows and acts as the short-circuited secondary of a *transformer. Eddy currents induced in the material within the coil cause the temperature of the material to rise.

induction motor See electric motor.

inelastic collision A collision in which some of the kinetic energy of the colliding bodies is converted into internal energy in one body so that kinetic energy is not conserved. In collisions of macroscopic bodies some kinetic energy is turned into vibrational energy of the atoms, causing a heating effect. Collisions between molecules of a gas or liquid may also be inelastic as they cause changes in vibrational and rotational *energy levels. In nuclear physics, an inelastic collision is one in which the incoming particle causes the nucleus it strikes to become excited or to break up.

inertia The property of matter that causes it to resist any change in its motion. Thus, a body at rest remains at rest unless it is acted upon by an external force and a body in motion continues to move at constant speed in a straight line unless acted upon by an external force. This is a statement of Newton's first law of motion. The *mass of a body is a measure of

its inertia. See Mach's principle; inertial frame.

inertial frame A *frame of reference in which bodies move in straight lines with constant speeds unless acted upon by external forces, i.e. a frame of reference in which free bodies are not accelerated. Newton's laws of motion are valid in an inertial system but not in a system that is itself accelerated with respect to such a frame.

inertial mass See mass.

infinite series See series.

infinitesimal Vanishingly small but not zero. Infinitesimal changes are notionally made in the *calculus, which is sometimes called the infinitesimal calculus.

infinity Symbol ∞. A quantity having a value that is greater than any assignable value. Minus infinity, $-\infty$, is a quantity having a value that is less than any assignable value.

inflation See early universe.

inflationary universe See early universe.

inflection A point on a curve at which the tangent changes from rotation in one direction to rotation in the opposite direction. If the curve $y = f(x)$ has a stationary point $dy/dx = 0$, there is either a maximum, minimum, or inflection at this point. If $d^2y/dx^2 = 0$, the stationary point is a point of inflection.

infrared astronomy The study of radiation from space in the infrared region of the spectrum (see infrared radiation). Some infrared radiation is absorbed by water and carbon dioxide molecules in the atmosphere but there are several narrow atmospheric *windows in the near-infrared (1.15–1.3 μm, 1.5–1.75 μm, 2–2.4 μm, 3.4–4.2 μm, 4.6–4.8 μm, 8–13 μm, and 16–18 μm). Longer wavelength observations must be made from balloons, rockets, or satellites. Infrared sources are either thermal, i.e. emitted

by gas or dust atoms or molecules in the temperature range 100–3000 K, or electronic, i.e. emitted by high-energy electrons interacting with magnetic fields as in *synchrotron radiation. Detectors are either modified reflecting *telescopes or solid-state photon detectors, usually incorporating *photovoltaic devices.

infrared radiation (IR) Electromagnetic radiation with wavelengths longer than that of red light but shorter than that radiowaves, i.e. radiation in the wavelength range 0.7 micrometre to 1 millimetre. It was discovered in 1800 by William Herschel (1738–1822) in the sun's spectrum. The natural vibrational frequencies of atoms and molecules and the rotational frequencies of some gaseous molecules fall in the infrared region of the electromagnetic spectrum. The infrared absorption spectrum of a molecule is highly characteristic of it and the spectrum can therefore be used for molecular identification. Glass is opaque to infrared radiation of wavelength greater than 2 micrometres and other materials, such as germanium, quartz, and polyethylene, have to be used to make lenses and prisms. Photographic film can be made sensitive to infrared up to about 1.2 μm.

infrasound Soundlike waves with frequencies below the audible limit of about 20 hertz.

insolation (from *in*coming *sol*ar radi*ation*) The solar radiation that is received at the earth's surface per unit area. It is related to the *solar constant, the duration of daylight, the altitude of the sun, and the latitude of the receiving surface. It is measured in MJ m^{-2}.

instantaneous value The value of any varying quantity at a specified instant.

insulator A substance that is a poor conductor of heat and electricity. Both properties usually occur as a

consequence of a lack of mobile electrons. *See* energy bands.

integral calculus *See* calculus.

integrand *See* integration.

integrated circuit A miniature electronic circuit produced within a single crystal of a *semiconductor, such as silicon. They range from simple logic circuits, little more than 1 mm square, to large-scale circuits measuring up to 8 mm square and containing a million or so transistors (active components) and resistors or capacitors (passive components). They are widely used in memory circuits, microcomputers, pocket calculators, and electronic watches on account of their low cost and bulk, reliability, and high speed. They are made by introducing impurities into specific regions of the semiconductor crystal by a variety of techniques.

integration The process of continuously summing changes in a function f(x). It is the basis of the integral *calculus and the opposite process to *differentiation. The function to be integrated is called the *integrand* and the result of integration on the integrand is called the *integral*. For example, the integration of f(x) is written $\int f(x)dx$, the differential dx being added to indicate that f(x) must be integrated with respect to x. To complete the integration, a *constant of integration*, C, must be added where no interval over which the integration takes place is given. This is called an *indefinite integral*. If the interval is specified, e.g.

$$\int_{-r}^{r} f(x)dx,$$

no constant of integration is required and the result is a *definite integral*. This means that f(x) is to be integrated between the values x = +r and x = −r.

intensity 1. The rate at which radiant energy is transferred per unit area. *See* radiant intensity. **2.** The rate at which sound energy is trans-

interaction

ferred as measured relative to some reference value. *See* decibel. **3.** Magnetic intensity. *See* magnetic field. **4.** Electric intensity. *See* electric field. **5.** *See* luminous intensity.

interaction An effect involving a number of bodies, particles, or systems as a result of which some physical or chemical change takes place to one or more of them. *See also* fundamental interaction.

interference The interaction of two or more wave motions affecting the same part of a medium so that the instantaneous disturbances in the resultant wave are the vector sum of the instantaneous disturbances in the interfering waves.

The phenomenon was first described by Thomas Young (1773–1829) in 1801 in light waves; it provided strong evidence for the wave theory of light. In the apparatus known as *Young's slits*, light is passed from a small source through a slit in a screen and the light emerging from this slit is used to illuminate two adjacent slits on a second screen. By allowing the light from these two slits to fail on a third screen, a series of parallel interference fringes is formed. Where the maximum values of the two waves from the slits coincide a bright fringe occurs (*constructive interference*) and where the maxima of one wave coincide with the minima of the other dark fringes are produced (*destructive interference*). *Newton's rings are also an interference effect. Because *lasers produce *coherent radiation they are also used to produce interference effects, one application of their use being *holography. *See also* interferometer.

interferometer An instrument designed to produce optical *interference fringes for measuring wavelengths, testing flat surfaces, measuring small distances, etc. *See also* echelon; Fabry–Pérot interferometer; Michelson–Morley experiment.

In astronomy, radio interferometers are one of the two basic types of *radio telescopes.

intermediate frequency *See* heterodyne; superheterodyne.

intermediate neutron A *neutron with kinetic energy in the range 10^2–10^5 electronvolts (1.6×10^{-17} – 1.6×10^{-14} joule).

intermediate vector boson *See* W boson; Z boson.

intermetallic compound A compound consisting of two or more metallic elements present in definite proportions in an alloy.

intermolecular forces Weak forces occurring between molecules. *See* van der Waals' forces.

internal-combustion engine A *heat engine in which fuel is burned in combustion chambers within the engine rather than in a separate furnace (as with the steam engine). The first working engine was the four-stroke *Otto engine* produced in 1876 by Nikolaus Otto (1832–91). In this type of engine a piston descends in a cylinder, drawing in a charge of fuel and air through an inlet valve; after reaching the bottom of its stroke the piston rises in the cylinder with the valves closed and compresses the charge; at or near the top of its stroke the charge is ignited by a spark and the resulting increase in pressure from the explosion forces the piston down again; on the subsequent upstroke the exhaust valve opens and the burnt gases are pushed out of the combustion chamber. The cycle is then repeated. Otto's engine used gas as a fuel; however, the invention of the carburettor and the development of the oil industry at the end of the 19th century enabled the Otto engine to become the source of power for the emerging motor car. A variation of the Otto four-stroke engine is the two-stroke engine that has no complicated valve system, the explosive

charge entering and leaving the cylinder through ports in the cylinder that are covered and uncovered by the moving piston.

An alternative to the Otto engine, especially for heavy vehicles where weight is not a problem, is the compression-ignition *Diesel engine* invented by Rudolf Diesel (1858–1913) in about 1896. In this type of engine there are no sparking plugs; instead air is compressed in the cylinder, causing its temperature to rise to about 550°C. Oil is then sprayed into the combustion chamber and ignites on contact with the hot air. While the spark-ignition petrol engine typically works on a *compression ratio of 8 or 9 to 1, the Diesel engine has to have a compression ratio of 15 to 20 to 1. This requires a much heavier, and therefore more expensive, engine. *See also* Wankel engine; gas turbine.

internal conversion A process in which an excited atomic nucleus (*see* excitation) decays to the *ground state and the energy released is transferred by electromagnetic coupling to one of the bound electrons of that atom rather than being released as a photon. The coupling is usually with an electron in the K-, L-, or M-shell of the atom, and this *conversion electron* is ejected from the atom with a kinetic energy equal to the difference between the nuclear transition energy and the binding energy of the electron. The resulting ion is itself in an excited state and usually subsequently emits an *Auger electron or an X-ray photon.

internal energy Symbol U. The total of the kinetic energies of the atoms and molecules of which a system consists and the potential energies associated with their mutual interactions. It does not include the kinetic and potential energies of the system as a whole nor their nuclear energies or other intra-atomic energies. The value of the absolute internal energy of a system in any particular state cannot be measured; the significant quantity is the change in internal energy, ΔU. For a closed system (i.e. one that is not being replenished from outside its boundaries) the change in internal energy is equal to the heat absorbed by the system (Q) from its surroundings, less the work done (W) by the system on its surroundings, i.e. $\Delta U = Q - W$. *See also* energy; heat.

internal resistance The resistance within a source of electric current, such as a cell or generator. It can be calculated as the difference between the e.m.f. (E) and the potential difference (V) between the terminals divided by the current being supplied (I), i.e. $r = (E - V)/I$, where r is the internal resistance.

international candle A former unit of *luminous intensity. It has now been replaced by the *candela, to which it is approximately equal.

international date line An imaginary line on the earth's surface that joins the north and south poles and approximately follows the 180° meridian through the Pacific Ocean. This line has been agreed internationally to mark the beginning and end of a day. A traveller moving towards the east, against the sun's apparent movement, gains 1 hour for every 15° of longitude; westward he loses time at the same rate. In crossing the dateline therefore he is deemed to compensate for this by losing or gaining (respectively) one day. The 180° meridian was chosen as the date line by the International Meridian Conference in 1884.

International Practical Temperature Scale *See* temperature scales.

interplanetary space The space between the sun and the planets within the *solar system. The *interplanetary matter* that occupies this region of space mostly originates in

the sun, from which it flows as the *solar wind. The solar wind consists primarily of protons emerging from the sun at a rate of about 10^9 kilograms per second. At the earth's distance from the sun the particle density has fallen to a few particles per cm³. Apart from this very tenuous gas, there are also dust particles in interplanetary space, largely believed to originate in the belt of asteroids. Particles weighing about 1 g produce visible meteors in the earth's atmosphere; micrometeorites as small as 1 nanogram can be detected by their impact on spacecraft.

interstellar space The space between the stars. The *interstellar matter* that occupies this space constitutes several percent of the Galaxy's total mass and it is from this matter that new stars are formed. The matter is primarily hydrogen, in which a number of other molecules and radicals have been detected, together with small solid dust grains. On average the density of matter in interstellar space is about 10^6 hydrogen atoms per cubic metre, but the gas is not uniformly distributed, being clumped into *interstellar clouds* of various sizes and densities.

interstitial See defect.

interstitial compound A compound in which ions or atoms of a nonmetal occupy interstitial positions in a metal lattice. Such compounds often have metallic properties. Examples are found in the carbides, borides, and silicides.

intrinsic semiconductor See semiconductor.

Invar A tradename for an alloy of iron (63.8%), nickel (36%), and carbon (0.2%) that has a very low *expansivity over a a restricted temperature range. It is used in watches and other instruments to reduce their sensitivity to changes in temperature.

inverse Compton effect The gain in energy of low-energy photons when they are scattered by free electrons of much higher energy. As a consequence, the electrons lose energy. *See also* Compton effect.

inverse functions If $y = f(x)$ and a function can be found so that $x = g(y)$, then $g(y)$ is said to be the inverse function of $f(x)$. If y is a trigonometrical function of the angle x, say $y = \sin x$, then x is the *inverse trigonometrical function* of y, written $x = \arcsin y$ or $\sin^{-1} y$. Similarly, the other trigonometrical functions form the inverse trigonometrical functions $\cos^{-1} y$, $\tan^{-1} y$, $\cot^{-1} y$, $\sec^{-1} y$, and $\csc^{-1} y$. *Inverse hyperbolic functions* are also formed in this way, e.g. $\text{arcsinh} y$ or $\sinh^{-1} y$, $\cosh^{-1} y$, and $\tanh^{-1} y$.

inverse-square law A law in which the magnitude of a physical quantity is proportional to the reciprocal of the square of the distance from the source of that property. *Newton's law of gravitation and *Coulomb's law are both examples.

inversion layer See transistor.

inversion temperature See Joule–Kelvin effect.

involute See evolute.

ion An atom or group of atoms that has either lost one or more electrons, making it positively charged (a cation), or gained one or more electrons, making it negatively charged (an anion). *See also* ionization.

ion engine A type of jet-propulsion engine that may become important for propelling or controlling spacecraft. It consists of a unit producing a beam of ions, which are accelerated by an electric or electromagnetic field. Reaction forces from the high-speed ions causes propulsion in much the same way as that caused by exhaust gas of a rocket. However, a separate beam of electrons or ions of opposite polarity to the propelling beam must also be ejected from the engine to

enable recombination to take place behind the vehicle (to avoid the vehicle becoming charged). Ion engines provide high *specific impulse and therefore low propellant consumption. The three main components of an ion engine are the power generator, the propellant feed, and the thruster. The power generator may be a nuclear reactor or a solar-energy collector. If it is the former, a gas turbine is coupled to the reactor and the turbine drives an electric generator. A solar-energy unit provides electricity direct. The propellant chosen needs to have an ion of medium mass (low mass for high specific impulse, high mass for high thrust) and a low first *ionization potential. Caesium and mercury are materials currently envisaged as suitable propellants. The thruster consists of an ionizer to produce the ions, an accelerator to provide and shape the accelerating field, and a neutralizer (usually an electron emitter) to neutralize the fast-moving ion beam after ejection.

ion exchange The exchange of ions of the same charge between a solution (usually aqueous) and a solid in contact with it. The process occurs widely in nature, especially in the absorption and retention of water-soluble fertilizers by soils. For example, if a potassium salt is dissolved in water and applied to soil, potassium ions are absorbed by the soil and sodium and calcium ions are released from it.

The soil, in this case, is acting as an ion exchanger. Synthetic *ion-exchange resins* consist of various copolymers having a cross-linked three-dimensional structure to which ionic groups have been attached. An *anionic resin* has negative ions built into its structure and therefore exchanges positive ions. A *cationic resin* has positive ions built in and exchanges negative ions. Ion-exchange resins, which are used in sugar refining to remove salts, are

synthetic organic polymers containing side groups that can be ionized. In anion exchange, the side groups are ionized basic groups, such as $-NH_3^+$ to which anions X^- are attached. The exchange reaction is one in which different anions in the solution displace the X^- from the solid. Similarly, cation exchange occurs with resins that have ionized acidic side groups such as $-COO^-$ or $-SO_2O^-$, with positive ions M^+ attached.

Ion exchange also occurs with inorganic polymers such as *zeolites, in which positive ions are held at sites in the silicate lattice. These are used for water-softening, in which Ca^{2+} ions in solution displace Na^+ ions in the zeolite. The zeolite can be regenerated with sodium chloride solution. *Ion-exchange membranes* are used as separators in electrolytic cells to remove salts from sea water (*see also* desalination) and in producing deionized water.

ionic radius A value assigned to the radius of an ion in a crystalline solid, based on the assumption that the ions are spherical with a definite size. X-ray diffraction can be used to measure the internuclear distance in crystalline solids. For example, in NaF the Na – F distance is 0.231 nm, and this is assumed to be the sum of the Na^+ and F^- radii. By making certain assumptions about the shielding effect that the inner electrons have on the outer electrons, it is possible to assign individual values to the ionic radii – Na^+ 0.096 nm; F^- 0.135 nm. In general, negative ions have larger ionic radii than positive ions. The larger the negative charge, the larger the ion; the larger the positive charge, the smaller the ion.

ionic strength Symbol I. A function expressing the effect of the charge of the ions in a solution, equal to the sum of the molality of each type of ion present multiplied by the square of its charge. $I = \Sigma m_i z_i^2$.

ion implantation The technique of implanting ions in the lattice of a semiconductor crystal in order to modify its electronic properties. It is used as an alternative to diffusion, or in conjunction with it, in the manufacture of integrated circuits and solid-state components.

ionization The process of producing *ions. Certain molecules (see electrolytes) ionize in solution; for example, acids ionize when dissolved in water:

$$HCl \rightarrow H^+ + Cl^-$$

Electron transfer also causes ionization in certain reactions; for example, sodium and chlorine react by the transfer of a valence electron from the sodium atom to the chlorine atom to form the ions that constitute a sodium chloride crystal:

$$Na + Cl \rightarrow Na^+Cl^-$$

Ions may also be formed when an atom or molecule loses one or more electrons as a result of energy gained in a collision with another particle or a quantum of radiation (see photoionization). This may occur as a result of the impact of *ionizing radiation or of *thermal ionization and the reaction takes the form

$$A \rightarrow A^+ + e$$

Alternatively, ions can be formed by electron capture, i.e.

$$A + e \rightarrow A^-$$

ionization chamber An instrument for detecting *ionizing radiation. It consists of two electrodes contained in a gas-filled chamber with a potential difference maintained between them. Ionizing radiation entering the chamber ionizes gas atoms, creating electrons and positive ions. The electric field between the electrodes drives the electrons to the anode and the positive ions to the cathode. This current is, in suitable conditions, proportional to the intensity of the radiation. See also Geiger counter.

ionization gauge A vacuum gauge consisting of a three-electrode system inserted into the container in which the pressure is to be measured. Electrons from the cathode are attracted to the grid, which is positively biased. Some pass through the grid but do not reach the anode, as it is maintained at a negative potential. Some of these electrons do, however, collide with gas molecules, ionizing them and converting them to positive ions. These ions are attracted to the anode; the resulting anode current can be used as a measure of the number of gas molecules present. Pressure as low as 10^{-6} pascal can be measured in this way.

ionization potential (IP) Symbol I. The minimum energy required to remove an electron from a specified atom or molecule to such a distance that there is no electrostatic interaction between ion and electron. Originally defined as the minimum potential through which an electron would have to fall to ionize an atom, the ionization potential was measured in volts. It is now, however, defined as the energy to effect an ionization and is conveniently measured in electronvolts (although this is not an SI unit).

The energy to remove the least strongly bound electrons is the *first ionization potential*. Second, third, and higher ionization potentials can also be measured, although there is some ambiguity in terminology. Thus, in chemistry the second ionization potential is often taken to be the minimum energy required to remove an electron from the singly charged ion; the second IP of lithium would be the energy for the process

$$Li^+ \rightarrow Li^{2+} + e$$

In physics, the second ionization potential is the energy required to remove an electron from the next to highest energy level in the neutral atom or molecule; e.g.

$$Li \rightarrow Li^{*+} + e,$$

where Li^{*+} is an excited singly charged ion produced by removing an electron from the K-shell.

ionizing radiation Radiation of sufficiently high energy to cause *ionization in the medium through which it passes. It may consist of a stream of high-energy particles (e.g. electrons, protons, alpha-particles) or short-wavelength electromagnetic radiation (ultraviolet, X-rays, gamma-rays). This type of radiation can cause extensive damage to the molecular structure of a substance either as a result of the direct transfer of energy to its atoms or molecules or as a result of the *secondary electrons released by ionization. In biological tissue the effect of ionizing radiation can be very serious, usually as a consequence of the ejection of an electron from a water molecule and the oxidizing or reducing effects of the resulting highly reactive species:

$$H_2O \rightarrow e^- + H_2O^* + H_2O^+ \rightarrow$$
$$\cdot OH + H_3O^+ + \cdot H,$$

where the dot before a radical indicates an unpaired electron and an * denotes an excited species.

ion-microprobe analysis A technique for analysing the surface composition of solids. The sample is bombarded with a narrow beam (as small as 2 μm diameter) of high-energy ions. Ions ejected from the surface by sputtering are detected by mass spectrometry. The technique allows quantitative analysis of both chemical and isotopic composition for concentrations as low as a few parts per million.

ionosphere See earth's atmosphere; radio transmission.

ionospheric wave See radio transmission.

ion pair A pair of oppositely charged ions produced as a result of a single ionization; e.g.

$$HCl \rightarrow H^+ + Cl^-.$$

Sometimes a positive ion and an electron are referred to as an ion pair, as in

$$A \rightarrow A^+ + e^-.$$

ion pump A type of *vacuum pump that can reduce the pressure in a container to about 1 nanopascal by passing a beam of electrons through the residual gas. The gas is ionized and the positive ions formed are attracted to a cathode within the container where they remain trapped. The pump is only useful at very low pressures, i.e. below about 1 micropascal. The pump has a limited capacity because the absorbed ions eventually saturate the surface of the cathode. A more effective pump can be made by simultaneously *sputtering a film of metal, so that fresh surface is continuously produced. The device is then known as a *sputter-ion pump*.

IP See ionization potential.

IR See infrared radiation.

iris See diaphragm.

irradiance Symbol E. The *radiant flux per unit area reaching a surface; in SI units it is measured in watts per square metre (W m^{-2}). Irradiance refers to electromagnetic radiation of all kinds, whereas *illuminance refers only to visible radiation.

irradiation Exposure to any form of radiation, often exposure to *ionizing radiation is implied.

irrational number A number that cannot be expressed as the ratio of two integers. An irrational number may be a *surd, such as $\sqrt{2}$ or $\sqrt{3}$, which can be expressed to any desired degree of accuracy but cannot be assigned an exact value. Alternatively, it may be a *transcendental, such as π or e. Compare rational number.

irreversible process See reversible process.

isentropic process Any process that takes place without a change of *entropy. The quantity of heat trans-

ferred, δQ, in a reversible process is proportional to the change in entropy, δS, i.e. $\delta Q = T\delta S$, where T is the thermodynamic temperature. Therefore, a reversible *adiabatic process is isentropic, i.e. when $\delta Q = 0$, δS also equals 0.

isobar **1.** A line on a map or chart that joints points or places that have the same atmospheric pressure. **2.** A curve on a graph representing readings taken at constant pressure. **3.** One of two or more nuclides that have the same number of nucleons but different *atomic numbers. Radium–88, actinium–89, and thorium–90 are isobars as each has a *nucleon number of 228.

isobaric spin *See* isotopic spin.

isocline A line on a map or chart joining points or places of equal magnetic dip (*see* geomagnetism).

isodiaphere One of two or more nuclides in which the difference between the number of neutrons and the number of protons is the same. A nuclide and its product after losing an *alpha particle are isodiapheres.

isodynamic line A line on a map or chart joining points or places at which the total strengths of the earth's magnetic field are equal (*see* geomagnetism).

isoelectronic Describing compounds that have the same numbers of valence electrons. For example, nitrogen (N_2) and carbon monoxide (CO) are isoelectronic molecules.

isogonal line A line on a map or chart joining points or places of equal magnetic declination (*see* geomagnetism).

isomerism The existence of atomic nuclei that have the same atomic number and the same mass number but different energy states.

isomers *See* isomerism.

isometric **1.** (in technical drawing) Denoting a projection in which the three axes are equally inclined to the surface of the drawing and lines are drawn to scale. **2.** (in crystallography) Denoting a system in which the axes are perpendicular to each other, as in cubic crystals. **3.** (in physics) Denoting a line on a graph illustrating the way in which temperature and pressure are interrelated at constant volume.

isomorphism The existence of two or more substances (*isomorphs*) that have the same crystal structure, so that they are able to form *solid solutions.

isospin *See* isotopic spin.

isotherm **1.** A line on a map or chart joining points or places of equal temperature. **2.** A curve on a graph representing readings taken at constant temperature (e.g. the relationship between the pressure and volume of a gas at constant temperature).

isothermal process Any process that takes place at constant temperature. In such a process heat is, if necessary, supplied or removed from the system at just the right rate to maintain constant temperature. *Compare* adiabatic process.

isotone One of two or more nuclides that contain the same number of neutrons but different numbers of protons. The naturally occurring isotones, for example, strontium–88 and yttrium–89 (both with 50 neutrons), give an indication of the stability of certain nuclear configurations.

isotonic Describing solutions that have the same osmotic pressure.

isotope One of two or more atoms of the same element that have the same number of protons in their nucleus but different numbers of neutrons. Hydrogen (1 proton, no neutrons), deuterium (1 proton, 1 neutron), and tritium (1 proton, 2 neutrons) are isotopes of hydrogen. Most elements in nature consist of a mix-

ture of isotopes. *See* isotope separation.

isotope separation The separation of the *isotopes of an element from each other on the basis of slight differences in their physical properties. For laboratory quantities the most suitable device is often the mass spectrometer. On a larger scale the methods used include gaseous diffusion (widely used for separating isotopes of uranium in the form of the gas uranium hexafluoride), distillation (formerly used to produce heavy water), electrolysis (requiring cheap electrical power), thermal diffusion (formerly used to separate uranium isotopes, but now considered uneconomic), centrifuging (a method in which there is renewed interest), and laser methods (involving the excitation of one isotope and its subsequent separation by electromagnetic means).

isotopic number (neutron excess) The difference between the number of neutrons in an isotope and the number of protons.

isotopic spin (isospin; isobaric spin) A quantum number applied to hadrons (*see* elementary particles) to distinguish between members of a set of particles that differ in their electromagnetic properties but are otherwise apparently identical. For example if electromagnetic interactions and weak interactions are ignored, the proton cannot be distinguished from the neutron in their strong interactions: isotopic spin was introduced to make a distinction between them. The use of the word 'spin' implies only an analogy to angular momentum, to which isotopic spin has a formal resemblance.

isotropic Denoting a medium whose physical properties are independent of direction. *Compare* anisotropic.

iteration The process of successive approximations used as a technique for solving a mathematical problem.

The technique can be used manually but is widely used by computers.

J

jet propulsion (reaction propulsion) The propulsion of a body by means of a force produced by discharging a fluid in the form of a jet. The backward-moving jet of fluid reacts on the body in which it was produced, in accordance with Newton's third law of motion, to create a reactive force that drives the body forward. Jet propulsion occurs in nature, the squid using a form of it to propel itself through water. Although jet-propelled boats and cars have been developed, the main use of jet propulsion is in aircraft and spacecraft. Jet propulsion is the only known method of propulsion in space. In the atmosphere, jet propulsion becomes more efficient at higher altitudes, as efficiency is inversely proportional to the density of the medium through which a body is flying. The three principal means of providing jet propulsion are the turbojet, the ramjet, and the rocket. The *turbojet* is an air-breathing *heat engine based on the *gas turbine, used to power jet aircraft. The *ramjet* is also an air-breathing engine, but compression of the oxidant is achieved by the forward motion of the device through the atmosphere. This enables the compressor and turbine of the gas turbine to be dispensed with and the remaining system consists simply of an inlet diffuser, a combustion chamber in which fuel is burnt, and a jet nozzle through which the products of combustion are discharged. Used in guided missiles, the ramjet must be accelerated to its operating velocity before it can fly (*see also* pulse jet). These two forms of jet propulsion, being air-breathing

engines, can only be used in the earth's atmosphere. The *rocket, however, carries its own oxidant and can therefore be used in space. *See also* ion engine.

Joly's steam calorimeter An apparatus invented by John Joly (1857–1933) to measure the specific heat capacity of a gas at constant volume. Two equal spherical containers are suspended from the opposite ends of a balance arm. One sphere is evacuated and the other contains the sample gas. The whole apparatus is enclosed in a steam bath, the specific heat capacity of the sample gas being calculated from the difference between the masses of the water that condenses on each sphere.

Josephson effects Electrical effects observed when two superconducting materials (at low temperature) are separated by a thin layer of insulating material (typically a layer of oxide less than 10^{-8} m thick). If normal metallic conductors are separated by such a barrier it is possible for a small current to flow between the conductors by the *tunnel effect. If the materials are superconductors (*see* superconductivity), several unusual phenomena occur:

(1) A supercurrent can flow through the barrier; i.e. it has zero resistance.
(2) If this current exceeds a critical value, this conductivity is lost; the barrier then only passes the 'normal' low tunnelling current and a voltage develops across the junction.
(3) If a magnetic field is applied below the critical current value, the current density changes regularly with distance across the junction. The net current through the barrier depends on the magnetic field applied. As the field is increased the net current increases from zero to a maximum, decreases to zero, increases again to a (lower) maximum, decreases, and so on. If the field exceeds a critical value the superconductivity in the barrier

vanishes and a potential difference develops across the junction.
(4) If a potential difference is applied across the junction, a high-frequency alternating current flows through the junction. The frequency of this current depends on the size of the potential difference.

A junction of this type is called a *Josephson junction*; two or more junctions joined by superconducting paths form a *Josephson interferometer*. Such junctions can be used in measuring fundamental constants, in defining a voltage standard, and in the highly accurate measurement of magnetic fields. An important potential use is in logic components in high-speed computers. Josephson junctions can switch states very quickly (as low as 6 picoseconds). Moreover they have very low power consumption and can be packed closely without generating too much heat. It is possible that computers based on such devices could operate 50 times faster than the best existing machines. The effects are named after B. D. Josephson (1940–), who predicted them theoretically in 1962.

joule Symbol J. The *SI unit of work and energy equal to the work done when the point of application of a force of one newton moves, in the direction of the force, a distance of one metre. 1 joule = 10^7 ergs = 0.2388 calorie. It is named after James Prescott Joule (1818–89).

Joule heating The production of heat in a conductor as a result of the passage of an electric current through the conductor. The quantity of heat produced is given by *Joule's law.

Joule's laws 1. The heat (Q) produced when an electric current (I) flows through a resistance (R) for a time (t) is given by $Q = I^2Rt$. **2.** The *internal energy of a given mass of gas is independent of its volume and pressure, being a function of temperature alone. This law applies only to

*ideal gases (for which it provides a definition of thermodynamic temperature) as in a real gas intermolecular forces would cause changes in the internal energy should a change of volume occur. *See also* Joule–Thomson effect.

Joule–Thomson effect (Joule–Kelvin effect) The change in temperature that occurs when a gas expands through a porous plug into a region of lower pressure. For most real gases the temperature falls under these circumstances as the gas has to do internal work in overcoming the intermolecular forces to enable the expansion to take place. This is a deviation from *Joule's law. There is usually also a deviation from *Boyle's law, which can cause either a rise or a fall in temperature since any increase in the product of pressure and volume is a measure of external work done. At a given pressure, there is a particular temperature, called the *inversion temperature* of the gas, at which the rise in temperature from the Boyle's law deviation is balanced by the fall from the Joule's law deviation. There is then no temperature change. Above the inversion temperature the gas is heated by expansion, below it, it is cooled. The effect was discovered by James Joule working in collaboration with William Thomson (later Lord Kelvin; 1824–1907).

Jovian Relating to the planet Jupiter.

JUGFET *See* transistor.

junction detector (solid-state detector) A sensitive detector of *ionizing radiation in which the output is a current pulse proportional to the energy falling in or near the depletion region of a reverse-biased *semiconductor junction. The first types were made by evaporating a thin layer of gold on to a polished wafer of *n*-type germanium; however, gold–silicon devices can be operated at room temperature and these have superseded the germanium type,

which have to be operated at the temperature of liquid nitrogen to reduce noise. When the gold–silicon junction is reverse-biased a depletion region, devoid of charge carriers (electrons and holes), forms in the silicon. Incoming ionizing radiation falling in this depletion region creates pairs of electrons and holes, which both have to be collected in order to give an output pulse proportional to the energy of the detected particle. Junction detectors are used in medicine and biology as well as in space systems.

junction transistor *See* transistor.

K

Kaluza–Klein theory A type of *unified-field theory that postulates a generalization of the general theory of relativity to higher than four space–time dimensions. In five space–time dimensions this gives general relativity and electromagnetic interactions. In higher space–time dimensions Kaluza–Klein theories give general relativity and more general *gauge theories. A combination of Kaluza–Klein theory and *supersymmetry gives rise to *supergravity, which needs eleven space–time dimensions. In these theories it is proposed that the higher dimensions are 'rolled up' to become microscopically small (a process known as *spontaneous compactification*) with four macroscopic space–time dimensions remaining.

kaon A K-meson. *See* meson.

Kater's pendulum A complex *pendulum designed by Henry Kater (1777–1835) to measure the acceleration of free fall. It consists of a metal bar with knife edges attached near the ends and two weights that can slide between the knife edges. The bar is pivoted from each knife edge

in turn and the positions of the weights are adjusted so that the period of the pendulum is the same with both pivots. The period is then given by the formula for a simple pendulum, which enables g to be calculated.

katharometer An instrument for comparing the thermal conductivities of two gases by comparing the rate of loss of heat from two heating coils surrounded by the gases. The instrument can be used to detect the presence of a small amount of an impurity in air and is also used as a detector in gas chromatography.

keeper A piece of soft iron used to bridge the poles of a permanent magnet when it is not in use. It reduces the leakage field and thus preserves the magnetization.

kelvin Symbol K. The *SI unit of thermodynamic *temperature equal to the fraction 1/273.16 of the thermodynamic temperature of the *triple point of water. The magnitude of the kelvin is equal to that of the degree celsius (centigrade), but a temperature expressed in degrees celsius is numerically equal to the temperature in kelvins less 273.15 (i.e. °C = K – 273.15). The *absolute zero of temperature has a temperature of 0 K (–273.15°C). The former name *degree kelvin* (symbol °K) became obsolete by international agreement in 1967. The unit is named after Lord Kelvin (1824–1907).

Kelvin effect *See* Thomson effect.

Kepler's laws Three laws of planetary motion formulated by Johannes Kepler (1571–1630) in about 1610 on the basis of observations made by Tycho Brahe (1546–1601). They state that: (1) the orbits of the planets are elliptical with the sun at one *focus of the ellipse; (2) each planet revolves around the sun so that an imaginary line (the *radius vector*) connecting the planet to the sun sweeps out equal areas in equal times; (3) the ratio of the square of each planet's *sidereal period to the cube of its distance from the sun is a constant for all the planets.

Kerr effect The ability of certain substances to refract differently light waves whose vibrations are in two directions (*see* double refraction) when the substance is placed in an electric field. The effect, discovered in 1875 by John Kerr (1824–1907), is caused by the fact that certain molecules have electric *dipoles, which tend to be orientated by the applied field; the normal random motions of the molecules tends to destroy this orientation and the balance is struck by the relative magnitudes of the field strength, the temperature, and the magnitudes of the dipole moments.

The Kerr effect is observed in a *Kerr cell*, which consists of a glass cell containing the liquid or gaseous substance; two capacitor plates are inserted into the cell and light is passed through it at right angles to the electric field. There are two principal indexes of refraction: n_o (the ordinary index) and n_e (the extraordinary index). The difference in the velocity of propagation in the cell causes a phase difference, δ, between the two waves formed from a beam of monochromatic light, wavelength λ, such that

$$\delta = (n_o - n_e)x/\lambda,$$

where x is the length of the light path in the cell. Kerr also showed empirically that the ratio

$$(n_o - n_e)\lambda = BE^2,$$

where E is the field strength and B is a constant, called the *Kerr constant*, which is characteristic of the substance and approximately inversely proportional to the thermodynamic temperature.

The *Kerr shutter* consists of a Kerr cell filled with a liquid, such as nitrobenzene, placed between two crossed polarizers; the electric field is arranged to be perpendicular to the

axis of the light beam and at 45° to the axis of the polarizers. In the absence of a field there is no optical path through the device. When the field is switched on the nitrobenzene becomes doubly refracting and a path opens between the crossed polarizers.

kilo- Symbol k. A prefix used in the metric system to denote 1000 times. For example, 1000 volts = 1 kilovolt (kV).

kilogram Symbol kg. The *SI unit of mass defined as a mass equal to that of the international platinum–iridium prototype kept by the International Bureau of Weights and Measures at Sèvres, near Paris.

kiloton weapon A nuclear weapon with an explosive power equivalent to one thousand tons of TNT. *Compare* megaton weapon.

kilowatt-hour Symbol kWh. The commercial unit of electrical energy. It is equivalent to a power consumption of 1000 watts for 1 hour.

kinematic equation *See* equation of motion.

kinematics The branch of mechanics concerned with the motions of objects without being concerned with the forces that cause the motion. In this latter respect it differs from *dynamics, which is concerned with the forces that affect motion. *See also* equation of motion.

kinematic viscosity Symbol ν. The ratio of the *viscosity of a liquid to its density. The SI unit is m^2 s^{-1}.

kinetic effect A chemical effect that depends on reaction rate rather than on thermodynamics. For example, diamond is thermodynamically less stable than graphite; its apparent stability depends on the vanishingly slow rate at which it is converted. *Overvoltage in electrolytic cells is another example of a kinetic effect. *Kinetic isotope effects* are changes in reaction rates produced by isotope substitution. For example, if the slow

step in a chemical reaction is the breaking of a C–H bond, the rate for the deuterated compound would be slightly lower because of the lower vibrational frequency of the C–D bond.

kinetic energy *See* energy.

kinetics The branch of physical chemistry concerned with measuring and studying the rates of chemical reactions. The main aim of chemical kinetics is to determine the mechanism of reactions by studying the rate under different conditions (temperature, pressure, etc.).

kinetic theory A theory, largely the work of Count Rumford (1753–1814), James Joule (1818–89), and James Clerk Maxwell (1831–79), that explains the physical properties of matter in terms of the motions of its constituent particles. In a gas, for example, the pressure is due to the incessant impacts of the gas molecules on the walls of the container. If it is assumed that the molecules occupy negligible space, exert negligible forces on each other except during collisions, are perfectly elastic, and make only brief collisions with each other, it can be shown that the pressure p exerted by one mole of gas containing n molecules each of mass m in a container of volume V, will be given by:

$$p = nm\bar{c}^2/3V,$$

where $\bar{c}^2$ is the mean square speed of the molecules. As according to the *gas laws for one mole of gas: $pV = RT$, where T is the thermodynamic temperature, and R is the molar *gas constant, it follows that:

$$RT = nm\bar{c}^2/3$$

Thus, the thermodynamic temperature of a gas is proportional to the mean square speed of its molecules. As the average kinetic *energy of translation of the molecules is $m\bar{c}^2/2$, the temperature is given by:

$$T = (m\bar{c}^2/2)(2n/3R)$$

Kirchhoff's law of radiation

The number of molecules in one mole of any gas is the *Avogadro constant, N_A; therefore in this equation $n = N_A$. The ratio R/N_A is a constant called the *Boltzmann constant (k). The average kinetic energy of translation of the molecules of one mole of any gas is therefore $3kT/2$. For monatomic gases this is proportional to the *internal energy (U) of the gas, i.e.

$$U = N_A 3kT/2$$
and as $k = R/N_A$
$$U = 3RT/2$$

For diatomic and polyatomic gases the rotational and vibrational energies also have to be taken into account (see degrees of freedom).

In liquids, according to the kinetic theory, the atoms and molecules still move around at random, the temperature being proportional to their average kinetic energy. However, they are sufficiently close to each other for the attractive forces between molecules to be important. A molecule that approaches the surface will experience a resultant force tending to keep it within the liquid. It is, therefore, only some of the fastest moving molecules that escape; as a result the average kinetic energy of those that fail to escape is reduced. In this way evaporation from the surface of a liquid causes its temperature to fall.

In a crystalline solid the atoms, ions, and molecules are able only to vibrate about the fixed positions of a *crystal lattice; the attractive forces are so strong at this range that no free movement is possible.

Kirchhoff's law of radiation A law stating that the emissivity of a body is equal to its absorptance at the same temperature.

Kirchhoff's laws Two laws relating to electric circuits, first formulated by G. R. Kirchhoff (1824–87). (a) The current law states that the algebraic sum of the currents flowing through all the wires in a network that meet at a point is zero. (b) The voltage law states that the algebraic sum of the e.m.f.s within any closed circuit is equal to the sum of the products of the currents and the resistances in the various portions of the circuit.

klystron An electron tube that generates or amplifies microwaves by *velocity modulation*. Several types are used; in the simple two-cavity klystron a beam of high-energy electrons from an electron gun is passed through a *resonant cavity, where it interacts with high-frequency radio waves. This microwave energy modulates the velocities of the electrons in the beam, which then enters a drift space where the faster electrons overtake the slower ones to form bunches. The bunched beam now has an alternating component, which is transferred to an output cavity and thence to an output waveguide.

knocking The metallic sound produced by a spark-ignition petrol engine under certain conditions. It is caused by rapid combustion of the unburnt explosive mixture in the combustion chambers ahead of the flame front. As the flame travels from the sparking plug towards the piston it compresses and heats the unburnt gases ahead of it. If the flame front moves fast enough, normal combustion occurs and the explosive mixture is ignited progressively by the flame. If it moves too slowly, ignition of the last part of the unburnt gas can occur very rapidly before the flame reaches it, producing a shock wave that travels back and forth across the combustion chamber. The result is overheating, possible damage to the plugs, an undesirable noise, and loss of power (probably due to preignition caused by overheated plugs). Knocking can be avoided by an engine design that increases turbulence in the combustion chamber and thereby increases flame speed. It also can be avoided by reducing the compression

ratio, but this involves loss of efficiency. The most effective method is to use high-octane fuel (*see* octane number), which has a longer self-ignition delay than low-octane fuels. This is usually achieved by the addition of lead(IV) tetraethyl to the fuel.

Knudsen flow *See* molecular flow.

Kohlrausch's law If a salt is dissolved in water, the conductivity of the (dilute) solution is the sum of two values – one depending on the positive ions and the other on the negative ions. The law, which depends on the independent migration of ions, was deduced experimentally by the German chemist Friedrich Kohlrausch (1840–1910).

Kovar A tradename for an alloy of iron, cobalt, and nickel with an *expansivity similar to that of glass. It is therefore used in making glass-to-metal seals, especially in circumstances in which a temperature variation can be expected.

Kundt's tube An apparatus designed by August Kundt (1839–94) in 1866 to measure the speed of sound in various fluids. It consists of a closed glass tube into which a dry powder (such as lycopodium) has been sprinkled. The source of sound in the original device was a metal rod clamped at its centre with a piston at one end, which is inserted into the tube. When the rod is stroked, sound waves generated by the piston enter the tube. If the position of the piston in the tube is adjusted so that the gas column is a whole number of half wavelengths long, the dust will be disturbed by the resulting *stationary waves forming a series of striations, enabling distances between *nodes to be measured. The vibrating rod can be replaced by a small loudspeaker fed by an oscillator.

L

labelling The process of replacing a stable atom in a compound with a radioisotope of the same element to enable its path through a biological or mechanical system to be traced by the radiation it emits. In some cases a different stable isotope is used and the path is detected by means of a mass spectrometer. A compound containing either a radioactive or stable isotope is called a *labelled compound*. If a hydrogen atom in each molecule of the compound has been replaced by a tritium atom, the compound is called a *tritiated compound*. A radioactive labelled compound will behave chemically and physically in the same way as an otherwise identical stable compound, and its presence can easily be detected using a *Geiger counter. This process of *radioactive tracing* is widely used in chemistry, biology, medicine, and engineering. For example, it can be used to follow the course of the reaction of a carboxylic acid with an alcohol to give an ester, e.g.

$$CH_3COOH + C_2H_5OH \rightarrow$$
$$C_2H_5COOCH_3 + H_2O$$

To determine whether the non-carbonyl oxygen in the ester comes from the acid or the alcohol, the reaction is performed with the labelled compound $CH_3CO^{18}OH$, in which the oxygen in the hydroxyl group of the acid has been 'labelled' by using the ^{18}O isotope. It is then found that the water product is $H_2^{18}O$; i.e. the oxygen in the ester comes from the alcohol, not the acid.

laevorotatory Designating a chemical compound that rotates the plane of plane-polarized light to the left (anticlockwise for someone facing the oncoming radiation). *See* optical activity.

lag 1. The time delay between a specified maximum value of one wave

or vibration and the maximum value of another wave or vibration. A *lagging current* is an alternating current that reaches its maximum at a later instant in the cycle than the e.m.f. producing it. **2.** This time delay expressed as an angle.

Lagrangian Symbol L. A function used to define a dynamical system in terms of functions of coordinates, velocities, and times given by:

$$L = T - V$$

where T is the kinetic energy of the system and V is the potential energy of the system. The Lagrangian formulation of dynamics has the advantage that it does not deal with many vector quantities, such as forces and accelerations, but only with two scalar functions, T and V. This leads to great simplifications. *Lagrangian dynamics* was formulated by J. L. Lagrange (1736–1813).

lambda point Symbol λ. The temperature of 2.186 K below which helium–4 becomes a superfluid. The name derives from the shape of the curve of specific heat capacity against temperature, which is shaped like a Greek letter lambda (λ) at this point. *See* superfluidity.

lambert A former unit of *luminance equal to the luminance of a uniformly diffusing surface that emits or reflects one lumen per square centimetre. It is approximately equal to 3.18×10^3 Cd m^{-2}. It is named after Johann H. Lambert (1728–77).

Lambert's laws (1) The *illuminance of a surface illuminated by light falling on it perpendicularly from a point source is inversely proportional to the square of the distance between the surface and the source. (2) If the rays make an angle θ with the normal to the surface, the illuminance is proportional to cosθ. (3) (Also called *Bouquer's law*) The *luminous intensity (I) of light (or other electromagnetic radiation) decreases exponentially

with the distance d that it enters an absorbing medium, i.e.

$$I = I_0\exp(-\alpha d)$$

where I_0 is the intensity of the radiation that enters the medium and α is its *linear absorption coefficient*. These laws were first stated (for light) by Johann H. Lambert (1728–77).

Lamb shift A small energy difference between two levels ($^2S_{1/2}$ and $^2P_{1/2}$) in the *hydrogen spectrum. The shift results from the quantum interaction between the atomic electron and the electromagnetic radiation. It was first explained by Willis Eugene Lamb (1913–).

laminar flow *Streamline flow of a fluid in which the fluid moves in layers without fluctuations or turbulence so that successive particles passing the same point have the same velocity. It occurs at low *Reynolds numbers, i.e. low velocities, high viscosities, low densities or small dimensions. The flow of lubricating oil in bearings is normally laminar because of the thinness of the lubricant layer.

laminated core A core for a transformer or other electrical machine in which the ferromagnetic alloy is made into thin sheets (laminations), which are oxidized or varnished to provide a relatively high resistance between them. This has the effect of reducing *eddy currents, which occur when alternating currents are used.

Laplace equation The partial differential equation:

$$\partial^2u/\partial x^2 + \partial^2u/\partial y^2 + \partial^2u/\partial z^2 = 0$$

It may also be written in the form $\nabla^2u = 0$, where ∇^2 is called the *Laplace operator*. It was formulated by the French mathematician P. S. Laplace (1749–1827).

Larmor precession A precession of the motion of charged particles in a magnetic field. It was first deduced in 1897 by Sir Joseph Larmor (1857–1942). Applied to the orbital motion of an electron around the nucleus of an atom in a magnetic field of flux

density B, the frequency of precession is given by $eB/4\pi m\nu\mu$, where e and m are the electronic charge and mass respectively, μ is the permeability, and ν is the velocity of the electron. This is known as the *Larmor frequency*.

laser (*l*ight *a*mplification by *s*timulated *e*mission of *r*adiation) A light amplifier usually used to produce monochromatic coherent radiation in the infrared, visible, and ultraviolet regions of the *electromagnetic spectrum.

Nonlaser light sources emit radiation in all directions as a result of the spontaneous emission of photons by thermally excited solids (filament lamps) or electronically excited atoms, ions, or molecules (fluorescent lamps, etc.). The emission accompanies the spontaneous return of the excited species to the *ground state and occurs randomly, i.e. the radiation is not coherent. In a laser, the atoms, ions, or molecules are first 'pumped' to an excited state and then stimulated to emit photons by collision of a photon of the same energy. This is called *stimulated emission*. In order to use it, it is first necessary to create a condition in the amplifying medium, called *population inversion*, in which the majority of the relevant entities are excited. Random emission from one entity can then trigger coherent emission from the others that it passes. In this way amplification is achieved.

The laser amplifier is converted to an oscillator by enclosing the amplifying medium within a resonator. Radiation then introduced along the axis of the resonator is reflected back and forth along its path by a mirror at one end and by a partially transmitting mirror at the other end. Between the mirrors the waves are amplified by stimulated emission. The radiation emerges through the semitransparent mirror at one end as a powerful coherent monochromatic parallel beam of light.

The emitted beam is uniquely parallel because waves that do not bounce back and forth between the mirrors quickly escape through the sides of the oscillating medium without amplification.

Some lasers are solid, others are liquid or gas devices. Population inversion can be achieved by *optical pumping* with flashlights or with other lasers. It can also be achieved by such methods as chemical reactions, discharges in gases, and recombination emission in semiconducting materials (*see* recombination process).

Lasers have found many uses since their invention in 1960, including laser welding, surgery, *holography, printing, optical communications, and the reading of digital information.

latent heat Symbol L. The quantity of heat absorbed or released when a substance changes its physical phase at constant temperature (e.g. from solid to liquid at the melting point or from liquid to gas at the boiling point). For example, the latent heat of vaporization is the energy a substance absorbs from its surroundings in order to overcome the attractive forces between its molecules as it changes from a liquid to a gas and in order to do work against the external atmosphere as it expands. In thermodynamic terms the latent heat is the *enthalpy of evaporation (ΔH), i.e. $L = \Delta H = \Delta U + p\Delta V$, where ΔU is the change in the internal energy, p is the pressure, and ΔV is the change in volume.

The *specific latent heat* (symbol l) is the heat absorbed or released per unit mass of a substance in the course of its isothermal change of phase. The *molar latent heat* is the heat absorbed or released per unit amount of substance during an isothermal change of state.

lateral inversion (perversion) The type of reversal that occurs with an image formed by a plane mirror. A

lateral velocity

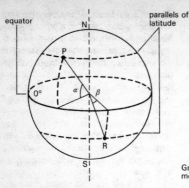

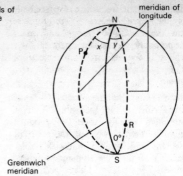

The latitude of P is given by the angle α. In this case it would be $\alpha°$ N. The latitude of R is $\beta°$ S.

The longitude of P is given by the angle x. In this case it would be $x°$ W. R has a longitude of $y°$ E.

Latitude and longitude

person with a mole on his left cheek sees an image in a plane mirror of a person with a mole on his right cheek. Since, however, that is (correctly) to the observer's left, the real reversal is of front and back; the image is 'turned through' itself to face the object – hence the alternative name.

lateral velocity The component of a celestial body's velocity that is at 90° to its *line-of-sight velocity.

latitude and longitude 1. (in geography) Imaginary lines on the earth's surface, enabling any point to be defined in terms of two angles subtended at its centre (see illustration). *Parallels of latitude* are circles drawn round the earth parallel to the equator; their diameters diminish as they approach the poles. These parallels are specified by the angle subtended at the centre of the earth by the arc formed between a point on the parallel and the equator. All points on the equator therefore have a latitude of 0°, while the north pole has a latitude of 90°N and the south pole of 90°S. Parallels of latitude 1° apart are separated on the earth's surface by about 100 km.

Meridians of longitude are half *great circles passing through both poles; they cross parallels of latitude at right angles. In 1884 the meridian through Greenwich, near London, was selected as the prime meridian and designated as 0°. Other meridians are defined by the angle between the plane of the meridian and the plane of the prime meridian specifying whether it is E or W of the prime meridian. At the equator meridians 1° apart are separated by about 112 km.

2. (in astronomy) The *celestial latitude* of a star, or other celestial body, is its angular distance north (taken as positive) or south (taken as negative) of the ecliptic measured along the great circle through the body and the poles of the ecliptic. The *celestial longitude* is the angular distance from the vernal equinox measured eastwards along the ecliptic to the intersection of the body's circle of longitude; it is measured in the same direction as the sun's apparent annual motion.

lattice The regular arrangement of atoms, ions, or molecules in a crystalline solid. *See* crystal lattice.

lattice energy A measure of the stability of a *crystal lattice, given by

the energy that would be released per mole if atoms, ions, or molecules of the crystal were brought together from infinite distances apart to form the lattice. *See* Born–Haber cycle.

lattice vibrations The periodic vibrations of the atoms, ions, or molecules in a *crystal lattice about their mean positions. On heating, the amplitude of the vibrations increases until they are so energetic that the lattice breaks down. The temperature at which this happens is the melting point of the solid and the substance becomes a liquid. On cooling, the amplitude of the vibrations diminishes. At *absolute zero a residual vibration persists, associated with the *zero-point energy of the substance. The increase in the electrical resistance of a conductor is due to increased scattering of the free conduction electrons by the vibrating lattice particles.

latus rectum *See* ellipse; hyperbola; parabola.

launch vehicle A rocket used to launch a satellite, spaceprobe, space station, etc. Multistage rockets are usually used, the empty tanks and engine of the first two stages being jettisoned before the desired orbit is reached. The *launch window* is the time interval during which the vehicle must be launched to achieve the orbit.

lawrencium Symbol Lr. A radioactive metallic transuranic element belonging to the actinoids; a.n. 103; mass number of only known isotope 257 (half-life 8 seconds). The element was identified by A. Ghiorso and associates in 1961. The alternative name *unniltrium* has been proposed.

Lawson criterion A condition for the release of energy from a *thermonuclear reactor first laid down by J. D. Lawson. It is usually stated as the minimum value for the product of the density (n_G) of the fusion-fuel particles and the *containment time (τ) for energy breakeven, i.e. it is a meas-

ure of the density of the reacting particles required and the time for which they need to react in order to produce more energy than was used in raising the temperature of the reacting particles to the *ignition temperature. For a 50:50 mixture of deuterium and tritium at the ignition temperature, the value of $n_G\tau$ is between 10^{14} and 10^{15} cm^{-3} s.

L–D process *See* basic-oxygen process.

lead–acid accumulator An accumulator in which the electrodes are made of lead and the electrolyte consists of dilute sulphuric acid. The electrodes are usually cast from a lead alloy containing 7–12% of antimony (to give increased hardness and corrosion resistance) and a small amount of tin (for better casting properties). The electrodes are coated with a paste of lead(II) oxide (PbO) and finely divided lead; after insertion into the electrolyte a 'forming' current is passed through the cell to convert the PbO on the negative plate into a sponge of finely divided lead. On the positive plate the PbO is converted to lead(IV) oxide (PbO_2). The equation for the overall reaction during discharge is:

$$PbO_2 + 2H_2SO_4 + Pb \rightarrow$$
$$2PbSO_4 + 2H_2O$$

The reaction is reversed during charging. Each cell gives an e.m.f. of about 2 volts and in motor vehicles a 12-volt battery of six cells is usually used. The lead–acid battery produces 80–120 kJ per kilogram. *Compare* nickel–iron accumulator.

lead equivalent A measure of the absorbing power of a radiation screen, expressed as the thickness of a lead screen in millimetres that would afford the same protection as the material being considered.

Le Chatelier's principle If a system is in equilibrium, any change imposed on the system tends to shift the equilibrium to nullify the effect of the

Leclanché cell

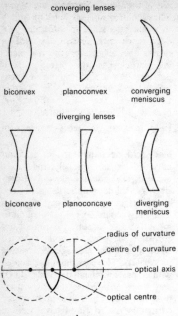

converging lenses

biconvex   planoconvex   converging meniscus

diverging lenses

biconcave   planoconcave   diverging meniscus

radius of curvature
centre of curvature
optical axis
optical centre

Lenses

applied change. The principle, which is a consequence of the law of conservation of energy, was first stated in 1888 by Henri Le Chatelier (1850–1936). It is applied to chemical equilibria. For example, in the gas reaction

$$2SO_2 + O_2 \leftrightarrows 2SO_3$$

an increase in pressure on the reaction mixture displaces the equilibrium to the right, since this reduces the total number of molecules present and thus decreases the pressure. The standard enthalpy change for the forward reaction is negative (i.e. the reaction is exothermic). Thus, an increase in temperature displaces the equilibrium to the left since this tends to reduce the temperature. The equilibrium constant thus falls with increasing temperature.

Leclanché cell A primary *voltaic cell consisting of a carbon rod (the anode) and a zinc rod (the cathode) dipping into an electrolyte of a 10–20% solution of ammonium chloride. *Polarization is prevented by using a mixture of manganese dioxide mixed with crushed carbon, held in contact with the anode by means of a porous bag or pot; this reacts with the hydrogen produced. This wet form of the cell, devised in 1867 by Georges Leclanché (1839–82), has an e.m.f. of about 1.5 volts. The *dry cell based on it is widely used in torches, radios, and calculators.

LED See light-emitting diode.

LEED Low-energy electron diffraction. See electron diffraction.

lens A curved, ground, and polished piece of glass, moulded plastic, or other transparent material used for the refraction of light. A *converging lens* is one that brings the rays of a parallel beam of light to a real *principal focus. They include biconvex, planoconvex, and converging meniscus lenses. *Diverging lenses* cause the rays of a parallel beam to diverge as if from a virtual principal focus; these include biconcave, planoconcave, and diverging meniscus lenses. See illustrations.

The *centre of curvature* of a lens face is the centre of the sphere of which the surface of the lens is a part. The *optical axis* is the line joining the two centres of curvature of a lens or, in the case of a lens with one plane surface, the line through one centre of curvature that is normal to the plane surface. The *optical centre* of a lens is the point within a lens on the optical axis through which any rays entering the lens pass without deviation. The distance between the optical centre and the principal focus of a lens is called the *focal length* (f). The distance (v) between the lens and the image it forms is related to the distance (u) between the lens and the object by:

$$1/v + 1/u = 1/f,$$

provided that the *real-is-positive convention is used. This takes distances to real objects, images, and foci as positive; those to virtual objects, images, and foci as negative. The equation does not always apply if the alternative New Cartesian convention (see sign convention) is used.

Lenz's law An induced electric current always flows in such a direction that it opposes the change producing it. This law, first stated by Heinrich Lenz (1804–65) in 1835, is essentially a form of the law of conservation of energy.

lepton Any of a class of *elementary particles that consists of the *electron, muon, tau particle, and three types of *neutrino (one associated with each of the other types of lepton). For each lepton there is an equivalent antiparticle. The antileptons have a charge opposite that of the leptons; the antineutrinos, like the neutrinos, have no charge. The electron, muon, and tau particle all have a charge of −1. These three particles differ from each other only in mass: the muon is 200 times more massive than the electron and the tau particle is 3500 times more massive than the electron. Leptons interact by the electromagnetic interaction and the weak interaction (see fundamental interactions).

Leslie's cube A metal box in the shape of a cube in which each of the four vertical sides have different surface finishes. When hot water is placed in the cube, the emissivity of the finishes can be compared. The device was first used by Sir John Leslie (1766–1832).

level An instrument used in *surveying to determine heights. It usually consists of a telescope and attached spirit level mounted on a tripod. The level is set up between a point of known height and a point for which the height is required. Before use it is adjusted until the line of sight is exactly horizontal. Sightings are then made onto a graduated levelling staff at the two points. The difference in elevation between the two points can then be calculated from the readings taken at these points.

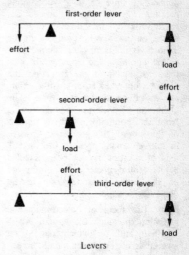

Levers

lever A simple machine consisting of a rigid bar pivoted about a fulcrum. The mechanical advantage or *force ratio of a lever (the ratio of load to effort) is equal to the ratio of the perpendicular distance of the line of action of the effort from the fulcrum to the perpendicular distance of the line of action of the load from the fulcrum. In a first-order lever the fulcrum comes between load and effort. In a second-order lever the load comes between the fulcrum and the effort. In a third-order lever the effort comes between the fulcrum and the load. See illustrations.

Leyden jar An early form of *capacitor consisting of a glass jar with a layer of metal foil on the outside and a similar layer on the inside. Contact to the inner foil is by means of a loose chain hanging inside the jar. It was invented in the Dutch town of Leyden in about 1745.

LF *See* low frequency.

***l*-form** *See* optical activity.

libration The phenomenon that enables 59% of the moon's surface to be observed from earth over a 30-year period, in spite of its *synchronous rotation. *Physical libration* arises from slight variations in the rotation of the moon on its axis, caused by minor distortions in its physical shape. *Geometric librations* are apparent oscillations arising from the fact that the moon is observed from slightly different directions at different times. The geometric *libration in longitude* results from the nonuniform orbital motion of the moon. The geometric *libration in latitude* arises because the moon's axis of rotation is not perpendicular to its orbital plane; it enables more of the lunar polar regions to be observed.

light The form of *electromagnetic radiation to which the human eye is sensitive and on which our visual awareness of the universe and its contents relies (*see* colour).

The finite velocity of light was suspected by many early experimenters in optics, but it was not established until 1676 when Ole Roemer (1644–1710) measured it. Sir Isaac Newton (1642–1727) investigated the optical *spectrum and used existing knowledge to establish a primarily *corpuscular theory* of light, in which it was regarded as a stream of particles that set up disturbances in the 'aether' of space. His successors adopted the corpuscles but ignored the wavelike disturbances until Thomas Young (1773–1829) rediscovered the *interference of light in 1801 and showed that a *wave theory* was essential to interpret this type of phenomenon. This view was accepted for most of the 19th century and it enabled James Clerk Maxwell (1831–79) to show that light forms part of the *electromagnetic spectrum. He believed that waves of electromagnetic radiation required a special medium to travel through, and revived the name 'luminiferous ether' for such a medium. The *Michelson–Morley experiment in 1887 showed that, if the medium existed, it could not be detected; it is now generally accepted that the ether is an unnecessary hypothesis. In 1905 Albert Einstein (1879–1955) showed that the *photoelectric effect could only be explained on the assumption that light consists of a stream of discrete *photons of electromagnetic energy. This renewed conflict between the corpuscular and wave theories has gradually been resolved by the evolution of the *quantum theory and *wave mechanics. While it is not easy to construct a model that has both wave and particle characteristics, it is accepted, according to Bohr's theory of *complementarity, that in some experiments light will appear wavelike, while in others it will appear to be corpuscular. During the course of the evolution of wave mechanics it has also become evident that electrons and other elementary particles have dual wave and particle properties.

light bulb *See* electric lighting.

light-emitting diode (LED) A rectifying *semiconductor device that converts electrical energy into light or infrared radiation in the range 550 nm (green light) to 1300 nm (infrared radiation). The most commonly used LED (see illustration) emits red light and consists of gallium arsenide–phosphide on a gallium arsenide substrate, light being emitted at a *p–n* junction, when electrons and holes recombine (*see* recombination process). LEDs are extensively used for displaying letters and numbers in digital instruments in which a self-luminous display is required.

lightning A high-energy luminous electrical discharge that passes between a charged cloud and a point

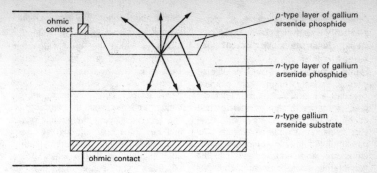

ohmic contact

p-type layer of gallium arsenide phosphide

n-type layer of gallium arsenide phosphide

n-type gallium arsenide substrate

ohmic contact

Light-emitting diode

on the surface of the earth, between two charged clouds, or between oppositely charged layers of the same cloud. In general, the upper parts of clouds are positively charged and the lower parts are negatively charged; the reasons for this separation of charge are complex.

Lightning usually occurs in the form of a downward step leader followed by an intensely luminous return stroke, which can produce instantaneous temperatures as high as 30 000°C. In the typical step leader a surge of electrons descends in approximately 50-metre steps with about 50-microsecond pauses between steps. When this leader reaches the earth a surge of charge returns up the preionized path taken by the leader. Cloud-to-cloud strokes also involve a leader and return stroke. The average current in a lightning stroke is about 10 000 amperes, but maximum currents in the return stroke can reach 20 000 A.

light year A unit of distance used in astronomy; the distance travelled by light in a vacuum during one year. It is equal to 9.4650×10^{15} metres or 5.8785×10^{12} miles.

limit The value that a function approaches as the independent variable approaches a specified value.

limit cycle *See* attractor.

limiting friction The friction force that just balances a moving force applied to a solid body resting on a solid surface when the body fails to move. If the moving force exceeds the limiting friction, the body will begin to move.

linac *See* linear accelerator.

Linde process A process for the *liquefaction of gases by the Joule–Thomson effect. In this process, devised by Carl von Linde (1842–1934) for liquefying air, the air is freed of carbon dioxide and water and compressed to 150 atmospheres. The compressed gas is passed through a copper coil to an expansion nozzle within a Dewar flask. The emerging air is cooled by the Joule–Thomson effect as it expands and then passes back within a second copper coil that surrounds the first coil. Thus the expanded gas cools the incoming gas in a process that is said to be *regenerative*. Eventually the air is reduced to its *critical temperature and, at the pressure of 150 atmospheres (well above its critical pressure), liquefies. The process is also used for other gases, especially hydrogen and helium. Hydrogen has first to be cooled below its inversion temperature (*see* Joule–Thomson effect) using liquid air; helium has first to be

cooled below its inversion temperature using liquid hydrogen.

linear absorption coefficient *See* Lambert's laws.

linear accelerator (linac) A type of particle *accelerator in which charged particles are accelerated in a straight line, either by a steady electric field or by means of radio-frequency electric fields. In the latter variety the passage of the particles is synchronized with the phase of the accelerating field by means of either travelling-wave acceleration or standing-wave acceleration. In the first of these the particles are carried forward by the electric component of the field, the phase velocity of which is equal to the particle velocity. In the standing-wave type, forward and backward waves are superimposed so that the particles are alternately repelled by cylindrical electrodes through which they have passed and attracted by the cylindrical electrodes they are approaching. At room temperatures megawatt radio-frequency powers are required but in recent superconducting linacs only a few watts are needed.

linear energy transfer (LET) The energy transferred per unit path length by a moving high-energy charged particle (such as an electron or a proton) to the atoms and molecules along its path. It is of particular importance when the particles pass through living tissue as the LET modifies the effect of a specific dose of radiation. LET is proportional to the square of the charge on the particle and increases as the velocity of the particle decreases.

linear equation An equation between two variables that gives a straight line when plotted on a graph. It has the general form $y = mx + c$, where m is the gradient of the line and c is the intercept of the line on the y-axis (in Cartesian coordinates).

linear expansivity *See* expansivity.

linear momentum *See* momentum.

linear motor A form of induction motor in which the stator and armature are linear and parallel, rather than cylindrical and coaxial. In some experimental trains the magnetic force between the primary winding in the vehicle and the secondary winding on the ground support the vehicle on an air cushion thus eliminating track friction. However, because of the high cost of the installation and the low efficiency the device has not yet found commercial application.

line defect *See* defect.

line-of-sight velocity (radial velocity) The component of a celestial body's velocity along the line of sight of the observer. It is usually given in relation to the sun to avoid complications arising from the earth's orbital motion. Line-of-sight velocity is normally calculated from the *Doppler effect on the body's spectrum, a *redshift indicating a receding body (taken as a positive velocity) and a blueshift indicating an approaching body (taken as negative).

line printer An output device used with computers. It prints a line of characters at a time, typically operating at 200 to 3000 lines per minute.

lines of force Imaginary lines in a *field of force that enable the direction and strength of the field to be visualized. They are used primarily in electric and magnetic fields; in electric fields they are sometimes called *tubes of force*, to express their characteristic of being perpendicular to a conducting surface. The tangent to a line of force at any point gives the direction of the field at that point and the number of lines per unit area perpendicular to the force represents the *intensity of the field.

line spectrum *See* spectrum.

Linnz–Donnewitz process *See* basic-oxygen process.

liquation The separation of mixtures of solids by heating to a temperature at which lower-melting components liquefy.

liquefaction of gases The conversion of a gaseous substance into a liquid. This is usually achieved by one of four methods or by a combination of two of them:

(1) by vapour compression, provided that the substance is below its *critical temperature;

(2) by refrigeration at constant pressure, typically by cooling it with a colder fluid in a countercurrent heat exchanger;

(3) by making it perform work adiabatically against the atmosphere in a reversible cycle;

(4) by the *Joule–Thomson effect (*see also* Linde process).

Large quantities of liquefied gases are now used commercially, especially *liquefied petroleum gas and liquefied natural gas.

liquefied petroleum gas (LPG) Various petroleum gases, principally propane and butane, stored as a liquid under pressure. It is used as an engine fuel and has the advantage of causing very little cylinder-head deposits.

Liquefied natural gas (LNG) is a similar product and consists mainly of methane. However, it cannot be liquefied simply by pressure as it has a low critical temperature of 190 K and must therefore be cooled to below this temperature before it will liquefy. Once liquefied it has to be stored in well-insulated containers. It provides a convenient form in which to ship natural gas in bulk from oil wells to users. It is also used as an engine fuel.

liquid A phase of matter between that of a crystalline solid and a *gas. In a liquid, the large-scale three-dimensional atomic (or ionic or molecular) regularity of the solid is absent but, on the other hand, so is the total disorganization of the gas. Although liquids have been studied for many years there is still no comprehensive theory of the liquid state. It is clear, however, from diffraction studies that there is a short-range structural regularity extending over several molecular diameters. These bundles of ordered atoms, molecules, or ions move about in relation to each other, enabling liquids to have almost fixed volumes, which adopt the shape of their containers.

liquid crystal A substance that flows like a liquid but has some order in its arrangement of molecules. *Nematic crystals* have long molecules all aligned in the same direction, but otherwise randomly arranged. *Cholesteric* and *smectic* liquid crystals also have aligned molecules, which are arranged in distinct layers. In cholesteric crystals, the axes of the molecules are parallel to the plane of the layers; in smectic crystals they are perpendicular.

liquid-crystal display A digital display unit used in watches, calculators, etc. It provides a source of clearly displayed digits for a very low power consumption. In the display unit a thin film of *liquid crystal is sandwiched between two transparent electrodes (glass with a thin metal or oxide coating). In the commonly used field-effect display, twisted nematic crystals are used. The nematic liquid crystal cell is placed between two crossed polarizers. Polarized light entering the cell follows the twist of the nematic liquid crystal, is rotated through 90°, and can therefore pass through the second polarizer. When an electric field is applied the molecular alignment in the liquid crystal is altered, the polarization of the entering light is unchanged, and no light is therefore transmitted. In these circumstances, a mirror placed behind the second polarizer will cause the display to appear black. One of the

electrodes, shaped in the form of a digit, will then provide a black digit when the voltage is applied.

liquid-drop model A model of the atomic nucleus in which the nucleons are regarded as being analogous to the molecules in a liquid, the interactions between which maintain the droplet shape by surface tension. The model has been useful in the theory of nuclear fission.

Lissajous figures A curve in one plane traced by a point moving under the influence of two independent harmonic motions. In the common case the harmonic motions are simple, perpendicular to each other, and have a simple frequency ratio. They can be displayed by applying sinusoidal alternating potentials to the X- and Y-inputs of a *cathode-ray oscilloscope.

litre Symbol l or L. A unit of volume in the metric system regarded as a special name for the cubic decimetre. It was formerly defined as the volume of 1 kilogram of pure water at 4°C at standard pressure, which is equivalent to 1.000 028 dm^3.

Lloyd's mirror An optical arrangement for producing interference fringes. A slit is illuminated by monochromatic light and placed close to a plane mirror. Interference occurs between direct light from the slit and light reflected from the mirror. It was first used by Humphrey Lloyd (1800–81) in 1834.

loaded concrete Concrete containing elements (such as iron or lead) with a high mass number; it is used in making the radiation shield around nuclear reactors.

Local Group The group of *galaxies of which our own Galaxy is a member. It consists of some 25 galaxies, the most massive of which are the Galaxy and the Andromeda galaxy.

local oscillator An *oscillator in a *heterodyne or *superheterodyne

radio receiver. It supplies the radio-frequency signal that beats with the incoming signal to produce the intermediate frequency.

locus A set of points whose location is specified by an equation. For example, if a point moves so that the sum of its distances from two fixed points is constant, the locus of the point is an *ellipse.

logarithm The power to which a number, called the *base*, has to be raised to give another number. Any number y can be written in the form $y = x^n$. n is then the logarithm to the base x of y, i.e. $n = \log_x y$. If the base is 10, the logarithms are called *common logarithms. Natural* (or *Napierian) logarithms* are to the base e $= 2.718\ 28\ldots$, written $\log_e y$ or $\ln y$. Logarithms were formerly used to facilitate calculations, before the advent of electronic calculators.

A logarithm contains two parts, an integer and a decimal. The integer is called the *characteristic*, and the decimal is called the *mantissa*. For example, the logarithm to the base 10 of 210 is 2.3222, where 2 is the characteristic and 0.3222 is the mantissa.

logarithmic scale 1. A scale of measurement in which an increase or decrease of one unit represents a tenfold increase or decrease in the quantity measured. Decibels and pH measurements are common examples of logarithmic scales of measurement. **2.** A scale on the axis of a graph in which an increase of one unit represents a tenfold increase in the variable quantity. If a curve $y = x^n$ is plotted on graph paper with logarithmic scales on both axes, the result is a straight line of slope n, i.e. $\log y = n\log x$, which enables n to be determined.

logarithmic series The expansion of a logarithmic function, such as $\log_e(1 + x)$, i.e. $x - x^2/2 + x^3/3 - \ldots + (-1)^n x^n/n$, or $\log_e(1 - x)$, i.e. $-x - x^2/2 - x^3/3 \ldots - x^n/n$.

logic circuits The basic switching circuits or *gates used in digital computers and other digital electronic devices. The output signal, using a *binary notation, is controlled by the logic circuit in accordance with the input system. The three basic logic circuits are the *and*, *or*, and *not* circuits. The *and* circuit gives a binary 1 output if a binary 1 is present on each input circuit; otherwise the output is a binary 0. The *or* circuit gives a binary 1 output if a binary 1 is present on at least one input circuit; otherwise the output is binary 0. The *not* circuit inverts the input signal, giving a binary 1 output for a binary 0 input or a 0 output for a 1 input.

Often these basic logic circuits are used in combination, e.g. a *nand* circuit consists of *not* + *and* circuits. In terms of electronic equipment, logic circuits are now almost exclusively embodied into *integrated circuits. They formerly made use of discrete transistors, although they were originally based on thermionic valves.

longitude *See* latitude and longitude.

longitudinal wave *See* wave.

long-sightedness *See* hypermetropia.

Lorentz–Fitzgerald contraction (Fitzgerald contraction) The contraction of a moving body in the direction of its motion. It was proposed independently by H. A. Lorentz (1853–1928) and G. F. Fitzgerald (1851–1901) in 1892 to account for the null result of the *Michelson–Morley experiment. The contraction was given a theoretical background in Einstein's special theory of *relativity. In this theory, an object of length l_0 at rest in one *frame of reference will appear, to an observer in another frame moving with relative velocity v with respect to the first, to have length $l_0\sqrt{(1 - v^2/c^2)}$, where c is the speed of light. The original hypothesis regarded this contraction as a real one accompanying the absolute motion of the body. The

contraction is in any case negligible unless v is of the same order as c.

Lorentz transformations A set of equations for transforming the position and motion parameters from a frame of reference with origin at O and coordinates (x,y,z) to a frame moving relative to it with origin at O' and coordinates (x',y',z'). They replace the *Galilean transformations used in *Newtonian mechanics and are used in relativistic mechanics. They are:
$$x' = \beta(x - vt)$$
$$y' = y$$
$$z' = z$$
$$t' = \beta(t - vx/c^2),$$
where v is the relative velocity of separation of O and O', c is the speed of light, and $\beta = 1/\sqrt{(1 - v^2/c^2)}$. The above equations apply for constant v in the xx' direction with O and O' coinciding at $t = t' = 0$.

Loschmidt's constant (Loschmidt number) Symbol N_L. The number of particles per unit volume of an *ideal gas at STP. It has the value $2.686\,763 \times 10^{25}$ m^{-3} and was first worked out by Joseph Loschmidt (1821–95).

loudness The physiological perception of sound intensity. As the ear responds differently to different frequencies, for a given intensity loudness is dependent on frequency. Sounds with frequencies between 1000 hertz and 5000 Hz are louder than sounds of the same intensity at higher or lower frequencies. Duration is also a factor in loudness, long bursts of sound being louder than short bursts. Loudness increases up to a duration of about 0.2 second; above this limit loudness does not increase with duration.

Relative loudness is usually measured on the assumption of proportionality to the logarithm of the intensity (for a given frequency), i.e. proportionality to the relative intensity on the *decibel scale. A subjective judgment is made of the relative intensity above threshold that a note of 1000 Hz

loudspeaker

must have to match the specimen sound; the loudness of this, in *phons, is then equal to that relative intensity in decibels.

loudspeaker A transducer for converting an electrical signal into an acoustic signal. Usually it is important to preserve as many characteristics of the electrical waveform as possible. The device must be capable of reproducing frequencies in the range 150–8000 hertz for speech and 20–20 000 Hz for music.

The most common loudspeaker consists of a moving-coil device. In this a cone-shaped diaphragm is attached to a coil of wire and made to vibrate in accordance with the electrical signal by the interaction between the current passing through the coil and a steady magnetic field from a permanent magnet surrounding it.

lowering of vapour pressure A reduction in the saturated vapour pressure of a pure liquid when a solute is introduced. If the solute is a solid of low vapour pressure, the decrease in vapour pressure of the liquid is proportional to the concentration of particles of solute; i.e. to the number of dissolved molecules or ions per unit volume. To a first approximation, it does not depend on the nature of the particles. *See* colligative property; Raoult's law.

low frequency (LF) A radio frequency in the range 30–300 kilohertz; i.e. having a wavelength in the range 1–10 kilometre.

lubrication The use of a substance to prevent contact between solid surfaces in relative motion in order to reduce friction, wear, overheating, and rusting. Liquid hydrocarbons (oils), either derived from petroleum or made synthetically, are the most widely used lubricants as they are relatively inexpensive, are good coolants, provide the appropriate range of viscosities, and are thermally stable. Additives include polymeric substances that maintain the desired viscosity as the temperature increases, antioxidants that prevent the formation of a sludge, and alkaline-earth phenates that neutralize acids and reduce wear. At high temperatures, solid lubricants, such as graphite or molybdenum disulphide, are often used. Semifluid lubricants (greases) are used to provide a seal against moisture and dirt and to remain attached to vertical surfaces. They are made by adding gelling agents, such as metallic soaps, to liquid lubricants.

Recent technology has made increasing use of gases as lubricants, usually in air bearings. Their very low viscosities minimize energy losses at the bearings but necessitate some system for pumping the gas continuously to the bearings. The principle is that of the hovercraft.

lumen Symbol lm. The SI unit of *luminous flux equal to the flux emitted by a uniform point source of 1 candela in a solid angle of 1 steradian.

luminance (photometric brightness) Symbol L. The *luminous intensity of any surface in a given direction per unit projected area of the surface, viewed from that direction. It is given by the equation $L = dI/(dA\cos\theta)$, where I is the luminous intensity and θ is the angle between the line of sight and the normal to the surface area A being considered. It is measured in candela per square metre.

luminescence The emission of light by a substance for any reason other than a rise in its temperature. In general, atoms of substances emit *photons of electromagnetic energy when they return to the *ground state after having been in an excited state (*see* excitation). The causes of the excitation are various. If the exciting cause is a photon, the process is called *photoluminescence*; if it is an electron it is called *electroluminescence*.

Chemiluminescence is luminescence resulting from a chemical reaction (such as the slow oxidation of phosphorus); *bioluminescence is the luminescence produced by a living organism (such as a firefly). If the luminescence persists significantly after the exciting cause is removed it is called *phosphorescence*; if it does not it is called *fluorescence*. This distinction is arbitrary since there must always be some delay; in some definitions a persistence of more than 10 nanoseconds (10^{-8} s) is treated as phosphorescence.

luminosity 1. *Luminous intensity in a particular direction; the apparent brightness of an image. **2.** The brightness of a star defined as the total energy radiated in unit time. It is related to the surface area (A) and the *effective temperature* (T_e; the temperature of a black body having the same radius as the star and radiating the same amount of energy per unit area in one second) by a form of *Stefan's law, i.e.

$$L = A\sigma T_e^4$$

where σ is the Stefan constant and L is the luminosity.

luminous exitance *See* exitance.

luminous flux Symbol Φ_v. A measure of the rate of flow of light, i.e. the radiant flux in the wavelength range 380–760 nanometres, corrected for the dependence on wavelength of the sensitivity of the human eye. It is measured by reference to emission from a standard source, usually in lumens.

luminous intensity Symbol I_v. A measure of the light-emitting ability of a light source, either generally or in a particular direction. It is measured in candelas.

lunar eclipse *See* eclipse.

lunation *See* synodic month.

lux Symbol lx. The SI unit of *illuminance equal to the illumination produced by a *luminous flux of 1 lumen distributed uniformly over an area of 1 square metre.

Lyman series *See* hydrogen spectrum.

M

machine A device capable of making the performance of mechanical work easier, usually by overcoming a force of resistance (the load) at one point by the application of a more convenient force (the effort) at some other point. In physics, the six so-called *simple machines* are the lever, wedge, inclined plane, screw, pulley, and wheel and axle.

Mach number The ratio of the relative speeds of a fluid and a rigid body to the speed of sound in that fluid under the same conditions of temperature and pressure. If the Mach number exceeds 1 the fluid or body is moving at a *supersonic speed*. If the Mach number exceeds 5 it is said to be *hypersonic*. The number is named after Ernst Mach (1838–1916).

Mach's principle The *inertia of any particular piece of matter is attributable to the interaction between that piece of matter and the rest of the universe. A body in isolation would have zero inertia. This principle was stated by Ernst Mach in the 1870s and was made use of by Einstein in his general theory of *relativity.

Maclaurin's series *See* Taylor series.

Magellanic clouds Two small galaxies situated close to the Milky Way that are only visible from the southern hemisphere. They were first recorded by Ferdinand Magellan (1480–1521) in 1519.

magic numbers Numbers of neutrons or protons that occur in atomic nuclei to produce very stable structures. The magic numbers for both

protons and neutrons are 2, 8, 20, 28, 50, and 82. For neutrons 126 and 184 are also magic numbers and for protons 114 is a magic number. The relationship between stability and magic numbers led to a nuclear *shell model in analogy to the electron shell model of the atom.

Magnadur A tradename for a ceramic material used to make permanent magnets. It consists of sintered iron oxide and barium oxide.

Magnalium A tradename for an aluminium-based alloy of high reflectivity for light and ultraviolet radiation that contains 1–2% of copper and between 5% and 30% of magnesium. Strong and light, these alloys also sometimes contain other elements, such as tin, lead, and nickel.

magnet A piece of magnetic material (*see* magnetism) that has been magnetized and is therefore surrounded by a *magnetic field. A magnet, often in the shape of a bar or horseshoe, that retains appreciable magnetization indefinitely (provided it is not heated, beaten, or exposed to extraneous magnetic fields) is called a *permanent magnet. See also* electromagnet.

magnetic bottle A nonuniform *magnetic field used to contain the *plasma in a thermonuclear experimental device. At the temperature of a thermonuclear reaction (10^8 K) any known substance would vaporize and the plasma has therefore to be contained in such a way that it does not come into contact with a material surface. The magnetic bottle provides a means of achieving this, by deflecting away from its boundaries the moving charged particles that make up the plasma.

magnetic bubble memory A form of computer memory in which a small magnetized region of a substance is used to store information. Bubble memories consist of materials, such as magnetic garnets, that are easily magnetized in one direction but hard

to magnetize in the perpendicular direction. A thin film of these materials deposited on a nonmagnetic substrate constitutes a bubble-memory chip. When a magnetic field is applied to such a chip, by placing it between two permanent magnets, cylindrical domains (called magnetic bubbles) are formed. These bubbles constitute a magnetic region of one polarity surrounded by a magnetic region of the opposite polarity. Information is represented as the presence or absence of a bubble at a specified storage location and is retrieved by means of a rotating magnetic field. Typically a chip measures 15 mm², or 25 mm² enclosed in two permanent magnets and two rotating field coils; each chip can store up to one million bits.

magnetic circuit A closed path containing a *magnetic flux. The path is clearly delimited only if it consists mainly or wholly of ferromagnetic or other good magnetic materials; examples include transformer cores and iron parts in electrical machines. The design of these parts can often be assisted by analogy with electrical circuits, treating the *magnetomotive force as the analogue of e.m.f., the magnetic flux as current, and the *reluctance as resistance. There is, however, no actual flow around a magnetic circuit.

magnetic compass *See* compass.

magnetic constant *See* permeability.

magnetic declination *See* geomagnetism.

magnetic dip *See* geomagnetism.

magnetic disk A smooth aluminium disk, usually 35.6 cm in diameter, both surfaces of which are coated with magnetic iron oxide. The disks are used as a recording medium in computers, up to ten such disks being mounted in a disk pack. Data is recorded in concentric tracks on both surfaces with up to 236 tracks per

centimetre. The disks rotate at 3600 revolutions per minute, information being put onto the disk and removed from it by means of a record-playback head. *See also* floppy disk.

magnetic domain *See* magnetism.

magnetic elements *See* geomagnetism.

magnetic equator *See* equator; geomagnetism.

magnetic field A *field of force that exists around a magnetic body (*see* magnetism) or a current-carrying conductor. Within a magnetic field a magnetic dipole may experience a torque and a moving charge may experience a force. The strength and direction of the field can be given in terms of the *magnetic flux density* (or *magnetic induction*), symbol B; it can also be given in terms of the *magnetic field strength* (*magnetizing force* or *magnetic intensity*), symbol H.

The magnetic flux density is a vector quantity and is the *magnetic flux per unit area of a magnetic field at right angles to the magnetic force. It can be defined in terms of the effects the field has, for example by $B = F/qv\sin\theta$, where F is the force a moving charge q would experience if it was travelling at a velocity v in a direction making an angle θ with that of the field. The *SI unit is the tesla.

The magnetic field strength is also a vector quantity and is related to B by: $H = B/\mu$, where μ is the *permeability of the medium. The SI unit of field strength is the ampere per metre $(A\ m^{-1})$.

magnetic field strength *See* magnetic field.

magnetic flux Symbol Φ. A measure of quantity of magnetism, taking account of the strength and the extent of a *magnetic field. The flux $d\Phi$ through an element of area dA perpendicular to B is given by $d\Phi = BdA$. The *SI unit of magnetic flux is the weber.

magnetic flux density *See* magnetic field.

magnetic force The attractive or repulsive force exerted on a *magnetic pole or a moving electric charge in a *magnetic field.

magnetic induction *See* magnetic field.

magnetic intensity *See* magnetic field.

magnetic meridian *See* meridian.

magnetic mirror A device used to contain *plasma in thermonuclear experimental devices. It consists of a region of high magnetic field strength at the end of a containment tube. Ions entering the region reverse their motion and return to the plasma from which they have emerged. *See also* magnetic bottle.

magnetic moment The ratio between the maximum torque (T_{max}) exerted on a magnet, current-carrying coil, or moving charge situated in a *magnetic field and the strength of that field. It is thus a measure of the strength of a magnet or current-carrying coil. In the Sommerfeld approach this quantity (also called *electromagnetic moment* or *magnetic area moment*) is T_{max}/B. In the Kennelly approach the quantity (also called *magnetic dipole moment*) is T_{max}/H.

In the case of a magnet placed in a magnetic field of field strength H, the maximum torque T_{max} occurs when the axis of the magnet is perpendicular to the field. In the case of a coil of N turns and area A carrying a current I, the magnetic moment can be shown to be $m = T/B = NIA$ or $m = T/H = \mu NIA$. Magnetic moments are measured in *SI units in $A\ m^2$.

An orbital electron has an orbital magnetic moment IA, where I is the equivalent current as the electron moves round its orbit. It is given by $I = q\omega/2\pi$, where q is the electronic

charge and ω is its angular velocity. The orbital magnetic moment is therefore $IA = q\omega A/2\pi$, where A is the orbital area. If the electron is spinning there is also a spin magnetic moment (*see* spin); atomic nuclei also have magnetic moments (*see* nuclear moment).

magnetic monopole A hypothetical magnetic entity consisting of an isolated elementary north or south pole. It has been postulated as a source of a *magnetic field by analogy with the way in which an electrically charged particle produces an electric field. Numerous ingenious experiments have been designed to detect the monopole but so far none has produced an unequivocal result. Magnetic monopoles are predicted to exist in certain *gauge theories with *Higgs bosons. In particular, some *grand unified theories predict very heavy monopoles (with mass of order 10^{16} GeV). Magnetic monopoles are also predicted to exist in *Kaluza–Klein theories and *superstring theory.

magnetic permeability *See* permeability.

magnetic poles 1. *See* geomagnetism. **2.** The regions of a *magnet from which the magnetic forces appear to originate. A magnetized bar has a pole at each end; if it is freely suspended in the earth's magnetic field (*see* geomagnetism) it will rotate so that one end points approximately towards the earth's geographical north pole. This end is called the north-seeking end or the north pole of the magnet. The other end is accordingly called the south-seeking end or south pole. In the obsolete theory associated with the *c.g.s. electromagnetic system of units, a *unit magnetic pole* was treated as one of a pair, which repelled each other with a force of 1 dyne when separated by 1 cm in space.

magnetic potential *See* magnetomotive force.

magnetic quantum number *See* atom.

magnetic susceptibility *See* susceptibility.

magnetic tape A plastic tape coated with a ferromagnetic iron oxide powder. The tape is used for recording data in tape recorders and computers. To record, the tape is passed over a recording head containing a gap in a magnetic circuit whose magnetization is modulated by the information to be recorded; the information is imprinted on the tape in the form of the direction of magnetization of the individual particles of iron oxide. The particles themselves are not rotated by the magnetizing field: it is their directions of magnetization that are orientated in accordance with the information. In audio-frequency recorders a high-frequency bias (in the range 75–100 kHz) is used to reduce distortion by facilitating the re-orientation. The playback procedure is the reverse of recording; the tape containing its orientation of tiny magnets is fed over the gap of the same (now the playback) head, in whose coil corresponding e.m.f.s are generated by induction.

magnetic variation (secular magnetic variation) *See* geomagnetism.

magnetism A group of phenomena associated with *magnetic fields. Whenever an electric current flows a magnetic field is produced; as the orbital motion and the *spin of atomic electrons are equivalent to tiny current loops, individual atoms create magnetic fields around them, when their orbital electrons have a net *magnetic moment as a result of their angular momentum. The magnetic moment of an atom is the vector sum of the magnetic moments of the orbital motions and the spins of all the electrons in the atom. The macroscopic magnetic properties of a substance arise from the magnetic moments of its component atoms and

molecules. Different materials have different characteristics in an applied magnetic field; there are four main types of magnetic behaviour:

(a) In *diamagnetism* the magnetization is in the opposite direction to that of the applied field, i.e. the *susceptibility is negative. Although all substances are diamagnetic, it is a weak form of magnetism and may be masked by other, stronger, forms. It results from changes induced in the orbits of electrons in the atoms of a substance by the applied field, the direction of the change (in accordance with *Lenz's law) opposing the applied flux. There is thus a weak negative susceptibility (of the order of -10^{-8} m^3 mol^{-1}) and a relative permeability of slightly less than one.

(b) In *paramagnetism* the atoms or molecules of the substance have net orbital or spin magnetic moments that are capable of being aligned in the direction of the applied field. They therefore have a positive (but small) susceptibility and a relative permeability slightly in excess of one. Paramagnetism occurs in all atoms and molecules with unpaired electrons; e.g. free atoms, free radicals, and compounds of transition metals containing ions with unfilled electron shells. It also occurs in metals as a result of the magnetic moments associated with the spins of the conducting electrons.

(c) In *ferromagnetic* substances, within a certain temperature range, there are net atomic magnetic moments, which line up in such a way that magnetization persists after the removal of the applied field. Below a certain temperature, called the *Curie point (or Curie temperature) an increasing magnetic field applied to a ferromagnetic substance will cause increasing magnetization to a high value, called the *saturation magnetization*. This is because a ferromagnetic substance consists of small (1–0.1 mm across) magnetized regions called *domains*.

The total magnetic moment of a sample of the substance is the vector sum of the magnetic moments of the component domains. Within each domain the individual atomic magnetic moments are spontaneously aligned by *exchange forces*, related to whether or not the atomic electron spins are parallel or antiparallel. However, in an unmagnetized piece of ferromagnetic material the magnetic moments of the domains themselves are not aligned; when an external field is applied those domains that are aligned with the field increase in size at the expense of the others. In a very strong field all the domains are lined up in the direction of the field and provide the high observed magnetization. Iron, nickel, cobalt, and their alloys are ferromagnetic. Above the Curie point, ferromagnetic materials become paramagnetic.

(d) Some metals, alloys, and transition-element salts exhibit another form of magnetism called *antiferromagnetism*. This occurs below a certain temperature, called the *Néel temperature, when an ordered array of atomic magnetic moments spontaneously forms in which alternate moments have opposite directions. There is therefore no net resultant magnetic moment in the absence of an applied field. In manganese fluoride, for example, this antiparallel arrangement occurs below a Néel temperature of 72 K. Below this temperature the spontaneous ordering opposes the normal tendency of the magnetic moments to align with the applied field. Above the Néel temperature the substance is paramagnetic.

A special form of antiferromagnetism is *ferrimagnetism*, a type of magnetism exhibited by the *ferrites. In these materials the magnetic moments of adjacent ions are antiparallel and of unequal strength, or the number of magnetic moments in one direction is greater than those in the opposite

direction. By suitable choice of rare-earth ions in the ferrite lattices it is possible to design ferrimagnetic substances with specific magnetizations for use in electronic components. *See also* geomagnetism.

magneto An alternating-current generator used as a high-tension source in the ignition systems of petrol engines in which there are no batteries, e.g. in some tractor, marine, and aviation engines. Most modern magnetos consist of a permanent-magnet rotor revolving within a primary (low-voltage) winding around which a secondary winding is placed in which to induce the high voltage needed to produce the spark across the points of the plugs. Magnetos are geared to the engine shaft, the speed depending on the number of poles of the magneto and the number of engine cylinders. A make-and-break device is incorporated in the primary winding; when the primary current stops the change of flux within the secondary induces in it a large e.m.f.

magnetobremsstrahlung *See* synchrotron radiation.

magnetocaloric effect A reversible change of temperature resulting from a change in the magnetization of a ferromagnetic or paramagnetic substance (*see* magnetism). The change in temperature ΔT, accompanying an adiabatic change of magnetic field ΔH, is:

$$\Delta T/\Delta H = -T/C_H(\partial M/\partial T)_H$$

C_H is the specific heat capacity per unit volume at constant H and M is the magnetization.

magnetochemistry The branch of physical chemistry concerned with measuring and investigating the magnetic properties of compounds. It is used particularly for studying transition-metal complexes, many of which are paramagnetic because they have unpaired electrons. Measurement of the magnetic susceptibility allows the magnetic moment of the metal atom

to be calculated, and this gives information about the bonding in the complex.

magnetohydrodynamics (MHD) The study of the interactions between a conducting fluid and a *magnetic field. MHD is important in the study of controlled thermonuclear reactions in which the conducting fluid is a *plasma confined by a magnetic field. Other important applications include the *magnetohydrodynamic power generator* (see illustration). In the open-cycle MHD generator a fossil fuel, burnt in oxygen or preheated compressed air, is seeded with an element of low *ionization potential (such as potassium or caesium). This element is thermally ionized at the combustion temperature (usually over 2500 K) producing sufficient free electrons (e.g. $K \rightarrow K^+ + e$) to provide adequate electrical conductivity. The interaction between the moving conducting fluid and the strong applied magnetic field across it generates an e.m.f. on the Faraday principle, except that the solid conductor of the conventional generator is replaced by a fluid conductor. The power output per unit fluid volume (W) is given by $W = k\sigma v^2 B^2$, where σ is the conductivity of the fluid, v is its velocity, B is the magnetic flux density, and K is a constant. Devices of this kind are in use in some power stations, where they are suitable for helping to meet high short-term demands and have the ability of increasing the thermal efficiency of a steam-turbine generator from about 40% to 50%. In experimental closed-cycle systems the fluid is continuously recirculated through a compressor; the fluid consists of a heated and seeded noble gas or a liquid metal.

magnetomechanical ratio *See* gyromagnetic ratio.

magnetometer An instrument for measuring the magnitude, and sometimes the direction, of a magnetic

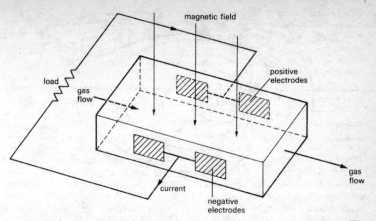

magnetic field

load

gas flow

positive electrodes

current

negative electrodes

gas flow

Magnetohydrodynamic generator

field. *Absolute magnetometers* measure the field without reference to a standard magnetic instrument. The most widely used are the *vibration magnetometer*, the *deflection galvanometer*, and the more modern *nuclear magnetometer*. The vibration instrument was devised by Gauss in 1832 and depends on the rate of oscillation of a small bar magnet suspended in a horizontal plane. The same magnet is then used as a fixed deflector to deflect a second similarly suspended magnet. The deflection galvanometer uses a Helmholtz coil system of known dimensions with a small magnet suspended at its centre. The deflected magnet comes to rest at a position controlled by the earth's magnetic field, the coil's magnetic field, and the angle through which the coil must be turned to keep the magnet and the coil in alignment. The sensitive nuclear magnetometers are based on measuring the audiofrequency voltage induced in a coil by the precessing protons in a sample of water. Various *relative magnetometers* are also in use, especially for measuring the earth's magnetic field and in calibrating other equipment.

magnetomotive force (m.m.f.) The analogue of *electromotive force in a *magnetic circuit. Mathematically, it is the circular integral of $H\cos\theta$ ds, where $H\cos\theta$ is the component of the *magnetic field strength in the direction of a path of length ds. The m.m.f. is measured in *SI units in ampere-turns. It was formerly called the *magnetic potential*.

magneton A unit for measuring *magnetic moments of nuclear, atomic, or molecular magnets. The *Bohr magneton* μ_B has the value of the classical magnetic moment of an electron, given by

$$\mu_B = eh/4\pi m_e = 9.274 \times 10^{-24} \text{ A m}^2,$$

where e and m_e are the charge and mass of the electron and h is the Planck constant. The *nuclear magneton*, μ_N is obtained by replacing the mass of the electron by the mass of the proton and is therefore given by

$$\mu_N = \mu_B m_e/m_p = 5.05 \times 10^{-27} \text{ A m}^2.$$

magneto-optical effects Effects resulting from the influence of a *magnetic field upon matter that is in the process of emitting or absorbing light. Examples are the *Faraday effect and the *Zeeman effect.

165

magnetosphere

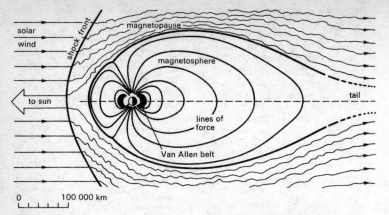

Magnetosphere and magnetopause

magnetosphere A comet-shaped region surrounding the earth and other magnetic planets in which the charged particles of the *solar wind are controlled by the planet's magnetic field rather than the sun's magnetic field. It extends for some 60 000 km on the side facing the sun but on the opposite side it extends to a much greater extent. The boundary of the magnetosphere is known as the *magnetopause* (see illustration). The magnetosphere of the earth includes the *Van Allen belts.

magnetostriction The change in length of a ferromagnetic material (*see* magnetism) when it is magnetized. It results from changes in the boundaries of the domains. A ferromagnetic rod exposed to an alternating field will vibrate along its length. This appears to be a major source of transformer hum, which can be removed by using a magnetic steel containing 6.5% silicon. Magnetostriction of a nickel transducer is used to generate and receive ultrasonic waves.

magnetron A microwave generator in which electrons, generated by a heated cathode, move under the combined force of an electric field and a magnetic field. The cathode consists of a central hollow cylinder, the outer surface of which carries the barium and strontium oxide electron emitters. The anode is also a cylinder, arranged concentrically around the cathode, and it contains a series of quarter-wavelength *resonant cavities arranged around its inner surface. The electric field is applied radially between anode and cathode, the magnetic field is coaxial with the cathode. The whole device is maintained in a vacuum enclosure. The magnetron is extensively used as a generator for radar installations and can produce microsecond pulses of up to 10 MW.

magnification A measure of the extent to which an optical system enlarges or reduces an image. The *linear magnification*, m, is the ratio of the image height to the object height. If this ratio is greater than one the system is enlarging, if it is less than one, it is reducing. The *angular magnification*, M or γ, is the ratio of the angles formed by the final image and the object (when viewed directly, in the most favourable position available) at the eye. This is also sometimes called the *magnifying power* of an optical system.

magnifying power *See* magnification.

166

magnitude A measure of the relative brightness of a star or other celestial object. The *apparent magnitude* depends on the star's *luminosity, its distance, and the absorption of light between the object and the earth. In 1856 the astronomer N. R. Pogson devised a scale in which a difference of five magnitudes corresponds to a brightness ratio of 100 to 1. Two stars that differ by one magnitude therefore have a brightness ratio of $(100)^{0.2}:1 = 2.512$, known as the *Pogson ratio*. This scale is now universally adopted. Apparent magnitudes are not a measure of luminosity, which is defined in terms of the *absolute magnitude*. This is the apparent magnitude of a body if it was situated at a standard distance of 10 parsecs.

magnon *See* spin wave.

Magnox A group of magnesium alloys used to enclose uranium fuel elements in *nuclear reactors. They usually contain some aluminium as well as other elements, such as beryllium.

mainframe computer *See* computer.

main-sequence stars *See* Hertzsprung–Russell diagram.

majority carrier *See* semiconductor.

Maksutov telescope *See* telescope.

manganin A copper alloy containing 13–18% of manganese and 1–4% of nickel. It has a high electrical resistance, which is relatively insensitive to temperature changes. It is therefore suitable for use as a resistance wire.

manometer A device for measuring pressure differences, usually by the difference in height of two liquid columns. The simplest type is the U-tube manometer, which consists of a glass tube bent into the shape of a U. If a pressure to be measured is fed to one side of the U-tube and the other is open to the atmosphere, the difference in level of the liquid in the two

limbs gives a measure of the unknown pressure.

mantissa *See* logarithm.

martensite A solid solution of carbon in alpha-iron (*see* iron) formed when *steel is cooled too rapidly for pearlite to form from austenite. It is responsible for the hardness of quenched steel.

mascon A gravitational anomaly on the surface of the moon resulting from a concentration of mass below the lunar surface. They occur in circular lunar maria and were caused either by the mare basalt as it flooded the basins or by uplift of high-density mantle material when the basins were formed.

maser (*m*icrowave *a*mplification by *s*timulated *e*mission of *r*adiation) A device for amplifying or generating *microwaves by means of stimulated emission (*see* laser). As oscillators, masers are used in *atomic clocks, while they are used as amplifiers in *radio astronomy, being especially suitable for amplifying feeble signals from space.

In the *ammonia gas maser* (devised in 1954) a molecular beam of ammonia passes through a small orifice into a vacuum chamber, where it is subjected to a nonuniform electric field. This field deflects ground-state ammonia molecules, shaped like a pyramid with the three hydrogen atoms forming the plane of the base and the single nitrogen atom forming the apex. The ground-state molecule has a dipole moment on account of its lack of symmetry and it is for this reason that it suffers deflection. Excited molecules, in which the nitrogen atom vibrates back and forth through the plane of the hydrogen atoms, have no resultant dipole moment and are not deflected. The beam, now consisting predominately of excited molecules, is passed to a resonant cavity fed with the microwave radiation corresponding to the energy difference between

mass

the excited and the ground states. This causes stimulated emission as the excited molecules fall to the ground state and the input microwave radiation is amplified coherently. This arrangement can also be made to oscillate and in this form is the basis of the *ammonia clock.

In the more versatile *solid-state maser* a magnetic field is applied to the electrons of paramagnetic (*see* magnetism) atoms or molecules. The energy of these electrons is quantized into two levels, depending on whether or not their spins are parallel to the magnetic field. The situation in which there are more parallel magnetic moments than antiparallel can be reversed by sudden changes in the magnetic field. This electron-spin resonance in paramagnetic materials allows amplification over broader bandwidths than gas masers.

mass A measure of a body's *inertia, i.e. its resistance to acceleration. According to Newton's laws of motion, if two unequal masses, m_1 and m_2, are allowed to collide, both will experience the same force of collision. If the two bodies acquire accelerations a_1 and a_2 as a result of the collision, then $m_1a_1 = m_2a_2$. This equation enables two masses to be compared. If one of the masses is regarded as a standard of mass, the mass of all other masses can be measured in terms of this standard. The body used for this purpose is a 1-kg cylinder of platinum–iridium alloy, called the international standard of mass. Mass defined in this way is called the *inertial mass* of the body. Mass can also be defined in terms of the gravitational force it produces. Thus, according to Newton's law of gravitation, $m_g = Fd^2/MG$, where M is the mass of a standard body situated a distance d from the body of mass m_g; F is the gravitational force between them and G is the *gravita-

tional constant. The mass defined in this way is the *gravitational mass*. In the 19th century Roland Eötvös (1848–1919) showed experimentally that gravitational and inertial mass are indistinguishable, i.e. $m_i = m_g$.

Although mass is formally defined in terms of its inertia, it is usually measured by gravitation. The *weight* (W) of a body is the force by which a body is gravitationally attracted to the earth corrected for the effect of rotation and equals the product of the mass of the body and the *acceleration of free fall (g), i.e. $W = mg$. In the general language, weight and mass are often used synonymously; however, for scientific purposes they are different. Mass is measured in kilograms; weight, being a force, is measured in newtons. Weight, moreover, depends on where it is measured, because the value of g varies at different localities on the earth's surface. Mass, on the other hand, is constant wherever it is measured, subject to the special theory of *relativity. According to this theory, announced by Albert Einstein in 1905, the mass of a body is a measure of its total energy content. Thus, if the energy of a body increases, for example by an increase in kinetic energy or temperature, then its mass will increase. According to this law an increase in energy ΔE is accompanied by an increase in mass Δm, according to the *mass–energy equation* $\Delta m = \Delta E/c^2$, where c is the speed of light. Thus, if 1 kg of water is raised in temperature by 100 K, its internal energy will increase by 4×10^{-12} kg. This is, of course, a negligible increase and the mass–energy equation is only significant for extremely high energies. For example, the mass of an electron is increased sevenfold if it moves relative to the observer at 99% of the speed of light.

mass action The law of mass action states that the rate at which a chemi-

cal reaction takes place at a given temperature is proportional to the product of the *active masses* of the reactants. The active mass of a reactant is taken to be its molar concentration. For example, for a reaction

$$A + B \rightarrow C$$

the rate is given by

$$R = k[A][B]$$

where k is the rate constant. The principle was introduced by C. M. Guldberg and P. Waage in 1863. It is strictly correct only for ideal gases. In real cases *activities can be used.

mass decrement *See* mass defect.

mass defect 1. The difference between the rest mass of an atomic nucleus and the sum of the rest masses of its individual nucleons in the unbound state. It is thus the mass equivalent of the *binding energy on the basis of the mass–energy equation (*see* mass; relativity). **2.** (*or* **mass decrement**) The difference between the rest mass of a radioactive nucleus before decay and the total rest mass of the decay products.

mass–energy equation *See* mass; relativity.

mass number *See* nucleon number.

mass spectrum *See* spectrum.

matrix (*pl.* **matrices**) **1.** (in mathematics) A set of quantities in a rectangular array, used in certain mathematical operations. The array is usually enclosed in large parentheses or in square brackets. **2.** (in geology) The fine-grained material of rock in which the coarser-grained material is embedded.

maximum and minimum thermometer A thermometer designed to record both the maximum and minimum temperatures that have occurred over a given time period. It usually consists of a graduated capillary tube at the base of which is a bulb containing ethanol. The capillary contains a thin thread of mercury with a steel index at each end. As the tem-

perature rises the index is pushed up the tube, where it remains in position to show the maximum temperature reached; as the temperature falls the lower index is pushed down the tube and similarly remains in position at the lowest temperature. The indexes are reset by means of a permanent magnet.

maximum permissible dose *See* dose.

maxwell A unit of magnetic flux in the *c.g.s. system, equal to the flux through 1 square centimetre perpendicular to a magnetic field of 1 gauss. 1 maxwell is equal to 10^{-8} weber. It is named after James Clerk Maxwell (1831–79).

Maxwell–Boltzmann distribution A law describing the distribution of speeds among the molecules of a gas. In a system consisting of N molecules that are independent of each other except that they exchange energy on collision, it is clearly impossible to say what velocity any particular molecule will have. However, statistical statements regarding certain functions of the molecules were worked out by James Clerk Maxwell (1831–79) and Ludwig Boltzmann (1844–1906). One form of their law states that $n = N\exp(-E/RT)$, where n is the number of molecules with energy in excess of E, T is the thermodynamic temperature, and R is the *gas constant.

Maxwell's equations A set of differential equations describing the space and time dependence of the electromagnetic field and forming the basis of classical electrodynamics. In *SI units the equations are:

(1) $\text{div}\boldsymbol{D} = \rho$
(2) $\text{curl}\boldsymbol{E} = -\partial \boldsymbol{B}/\partial t$
(3) $\text{div}\boldsymbol{B} = 0$
(4) $\text{curl}\boldsymbol{H} = \partial \boldsymbol{D}/\partial t + \boldsymbol{J}$

where $\boldsymbol{D}$ is the electric displacement, $\boldsymbol{E}$ is the electric field strength, $\boldsymbol{B}$ is the magnetic flux density, $\boldsymbol{H}$ is the magnetic field strength, ρ is the volume charge density, and $\boldsymbol{J}$ is the elec-

tric current density. Note that in relativity and particle physics it is common to use *Gaussian or *Heaviside–Lorentz units, in which case Maxwell's equations include 4π and the speed of light c. Maxwell's equations have the following interpretation. Equation (1) represents *Coulomb's law; equation (2) represents *Faraday's laws of electromagnetic induction; equation (3) represents the absence of *magnetic monopoles; equation (4) represents a generalization of *Ampère's law.

McLeod gauge A vacuum pressure gauge in which a relatively large volume of a low-pressure gas is compressed to a small volume in a glass apparatus (see illustration). The volume is reduced to an extent that causes the pressure to rise sufficiently to support a column of fluid high enough to read. This simple device, which relies on *Boyle's law, is suit-

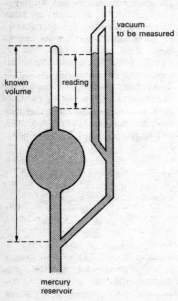

McLeod gauge

able for measuring pressures in the range 10^3 to 10^{-3} pascal.

mean *See* average.

mean free path The average distance travelled between collisions by the molecules in a gas, the electrons in a metallic crystal, the neutrons in a moderator, etc. According to the *kinetic theory the mean free path between elastic collisions of gas molecules of diameter d (assuming they are rigid spheres) is $1/\sqrt{2}n\pi d^2$, where n is the number of molecules per unit volume in the gas. As n is proportional to the pressure of the gas, the mean free path is inversely proportional to the pressure.

mean free time The average time that elapses between the collisions of the molecules in a gas, the electrons in a crystal, the neutrons in a moderator, etc. *See* mean free path.

mean life *See* decay.

mean solar day *See* day.

mechanical advantage *See* force ratio.

mechanical equivalent of heat Symbol J. The ratio of a unit of mechanical energy to the equivalent unit of thermal energy, when a system of units is used in which they differ. J has the value 4.1868×10^7 ergs per calorie. The concept loses its usefulness in *SI units in which all forms of energy are expressed in joules and J therefore has a value of 1.

mechanics The study of the interactions between matter and the forces acting on it. *Statics is broadly concerned with the action of forces when no change of momentum is concerned, while *dynamics deals with cases in which there is a change of momentum. *Kinematics is the study of the motion of bodies without reference to the forces affecting the motion. These classical sciences are concerned with macroscopic bodies in the solid state, while *fluid mechanics

The labels on the illustration read: vacuum to be measured; known volume; reading; mercury reservoir.

is the science of the interaction between forces and fluids.

median 1. The middle number or value in a series of numbers or values. **2.** A straight line in a triangle that joins the vertex to the mid-point of the base.

medium frequency (MF) A radio frequency in the range 0.3–3 megahertz; i.e. having a wavelength in the range 100–1000 metres.

mega- Symbol M. A prefix used in the metric system to denote one million times. For example, 10^6 volts = 1 megavolt (MV).

megaton weapon A nuclear weapon with an explosive power equivalent to one million tons of TNT. *Compare* kiloton weapon.

Meissner effect The falling off of the magnetic flux within a superconducting metal when it is cooled to a temperature below the critical temperature in a magnetic field. It was discovered by Walther Meissner in 1933 when he observed that the earth's magnetic field was expelled from the interior of tin crystals below 3.72 K, indicating that as *superconductivity appeared the material became perfectly diamagnetic. *See* magnetism.

melting point (m.p.) The temperature at which a solid changes into a liquid. A pure substance under standard conditions of pressure (usually 1 atmosphere) has a single reproducible melting point. If heat is gradually and uniformly supplied to a solid the consequent rise in temperature stops at the melting point until the fusion process is complete.

mendelevium Symbol Md. A radioactive metallic transuranic element belonging to the actinoids; a.n. 101; mass number of the only known nuclide 256 (half-life 1.3 hours). It was first identified by A. Ghiorso, G. T. Seaborg, and associates in 1955.

The alternative name *unnilunium* has been proposed.

meniscus 1. A concave or convex upper surface that forms on a liquid in a tube as a result of *surface tension. **2.** *See* concave.

mercury cell A primary *voltaic cell consisting of a zinc anode and a cathode of mercury(II) oxide (HgO) mixed with graphite. The electrolyte is potassium hydroxide (KOH) saturated with zinc oxide, the overall reaction being:

$$Zn + HgO \rightarrow ZnO + Hg$$

The e.m.f. is 1.35 volts and the cell will deliver about 0.3 ampere-hour per cm^3.

mercury-vapour lamp A type of discharge tube in which a glow discharge takes place in mercury vapour. The discharge takes place in a transparent tube of fused silica or quartz into the ends of which molybdenum and tungsten electrodes are sealed; this tube contains argon and a small amount of pure mercury. A small arc is struck between a starter electrode and one of the main electrodes causing local ionization of some argon atoms. The ionized atoms diffuse through the tube causing the main discharge to strike; the heat from this vaporizes the mercury droplets, which become ionized current carriers. Radiation is confined to four visible wavelengths in the visible spectrum and several strong ultraviolet lines. The light is bluish but can be changed by the use of *phosphors on an outer tube. The outer tube is also usually used to filter out excessive ultraviolet radiation. The lamp is widely used for street lighting on account of its low cost and great reliability and as a source of ultraviolet radiation.

meridian 1. *See* latitude and longitude. **2. (magnetic meridian)** An imaginary great circle on the earth's surface that passes through the north and south magnetic poles. A compass

needle on the earth's surface influenced only by the earth's magnetic field (*see* geomagnetism) comes to rest along a magnetic meridian. **3. (celestial meridian)** A great circle of the *celestial sphere that passes through the zenith and the celestial poles. It meets the horizon at the north and south points.

meso form *See* optical activity.

meson Any of a class of *elementary particles that are a subclass of the *hadrons. According to current quark theory mesons consist of quark–antiquark pairs. They exist with positive, negative, and zero charges, but when charged the charge has the same magnitude as that of the electron. They include the *kaon*, *pion*, and *psi* particles. Mesons are believed to participate in the forces that hold nucleons together in the nucleus. The muon, originally called a mu-meson, was thought to be a meson but is now recognized as a *lepton.

meson-catalysed fusion *See* nuclear fusion.

metal fatigue A cumulative effect causing a metal to fail after repeated applications of *stress, none of which exceeds the ultimate *tensile strength. The *fatigue strength* (or *fatigue limit*) is the stress that will cause failure after a specified number (usually 10^7) of cycles. The number of cycles required to produce failure decreases as the level of stress or strain increases. Other factors, such as corrosion, also reduce the fatigue life.

metallography The microscopic study of the structure of metals and their alloys. Both optical *microscopes and *electron microscopes are used in this work.

metallurgy The branch of engineering concerned with the production of metals from their ores, the purification of metals, the manufacture of alloys, and the use and performance of metals in engineering practice. *Process metallurgy* is concerned with the extraction and production of metals, while *physical metallurgy* concerns the mechanical behaviour of metals.

metamict state The amorphous state of a substance that has lost its crystalline structure as a result of the radioactivity of uranium or thorium. *Metamict minerals* are minerals whose structure has been disrupted by this process. The metamictization is caused by alpha-particles and the recoil nuclei from radioactive disintegration.

metastable state A condition of a system in which it has a precarious stability that can easily be disturbed. It is unlike a state of stable equilibrium in that a minor disturbance will cause a system in a metastable state to fall to a lower energy level. A book lying on a table is in a state of stable equilibrium; a thin book standing on edge is in metastable equilibrium. Supercooled water is also in a metastable state. It is liquid below $0°C$; a grain of dust or ice introduced into it will cause it to freeze. An excited state of an atom or nucleus that has an appreciable lifetime is also metastable.

meteor A streak of light observable in the sky when a particle of matter enters the earth's atmosphere and becomes incandescent as a result of friction with atmospheric atoms and molecules. These particles of matter are known collectively as *meteoroids*. Meteoroids that survive their passage through the atmosphere and strike the earth's surface are known as *meteorites*. Only some 2500 meteorites are known, excluding the *micrometeorites* (bodies less than 1 mm in diameter). Meteorites consist mainly of silicate materials (stony meteorites) or iron (iron meteorites). It is estimated that the earth collects over 10^8 kg of meteoritic material every year, mostly in the form of micrometeorites. Micrometeorites survive atmospheric

friction because their small size enables them to radiate away the heat generated by friction before they vaporize.

meteorite *See* meteor.

method of mixtures A method of determining the specific heat capacities of liquids or a liquid and a solid by mixing known masses of the substances at different temperatures and measuring the final temperature of the mixture.

metre Symbol m. The SI unit of length, being the length of the path travelled by light in vacuum during a time interval of $1/(2.99\,792\,458 \times 10^8)$ second. This definition, adopted by the General Conference on Weights and Measures in October, 1983, replaced the 1967 definition based on the krypton lamp, i.e. $1\,650\,763.73$ wavelengths in a vacuum of the radiation corresponding to the transition between the levels $2p^{10}$ and $5d^5$ of the nuclide krypton–86. This definition (in 1958) replaced the older definition of a metre based on a platinum–iridium bar of standard length. When the *metric system was introduced in 1791 in France, the metre was intended to be one ten-millionth of the earth's meridian quadrant passing through Paris. However, the original geodetic surveys proved the impractibility of such a standard and the original platinum metre bar, the *mètre des archives*, was constructed in 1793.

metre bridge *See* Wheatstone bridge.

metric system A decimal system of units originally devised by a committee of the French Academy, which included J. L. Lagrange and P. S. Laplace, in 1791. It was based on the *metre, the gram defined in terms of the mass of a cubic centimetre of water, and the second. This centimetre-gram-second system (*see* c.g.s. units) later gave way for scientific work to the metre-kilogram-second

system (*see* m.k.s. units) on which *SI units are based.

metric ton (tonne) A unit of mass equal to 1000 kg or 2204.61 lb. 1 tonne = 0.9842 ton.

metrology The scientific study of measurement, especially the definition and standardization of the units of measurement used in science.

MHD *See* magnetohydrodynamics.

mho A reciprocal ohm, the former name of the unit of electrical *conductance now known as the siemens.

Michelson–Morley experiment An experiment, conducted in 1887 by Albert Michelson (1852–1931) and Edward Morley (1838–1923), that attempted to measure the velocity of the earth through the *ether. Using a modified *Michelson interferometer* (see illustration) they expected to observe a shift in the interference fringes formed when the instrument was rotated through 90°, showing that the speed of light measured in the direction of the earth's rotation, or orbital motion, is not identical to its speed at right angles to this direction. No shift was observed. An explanation was finally provided by the *Lorentz–Fitzgerald contraction, which provided an important step in the formulation of Einstein's special

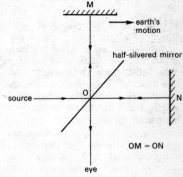

Michelson interferometer

theory of *relativity and the abandonment of the ether concept.

micro- Symbol μ. A prefix used in the metric system to denote one millionth. For example, 10^{-6} metre = 1 micrometre (μm).

microbalance A sensitive *balance capable of weighing masses of the order 10^{-6} to 10^{-9} kg.

microelectronics The techniques of designing and making electronic circuits of very small size. As a result of these techniques a single *silicon chip measuring less than a centimetre in either direction can contain many thousands of transistors and may constitute the central processing unit of a microcomputer. In addition to an enormous drop in size, compared to an equivalent valve-operated device, these microelectronic circuits are some 100 000 times more reliable than their thermionic predecessors.

micrometeorite *See* meteor.

micrometer A gauge for measuring small diameters, thicknesses, etc., accurately. It consists of a G-shaped device in which the gap between the measuring faces is adjusted by means of an accurately calibrated screw, the end of which forms one of the measuring faces.

micron The former name for the *SI unit now called the micrometre, i.e. 10^{-6} m.

microphone A *transducer in which sound waves are converted into corresponding variations in an electrical signal for amplification, transmission to a distant point, or recording. Various types of device are used. In the *dynamic microphone* the sound waves impinge on a conductor of low mass supported in a magnetic field and cause it to oscillate at the frequency of the sound waves. These movements induce an e.m.f. in the conductor that is proportional to its velocity. The moving conductor consists of a metal ribbon, a wire, or a coil of wire. In the *moving-iron microphone*, sound waves cause a light armature to oscillate so that it varies the reluctance of a magnetic circuit. In a coil surrounding this path the varying reluctance is experienced as a variation in the magnetic flux within it, which induces a corresponding e.m.f. In the *carbon microphone*, widely used in telephones, a diaphragm constitutes a movable electrode in contact with carbon granules, which are also in contact with a fixed electrode. The movement of the diaphragm, in response to the sound waves, varies the resistance of the path through the granules to the fixed electrode. *See also* capacitor microphone; crystal microphone.

microprocessor *See* computer.

microscope A device for forming a magnified image of a small object. The *simple microscope* consists of a

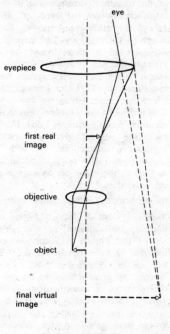

Compound microscope

biconvex magnifying glass or an equivalent system of lenses, either hand-held or in a simple frame. The *compound microscope* (see illustration) uses two lenses or systems of lenses, the second magnifying the real image formed by the first. The lenses are usually mounted at the opposite ends of a tube that has mechanical controls to move it in relation to the object. An optical condenser and mirror, often with a separate light source, provide illumination of the object. The widely used *binocular microscope* consists of two separate instruments fastened together so that one eye looks through one while the other eye looks through the other. This gives stereoscopic vision and reduces eye strain. *See also* atomic force microscope; electron microscope; field-emission microscope; field-ionization microscope; phase-contrast microscope; scanning tunnelling microscope; ultraviolet microscope.

microwave background radiation A cosmic background of radiation in the frequency range 3×10^{11} hertz to 3×10^{8} hertz discovered in 1965. Believed to have emanated from the primordial fireball of the big bang with which the universe is thought to have originated (*see* big-bang theory), the radiation has an energy density in intergalactic space of some 4×10^{-14} J m^{-3}.

microwave optics The study of the behaviour of microwaves by analogy with the behaviour of light waves. On the large scale microwaves are propagated in straight lines and, like light waves, they undergo reflection, refraction, diffraction, and polarization.

microwaves Electromagnetic waves with wavelengths in the range 10^{-3} to 0.03 m.

Milky Way *See* galaxy.

milli- Symbol m. A prefix used in the metric system to denote one thousandth. For example, 0.001 volt = 1 millivolt (mV).

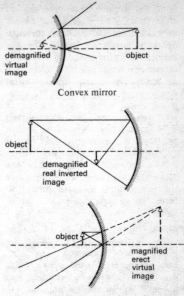

Convex mirror

Concave mirrors

millibar *See* bar.

minority carrier *See* semiconductor.

minor planets *See* asteroids.

minute 1. One sixtieth of an hour. **2.** One sixtieth of a degree (angle).

mirage An optical phenomenon that occurs as a result of the bending of light rays through layers of air having very large temperature gradients. An *inferior mirage* occurs when the ground surface is strongly heated and the air near the ground is much warmer that the air above. Light rays from the sky are strongly refracted upwards near the surface giving the appearance of a pool of water. A *superior mirage* occurs if the air close to the ground surface is much colder than the air above. Light is bent downwards from the object towards the viewer so that it appears to be elevated or floating in the air.

mirror A surface that reflects most of the light falling on it. A *plane mirror*

is a flat surface that produces an erect virtual *image of a real object, in which front and back are reversed. *Spherical mirrors* are formed from the surfaces of spheres and form images of real objects in much the same way as lenses. A convex mirror forms erect virtual images. They are commonly used as rear-view mirrors in road vehicles, and give a diminished wide-angle image. A concave mirror can form either inverted real images or erect virtual images. (See illustrations.) Spherical mirrors obey the *lens equation (using the real-positive sign convention) and are subject to some *aberrations similar to those of lenses.

misch metal An alloy of cerium (50%), lanthanum (25%), neodymium (18%), praseodymium (5%), and other rare earths. It is used alloyed with iron (up to 30%) in lighter flints, and in small quantities to improve the malleability of iron. It is also added to copper alloys to make them harder, to aluminium alloys to make them stronger, to magnesium alloys to reduce creep, and to nickel alloys to reduce oxidation.

missing mass The mass of matter in the universe that cannot be observed by direct observations of its emitted or absorbed electromagnetic radiation. There are a number of astrophysical observations that suggest that the actual mass of the universe is much greater than that estimated by observations using optical telescopes, radiotelescopes, etc. It is thought that there is a considerable amount of *dark matter* (or *hidden matter*) causing this discrepancy. Various explanations have been put forward for the missing mass, including black holes, brown dwarfs, cosmic strings, axions, neutrinos, monopoles, and various exotic particles, such as *weakly interacting massive particles* (*WIMPS*).

m.k.s. units A *metric system of units devised by A. Giorgi (and

sometimes known as *Giorgi units*) in 1901. It is based on the metre, kilogram, and second and grew from the earlier *c.g.s. units. The electrical unit chosen to augment these three basic units was the ampere and the *permeability of space (magnetic constant) was taken as 10^{-7} H m^{-1}. To simplify electromagnetic calculations the magnetic constant was later changed to $4\pi \times 10^{-7}$ H m^{-1} to give the *rationalized MKSA system*. This system, with some modifications, formed the basis of *SI units, now used in most scientific work.

m.m.f. *See* magnetomotive force.

mmHg A unit of pressure equal to that exerted under standard gravity by a height of one millimetre of mercury, or 133.322 pascals.

mobility (of an ion) Symbol *u*. The terminal speed of an ion in an electric field divided by the field strength.

moderator A substance that slows down free neutrons in a *nuclear reactor, making them more likely to cause fissions of atoms of uranium–235 and less likely to be absorbed by atoms of uranium–238. Moderators are light elements, such as deuterium (in heavy water), graphite, and beryllium, to which neutrons can impart some of their kinetic energy on collision without being captured. Neutrons that have had their energies reduced in this way (to about 0.025 eV, equivalent to a speed of 2200 m s^{-1}) are said to have been *thermalized* or to have become *thermal neutrons*.

modulation The process of superimposing the characteristics of a periodic signal onto a *carrier wave so that the information contained in the signal can be transmitted by the carrier wave. In *radio transmission, the simplest form of modulation is *amplitude modulation* (*AM*), in which the amplitude of the carrier is increased or diminished as the signal amplitude increases and diminishes. In *frequency*

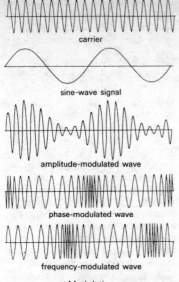

carrier

sine-wave signal

amplitude-modulated wave

phase-modulated wave

frequency-modulated wave

Modulation

modulation (FM), the frequency of the carrier is increased or diminished as the signal amplitude increases and diminishes but the carrier amplitude remains constant. In *phase modulation*, the relative phase of the carrier is varied in accordance with the signal amplitude. (See illustrations.) Both frequency modulation and phase modulation are forms of *angle modulation*.

In *pulse modulation* the information is transmitted by controlling the amplitude, duration, position, or presence of a series of pulses. Morse code is a simple form of a pulse modulation.

modulus *See* absolute value.

modulus of elasticity *See* elastic modulus.

Moho (Mohorovičić discontinuity) A discontinuity within the *earth that marks the junction between the crust and the underlying mantle. Below the discontinuity earthquake seismic waves undergo a sudden increase in velocity, a feature that was first observed in 1909 by the Yugoslavian geophysicist Andrija Mohorovičić (1857–1936), after whom the discontinuity was named. The Moho lies at a depth of about 10–12 km below the oceans and about 33–35 km below the continents.

Mohs' scale A hardness scale in which a series of ten minerals are arranged in order, each mineral listed being scratched by and therefore softer than those below it. The minerals are: (1) talc; (2) gypsum; (3) calcite; (4) fluorite; (5) apatite; (6) orthoclase; (7) quartz; (8) topaz; (9) corundum; (10) diamond. As a rough guide a mineral with a value up to 2.5 on this scale can be scratched by a fingernail, up to 4 can be scratched by a coin, and up to 6 by a knife. The scale was devised by Friedrich Mohs (1773–1839).

molar Denoting that an extensive physical property is being expressed per *amount of substance, usually per mole. For example, the molar heat capacity of a compound is the heat capacity of that compound per unit amount of substance, i.e. it is usually expressed in $J K^{-1} mol^{-1}$.

molar conductivity Symbol Λ. The conductivity of that volume of an electrolyte that contains one mole of solution between electrodes placed one metre apart.

molar heat capacity *See* heat capacity.

molar latent heat *See* latent heat.

molar volume (molecular volume) The volume occupied by a substance per unit amount of substance.

mole Symbol mol. The SI unit of *amount of substance. It is equal to the amount of substance that contains as many elementary units as there are atoms in 0.012 kg of carbon–12. The elementary units may be atoms, molecules, ions, radicals, electrons, etc., and must be specified. 1 mole of a compound has a mass equal to its

*relative molecular mass expressed in grams.

molecular beam A beam of atoms, ions, or molecules at low pressure, in which all the particles are travelling in the same direction and there are few collisions between them. They are formed by allowing a gas or vapour to pass through an aperture into an enclosure, which acts as a collimator by containing several additional apertures and vacuum pumps to remove any particles that do not pass through the apertures. Molecular beams are used in studies of surfaces and chemical reactions and in spectroscopy.

molecular distillation Distillation in high vacuum (about 0.1 pascal) with the condensing surface so close to the surface of the evaporating liquid that the molecules of the liquid travel to the condensing surface without collisions. This technique enables very much lower temperatures to be used than are used with distillation at atmospheric pressure and therefore heat-sensitive substances can be distilled. Oxidation of the distillate is also eliminated as there is no oxygen present.

molecular flow (Knudsen flow) The flow of a gas through a pipe in which the mean free path of gas molecules is large compared to the dimensions of the pipe. This occurs at low pressures; because most collisions are with the walls of the pipe rather than other gas molecules, the flow characteristics depend on the relative molecular mass of the gas rather than its viscosity. The effect was studied by M. H. C. Knudsen (1871–1949).

molecular formula *See* formula.

molecular orbital *See* orbital.

molecular volume *See* molar volume.

molecular weight *See* relative molecular mass.

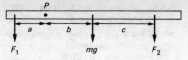

Moment of a force. For equilibrium $mgb + F_2(b+c) = F_1 a$, where mg is the weight of the beam acting through its centre of mass

molecule One of the fundamental units forming a chemical compound; the smallest part of a chemical compound that can take part in a chemical reaction. In most covalent compounds, molecules consist of groups of atoms held together by covalent or coordinate bonds. Covalent substances that form macromolecular crystals have no discrete molecules (in a sense, the whole crystal is a molecule). Similarly, ionic compounds do not have single molecules, being collections of oppositely charged ions.

mole fraction Symbol X. A measure of the amount of a component in a mixture. The mole fraction of component A is given by $X_A = n_A/N$, where n_A is the amount of substance of A (for a given entity) and N is the total amount of substance of the mixture (for the same entity).

moment of a force A measure of the turning effect produced by a force about an axis. The magnitude of the moment is the product of the force and the perpendicular distance from the axis to the line of action of the force. An object will be in rotational equilibrium if the algebraic sum of all the moments of the forces on it about any axis is zero. See illustration.

moment of inertia Symbol I. The moment of inertia of a massive body about an axis is the sum of all the products formed by multiplying the magnitude of each element of mass (δm) by the square of its distance (r) from the line, i.e. $I_m = \Sigma r^2 \delta m$. It is the analogue in rotational dynamics of mass in linear dynamics. The basic equation is $T = I\alpha$, where T is the

torque causing angular acceleration α about the specified axis.

momentum The *linear momentum* (p) of a body is the product of its mass (m) and its velocity (v), i.e. $p = mv$. *See also* angular momentum.

monochromatic radiation Electromagnetic radiation, especially visible radiation, of only one frequency or wavelength. Completely monochromatic radiation cannot be produced, but *lasers produce radiation within a very narrow frequency band. *Compare* polychromatic radiation.

monochromator A device that provides monochromatic radiation from a polychromatic source. In the case of visible radiation, for example, a prism can be used together with slits to select a small range of wavelengths.

monoclinic *See* crystal system.

moon The earth's only natural satellite, which orbits the earth at a mean distance of 384 400 km. It has a diameter of 3476 km. It has no atmosphere or surface water. Its surface temperature varies between 80 K (night minimum) and 400 K (noon at the equator). It is the only celestial body outside the earth to have been reached by man (1969).

Moseley's law The frequencies of the lines in the *X-ray spectra of the elements are related to the atomic numbers of the elements. If the square roots of the frequencies of corresponding lines of a set of elements are plotted against the atomic numbers a straight line is obtained. The law was discovered by H. G. Moseley (1887–1915).

Mössbauer effect The emission without recoil of a gamma-ray photon from a nucleus embedded in a solid. The emission of a gamma ray by a single atom in a gas causes the atom to recoil and reduces the energy of the gamma ray from its usual transition energy E_0 to $E_0 - R$, where R is the recoil energy. In 1957 R. L.

Mössbauer (1929–) discovered that if the emitting nucleus is held by strong forces in the lattice of a solid, the recoil energy is shared by all the nuclei in the lattice. As there may typically be 10^{10}–10^{20} atoms in the lattice the recoil will be negligible and the gamma-ray photon has the energy E_0. The same principle applies to the absorption of gamma rays and is used in *Mössbauer-effect spectroscopy* to elucidate problems in nuclear physics, solid-state physics, and chemistry.

motion A change in the position of a body or system with respect to time, as measured by a particular observer in a particular *frame of reference. Only relative motion can be measured; absolute motion is meaningless. *See also* equation of motion; Newton's laws of motion.

motor Any device for converting chemical energy or electrical energy into mechanical energy. *See* electric motor; internal-combustion engine; linear motor.

motor generator An electric motor mechanically coupled to an electric generator. The motor is driven by a supply of specified voltage, frequency, or number of phases and the generator provides an output in which one or more of these parameters is different to suit a particular purpose.

moving-coil instrument A measuring instrument in which current or voltage is determined by the couple on a small coil pivoted between the poles of a magnet with curved poles, giving a radial magnetic field. When a current flows through the coil it turns against a return spring. If the angle through which it turns is α, the current I is given by $I = k\alpha/BAN$, where B is the magnetic flux density, A is the area of the coil and N is its number of turns; k is a constant depending on the strength of the return spring. The instrument is suitable for measuring d.c. but can be

converted for a.c. by means of a rectifier network. It is usually made as a *galvanometer and converted to an ammeter or voltmeter by means of a *shunt or a *multiplier.

moving-iron instrument A measuring instrument in which current or voltage is determined by the force of attraction on a bar of soft iron pivoted within the magnetic field of a fixed coil or by the repulsion between the poles induced in two soft iron rods within the coil. As the deflection caused by the passage of a current through the coil does not depend on the direction of the current, moving-iron instruments can be used with either d.c. or a.c. without a rectifier. They are, however, less sensitive than *moving-coil instruments.

moving-iron microphone See microphone.

multimeter An electrical measuring instrument designed to measure potential differences or currents over a number of ranges. It also usually has an internal dry cell enabling resistances to be measured. Most multimeters are moving-coil instruments with a switch to enable series resistors or parallel resistors to be incorporated into the circuit.

multiplet 1. A spectral line formed by more than two (see doublet) closely spaced lines. 2. A group of *elementary particles that are identical in all respects except that of electric charge.

multiplication factor Symbol k. The ratio of the average number of neutrons produced in a *nuclear reactor per unit time to the number of neutrons lost by absorption or leakage in the same time. If $k = 1$, the reactor is said to be *critical*. If $k > 1$ it is *supercritical* and if $k < 1$ it is *subcritical*. See also critical reaction.

multiplier A fixed resistance used with a voltmeter, usually a *moving-coil instrument, to vary its range.

Many voltmeters are provided with a series of multipliers from which the appropriate value can be selected. If the original instrument requires i amperes for full-scale deflection and the resistance of the moving coil is r ohms, the value R of the resistance of the multiplier required to give a full-scale deflection when a voltage V is applied across the terminals is given by $R = V/i - r$.

multivibrator An electronic *oscillator consisting of two active devices, usually transistors, interconnected in an electrical network. The purpose of the device is to generate a continuous square wave with which to store information in binary form in a logic circuit. This is achieved by applying a portion of the output voltage or current of each active device to the input of the other with the appropriate magnitude and polarity, so that the devices are conducting alternately for controllable periods.

Mumetal The original trade name for a ferromagnetic alloy, containing 78% nickel, 17% iron, and 5% copper, that had a high *permeability and a low *coercive force. More modern versions also contain chromium and molybdenum. These alloys are used in some transformer cores and for shielding various devices from external magnetic fields.

Muntz metal A form of *brass containing 60% copper, 39% zinc, and small amounts of lead and iron. Stronger than alpha-brass, it is used for hot forgings, brazing rods, and large nuts and bolts. It is named after G. F. Muntz (1794–1857).

muon See lepton; elementary particles.

mutarotation Change of optical activity with time as a result of spontaneous chemical reaction.

mutual inductance See inductance.

myopia Short-sightedness. It results from the lens of the eye refracting the

parallel rays of light entering it to a focus in front of the retina generally because of an abnormally long eyeball. The condition is corrected by using diverging spectacle lenses to move the image back to the retina.

N

nadir The point opposite the *zenith on the *celestial sphere.

nand circuit *See* logic circuit.

nano- Symbol n. A prefix used in the metric system to denote 10^{-9}. For example, 10^{-9} second = 1 nanosecond (ns).

Napierian logarithm *See* logarithm.

natural abundance *See* abundance.

natural frequency 1. The frequency of the free oscillation of a system. **2.** The frequency at which resonance occurs in an electrical circuit.

natural logarithm *See* logarithm.

natural units A system of units, used principally in particle physics, in which all quantities that have dimensions involving length, mass, and time are given dimensions of a power of energy (usually expressed in electronvolts). This is equivalent to setting the rationalized *Planck constant and the speed of light both equal to unity. *See also* Gaussian units; geometrized units; Heaviside–Lorentz units; Planck units.

nautical mile A measure of distance used at sea. In the UK it is defined as 6080 feet but the international definition is 1852 metres. 1 international nautical mile is therefore equivalent to 1.15078 land (statute) miles.

near point The nearest point at which the human eye can focus an object. As the lens becomes harder with age, the extent to which accommodation can bring a near object into focus decreases. Therefore with advancing age the near point recedes – a condition known as *presbyopia.

nebula Originally a fixed, extended, and somewhat fuzzy white haze observed in the sky with a telescope. Many of these objects can now be resolved into clouds of individual stars and have been identified as *galaxies. They are still sometimes referred to as *extragalactic nebulae*. The *gaseous nebulae*, however, cannot be resolved into individual stars and consist, for the most part, of interstellar dust and gas. In some of these gaseous nebulae the gas atoms have been ionized by ultraviolet radiation from nearby stars and light is emitted as these ions interact with the free electrons in the gas. These are called *emission nebulae*. In the *dark nebulae*, there are no nearby stars and these objects are consequently dark; they can only be detected by what they obscure.

Néel temperature The temperature above which an antiferromagnetic substance becomes paramagnetic (*see* magnetism). The *susceptibility increases with temperature, reaching a maximum at the Néel temperature, after which it abruptly declines. The phenomenon was discovered around 1930 by L. E. F. Néel (1904–).

negative charge *See* charge.

negative feedback *See* feedback.

nematic crystal *See* liquid crystal.

neon lamp A small lamp consisting of a pair of electrodes, treated to emit electrons freely, sealed in a glass bulb containing neon gas at low pressure. When a minimum voltage of between 60 and 90 volts is applied across the electrodes, the kinetic energy of the electrons is sufficient to ionize the neon atoms around the cathode, causing the emission of a reddish light. With d.c. the glow is restricted to the cathode; with a.c. both electrodes act alternately as

cathodes and a glow appears to emanate from both electrodes. The device consumes a very low power and is widely used as an indicator light showing that a circuit is live.

neper A unit used to express a ratio of powers, currents, etc., used especially in telecommunications to denote the attenuation of an amplitude A_1 to an amplitude A_2 as N nepers, where

$$N = \ln(A_2/A_1).$$

1 neper = 8.686 decibels. The unit is named after John Napier (1550–1617), the inventor of natural logarithms.

neptunium Symbol Np. A radioactive metallic transuranic element belonging to the actinoids; a.n. 93; r.a.m. 237.0482. The most stable isotope, neptunium–237, has a half-life of 2.2×10^6 years and is produced in small quantities as a by-product in nuclear reactors. Other isotopes have mass numbers 229–236 and 238–241. The only other relatively long-lived isotope is neptunium–236 (half-life 5 $\times 10^3$ years). The element was first produced by McMillan and Abelson in 1940.

neptunium series *See* radioactive series.

Nernst effect An effect in which a temperature gradient along an electric conductor or semiconductor placed in a perpendicular magnetic field, causes a potential difference to develop in the third perpendicular direction between opposite edges of the conductor. This effect, an analogue of the *Hall effect, was discovered in 1886 by Walter Nernst (1864–1941).

Nernst heat theorem A statement of the third law of *thermodynamics in a restricted form: if a chemical change takes place between pure crystalline solids at *absolute zero there is no change of entropy.

Neumann's law The magnitude of an electromagnetically induced e.m.f. (E) is given by $E = -d\Phi/dt$, where Φ is the magnetic flux. This is a quantitative statement of *Faraday's second law of electromagnetic induction and is sometimes known as the Faraday–Neumann law.

neutrino A *lepton (*see also* elementary particles) that exists in three forms, one in association with the electron, one with the muon, and one with the tau particle. Each form has its own antiparticle. The neutrino, which was postulated in 1931 to account for the 'missing' energy in *beta decay, was identified tentatively in 1953 and, more definitely, in 1956. Neutrinos have no charge, are thought to have zero rest mass, and travel at the speed of light. In some *grand unified theories they are predicted to have nonzero mass, but there is no conclusive evidence for this.

neutron A neutral hadron (*see* elementary particles) that is stable in the atomic nucleus but decays into a proton, an electron, and an antineutrino with a mean life of 12 minutes outside the nucleus. Its rest mass (symbol m_n) is slightly greater than that of the proton, being 1.674 9286 (10) $\times 10^{-27}$ kg. Neutrons occur in all atomic nuclei except normal hydrogen. The neutron was first reported in 1932 by James Chadwick (1891–1974).

neutron diffraction The scattering of neutrons by atoms in solids, liquids, or gases. This process has given rise to a technique, analogous to *X-ray diffraction techniques, using a flux of thermal neutrons from a nuclear reactor to study solid-state phenomena. Thermal neutrons have average kinetic energies of about 0.025 eV (4 $\times 10^{-21}$ J) giving them an equivalent wavelength of about 0.1 nanometre, which is suitable for the study of interatomic interference. There are two types of interaction in the scattering of neutrons by atoms: one is the interaction between the neutrons

and the atomic nucleus, the other is the interaction between the *magnetic moments of the neutrons and the spin and orbital magnetic moments of the atoms. The latter interaction has provided valuable information on antiferromagnetic and ferrimagnetic materials (*see* magnetism). Interaction with the atomic nucleus gives diffraction patterns that complement those from X-rays. X-rays, which interact with the extranuclear electrons, are not suitable for investigating light elements (e.g. hydrogen), whereas neutrons do give diffraction patterns from such atoms because they interact with nuclei.

neutron drip *See* neutron star.

neutron excess *See* isotopic number.

neutron number Symbol N. The number of neutrons in an atomic nucleus of a particular nuclide. It is equal to the difference between the *nucleon number and the *atomic number.

neutron star A compact stellar object that is supported against collapse under self-gravity by the *degeneracy pressure of the neutrons of which it is primarily composed. Neutron stars are believed to be formed as the end products of the evolution of stars of mass greater than a few (4–10) solar masses. The core of the evolved star collapses and (assuming that its mass is greater than the *Chandrasekhar limit for a *white dwarf), at the very high densities involved (about 10^{14} kg m^{-3}), electrons react with protons in atomic nuclei to produce neutrons. The neutron-rich nuclei thus formed release free neutrons in a process known as *neutron drip*. The density increases to about 10^{17} kg m^{-3}, at which most of the electrons and protons have been converted to a *degenerate gas of neutrons and the atomic nuclei have lost their separate identities. If the mass of the core exceeds the Chandrasekhar limit for a neutron star,

then further collapse will occur, leading to the formation of a *black hole. *Pulsars are believed to be rapidly rotating magnetized neutron stars and many X-ray sources are thought to be neutron stars in binary systems with another star, from which material is drawn into an accretion disc. This material, heated to a very high temperature, emits radiation in the X-ray region.

neutron temperature A concept used to express the energies of neutrons that are in thermal equilibrium with their surroundings, assuming that they behave like a monatomic gas. The neutron temperature T, on the Kelvin scale, is given by $T = 2E/3k$, where E is average neutron energy and k the *Boltzmann constant.

newton Symbol N. The *SI unit of force, being the force required to give a mass of one kilogram an acceleration of 1 m s^{-2}. It is named after Sir Isaac Newton (1642–1727).

Newtonian fluid A fluid in which the velocity gradient is directly proportional to the shear stress. If two flat plates of area A are separated by a layer of fluid of thickness d and move relative to each other at a velocity v, then the rate of shear is v/d and the shear stress is F/A, where F is the force applied to each (see illustration). For a Newtonian fluid $F/A = \mu v/d$, where μ is the constant of proportionality and is called the Newtonian *viscosity. Many liquids are Newtonian fluids over a wide range of temperatures and pressures. However, some are not; these are called *non-Newtonian fluids*. In such fluids there is a departure from the

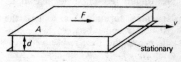

Newtonian fluid

simple Newtonian relationships. For example, in some liquids the viscosity increases as the velocity gradient increases, i.e. the faster the liquid moves the more viscous it becomes. Such liquids are said to be *dilatant* and the phenomenon they exhibit is called *dilatancy*. It occurs in some pastes and suspensions. More common, however, is the opposite effect in which the viscosity depends not only on the velocity gradient but also on the time for which it has been applied. These liquids are said to exhibit *thixotropy*. The faster a *thixotropic liquid* moves the less viscous it becomes. This property is used in nondrip paints (which are more viscous on the brush than on the wall) and in lubricating oils (which become thinner when the parts they are lubricating start to move). Another example is the non-Newtonian flow of macromolecules in solution or in polymer melts. In this case the shearing force F is not parallel to the shear planes and the linear relationship does not apply. In general, the many types of non-Newtonian fluid are somewhat complicated and no theory has been developed to accommodate them fully.

Newtonian mechanics The system of *mechanics that relies on *Newton's laws of motion. Newtonian mechanics is applicable to bodies moving at speeds relative to the observer that are small compared to the speed of light. Bodies moving at speeds comparable to the speed of light require an approach based on *relativistic mechanics, in which the mass of a body changes with its speed.

Newtonian telescope *See* telescope.

Newton's formula For a lens, the distances p and q between two conjugate points and their respective foci is given by $pq = f^2$, where f is the focal length of the lens.

Newton's law of cooling The rate at which a body loses heat is proportional to the difference in temperature between the body and the surroundings. It is an empirical law that is only true for substantial temperature differences if the heat loss is by forced convection or conduction.

Newton's law of gravitation There is a force of attraction between any two massive particles in the universe. For any two point masses m_1 and m_2, separated by a distance d, the force of attraction F is given by $F = m_1 m_2 G / d^2$, where G is the *gravitational constant. Real bodies having spherical symmetry act as point masses positioned at their centres of mass.

Newton's laws of motion The three laws of motion on which *Newtonian mechanics is based. (1) A body continues in a state of rest or uniform motion in a straight line unless it is acted upon by external forces. (2) The rate of change of momentum of a moving body is proportional to and in the same direction as the force acting on it, i.e. $F = \mathrm{d}(mv)/\mathrm{d}t$, where F is the applied force, v is the velocity of the body, and m its mass. If the mass remains constant, $F = m\mathrm{d}v/\mathrm{d}t$ or $F = ma$, where a is the acceleration. (3) If one body exerts a force on another, there is an equal and opposite force, called a *reaction*, exerted on the first body by the second.

Newton's rings 1. (in optics) *Interference fringes formed by placing a slightly convex lens on a flat glass plate. If monochromatic light is reflected by the two close surfaces into the observer's eye at a suitable angle, the point of contact of the lens is seen as a dark spot surrounded by a series of bright and dark rings. The radius of the nth dark ring is given by $r_n = \sqrt{nR\lambda}$, where λ is the wavelength and R is the radius of curvature of the lens. The phenomenon is

used in the quality testing of lens surfaces. With white light, coloured rings are formed. **2.** (in photography) The irregular patterns produced by thin film interference between a projected transparency and its cover glass.

Nichrome Trade name for a group of nickel–chromium alloys used for wire in heating elements as they possess good resistance to oxidation and have a high resistivity. Typical is Nichrome V containing 80% nickel and 19.5% chromium, the balance consisting of manganese, silicon, and carbon.

nickel–iron accumulator (Edison cell; NIFE cell) A *secondary cell devised by Thomas Edison (1847–1931) having a positive plate of nickel oxide and a negative plate of iron both immersed in an electrolyte of potassium hydroxide. The reaction on discharge is

$$2NiOOH.H_2O + Fe \rightarrow 2Ni(OH)_2 + Fe(OH)_2,$$

the reverse occurring during charging. Each cell gives an e.m.f. of about 1.2 volts and produces about 100 kJ per kilogram during each discharge. *Compare* lead–acid accumulator.

nickel silver *See* German silver.

Nicol prism A device for producing *plane-polarized light. It consists of two pieces of calcite cut with a 68° angle and stuck together with Canada balsam. The extraordinary ray (*see* double refraction) passes through the prism while the ordinary ray suffers total internal reflection at the interface between the two crystals, as the refractive index of the calcite is 1.66 for the ordinary ray and that of the Canada balsam is 1.53. Modifications of the prism using different shapes and cements are used for special purposes. It was devised in 1828 by William Nicol (1768–1851).

NIFE cell *See* nickel–iron accumulator.

nit A unit of *luminance equal to one *candela per square metre.

NMR *See* nuclear magnetic resonance.

nobelium Symbol No. A radioactive metallic transuranic element belonging to the actinoids; a.n. 102; mass number of most stable element 254 (half-life 55 seconds). Seven isotopes are known. The element was first identified with certainty by A. Ghiorso and G. T. Seaborg in 1966. The alternative name *unnilbium* has been proposed.

nodal points Two points on the axis of a system of lenses; if the incident ray passes through one, the emergent ray will pass through the other.

node 1. (in physics) A point of minimum disturbance in a *stationary-wave system. **2.** (in astronomy) Either of two points at which the orbit of a celestial body intersects a reference plane, usually the plane of the *ecliptic or the celestial equator (*see* celestial sphere).

noise 1. Any undesired sound. It is measured on a *decibel scale ranging from the threshold of hearing (0 dB) to the threshold of pain (130 dB). Between these limits a whisper registers about 20 dB, heavy urban traffic about 90 dB, and a heavy hammer on steel plate about 110 dB. A high noise level (industrial or from overamplified music, for example) can cause permanent hearing impairment. **2.** Any unwanted disturbance within a useful frequency band in a communication channel.

nomogram A graph consisting of three lines, each with its own scale, each line representing the values of a variable over a specified range. A ruler laid between two points on two of the lines enables the value of the third variable to be read off the third line.

non-Euclidean geometry A type of geometry that does not comply with

the basic postulates of *Euclidean geometry, particularly a form of geometry that does not accept Euclid's postulate that only one straight line can be drawn through a point in space parallel to a given straight line. Several types of non-Euclidean geometry exist.

non-Newtonian fluid See Newtonian fluid.

nonpolar compound A compound that has covalent molecules with no permanent dipole moment. Examples of nonpolar compounds are methane and benzene.

nonrelativistic quantum theory See quantum theory.

normal 1. (in mathematics) A line drawn at right angles to a surface. 2. (in chemistry) Having a concentration of one gram equivalent per dm^3.

normalizing The process of heating steel to above an appropriate critical temperature followed by cooling in still air. The process promotes the formation of a uniform internal structure and the elimination of internal stress.

not circuit See logic circuit.

note 1. A musical sound of specified pitch. 2. A representation of such a sound in a musical score. Such a representation has a specified duration as well as a specified pitch.

nova A star that, over a period of only a few days, becomes 10^3–10^4 times brighter than it was. Some 10–15 such events occur in the Milky Way each year. Novae are believed to be close *binaries, one component of which is usually a *white dwarf and the other a *red giant. Matter is transferred from the red giant to the white dwarf, on whose surface it accumulates, eventually leading to a thermonuclear explosion. See also supernova.

N.T.P. See s.t.p.

n-type conductivity See semiconductor; transistor.

nuclear battery A single cell, or battery of cells, in which the energy of particles emitted from the atomic nucleus is converted internally into electrical energy. In the high-voltage type, a beta-emitter, such as strontium–90, krypton–85, or tritium, is sealed into a shielded glass vessel, the electrons being collected on an electrode that is separated from the emitter by a vacuum or by a solid dielectric. A typical cell delivers some 160 picoamperes at a voltage proportional to the load resistance. It can be used to maintain the voltage of a charged capacitor. Of greater use, especially in space technology, are the various types of low-voltage nuclear batteries. Typical is the gas-ionization device in which a beta-emitter ionizes a gas in an electric field. Each beta-particle produces about 200 ions, thus multiplying the current. The electric field is obtained by the contact potential difference between two electrodes, such as lead dioxide and magnesium. Such a cell, containing argon and tritium, gives about 1.6 nanoamperes at 1.5 volts. Other types use light from a phosphor receiving the beta-particles to operate photocells or heat from the nuclear reaction to operate a thermopile.

nuclear energy Energy obtained as a result of *nuclear fission or *nuclear fusion. The nuclear fission of one uranium atom yields about 3.2×10^{-11} joule, whereas the combustion of one carbon atom yields about 6.4×10^{-19} joule. Mass for mass, uranium yields about 2 500 000 times more energy by fission than carbon does by combustion. The nuclear fusion of deuterium to form helium releases about 400 times as much energy as the fission of uranium (on a mass basis).

nuclear fission A nuclear reaction in which a heavy nucleus (such as uranium) splits into two parts (*fission*

products), which subsequently emit either two or three neutrons, releasing a quantity of energy equivalent to the difference between the rest mass of the neutrons and the fission products and that of the original nucleus. Fission may occur spontaneously or as a result of irradiation by neutrons. For example, the fission of a uranium–235 nucleus by a *slow neutron may proceed thus:

$$^{235}U + n \rightarrow {}^{148}La + {}^{85}Br + 3n$$

The energy released is approximately 3×10^{-11} J per ^{235}U nucleus. For 1 kg of ^{235}U this is equivalent to 20 000 megawatt-hours – the amount of energy produced by the combustion of 3×10^6 tonnes of coal. Nuclear fission is the process used in *nuclear reactors and atom bombs (*see* nuclear weapons).

nuclear force A strong attractive force between *nucleons in the atomic nucleus that holds the nucleus together. At close range (up to about 2×10^{-15} metre) these forces are some 100 times stronger than electromagnetic forces. *See* fundamental interactions.

nuclear fuel A substance that will sustain a fission chain reaction so that it can be used as a source of *nuclear energy. The *fissile isotopes are uranium–235, uranium–233, plutonium–241, and plutonium–239. The first occurs in nature as 1 part in 140 of natural uranium, the others have to be made artificially. ^{233}U is produced when thorium–232 captures a neutron and ^{239}Pu is produced by neutron capture in ^{238}U. ^{232}Th and ^{238}U are called *fertile isotopes.

nuclear fusion A type of *nuclear reaction in which atomic nuclei of low atomic number fuse to form a heavier nucleus with the release of large amounts of energy. In *nuclear fission reactions a neutron is used to break up a large nucleus, but in nuclear fusion the two reacting nuclei themselves have to be brought into

collision. As both nuclei are positively charged there is a strong repulsive force between them, which can only be overcome if the reacting nuclei have very high kinetic energies. These high kinetic energies imply temperatures of the order of 10^8 K. As the kinetic energy required increases with the nuclear charge (i.e. atomic number), reactions involving low atomic-number nuclei are the easiest to produce. At these elevated temperatures, however, fusion reactions are self-sustaining; the reactants at these temperatures are in the form of a *plasma (i.e. nuclei and free electrons) with the nuclei possessing sufficient energy to overcome electrostatic repulsion forces. The fusion bomb (*see* nuclear weapons) and the stars generate energy in this way. It is hoped that the method will be harnessed in the *thermonuclear reactor as a source of energy for man's use.

Typical fusion reactions with the energy release in joules are:

$$D + D = T + p + 6.4 \times 10^{-13} \text{ J}$$
$$T + D = {}^4He + n + 28.2 \times 10^{-13} \text{ J}$$
$$^6Li + D = 2{}^4He + 35.8 \times 10^{-13} \text{ J}$$

By comparison the formation of a water molecule from hydrogen and oxygen is accompanied by the release of 1.5×10^{-19} J.

A large amount of work is currently being done on *cold fusion*; i.e. fusion that can occur at lower temperatures than those necessary to overcome the electrostatic repulsion between nuclei. The most productive approach is *meson-catalysed fusion*, in which the deuterium atoms have their electrons replaced by negative muons to give 'muonic atoms' of deuterium. The muon is 207 times heavier than the electron, so the muonic deuterium atom is much smaller and is able to approach another deuterium atom more closely, allowing nuclear fusion to occur. The muon is released to form another muonic atom, and the process continues. The limiting factor

is the short lifetime of the muon, which restricts the number of fusion reactions it can catalyse. *See also* plasma physics.

nuclear isomerism A condition in which atomic nuclei with the same number of neutrons and protons have different lifetimes. This occurs when nuclei exist in different unstable quantum states, from which they decay to lower excited states or to the ground state, with the emission of gamma-ray photons. If the lifetime of a particular excited state is unusually long it is said to be isomeric, although there is no fixed limit separating isomeric decays from normal decays.

nuclear magnetic resonance (NMR) The absorption of electromagnetic radiation at a suitable precise frequency by a nucleus with a nonzero magnetic moment in an external magnetic field. The phenomenon occurs if the nucleus has nonzero *spin, in which case it behaves as a small magnet. In an external magnetic field, the nucleus's magnetic moment vector precesses about the field direction but only certain orientations are allowed by quantum rules. Thus, for hydrogen (spin of $\frac{1}{2}$) there are two possible states in the presence of a field, each with a slightly different energy. Nuclear magnetic resonance is the absorption of radiation at a photon energy equal to the difference between these levels, causing a transition from a lower to a higher energy state. For practical purposes, the difference in energy levels is small and the radiation is in the radiofrequency region of the electromagnetic spectrum. It depends on the field strength.

NMR can be used for the accurate determination of nuclear moments. It can also be used in a sensitive form of magnetometer to measure magnetic fields. In medicine, NMR *tomography is being developed, in which images of tissue are produced by magnetic-resonance techniques.

The main application of NMR is as a technique for chemical analysis and structure determination, known as *NMR spectroscopy*. It depends on the fact that the electrons in a molecule shield the nucleus to some extent from the field, causing different atoms to absorb at slightly different frequencies (or at slightly different fields for a fixed frequency). Such effects are known as *chemical shifts*. In an NMR spectrometer, the sample is subjected to a strong field, which can be varied in a controlled way over a small region. It is irradiated with radiation at a fixed frequency, and a detector monitors the field at the sample. As the field changes, absorption corresponding to transitions occurs at certain values, and this causes oscillations in the field, which induce a signal in the detector. The most common nucleus studied is ^{1}H. For instance, an NMR spectrum of ethanol (CH_3CH_2OH) has three peaks in the ratio 3:2:1, corresponding to the three different hydrogen-atom environments. The peaks also have a fine structure caused by interaction between spins in the molecule. Other nuclei can also be used for NMR spectroscopy (e.g. ^{13}C, ^{14}N, ^{19}F) although these generally have lower magnetic moment and natural abundance than hydrogen. *See also* electron spin resonance.

nuclear moment A property of atomic nuclei in which lack of spherical symmetry of the nuclear charge gives rise to electric moments and the intrinsic spin and rotational motion of the component nucleons give rise to magnetic moments.

nuclear physics The physics of atomic nuclei and their interactions, with particular reference to the generation of *nuclear energy.

nuclear power Electric power or motive power generated by a *nuclear reactor.

nuclear reaction Any reaction in which there is a change to an atomic nucleus. This may be a natural spontaneous disintegration or an artificial bombardment of a nucleus with an energetic particle, as in a *nuclear reactor. Nuclear reactions are commonly represented by enclosing within a bracket the symbols for the incoming and outgoing particles; the initial nuclide is shown before the bracket and the final nuclide after it. For example, the reaction:

$$^{12}C + {}^{2}H \rightarrow {}^{13}N + {}^{1}n$$

is shown as $^{12}C(d,n)^{13}N$, where d is the symbol for a deuteron.

nuclear reactor A device in which a *nuclear fission *chain reaction is sustained and controlled in order to produce *nuclear energy, radioisotopes, or new nuclides. The fuels available for use in a fission reactor are uranium–235, uranium–233, and plutonium–239; only the first occurs in nature (as 1 part in 140 of natural uranium), the others have to be produced artificially (*see* nuclear fuel). When a uranium–235 nucleus is made to undergo fission by the impact of a neutron it breaks into two roughly equal fragments, which release either two or three very high-energy neutrons. These *fast neutrons need to be slowed down to increase the probability that they will cause further fissions of ^{235}U nuclei and thus sustain the chain reaction. This slowing down process occurs naturally to a certain extent when the neutrons collide with other nuclei; unfortunately, however, the predominant uranium isotope, ^{238}U, absorbs fast neutrons to such an extent that in natural uranium the fission reaction is not self-sustaining. In order to create a controlled self-sustaining chain reaction it is necessary either to slow down the neutrons (using a *moderator in a *thermal reactor*) to greatly reduce the number absorbed by ^{238}U, or to reduce the predominance of ^{238}U in natural uranium by enriching it with more ^{235}U than it normally contains. In a *fast reactor* the fuel used is enriched uranium and no moderator is employed.

In thermal reactors, neutrons are slowed down by collisions with light moderator atoms (such as graphite, deuterium, or beryllium); they are then in thermal equilibrium with the surrounding material and are known as *thermal neutrons*. In a *heterogeneous thermal reactor* the fuel and moderator are in separate solid and liquid phases (e.g. solid uranium fuel and a heavy water moderator). In the *homogeneous thermal reactor* the fuel and moderator are mixed together, for example in a solution, molten dispersion, slurry, or suspension.

In the reactor *core* the *fuel elements* encase the fuel; in a heterogeneous reactor the fuel elements may fit into a lattice that also contains the moderator. The progress of the reaction is controlled by *control rods, which when lowered into the core absorb neutrons and so slow down or stop the chain reaction. The heat produced by the nuclear reaction in the core is used to generate electricity by the same means as in a conventional power station, i.e. by raising steam to drive a steam turbine that turns a generator. The heat is transferred to the steam-raising boiler or heat-exchanger by the *coolant. Water is frequently used as the coolant; in the case of the *boiling-water reactor* (BWR) and the *pressurized-water reactor* (PWR) water is both coolant and moderator. In the BWR the primary coolant drives the turbine; in the PWR the primary coolant raises steam in a secondary circuit for driving the turbine. In the *gas-cooled reactor* the coolant is a gas, usually carbon dioxide with an outlet temperature of about 350°C, or 600°C in

nuclear waste

the case of the *advanced gas-cooled reactor* (AGR).

In fast reactors, in which there is no moderator, the temperature is higher and a liquid-metal coolant is used, usually liquid sodium. Some fast reactors are used as converters or breeders. A *converter reactor* is one that converts *fertile material (such as ^{238}U) into *fissile material (such as ^{239}Pu). A *breeder reactor* produces the same fissile material as it uses. For example, a *fast breeder reactor* using uranium enriched with ^{239}Pu as the fuel can produce more ^{239}Pu than it uses by converting ^{238}U to ^{239}Pu. *See also* thermonuclear reactor.

nuclear waste *See* radioactive waste.

nuclear weapons Weapons in which an explosion is caused by *nuclear fission, *nuclear fusion, or a combination of both. In the fission bomb (*atomic bomb* or *A-bomb*) two subcritical masses (*see* critical mass) of a *fissile material (uranium–235 or plutonium–239) are brought together by a chemical explosion to produce one supercritical mass. The resulting nuclear explosion is typically in the *kiloton range with temperatures of the order 10^8 K being reached. The fusion bomb (*thermonuclear weapon, hydrogen bomb*, or *H-bomb*) relies on a nuclear-fusion reaction, which becomes self-sustaining at a critical temperature of about 35×10^6 K. This is achieved by means of an inner fission bomb, which is surrounded by a hydrogenous material, such as heavy hydrogen (deuterium) or lithium deuteride. The *megaton explosion produced in such a thermonuclear reaction has not yet been used in war, the largest explosion so far produced being the 58 megaton weapon exploded in the Arctic by the USSR in 1961.

nucleon A *proton or a *neutron.

nucleonics The technological aspects of *nuclear physics, including the design of nuclear reactors, devices to produce and detect radiation, and nuclear transport systems. It is also concerned with the technology of *radioactive waste disposal and with radioisotopes.

nucleon number (mass number) Symbol A. The number of *nucleons in an atomic nucleus of a particular nuclide.

nucleus (of atom) The central core of an atom that contains most of its mass. It is positively charged and consists of one or more nucleons (protons or neutrons). The positive charge of the nucleus is determined by the number of protons it contains (*see* atomic number) and in the neutral atom this is balanced by an equal number of electrons, which move around the nucleus. The simplest nucleus is the hydrogen nucleus, consisting of one proton only. All other nuclei also contain one or more neutrons. The neutrons contribute to the atomic mass (*see* nucleon number) but not to the nuclear charge. The most massive nucleus that occurs in nature is uranium–238, containing 92 protons and 146 neutrons. The symbol used for this *nuclide is $^{238}_{92}$U, the upper figure being the nucleon number and the lower figure the atomic number. In all nuclei the nucleon number (A) is equal to the sum of the atomic number (Z) and the neutron number (N), i.e. $A = Z + N$.

nuclide A type of atom as characterized by its *atomic number and its *neutron number. An *isotope refers to a member of a series of different atoms that have the same atomic number but different neutron numbers (e.g. uranium–238 and uranium–235 are isotopes of uranium), whereas a nuclide refers only to a particular nuclear species (e.g. the nuclides uranium–235 and plutonium–239 are fissile). The term is also used for a type of nucleus.

null method A method of making a measurement in which the quantity to be measured is balanced by another similar reading by adjusting the instrument to read zero (*see* Wheatstone bridge).

nutation An irregular periodic oscillation of the earth's poles. It causes an irregularity of the precessional circle traced by the celestial poles and results from the varying distances and relative directions of the sun and the moon.

O

objective The *lens or system of lenses nearest to the object being examined through an optical instrument.

occlusion 1. The trapping of small pockets of liquid in a crystal during crystallization. **2.** The absorption of a gas by a solid such that atoms or molecules of the gas occupy interstitial positions in the solid lattice. Palladium, for example, can occlude hydrogen.

occultation The disappearance of a star, planet, or other celestial body behind the moon or another planet, while it is being observed. A solar *eclipse is a form of occultation.

octane number A number that provides a measure of the ability of a fuel to resist *knocking when it is burnt in a spark-ignition engine. It is the percentage by volume of iso-octane (C_8H_{18}; 2,2,4-trimethylpentane) in a blend with normal heptane (C_7H_{16}) that matches the knocking behaviour of the fuel being tested in a single cylinder four-stroke engine of standard design. *Compare* cetane number.

octave The interval between two musical notes that have fundamental frequencies in the ratio 2:1; the word describes the interval in terms of the eight notes of the diatonic scale.

octet A stable group of eight electrons in the outer shell of an atom (as in an atom of an inert gas).

ocular *See* eyepiece.

odd–even nucleus An atomic nucleus containing an odd number of protons and an even number of neutrons.

odd–odd nucleus An atomic nucleus containing an odd number of protons and an odd number of neutrons.

oersted Symbol Oe. The unit of magnetic field strength in the *c.g.s. electromagnetic system. A field has a strength of one oersted if it exerts a force of one dyne on a unit magnetic pole placed in it. It is equivalent to $10^3/4\pi$ A m^{-1}. The unit was named after Hans Christian Oersted (1777–1851).

ohm Symbol Ω. The derived *SI unit of electrical resistance, being the resistance between two points on a conductor when a constant potential difference of one volt, applied between these points, produces a current of one ampere in the conductor. The former *international ohm* (sometimes called the 'mercury ohm') was defined in terms of the resistance of a column of mercury. The unit is named after Georg Ohm (1787–1854).

ohmmeter Any direct-reading instrument for measuring the value of a resistance in ohms. The instrument commonly used is a *multimeter capable of measuring also both currents and voltages. To measure resistance a dry cell and resistor are switched in series with the moving coil *galvanometer and the unknown resistance is connected across the instrument's terminals. The value of the resistance is then read off an ohms scale. Such instruments are increasingly being replaced by electronic digital multimeters.

Ohm's law The ratio of the potential difference between the ends of a conductor to the current flowing through it is constant. This constant is the *resistance of the conductor, i.e. $V = IR$, where V is the potential difference in volts, I is the current in amperes, and R is the resistance in ohms. The law was discovered in 1827 by Georg Ohm. Most materials do not obey this simple linear law; those that do are said to be *ohmic* but remain so only if physical conditions, such as temperature, remain constant. Metals are the most accurately ohmic conductors.

oil-immersion lens *See* immersion objective.

Olbers' paradox If the universe is infinite, uniform, and unchanging the sky at night would be bright, as in whatever direction one looked one would eventually see a star. The number of stars would increase in proportion to the square of the distance from the earth; the intensity of light reaching the earth from a given star is inversely proportional to the square of the distance. Consequently, the whole sky should be about as bright as the sun. The paradox, that this is not the case, was stated by Heinrich Olbers (1758–1840) in 1826. (It had been discussed earlier, in 1744, by J. P. L. Chesaux.) The paradox is resolved by the fact that, according to the *big-bang theory, the universe is not infinite, not uniform, and not unchanging. For instance, light from the most distant galaxies displays an extreme *redshift and ceases to be visible.

opacity The extent to which a medium is opaque to electromagnetic radiation, especially to light. It is the reciprocal of the *transmittance. A medium that is opaque to X-rays and gamma rays is said to be *radioopaque*.

open cluster (galactic cluster) *See* star cluster.

open-hearth process A traditional method for manufacturing steel by heating together scrap, pig iron, hot metal, etc., in a refractory-lined shallow open furnace heated by burning producer gas in air.

opera glasses *See* binoculars.

operator A mathematical symbol indicating that a specified operation should be carried out. For example, the operator $\sqrt{}$ in $\sqrt{x}$ indicates that the square root of x should be taken; the operator d/dx in dy/dx indicates that y should be differentiated with respect to x, etc.

opposition The moment at which a planet having its orbit outside that of the earth is in a line with the earth and the sun. When a planet is in opposition it can be observed during the night and is near to its closest point to the earth; it is therefore a favourable opportunity for observation.

optical activity The ability of certain substances to rotate the plane of plane-polarized light as it passes through a crystal, liquid, or solution. It occurs when the molecules of the substance are asymmetric, so that they can exist in two different structural forms each being a mirror image of the other. The two forms are *optical isomers* or *enantiomers*. The existence of such forms is also known as *enantiomorphism* (the mirror images being *enantiomorphs*). One form will rotate the light in one direction and the other will rotate it by an equal amount in the other. The two possible forms are described as *dextrorotatory or *laevorotatory according to the direction of rotation, and prefixes *d*- and *l*-, respectively, are used to designate the isomer, as in *d*-tartaric and *l*-tartaric acids (see formulae). An equimolar mixture of the two forms is not optically active. It is called a *racemic mixture* (or *racemate*) and designated by *dl*-. The alternative prefixes (+)-, (–)-, and (±)-, cor-

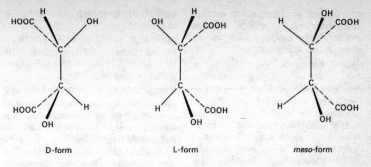

D-form   L-form   *meso*-form

Isomers of tartaric acid

responding to *d-*, *l-*, and *dl-*, respectively, are preferred and increasingly used. In addition, certain molecules can have a *meso form* in which one part of the molecule is a mirror image of the other. Such molecules are not optically active.

Molecules that show optical activity have no plane of symmetry. The commonest case of this is in organic compounds in which a carbon atom is linked to four different groups. An atom of this type is said to be a *chiral centre*. Asymmetric molecules showing optical activity can also occur in inorganic compounds. For example, an octahedral complex in which the central ion coordinates to eight different ligands would be optically active. Many naturally occurring compounds show optical isomerism and usually only one isomer occurs naturally. For instance, glucose is found in the dextrorotatory form. The other isomer, l- or (−)-glucose, can be synthesized in the laboratory, but cannot be synthesized by living organisms.

optical axis (principal axis; optic axis) The line passing through the *optical centre and the centre of a curvature of a *lens or spherical *mirror.

optical centre The point at the geometrical centre of a *lens through which a ray of light entering the lens passes without deviation.

optical fibre A *waveguide through which light can be transmitted with very little leakage through the sidewalls. In the *step-index fibre* a pure glass core, with a diameter between 6 and 250 micrometres, is surrounded by a coaxial glass or plastic cladding of lower refractive index. The cladding is usually between 10 and 150 micrometres thick. The interface between core and cladding acts as a cylindrical mirror at which *total internal reflection of the transmitted light takes place. This structure enables a beam of light to travel through many kilometres of fibre. In the *graded-index fibre*, each layer of glass, from the fibre axis to its outer wall, has a slightly lower refractive index than the layer inside it. This arrangement also prevents light from escaping through the fibre walls by a combination of refraction and total internal reflection, and can be made to give the same transit time for rays at different angles.

Fibre-optic systems use optical fibres to transmit information, in the form of coded pulses or fragmented images (using bundles of fibres), from a source to a receiver. Over moderate distances they are used in telecommunications, for which purpose they are becoming competitive with electric

cables. They are also used in medical instruments (*fibrescopes*) to examine internal body cavities, such as the stomach and bladder.

optical flat A flat glass disc having very accurately polished surfaces so that the deviation from perfect flatness does not exceed (usually) 50 nanometres. It is used to test the flatness of such plane surfaces as gauge anvils by means of the *interference patterns formed when parallel beams of light pass through the flat and are reflected by the surface being inspected.

Surfaces are said to be *optically flat* if the deviation from perfect flatness is smaller than the wavelength of light.

optical glass Glass used in the manufacture of lenses, prisms, and other optical parts. It must be homogeneous and free from bubbles and strain. Optical *crown glass* may contain potassium or barium in place of the sodium of ordinary crown glass and has a refractive index in the range 1.51 to 1.54. *Flint glass* contains lead oxide and has a refractive index between 1.58 and 1.72. Higher refractive indexes are obtained by adding lanthanoid oxides to glasses; these are now known as lanthanum crowns and flints.

optical isomers *See* optical activity.

optical maser *See* laser.

optical microscope *See* microscope.

optical pumping *See* laser.

optical pyrometer *See* pyrometer.

optical rotary dispersion (ORD) The effect in which the amount of rotation of plane-polarized light by an optically active compound depends on the wavelength. A graph of rotation against wavelength has a characteristic shape showing peaks or troughs.

optical rotation Rotation of plane-polarized light. *See* optical activity.

optical telescope *See* telescope.

optical temperature *See* radiation temperature.

optic axis 1. The direction in a doubly refracting crystal in which light is transmitted without double refraction. **2.** *See* optical axis.

optics The study of *light and the phenomena associated with its generation, transmission, and detection. In a broader sense, optics includes all the phenomena associated with infrared and ultraviolet radiation. *Geometrical optics* assumes that light travels in straight lines and is concerned with the laws controlling the reflection and refraction of rays of light. *Physical optics* deals with phenomena that depend on the wave nature of light, e.g. diffraction, interference, and polarization.

orbit 1. (in astronomy) The path through space of one celestial body about another. For one small body moving in the gravitational field of another the orbit is a *conic section. Most such orbits are elliptical and most planetary orbits in the solar system are nearly circular. The shape and size of an elliptical orbit is specified by its *eccentricity, e, and the length of its semimajor axis, a. **2.** (in physics) The path of an electron as it travels round the nucleus of an atom. *See* orbital.

orbital A region in which an electron may be found in an atom or molecule. In the original *Bohr theory of the atom the electrons were assumed to move around the nucleus in circular orbits, but further advances in quantum mechanics led to the view that it is not possible to give a definite path for an electron. According to *wave mechanics, the electron has a certain probability of being in a given element of space. Thus for a hydrogen atom the electron can be anywhere from close to the nucleus to out in space but the maximum probability, in spherical shells of equal thickness, occurs in a shell with a

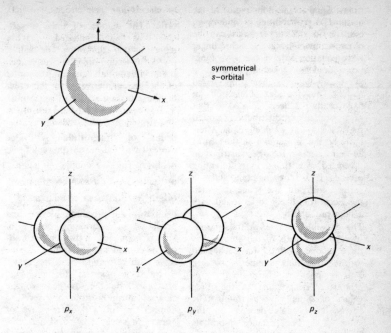

symmetrical
s−orbital

p_x

p_y

p_z

three equivalent p-orbitals, each having 2 lobes

Atomic orbitals

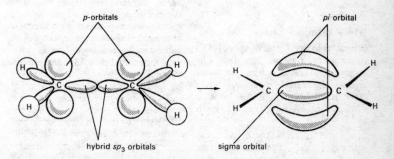

p-orbitals

pi orbital

hybrid sp₃ orbitals

sigma orbital

Molecular orbitals: formation of the double bond in ethene

Orbitals

radius equal to the Bohr radius of the atom. The probabilities of finding an electron in different regions can be obtained by solving the Schrödinger wave equation to give the wave function ψ, and the probability of location per unit volume is then proportional to $|\psi|^2$. Thus the idea of electrons in fixed orbits has been replaced by that of a probability distribution around the nucleus – an *atomic orbital*. Alternatively, the orbital can be thought of as an electric charge distribution (averaged over time). In representing orbitals it is convenient to take a surface enclosing the space in which the electron is likely to be found with a high probability.

The possible atomic orbitals correspond to subshells of the atom. Thus there is one *s*-orbital for each shell (orbital quantum number $l = 0$). This is spherical. There are three *p*-orbitals (corresponding to the three values of *l*) and five *d*-orbitals. The shapes of orbitals depend on the value of *l*. For instance, *p*-orbitals each have two lobes; most *d*-orbitals have four lobes.

In molecules, the valence electrons move under the influence of two nuclei (in a bond involving two atoms) and there are corresponding *molecular orbitals* for electrons. See illustration.

orbital quantum number *See* atom.

orbital velocity (orbital speed) The speed of a satellite, spacecraft, or other body travelling in an *orbit around the earth or around some other celestial body. If the orbit is elliptical, the orbital speed, v, is given by:

$$v = \sqrt{[gR^2(2/r - 1/a)]},$$

where g is the acceleration of free fall, R is the radius of the orbited body, a is the semimajor axis of the orbit, and r is the distance between the orbiting body and the centre of mass of the system. If the orbit is circular, $r = a$ and $v = \sqrt{(gR^2/r)}$.

or circuit *See* logic circuits.

order The number of times a variable is differentiated. dy/dx represents a first-order derivative, d^2y/dx^2 a second-order derivative, etc. In a *differential equation the order of the highest derivative is the order of the equation. $d^2y/dx^2 + 2dy/dx = 0$ is a second-order equation of the first degree. *See also* degree.

order of magnitude A value expressed to the nearest power of ten.

ordinary ray *See* double refraction.

ordinate *See* Cartesian coordinates.

origin *See* Cartesian coordinates.

oscillator An electronic device that produces an alternating output of known frequency. If the output voltage or current has the form of a sine wave with respect to time, the device is called a *sinusoidal* (or *harmonic*) *oscillator*. If the output voltage changes abruptly from one level to another (as in a *square wave or *sawtooth wave) it is called a *relaxation oscillator*. A harmonic oscillator consists of a frequency-determining circuit or device, such as a *resonant circuit, maintained in oscillation by a source of power that by positive feedback also makes up for the resistive losses. In some relaxation oscillators the circuit is arranged so that in each cycle energy is stored in a reactive element (a capacitor or inductor) and subsequently discharged over a different time interval. *See also* multivibrator.

oscilloscope *See* cathode-ray oscilloscope.

osmiridium A hard white naturally occurring alloy consisting principally of osmium (17–48%) and iridium (49%). It also contains small quantities of platinum, rhodium, and ruthenium. It is used for making small items subject to wear, e.g. electrical contacts or the tips of pen nibs.

osmometer *See* osmosis.

osmosis The passage of a solvent through a *semipermeable membrane* separating two solutions of different concentrations. A semipermeable membrane is one through which the molecules of a solvent can pass but the molecules of most solutes cannot. There is a thermodynamic tendency for solutions separated by such a membrane to become equal in concentration, the water (or other solvent) flowing from the weaker to the stronger solution. Osmosis will stop when the two solutions reach equal concentration, and can also be stopped by applying a pressure to the liquid on the stronger-solution side of the membrane. The pressure required to stop the flow from a pure solvent into a solution is a characteristic of the solution, and is called the *osmotic pressure* (symbol Π). Osmotic pressure depends only on the concentration of particles in the solution, not on their nature (i.e. it is a *colligative property). For a solution of n moles in volume V at thermodynamic temperature T, the osmotic pressure is given by $\Pi V = nRT$, where R is the gas constant. Osmotic-pressure measurements are used in finding the relative molecular masses of compounds, particularly macromolecules. A device used to measure osmotic pressure is called an *osmometer*.

The distribution of water in living organisms is dependent to a large extent on osmosis, water entering the cells through their membranes. A cell membrane is not truly semipermeable as it allows the passage of certain solute molecules; it is described as *differentially permeable*. Animals have evolved various means to counteract the effects of osmosis (*see* osmoregulation); in plant cells, excessive osmosis is prevented by the pressure exerted by the cell wall, which opposes the osmotic pressure.

osmotic pressure *See* osmosis.

Ostwald's dilution law An expression for the degree of dissociation of a weak electrolyte. For example, if a weak acid dissociates in water

$$HA \leftrightharpoons H^+ + A^-$$

the dissociation constant K_a is given by

$$K_a = \alpha^2 n/(1 - \alpha)V$$

where α is the degree of dissociation, n the initial amount of substance (before dissociation), and V the volume. If α is small compared with 1, then $\alpha^2 = KV/n$; i.e. the degree of dissociation is proportional to the square root of the dilution. The law was first put forward by W. Ostwald (1853–1932) to account for electrical conductivities of electrolyte solutions.

Otto engine *See* internal-combustion engine.

ounce 1. One sixteenth of a pound (avoirdupois), equal to 0.028 349 kg. **2.** Eight drachms (Troy), equal to 0.031 103 kg. **3. (fluid ounce)** Eight fluid drachms, equal to 0.028 413 dm³.

overdamped *See* damping.

overpotential A potential that must be applied in an electrolytic cell in addition to the theoretical potential required to liberate a given substance at an electrode. The value depends on the electrode material and on the current density. It occurs because of the significant activation energy for electron transfer at the electrodes, and is particularly important for the liberation of such gases as hydrogen and oxygen. For example, in the electrolysis of a solution of zinc ions, hydrogen ($E^\ominus = 0.00$ V) would be expected to be liberated at the cathode in preference to zinc ($E^\ominus = -0.76$ V). In fact, the high overpotential of hydrogen on zinc (about 1 V under suitable conditions) means that zinc can be deposited instead.

overtones *See* harmonic.

P

packing density 1. The number of devices (such as *logic circuits) or integrated circuits per unit area of a *silicon chip. **2.** The quantity of information stored in a specified space of a storage system associated with a computer, e.g. *bits per inch of magnetic tape.

packing fraction The algebraic difference between the relative atomic mass of an isotope and its mass number, divided by the mass number.

pair production The creation of an electron and a positron from a photon in a strong electric field, such as that surrounding an atomic nucleus. The electron and the positron each have a mass of about 9×10^{-31} kg, which is equivalent on the basis of the mass–energy equation ($E = mc^2$) to a total of 16×10^{-14} J. The frequency, ν, associated with a photon of this energy (according to $E = h\nu$) is 2.5×10^{20} Hz. Pair production thus requires photons of high quantum energy (Bremsstrahlung or gamma rays). Any excess energy is taken up as kinetic energy of the products.

palaeomagnetism The study of magnetism in rocks, which provides information on variations in the direction and intensity of the earth's magnetic field with time. During the formation of an igneous or sedimentary rock containing magnetic minerals the polarity of the earth's magnetic field at that time becomes 'frozen' into the rock. Studies of this fossil magnetism in samples of rocks have enabled the former positions of magnetic poles at various geological times to be located. It has also revealed that periodic reversals in the geomagnetic field have taken place (i.e. the N-pole becomes the S-pole and vice versa). This information has been important in plate tectonics in establishing the movements of lithospheric plates over the earth's surface. The magnetic reversals provided crucial evidence for the sea-floor spreading hypothesis proposed in the early 1960s.

para- Prefix denoting the form of diatomic molecules in which the nuclei have opposite spins, e.g. para-hydrogen. *Compare* ortho-.

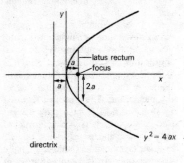

A parabola

parabola A *conic with eccentricity $e = 1$. It is the locus of a point that moves so that its distance from the *focus* is equal to its perpendicular distance from the *directrix*. A chord through the focus, perpendicular to the axis, is called the *latus rectum*. For a parabola with its vertex at the origin, lying symmetrically about the x-axis, the equation is $y^2 = 4ax$, where a is the distance from the vertex to the focus. The directrix is the line $x = -a$, and the latus rectum is $4a$. See illustration.

parabolic reflector (paraboloidal reflector) A reflector having a section that is a parabola. A concave parabolic reflector will reflect a parallel beam of radiation through its focus and, conversely, will produce a parallel beam if the source of the radiation is placed at its focus. Parabolic mirrors are used in reflecting optical *telescopes to collect the light and in some light sources that require a parallel beam of light. In radio

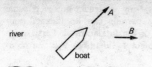

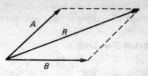

A is the velocity of the boat with respect to the water; B is the velocity of the water with respect to the bank

parallelogram of velocities. R is the resultant velocity of the boat with respect to the bank

Parallelogram of vectors

telescopes a dish aerial may also consist of a parabolic reflector.

paraboloid A solid formed by rotating a parabola about its axis of symmetry.

parallax 1. An apparent displacement of a distant object (with respect to a more distant background) when viewed from two different positions. If such an object is viewed from two points at either end of a base line, the angle between the lines joining the object to the ends of the base line is the *angle of parallax*. If the base line is the distance between the two eyes of an observer the angle is called the *binocular parallax*. 2. The angular displacement in the apparent position of a celestial body when observed from two different points. *Diurnal parallax* results from the earth's daily rotation, the celestial body being viewed from the surface of the earth rather than from its centre. *Annual parallax* is caused by the earth's motion round the sun, the celestial body being viewed from the earth rather than from the centre of the sun. *Secular parallax* is caused by the motion of the solar system relative to the fixed stars.

parallel circuits A circuit in which the circuit elements are connected so that the current divides between them. For resistors in parallel, the total resistance, R, is given by $1/R = 1/r_1 + 1/r_2 + 1/r_3 \ldots$, where r_1, r_2, and r_3 are the resistances of the individual elements. For capacitors in parallel, the total capacitance, C, is given by $C = c_1 + c_2 + c_3 \ldots$.

parallelepiped (parallelopiped) A solid with six faces, all of which are parallelograms.

parallelogram of forces *See* parallelogram of vectors.

parallelogram of vectors A method of determining the *resultant of two *vector quantities. The two vector quantities are represented by two adjacent sides of a parallelogram and the resultant is then the diagonal through their point of intersection. The magnitude and direction of the resultant is found by scale drawing or by trigonometry. The method is used for such vectors as forces (*parallelogram of forces*) and velocities (*parallelogram of velocities*). See illustration.

parallelogram of velocities *See* parallelogram of vectors.

paramagnetism *See* magnetism.

parametric equation An equation of a curve expressed in the form of the parameters that locate points on the curve. The parametric equations of a straight line are $x = a + bt, y = c + dt$. For a circle, they are $x = a\cos\theta, y = a\sin\theta$.

parasitic capture The absorption of a neutron by a nuclide that does not result in either fission or a useful artificial element.

paraxial ray A ray of light that falls on a reflecting or refracting surface close to and almost parallel to the axis. It is for such rays that simple

lens theory can be developed, by means of making small angle approximations.

parent *See* daughter.

parity Symbol *P*. The property of a *wave function that determines its behaviour when all its spatial coordinates are reversed in direction, i.e. when *x,y,z* are replaced by −*x*,−*y*,−*z*. If a wave function ψ satisfies the equation $\psi(x,y,z) = \psi(-x,-y,-z)$ it is said to have even parity, if it satisfies $\psi(x,y,z) = -\psi(-x,-y,-z)$ it has odd parity. In general, $\psi(x,y,z) = P\psi(-x,-y,-z)$, where *P* is a quantum number called parity that can have the value +1 or −1. The principle of *conservation of parity* (or *space-reflection symmetry*) would hold if all physical laws could be stated in a coordinate system independent of left- or right-handedness. If parity was conserved there would therefore be no fundamental way of distinguishing between left and right. In electromagnetic and strong interactions, parity is, in fact, conserved. In 1956, however, it was shown that parity is not conserved in weak interactions. In the beta decay of cobalt–60, for example, the electrons from the decay are emitted preferentially in a direction opposite to that of the cobalt spin. This experiment provides a fundamental distinction between left and right.

parsec A unit of length used to express astronomical distance. The distance at which the mean radius of the earth's orbit subtends an angle of one second of arc. One parsec is equal to 3.0857×10^{16} metres or 3.2616 light years.

partial A simple component of a complex tone. When a musical instrument produces a note, say, middle C, it will produce a complex tone in which the fundamental frequency is mixed with a number of partials. Some of these partials, for example, if the note is produced by bowing a taut string, will be *harmonics, i.e.

integral multiples of the fundamental. If the string is struck, however, some of the partials can be inexact multiples of the fundamental. Partials are not therefore identical with harmonics.

partial derivative The infinitesimal change in a function consisting of two or more variables when one of the variable changes and the others remain constant. If $z =$ f(x,y), $\partial z/\partial x$ is the partial derivative of z with respect to x, while y remains unchanged. A *partial differential equation*, such as *Laplace's equation, is an equation containing partial derivatives of a function.

partial eclipse *See* eclipse.

partial pressure *See* Dalton's law.

particle **1.** (in physics) One of the fundamental components of matter. *See* elementary particles. **2.** (in mechanics) A hypothetical body that has mass but no physical extension. As it is regarded as having no volume, a particle is incapable of rotation and therefore can only have translational motion. Thus a real body may often, for translational purposes, be regarded as a particle located at the body's centre of mass and having a mass equal to that of the whole body.

particle physics The study of *elementary particles.

partition If a substance is in contact with two different phases then, in general, it will have a different affinity for each phase. Part of the substance will be absorbed or dissolved by one and part by the other, the relative amounts depending on the relative affinities. The substance is said to be *partitioned* between the two phases. For example, if two immiscible liquids are taken and a third compound is shaken up with them, then an equilibrium is reached in which the concentration in one solvent differs from that in the other.

The ratio of the concentrations is the *partition coefficient* of the system. The *partition law* states that this ratio is a constant for given liquids.

partition coefficient *See* partition.

parton A pointlike, almost free, particle postulated as a component of nucleons. The parton model enabled the results of very high-energy experiments on nucleons to be understood. *See* quantum chromodynamics.

pascal The *SI unit of pressure equal to one newton per square metre.

Pascal's law In a confined fluid, externally applied pressure is transmitted uniformly in all directions. In a static fluid, force is transmitted at the speed of sound throughout the fluid and acts at right angles to any surface in or bounding the fluid. This principle is made use of in the hydraulic jack, the pneumatic tyre, and similar devices. The law was discovered in 1647 by Blaise Pascal (1623–62).

Paschen series *See* hydrogen spectrum.

passive device 1. An electronic component, such as a capacitor or resistor, that is incapable of amplification. **2.** An artificial *satellite that reflects an incoming signal without amplification. **3.** A solar-power device that makes use of an existing structure to collect and utilize solar energy without the use of pumps, fans, etc. **4.** A radar device that provides information for navigation, guidance, surveillance, etc., by receiving the microwave radiation emitted by a warm body or reflected by a body from some other source. Such a passive device emits no microwave energy itself and therefore does not disclose its position. *Compare* active device.

Pauli exclusion principle The quantum-mechanical principle, applying to fermions but not to bosons, that no two identical particles in a system, such as electrons in an atom or

quarks in a hadron, can possess an identical set of quantum numbers. It was first formulated by Wolfgang Pauli (1900–58) in 1925. The origin of the Pauli exclusion principle lies in the *spin–statistics theorem of relativistic quantum field theory.

p.d. (potential difference) *See* electric potential.

pearlite *See* steel.

Peltier effect The change in temperature produced at a junction between two dissimilar metals or semiconductors when an electric current passes through the junction. The direction of the current determines whether the temperature rises or falls. The first metals to be investigated were bismuth and copper; if the current flows from bismuth to copper the temperature rises. If the current is reversed the temperature falls. The effect was discovered in 1834 by J. C. A. Peltier (1785–1845) and has been used recently for small-scale refrigeration. *Compare* Seebeck effect.

pendulum Any rigid body that swings about a fixed point. The *ideal simple pendulum* consists of a bob of small mass oscillating back and forth through a small angle at the end of a string or wire of negligible mass. Such a device has a period $2\pi\sqrt{(l/g)}$, where l is the length of the string or wire and g is the *acceleration of free fall. This type of pendulum moves with *simple harmonic motion.

The *compound pendulum* consists of a rigid body swinging about a point within it. The period of such a pendulum is given by $T = 2\pi\sqrt{[(h^2 + k^2)/hg]}$, where k is the radius of gyration about an axis through the centre of mass and h is the distance from the pivot to the centre of mass. *See also* Kater's pendulum.

pentode A *thermionic valve with a *suppressor grid* between the anode and the screen grid of a tetrode. Its purpose is to suppress the loss of electrons from the anode as a result of

secondary emission. The suppressor grid is maintained at a negative potential relative to the anode and to the screen grid.

penumbra *See* shadow.

perfect gas *See* ideal gas; gas.

perfect pitch *See* absolute pitch.

perfect solution *See* Raoult's law.

pericynthion The point in the orbit around the moon of a satellite launched from the earth that is nearest to the moon. For a satellite launched from the moon the equivalent point is the *perilune*. *Compare* apocynthion.

perigee *See* apogee.

perihelion The point in the orbit of a planet, comet, or artificial satellite in solar orbit at which it is nearest to the sun. The earth is at perihelion on about 3 January. *Compare* aphelion.

period *See* periodic motion.

periodic law The principle that the physical and chemical properties of elements are a periodic function of their proton number. The concept was first proposed in 1869 by the Russian chemist Dimitri Mendeleev (1834–1907), using relative atomic mass rather than proton number, as a culmination of efforts to rationalize chemical properties by J. W. Döbereiner (1817), J. A. R. Newlands (1863), and Lothar Meyer (1864). One of the major successes of the periodic law was its ability to predict chemical and physical properties of undiscovered elements and unknown compounds that were later confirmed experimentally.

periodic motion Any motion of a system that is continuously and identically repeated. The time T that it takes to complete one cycle of an oscillation or wave motion is called the *period*, which is the reciprocal of the *frequency. See* pendulum; simple harmonic motion.

peripheral device Any device, such as an input or output device, connected to the central processing unit of a *computer. Backing store is also usually regarded as a peripheral.

periscope An optical device that enables an observer to see over or around opaque objects. The simplest type consists of a long tube with mirrors at each end set at 45° to the direction to be viewed. A better type uses internally reflecting prisms instead of plane mirrors. Periscopes are used in tanks (to enable the observer to see over obstacles without being shot at) and in submarines (when the vessel is submerged). Such periscopes are usually quite complicated instruments and include telescopes.

Permalloys A group of alloys of high magnetic permeability consisting of iron and nickel (usually 40–80%) often with small amounts of other elements (e.g. 3–5% molybdenum, copper, chromium, or tungsten). They are used in thin foils in electronic transformers, for magnetic shielding, and in computer memories.

permanent gas A gas, such as oxygen or nitrogen, that was formerly thought to be impossible to liquefy. A permanent gas is now regarded as one that cannot be liquefied by pressure alone at normal temperatures (i.e. a gas that has a critical temperature below room temperature).

permanent magnet *See* magnet.

permeability (magnetic permeability) Symbol μ. The ratio of the magnetic flux density, B, in a substance to the external field strength, H; i.e. $\mu = B/H$. The permeability of free space, μ_0, is also called the *magnetic constant* and has the value $4\pi \times 10^{-7}$ H m^{-1} in *SI units. The relative permeability of a substance, μ_r, is given by μ/μ_0 and is therefore dimensionless. *See* magnetism.

permittivity Symbol ε. The ratio of the *electric displacement in a medium to the intensity of the electric field producing it. It is important for electrical insulators used as *dielectrics.

If two charges Q_1 and Q_2 are separated by a distance r in a vacuum, the force F between the charges is given by:

$$F = Q_1Q_2/r^2 4\pi\varepsilon_0$$

In this statement of *Coulomb's law using *SI units, ε_0 is called the absolute permittivity of free space, which is now known as the *electric constant*. It has the value 8.854×10^{-12} F m^{-1}. If the medium between the charges is anything other than a vacuum the equation becomes:

$$F = Q_1Q_2/r^2 4\pi\varepsilon$$

and the force between the charges is reduced. ε is the *absolute permittivity* of the new medium. The *relative permittivity* (ε_r) of a medium, formerly called the *dielectric constant*, is given by $\varepsilon_r = \varepsilon/\varepsilon_0$.

permutations and combinations A combination is any subset of a particular set of objects, regardless of the order of selection. If the set consists of n objects, r objects can be selected giving $n!/r!(n-r)!$ different combinations. This can be written $_nC_r$.

A permutation is an ordered subset (i.e. attention is paid to the order of selection or arrangement) of a particular set of objects. If the set consists of n objects, r such objects can be selected to give $n!/(n-r)!$ permutations. This is written $_nP_r$.

perpetual motion 1. Perpetual motion of the first kind. Motion in which a mechanism, once started, would continue indefinitely to perform useful work without being supplied with energy from an outside source. Such a device would contravene the first law of *thermodynamics and is therefore not feasible. Many historical attempts, exercising great ingenuity, were constructed before the concept of energy and its conservation were understood. Some attempts have been made, since the first law of thermodynamics became generally accepted, by inventors seeking to establish loopholes in the laws of nature. **2.** Perpetual motion of the second kind. Motion in which a mechanism extracts heat from a source and converts all of it into some other form of energy. An example of such a mechanism would be a ship that utilized the internal energy of the oceans for propulsion. Such a device does not contravene the first law of thermodynamics but it does contravene the second law. In the case of the ship, the sea would have to be at a higher temperature than the ship to establish a useful flow of heat. This could not occur without an external energy source. **3.** Perpetual motion of the third kind. A form of motion that continues indefinitely but without doing any useful work. An example is the random molecular motion in a substance. This type postulates the complete elimination of friction. A mechanism consisting of frictionless bearings maintained in a vacuum could turn indefinitely, once started, without contravening the first or second laws of thermodynamics, provided it did no external work. Experience indicates that on the macroscopic scale such a condition cannot be achieved. On the microscopic scale, however, a superconducting ring of wire will apparently sustain a perpetual current flow without the application of an external force. This could be considered a form of perpetual motion of the third kind, if the energy required to cool the wire to superconducting temperatures is ignored.

perturbation A departure by a celestial body from the trajectory or orbit it would follow if it moved only under the influence of a single central force. According to *Kepler's law, for

perturbation theory

example, a single planet orbiting the sun would move in an elliptical orbit. In fact, planets are perturbed from elliptical orbits by the gravitational forces exerted on them by other planets. Similarly, the moon's orbit round the earth is perturbed by the gravitational effect of the sun and the trajectories of comets are perturbed when they pass close to planets.

perturbation theory A method used in calculations in both classical physics (e.g. planetary orbits) and quantum mechanics (e.g. atomic structure), in which the system is divided into a part that is exactly calculable and a small term, which prevents the whole system from being exactly calculable. The technique of perturbation theory enables the effects of the small term to be calculated by an infinite series (which in general is an asymptotic series). Each term in the series is a 'correction term' to the solutions of the exactly calculable system. In classical physics, perturbation theory can be used for calculating planetary orbits. In quantum mechanics, it can be used to calculate the energy levels in molecules. In the many-body problem in quantum mechanics and in relativistic quantum field theory, the terms in perturbation theory may be represented pictorially by Feynman diagrams (*see* quantum electrodynamics).

perversion *See* lateral inversion.

peta- Symbol P. A prefix used in the metric system to denote one thousand million million times. For example, 10^{15} metres = 1 petametre (Pm).

pewter An alloy of lead and tin. It usually contains 63% tin; pewter tankards and food containers should have less than 35% of lead so that the lead remains in solid solution with the tin in the presence of weak acids in the food and drink. Copper is sometimes added to increase ductility and antimony is added if a hard alloy is required.

pH *See* pH scale.

phase 1. A homogeneous part of a heterogeneous system that is separated from other parts by a distinguishable boundary. A mixture of ice and water is a two-phase system. A solution of salt in water is a single-phase system. **2.** A description of the stage that a periodic motion has reached, usually by comparison with another such motion of the same frequency. Two varying quantities are said to be *in phase* if their maximum and minimum values occur at the same instants; otherwise, there is said to be a *phase difference*. *See also* phase angle. **3.** One of the circuits in an electrical system or device in which there are two or more alternating currents that are not in phase with each other. In a three-phase system the displacement between the currents is one third of a period. **4.** *See* phases of the moon.

phase angle The difference in *phase between two sinusoidally varying quantities. The displacement x_1 of one quantity at time t is given by $x_1 = a\sin\omega t$, where ω is the angular frequency and a is the amplitude. The displacement x_2 of a similar wave that reaches the end of its period T, a fraction β of the period before the first is said to lead the first quantity by a time βT. The value of x_2 is then given by $x_2 = a\sin(\omega t + \phi)$. ϕ is called the phase angle and it is equal to $2\pi\beta$.

phase-contrast microscope A type of *microscope that is widely used for examining such specimens as biological cells and tissues. It makes visible the changes in phase that occur when nonuniformly transparent specimens are illuminated. In passing through an object the light is slowed down and becomes out of phase with the original light. With transparent specimens having some structure *diffraction occurs, causing a larger phase change in light outside the central

maximum of the pattern. The phase-contrast microscope provides a means of combining this light with that of the central maximum by means of an annular diaphram and a *phase-contrast plate*, which produces a matching phase change in the light of the central maximum only. This gives greater contrast to the final image, due to constructive interference between the two sets of light waves. This is *bright contrast*; in *dark contrast* a different phase-contrast plate is used to make the same structure appear dark, by destructive interference of the same waves.

phase diagram A graph showing the relationship between solid, liquid, and gaseous *phases over a range of conditions (e.g. temperature and pressure).

phase modulation *See* modulation.

phase rule For any system at equilibrium, the relationship $P + F = C + 2$ holds, where P is the number of distinct phases, C the number of components, and F the number of degrees of freedom of the system.

phases of the moon The shapes of the illuminated surface of the moon as seen from the earth. The shape changes as a result of the relative positions of the earth, sun, and moon. *New moon* occurs when the nearside is totally unilluminated by the sun. As the moon moves eastwards in its orbit the sunrise *terminator crosses the nearside from east to west producing a *crescent moon*. The moon is half illuminated at *first quarter*. When it is more than half-phase but less than full phase it is said to be a *gibbous moon*. When the moon is at *opposition the nearside is fully illuminated producing a *full moon*. The sunset terminator then follows to produce a waning gibbous moon, *last quarter*, a waning crescent moon, and eventually the next new moon.

phase space For a system with n degrees of freedom, the $2n$-dimensional space with coordinates (q_1, q_2, ..., q_n, p_1, p_2, ..., p_n), where the qs describe the degrees of freedom of the system and the ps are the corresponding momenta. Each point represents a state of the system. In a gas of N point particles, each particle has three positional coordinates and three corresponding momentum coordinates, so that the phase space has $6N$-dimensions. If the particles have internal degrees of freedom, such as the vibrations and rotations of molecules, then these must be included in the phase space, which is consequently of higher dimension than that for point particles. As the system changes with time the representative points trace out a curve in phase space known as a *trajectory*. *See also* attractor; configuration space; statistical mechanics.

phase speed (phase velocity) Symbol V_p. The speed of propagation of a pure sine wave. $V_p = \lambda f$, where λ is the wavelength and f is the frequency. The value of the phase speed depends on the nature of the medium through which it is travelling and may also depend on the mode of propagation. For electromagnetic waves travelling through space the phase speed c is given by $c^2 = 1/\varepsilon_0\mu_0$, where ε_0 and μ_0 are the *electric constant and the *magnetic constant respectively.

phasor A rotating *vector that represents a sinusoidally varying quantity. Its length represents the amplitude of the quantity and it is imagined to rotate with angular velocity equal to the angular frequency of the quantity, so that the instantaneous value of the quantity is represented by its projection upon a fixed axis. The concept is convenient for representing the *phase angle between two quantities; it is shown on a diagram as the angle between their phasors.

phlogiston theory A former theory of combustion in which all flammable objects were supposed to contain a substance called *phlogiston*, which was released when the object burned. The existence of this hypothetical substance was proposed in 1669 by Johann Becher, who called it 'combustible earth' (*terra pinguis*: literally 'fat earth'). For example, according to Becher, the conversion of wood to ashes by burning was explained on the assumption that the original wood consisted of ash and *terra pinguis*, which was released on burning. In the early 18th century Georg Stahl renamed the substance *phlogiston* (from the Greek for 'burned') and extended the theory to include the calcination (and corrosion) of metals. Thus, metals were thought to be composed of *calx* (a powdery residue) and phlogiston; when a metal was heated, phlogiston was set free and the calx remained. The process could be reversed by heating the metal over charcoal (a substance believed to be rich in phlogiston, because combustion almost totally consumed it). The calx would absorb the phlogiston released by the burning charcoal and become metallic again.

The theory was finally demolished by Antoine Lavoisier, who showed by careful experiments with reactions in closed containers that there was no *absolute* gain in mass – the gain in mass of the substance was matched by a corresponding loss in mass of the air used in combustion. After experiments with Priestley's dephlogisticated air, Lavoisier realized that this gas, which he named oxygen, was taken up to form a calx (now called an oxide). The role of oxygen in the new theory was almost exactly the opposite of phlogiston's role in the old. In combustion and corrosion phlogiston was released; in the modern theory, oxygen is taken up to form an oxide.

phon A unit of loudness of sound that measures the intensity of a sound relative to a reference tone of defined intensity and frequency. The reference tone usually used has a frequency of 1 kilohertz and a root-mean-square sound pressure of 2×10^{-5} pascal. The observer listens with both ears to the reference tone and the sound to be measured alternately. The reference tone is then increased until the observer judges it to be of equal intensity to the sound to be measured. If the intensity of the reference tone has been increased by n *decibels to achieve this, the sound being measured is said to have an intensity of n phons. The decibel and phon scales are not identical as the phon scale is subjective and relies on the sensitivity of the ear to detect changes of intensity with frequency.

phonon A quantum of *crystal-lattice vibrational energy having a magnitude hf, where h is the *Planck constant and f is the frequency of the vibration. Phonons are analogous to the quanta of light, i.e. *photons. The concept of phonons is useful in the treatment of the thermal conductivity of nonmetallic solids and, through consideration of electron–phonon interactions, the temperature dependence of the electrical conductivity of metals.

phosphor bronze An alloy of copper containing 4% to 10% of tin and 0.05% to 1% of phosphorus as a deoxidizing agent. It is used particularly for marine purposes and where it is exposed to heavy wear, as in gear wheels. *See also* bronze.

phosphorescence *See* luminescence.

phot A unit of illuminance equal to 10^4 lux or one lumen per square centimetre.

photino *See* supersymmetry.

photocathode A *cathode that emits electrons when light falls upon it, as

a result of the *photoelectric effect. *See* photoelectric cell.

photocell *See* photoelectric cell.

photochemical reaction A chemical reaction caused by light or ultraviolet radiation. The incident photons are absorbed by reactant molecules to give excited molecules or free radicals, which undergo further reaction.

photochemistry The branch of chemistry concerned with *photochemical reactions.

photochromism A change of colour occurring in certain substances when exposed to light. Photochromic materials are used in sunglasses that darken in bright sunlight.

photoconductive effect *See* photoelectric effect.

photodiode A *semiconductor diode used to detect the presence of light or to measure its intensity. It usually consists of a *p–n* junction device in a container that focuses any light in the environment close to the junction. The device is usually biased in reverse so that in the dark the current is small; when it is illuminated the current is proportional to the amount of light falling on it. *See* photoelectric effect.

photodisintegration The decay of a nuclide as a result of the absorption of a gamma-ray photon.

photoelasticity An effect in which certain materials exhibit double refraction when subjected to stress. It is used in a technique for detecting strains in transparent materials (e.g. Perspex, celluloid, and glass). When polarized white light is passed through a stressed sample, the birefringence causes coloured patterns to be seen on the viewing screen of a suitable *polariscope. If monochromatic polarized light is used, a complex pattern of light and dark fringes is produced.

photoelectric cell (photocell) Any of several devices that produce an electric signal in response to exposure to electromagnetic radiation. The original photocells utilized photoemission from a photosensitive cathode (*photocathode*). The electrons emitted are attracted to an anode. A positive potential on the anode enables a current to flow through an external circuit, the current being proportional to the intensity of the illumination on the cathode. The electrodes are enclosed in an evacuated glass tube (*see also* photomultiplier).

More modern light-sensitive devices utilize the photoconductive effect and the photovoltaic effect (*see* photoelectric effect; photodiode; phototransistor; solar cell).

photoelectric effect The liberation of electrons (*see* photoelectron) from a substance exposed to electromagnetic radiation. The number of electrons emitted depends on the intensity of the radiation. The kinetic energy of the electrons emitted depends on the frequency of the radiation. The effect is a quantum process in which the radiation is regarded as a stream of *photons, each having an energy hf, where h is the Planck constant and f is the frequency of the radiation. A photon can only eject an electron if the photon energy exceeds the *work function, ϕ, of the solid, i.e. if $hf_0 = \phi$ an electron will be ejected; f_0 is the minimum frequency (or *threshold frequency*) at which ejection will occur. For many solids the photoelectric effect occurs at ultraviolet frequencies or above, but for some materials (having low work functions) it occurs with light. The maximum kinetic energy, E_m, of the photoelectron is given by *Einstein's equation: $E_m = hf - \phi$ (*see also* photoionization).

Apart from the liberation of electrons from atoms, other phenomena are also referred to as photoelectric effects. These are the *photoconductive effect* and the *photovoltaic effect*. In

the photoconductive effect, an increase in the electrical conductivity of a semiconductor is caused by radiation as a result of the excitation of additional free charge carriers by the incident photons. *Photoconductive cells*, using such photosensitive materials as cadmium sulphide, are widely used as radiation detectors and light switches (e.g. to switch on street lighting).

In the photovoltaic effect, an e.m.f. is produced between two layers of different materials as a result of irradiation. The effect is made use of in *photovoltaic cells*, most of which consist of *p–n* *semiconductor junctions (*see also* photodiode; phototransistor). When photons are absorbed near a *p–n* junction new free charge carriers are produced (as in photoconductivity); however, in the photovoltaic effect the electric field in the junction region causes the new charge carriers to move, creating a flow of current in an external circuit without the need for a battery. *See also* photoelectric cell.

photoelectron An electron emitted from a substance by irradiation as a result of the *photoelectric effect or *photoionization.

photoelectron spectroscopy A technique for determining the *ionization potentials of molecules. The sample is a gas or vapour irradiated with a narrow beam of ultraviolet radiation (usually from a helium source at 58.4 nm, 21.21 eV photon energy). The photoelectrons produced in accordance with *Einstein's equation are passed through a slit into a vacuum region, where they are deflected by magnetic or electrostatic fields to give an energy spectrum. The photoelectron spectrum obtained has peaks corresponding to the ionization potentials of the molecule (and hence the orbital energies). The technique also gives information on the vibrational energy levels of the ions formed.

ESCA (electron spectroscopy for chemical analysis) is a similar analytical technique in which a beam of X-rays is used. In this case, the electrons ejected are from the inner shells of the atoms. Peaks in the electron spectrum for a particular element show characteristic chemical shifts, which depend on the presence of other atoms in the molecule.

photoemission The process in which electrons are emitted by a substance as a result of irradiation. *See* photoelectric effect; photoionization.

photofission A *nuclear fission that is caused by a gamma-ray photon.

photographic density A measure of the opacity of a photographic emulsion (negative or transparency). *See* densitometer.

photography The process of forming a permanent record of an image on specially treated film or paper. In normal black-and-white photography a camera is used to expose a film or plate to a focused image of the scene for a specified time. The film or plate is coated with an emulsion containing silver salts and the exposure to light causes the silver salts to break down into silver atoms; where the light is bright dark areas of silver are formed on the film after development (by a mild reducing agent) and fixing. The negative so formed is printed, either by a contact process or by projection. In either case light passing through the negative film falls on a sheet of paper also coated with emulsion. Where the negative is dark, less light passes through and the resulting positive is light in this area, corresponding with a light area in the original scene. As photographic emulsions are sensitive to ultraviolet and X-rays, they are widely used in studies involving these forms of electromagnetic radiation. *See also* colour photography.

photoionization The *ionization of an atom or molecule as a result of

irradiation by electromagnetic radiation. For a photoionization to occur the incident photon of the radiation must have an energy in excess of the *ionization potential of the species being irradiated. The ejected photoelectron will have an energy, E, given by $E = hf - I$, where h is the Planck constant, f is the frequency of the incident radiation, and I is the ionization potential of the irradiated species.

photolithography A technique used in the manufacture of semiconductor components, integrated circuits, etc. It depends on the principle of masking selected areas of a surface and exposing the unmasked areas to such processes as the introduction of impurities, deposition of thin films, removal of material by etching, etc. The technique has been developed for use on tiny structures (typically measured in micrometres), which can only be examined by means of an electron microscope.

photoluminescence See luminescence.

photolysis Chemical reaction produced by exposure to light or ultraviolet radiation. Photolytic reactions often involve free radicals, the first step being homolytic fission of a chemical bond.

photometer An instrument used to measure *luminous intensity, illumination, and other photometric quantities. The older types rely on visual techniques to compare a source of light with a standard source. More modern photometers use *photoelectric cells, of the photoconductive, photoemissive, or photovoltaic typess. The photovoltaic types do not require an external power source and are therefore very convenient to use but are relatively insensitive. The photoemissive type usually incorporates a *photomultiplier, especially for use in astronomy and with other weak sources. Photoconductive units require

only low-voltage supplies, which makes them convenient for commercial illumination meters and photographers' exposure meters.

photometric brightness See luminance.

photometry The study of visual radiation, especially the calculations and measurements of *luminous intensity, *luminous flux, etc. In some cases photometric calculations and measurements extend into the near infrared and the near ultraviolet.
In photometry, two types of measurement are used: those that measure *luminous* quantities rely on the use of the human eye (for example, to compare the illuminance of two surfaces); those called *radiant* quantities rely on the use of photoelectric devices to measure electromagnetic energy. See also photometer.

photomicrography The use of photography to obtain a permanent record (a *photomicrograph*) of the image of an object as viewed through a microscope.

photomultiplier A sensitive type of *photoelectric cell in which electrons emitted from a photocathode are accelerated to a second electrode where several electrons are liberated by each original photoelectron, as a result of *secondary emission. The whole process is repeated as many times as necessary to produce a useful electric current by secondary emission from the last electrode. A photomultiplier is thus a photocathode with the output amplified by an electron multiplier. The initial photocurrent can be amplified by a factor of 10^8. Photomultipliers are thus useful when it is necessary to detect low intensities of light, as in stellar photometry, star and planet tracking in guidance systems, and more mundanely in process control.

photon A particle with zero *rest mass consisting of a *quantum of electromagnetic radiation. The photon

may also be regarded as a unit of energy equal to hf, where h is the *Planck constant and f is the frequency of the radiation in hertz. Photons travel at the speed of light. They are required to explain the photoelectric effect and other phenomena that require *light to have particle character.

photoneutron A neutron emitted by an atomic nucleus undergoing a *photonuclear reaction.

photonuclear reaction A *nuclear reaction that is initiated by a (gamma-ray) photon.

photopic vision The type of vision that occurs when the cones in the eye are the principal receptors, i.e. when the level of illumination is high. Colours can be identified with photopic vision. *Compare* scotopic vision.

photoreceptor A sensory cell or group of cells that reacts to the presence of light. It usually contains a pigment that undergoes a chemical change when light is absorbed, thus stimulating a nerve. *See* eye.

photosensitive substance 1. Any substance that when exposed to electromagnetic radiation produces a photoconductive, photoelectric, or photovoltaic effect. **2.** Any substance, such as the emulsion of a photographic film, in which electromagnetic radiation produces a chemical change.

photosphere The visible surface of the *sun or other star and the source of its continuous spectrum. It is a gaseous layer several hundreds of kilometres thick with an average temperature of 5780 K. Where the photosphere merges with the *chromosphere the temperature is 4000 K.

phototransistor A junction *transistor that is photosensitive. When radiation falls on the emitter-base junction, new free charge carriers are created in the base region and the collector current is increased. Phototransistors are similar to *photodiodes

except that the primary photoelectric current is amplified internally and it is therefore more sensitive to light than the photodiode. Some types can be used as switching or bistable devices, a small intensity of radiation switching them from a low to high current state.

photovoltaic effect *See* photoelectric effect.

pH scale A logarithmic scale for expressing the acidity or alkalinity of a solution. To a first approximation, the pH of a solution can be defined as $-\log_{10}c$, where c is the concentration of hydrogen ions in moles per cubic decimetre. A neutral solution at 25°C has a hydrogen-ion concentration of 10^{-7} mol dm^{-3}, so the pH is 7. A pH below 7 indicates an acid solution; one above 7 indicates an alkaline solution. More accurately, the pH depends not on the concentration of hydrogen ions but on their *activity, which cannot be measured experimentally. For practical purposes, the pH scale is defined by using a hydrogen electrode in the solution of interest as one half of a cell, with a reference electrode (e.g. a calomel electrode) as the other half cell. The pH is then given by $(E - E_R)F/2.303RT$, where E is the e.m.f. of the cell, E_R the standard electrode potential of the reference electrode, and F the Faraday constant. In practice, a glass electrode is more convenient than a hydrogen electrode.

pH stands for 'potential of hydrogen'. The scale was introduced by S. P. Sørensen in 1909.

physical chemistry The branch of chemistry concerned with the effect of chemical structure on physical properties. It includes chemical thermodynamics and electrochemistry.

physics The study of the laws that determine the structure of the universe with reference to the matter and energy of which it consists. It is concerned not with chemical changes that

occur but with the forces that exist between objects and the interrelationship between matter and energy. Traditionally, the study was divided into separate fields: heat, light, sound, electricity and magnetism, and mechanics. Since the turn of the century, however, quantum mechanics and relativistic physics have become increasingly important; the growth of modern physics has been accompanied by the studies of atomic physics, nuclear physics, and particle physics. The physics of astronomical bodies and their interactions is known as *astrophysics*, the physics of the earth is known as *geophysics*, and the study of the physical aspects of biology is called *biophysics*.

physisorption *See* adsorption.

pi Symbol π. The ratio of the circumference of any circle to its diameter. It is a *transcendental number with the value 3.141 592 . . . .

pico- Symbol p. A prefix used in the metric system to denote 10^{-12}. For example, 10^{-12} farad = 1 picofarad (pF).

pie chart A diagram in which percentages are shown as sectors of a circle. If x percent of the electorate vote for party X, y percent for party Y, and z percent for party Z, a pie chart would show three sectors having central angles $3.6x°$, $3.6y°$, and $3.6z°$.

pi electron An electron in a pi orbital. *See* orbital.

piezoelectric effect The generation of a potential difference across the opposite faces of certain nonconducting crystals (*piezoelectric crystals*) as a result of the application of mechanical stress between these faces. The *electric polarization produced is proportional to the stress and the direction of the polarization reverses if the stress changes from compression to tension. The *reverse piezoelectric effect* is the opposite phenomenon: if the opposite faces of a piezoelectric crys-

tal are subjected to a potential difference, the crystal changes its shape. Rochelle salt and quartz are the most frequently used piezoelectric materials. While Rochelle salt produces the greater polarization for a given stress, quartz is more widely used as its crystals have greater strength and are stable at temperatures in excess of 100°C.

If a quartz plate is subjected to an alternating electric field, the reverse piezoelectric effect causes it to expand and contract at the field frequency. If this field frequency is made to coincide with the natural elastic frequency of the crystal, the plate resonates; the direct piezoelectric effect then augments the applied electric field. This is the basis of the *crystal oscillator and the *quartz clock. *See also* crystal microphone; crystal pickup.

pig iron The impure form of iron produced by a blast furnace, which is cast into pigs (blocks) for converting at a later date into cast iron, steel, etc. The composition depends on the ores used, the smelting procedure, and the use to which the pigs will later be put.

pi-meson *See* pion.

pinch effect A magnetic attraction between parallel conductors carrying currents flowing in the same direction. The force was noticed in early induction furnaces. Since the late 1940s it has been widely studied as a means of confining the hot plasma in a *thermonuclear reactor. In an experimental toroidal thermonuclear reactor a large electric current is induced in the plasma by electromagnetic induction; this current both heats the plasma and draws it away from the walls of the tube as a result of the pinch effect.

pion (pi-meson) An *elementary particle classified as a *meson. It exists in three forms: neutral, positively charged, and negatively charged. The charged pions decay

211

into muons and neutrinos; the neutral pion decays into two gamma-ray photons.

Pirani gauge An instrument used to measure low pressures (1–10^{-4} torr; 100–0.01 Pa). It consists of an electrically heated filament, which is exposed to the gas whose pressure is to be measured. The extent to which heat is conducted away from the filament depends on the gas pressure, which thus controls its equilibrium temperature. Since the resistance of the filament is dependent on its temperature, the pressure is related to the resistance of the filament. The filament is arranged to be part of a *Wheatstone bridge circuit and the pressure is read from a microammeter calibrated in pressure units. As the effect depends on the thermal conductivity of the gas, the calibration has to be made each time the pressure of a different gas is measured.

pitch 1. (in physics) The property of a sound that characterizes its highness or lowness to an observer. It is related to, but not identical with, frequency. Below about 1000 Hz the pitch is slightly higher than the frequency and above 1000 the position is reversed. The loudness of a sound also affects the pitch. Up to 1000 Hz an increase in loudness causes a decrease in pitch. From about 1000 to 3000 Hz the pitch is independent of loudness, while above 3000 Hz an increase in loudness seems to cause a raising of pitch. Pitch is usually measured in mels; a note of 1000 Hz frequency with a loudness of 40 decibels above the absolute threshold of hearing has a pitch of 1000 mels. **2.** (in mechanics) *See* screw.

Pitot tube A device for measuring the speed of a fluid. It consists of two tubes, one with an opening facing the moving fluid and the other with an opening at 90° to the direction of the flow. The two tubes are connected to the opposite sides of a manometer so that the difference between the dynamic pressure in the first tube and the static pressure in the second tube can be measured. The speed v of the flow of an incompressible fluid is then given by: $v^2 = 2(P_2 - P_1)/\rho$, where P_2 is the dynamic pressure, P_1 is the static pressure, and ρ is the density of the fluid. The device has a wide variety of applications. It was devised by Henri Pitot (1695–1771).

Planck constant Symbol h. The fundamental constant equal to the ratio of the energy E of a quantum of energy to its frequency v: $E = hv$. It has the value $6.626\,176 \times 10^{-34}$ J s. It is named after Max Planck (1858–1947). In quantum-mechanical calculations (especially particle physics) the *rationalized Planck constant* $\hbar = h/2\pi = 1.054\,589 \times 10^{-34}$ J s is frequently used.

Planck length The length scale at which a classical description of gravity ceases to be valid, and *quantum mechanics must be taken into account. It is given by $L_P = \sqrt{(G\hbar/c^3)}$ where G is the gravitational constant, $\hbar$ is the rationalized Planck constant, and c is the speed of light. The value of the Planck length is of order 10^{-35} m (twenty orders of magnitude smaller than the size of a proton, 10^{-15} m).

Planck mass The mass of a particle whose Compton wavelength is equal to the *Planck length. It is given by $m_P = \sqrt{(\hbar c/G)}$, where $\hbar$ is the rationalized Planck constant, c is the speed of light, and G is the gravitational constant. The description of an elementary particle of this mass, or particles interacting with energies per particle equivalent to it (through $E = mc^2$), requires a *quantum theory of gravity. Since the Planck mass is of order 10^{-8} kg (equivalent energy 10^{19} GeV), and, for example, the proton mass is of order 10^{-27} kg and the highest energies attainable in present-

day particle accelerators are of order 10^3 GeV, quantum-gravitational effects do not arise in laboratory particle physics. However, energies equivalent to the Planck mass did occur in the early universe according to *big-bang theory, and a quantum theory of gravity is important for discussing conditions there (see Planck time).

Planck's radiation law A law giving the distribution of energy radiated by a *black body. It introduced into physics the novel concept of energy as a quantity that is radiated by a body in small discrete packets rather than as a continuous emission. These small packets became known as quanta and the law formed the basis of *quantum theory. The *Planck formula* gives the energy radiated per unit time at frequency v per unit frequency interval per unit solid angle into an infinitesimal cone from an element of the black-body surface that is of unit area in projection perpendicular to the cone's axis. The expression for this *monochromatic specific intensity* I_v is:

$$I_v = 2hc^{-2}v^3/[\exp(hv/kT - 1],$$

where h is the *Planck constant, c is the *speed of light, k is the *Boltzmann constant, and T is the thermodynamic temperature of the black body. I_v has units of watts per square metre per steradian per hertz ($W\ m^{-2}\ sr^{-1}\ Hz^{-1}$). The monochromatic specific intensity can also be expressed in terms of the energy radiated at wavelength λ per unit wavelength interval; it is then written as I, and the Planck formula is:

$$I_\lambda = 2hc^2\lambda^{-5}/[\exp(hc/\lambda kT) - 1].$$

There are two important limiting cases of the Planck formula. For low frequencies $v << kT/h$ (equivalently, long wavelengths $\lambda >> hc/kT$) the *Rayleigh–Jeans formula* is valid:

$$I_v = 2c^{-2}v^2kT,$$

or

$$I_\lambda = 2c\lambda^{-4}kT.$$

Note that these expressions do not involve the Planck constant. They can be derived classically and do not apply at high frequencies, i.e. high energies, when the quantum nature of *photons must be taken into account. The second limiting case is the *Wien formula*, which applies at high frequencies $v >> kT/h$ (equivalently, short wavelengths $\lambda << hc/kT$):

$$I_v = 2hc^{-2}v^3 \exp(-hv/kT),$$

or

$$I_\lambda = 2hc^2\lambda^{-5} \exp(-hc/\lambda kT).$$

See also Wien's displacement law.

Planck time The time taken for a photon (travelling at the speed of light c) to move through a distance equal to the *Planck length. It is given by $t_P = \sqrt{(G\hbar/c^5)}$, where G is the gravitational constant and $\hbar$ is the rationalized Planck constant. The value of the Planck time is of order 10^{-43} s. In the *big-bang cosmology, up until a time t_P after the initial instant, it is necessary to use a *quantum theory of gravity to describe the evolution of the universe.

Planck units A system of *units, used principally in discussions of *quantum theories of gravity, in which length, mass, and time are expressed as multiples of the *Planck length, mass, and time respectively. This is equivalent to setting the gravitational constant, the speed of light, and the reduced Planck constant all equal to unity. All quantities that ordinarily have dimensions involving length, mass, and time become dimensionless in Planck units. Since, in the subject area where Planck units are used, it is normal to employ *Gaussian or *Heaviside–Lorentz units for electromagnetic quantities, these then become dimensionless. See also geometrized units; natural units.

plane A flat surface defined by the condition that any two points in the plane are joined by a straight line that lies entirely in the surface.

plane-polarized light *See* polarization of light.

planet A body that revolves around a central astronomical body, especially one of the nine bodies (Mercury; Venus; earth; Mars; Jupiter; Saturn; Uranus; Neptune; Pluto) that revolve in elliptical orbits around the sun. *See* solar system.

planimeter An instrument used to measure the area of a closed curve. The outline of the curve is followed by a pointer on the instrument and the area is given on a graduated disc.

plano-concave lens *See* concave; lens.

plano-convex lens *See* convex; lens.

plasma A highly ionized gas in which the number of free electrons is approximately equal to the number of positive ions. Sometimes described as the fourth state of matter, plasmas occur in interstellar space, in the atmospheres of stars (including the sun), in discharge tubes, and in experimental thermonuclear reactors.

Because the particles in a plasma are charged, its behaviour differs in some respects from that of a gas. Plasmas can be created in the laboratory by heating a low-pressure gas until the mean kinetic energy of the gas particles is comparable to the *ionization potential of the gas atoms or molecules. At very high temperatures, from about 50 000 K upwards, collisions between gas particles cause cascading ionization of the gas. However, in some cases, such as a fluorescent lamp, the temperature remains quite low as the plasma particles are continually colliding with the walls of the container, causing cooling and recombination. In such cases ionization is only partial and requires a large energy input. In *thermonuclear reactors an enormous plasma temperature is maintained by confining the plasma away from the container walls using electromagnetic fields (*see*

pinch effect). The study of plasmas is known as *plasma physics*.

plasmon A *collective excitation for quantized oscillations of the electrons in a metal.

plasticity The property of solids that causes them to change permanently in size or shape as a result of the application of a stress in excess of a certain value, called the *yield point*.

pleochroic Denoting a crystal that appears to be of different colours, depending on the direction from which it is viewed. It is caused by polarization of light as it passes through an anisotropic medium.

plutonium Symbol Pu. A dense silvery radioactive metallic transuranic element belonging to the actinoids; a.n. 94; mass number of most stable isotope 244 (half-life 7.6×10^7 years); r.d. 19.84; m.p. 641°C; b.p. 3232°C. Thirteen isotopes are known, by far the most important being plutonium–239 (half-life 2.44×10^4 years), which undergoes *nuclear fission with slow neutrons and is therefore a vital power source for *nuclear weapons and some *nuclear reactors. About 20 tonnes of plutonium are produced annually by the world's nuclear reactors, a detailed inventory of every gram of which is kept in order to prevent its military misuse. The element was first produced by Seaborg, McMillan, Kennedy, and Wahl in 1940.

point-contact transistor *See* transistor.

point defect *See* defect.

point discharge *See* corona.

poise A *c.g.s. unit of viscosity equal to the tangential force in dynes per square centimetre required to maintain a difference in velocity of one centimetre per second between two parallel planes of a fluid separated by one centimetre. 1 poise is equal to 10^{-1} N s m^{-2}.

Poiseuille's equation An equation relating the volume flow rate, V, of a fluid through a cylindrical tube to the pressure difference, p, between the ends of the tube: $V = \pi p r^4/8\eta$, where r is the radius and l the length of the tube; η is the viscosity of the fluid. It applies if the Reynolds number is less than 2000 and was first stated by Jean Louis Poiseuille (1799–1869).

poison A substance that absorbs neutrons in a nuclear reactor and therefore slows down the reaction. It may be added intentionally for this purpose or may be formed as a fission product and need to be periodically removed.

Poisson's ratio The ratio of the lateral strain to the longitudinal strain in a stretched rod. If the original diameter of the rod is d and the contraction of the diameter under stress is Δd, the lateral strain $\Delta d/d = s_d$; if the original length is l and the extension under stress Δl, the longitudinal strain is $\Delta l/l = s_l$. Poisson's ratio is then s_d/s_l. For steels the value is between 0.28 and 0.30 and for aluminium alloys it is about 0.33. It was first introduced by Simeon Poisson (1781–1840).

polar coordinates A system used in analytical geometry to locate a point P, with reference to two or three axes. The distance of P from the origin is r, and the angle between the x-axis and the *radius vector OP* is θ, thus in two-dimensional polar coordinates the coordinates of P are (r,θ). If the *Cartesian coordinates of P are (x,y) then, $x = r\cos\theta$ and $y = r\sin\theta$. In three dimensions the point P may be regarded as lying on the surface of a cylinder, giving *cylindrical polar coordinates*, or on the surface of a sphere, giving *spherical polar coordinates*. In the former the coordinates of P would be (r,θ,z); in the latter they would be (r,θ,ϕ) (see illustration).

polariscope (polarimeter) A device used to study optically active substances (*see* optical activity). The simplest type of instrument consists of a light source, collimator, polarizer, and analyser. The specimen is placed between polarizer and analyser, so that any rotation of the plane of polarization of the light can be assessed by turning the analyser. *See also* photoelasticity.

polarization 1. The process of confining the vibrations of the vector constituting a transverse wave to one direction. In unpolarized radiation the vector oscillates in all directions perpendicular to the direction of propagation. *See* polarization of light. **2.** The formation of products of the chemical reaction in a *voltaic cell in the vicinity of the electrodes resulting in increased resistance to current flow and, frequently, to a reduction in the e.m.f. of the cell. *See also* depolarization. **3.** The partial separation of electric charges in an insulator subjected to an electric field.

polarization of light The process of confining the vibrations of the electric vector of light waves to one direction. In unpolarized light the electric field vibrates in all directions perpendicular to the direction of propagation. After reflection or transmission through certain substances (*see* Polaroid) the electric field is confined to one direction and the radiation is said to be *plane-polarized light*. The plane of plane-polarized light can be rotated when it passes through certain substances (*see* optical activity).

In *circularly polarized light*, the tip of the electric vector describes a circular helix about the direction of propagation with a frequency equal to the frequency of the light. The magnitude of the vector remains constant. In *elliptically polarized light*, the vector also rotates about the direction of propagation but the amplitude changes; a projection of the vector on

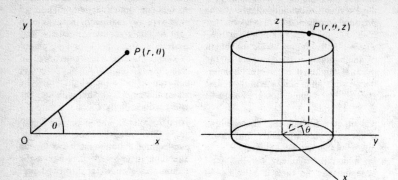

two-dimensional coordinates

cylindrical polar coordinates

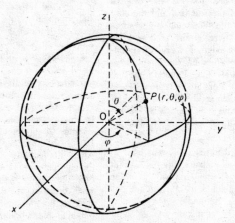

spherical polar coordinates

Polar coordinates

a plane at right angles to the direction of propagation describes an ellipse. Circularly and elliptically polarized light are produced using a *retardation plate.

polarizing angle *See* Brewster's law.

polar molecule A molecule that has a dipole moment; i.e. one in which there is some separation of charge in the chemical bonds, so that one part of the molecule has a positive charge and the other a negative charge.

216

Polaroid A doubly refracting material that plane-polarizes unpolarized light passed through it. It consists of a plastic sheet strained in a manner that makes it birefringent by aligning its molecules. Sunglasses incorporating a Polaroid material absorb light that is vibrating horizontally – produced by reflection from horizontal surfaces – and thus reduce glare.

polaron A coupled electron–ion system that arises when an electron is introduced into the conduction band of a perfect ionic crystal and induces lattice polarization around itself.

pole 1. *See* magnetic poles; magnetic monopole. **2.** The *optical centre of a curved mirror.

polonium Symbol Po. A rare radioactive metallic element; a.n. 84; r.a.m. 210; r.d. 9.32; m.p. 254°C; b.p. 962°C. The element occurs in uranium ores to an extent of about 100 micrograms per 1000 kilograms. It has 27 isotopes, more than any other element. The longest-lived isotope is polonium–209 (half-life 103 years). Polonium has attracted attention as a possible heat source for spacecraft as the energy released as it decays is 1.4 $\times$ 10^5 J kg^{-1} s^{-1}. It was discovered by Marie Curie in 1898 in a sample of pitchblende.

polychromatic radiation Electromagnetic radiation that consists of a mixture of different wavelengths. This need not refer only to visible radiation. *Compare* monochromatic radiation.

polygon A plane figure with a number of sides. In a *regular polygon* all the sides and internal angles are equal. For such a polygon with n sides, the interior angle is $(180 - 360/n)$ degrees and the sum of the interior angles is $(180n - 360)$ degrees.

polygon of forces A polygon in which the sides represent, in magnitude and direction, all forces acting on a rigid body. The side required to close the polygon represents the resultant of a system of forces.

polyhedron A solid bounded by polygonal faces. In a *regular polyhedron* all the faces are congruent regular polygons. The cube is one of five possible regular polyhedrons. The others are the *tetrahedron* (four triangular faces), the *octahedron* (eight triangular faces), the *dodecahedron* (twelve pentagonal faces), and the *icosahedron* (twenty triangular faces).

polynomial A mathematical expression containing three or more terms. It has the general form $a_0 x^n + a_1 x^{n-1} + a_2 x^{n-2} + \ldots + a_n$, where a_0, a_1, etc., are constants and n is the highest power of the variable, called the *degree* of the polynomial.

population inversion *See* laser.

population type A method of classifying stars as either population I or population II bodies, devised in 1944 by Wilhelm Baade (1893–1960). Population I stars are the young metal-rich highly luminous stars found in the spiral arms of galaxies. Population II stars are older metal-deficient stars that occur in the centres of galaxies.

positive charge *See* charge.

positive feedback *See* feedback.

positron The antiparticle of the *electron. *See also* annihilation; elementary particles; pair production.

potassium–argon dating A *dating technique for certain rocks that depends on the decay of the radioisotope potassium–40 to argon–40, a process with a half-life of about 1.27 $\times$ 10^{10} years. It assumes that all the argon–40 formed in the potassium-bearing mineral accumulates within it and that all the argon present is formed by the decay of potassium–40. The mass of argon–40 and potassium–40 in the sample is estimated and the sample is then dated from the equation:

$$^{40}\text{Ar} = 0.1102\ ^{40}\text{K}(e^{\lambda t} - 1),$$

potential barrier

where λ is the decay constant and t is the time in years since the mineral cooled to about 300°C, when the ^{40}Ar became trapped in the crystal lattice. The method is effective for micas, feldspar, and some other minerals.

potential barrier A region containing a maximum of potential that prevents a particle on one side of it from passing to the other side. According to classical theory a particle must possess energy in excess of the height of the potential barrier to pass it. However, in quantum theory there is a finite probability that a particle with less energy will pass through the barrier (*see* tunnel effect). A potential barrier surrounds the atomic nucleus and is important in nuclear physics; a similar but much lower barrier exists at the interface between *semiconductors and metals and between differently doped semiconductors. These barriers are important in the design of electronic devices.

potential difference *See* electric potential.

potential divider *See* voltage divider.

potential energy *See* energy.

potentiometer 1. *See* voltage divider. **2.** An instrument for measuring, comparing, or dividing small potential differences. A typical example of its use is the measurement of the e.m.f. (E_1) of a cell by comparing it with the e.m.f. (E_2) of a standard cell. In this case a circuit is set up as illustrated, in which AB is a wire of uni-

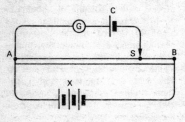

Potentiometer

form resistance and S is a sliding contact onto this wire. An accumulator X maintains a steady current through the wire. To measure the e.m.f. of a cell C, it is connected up as shown in the diagram and the sliding contact moved until the e.m.f. of C exactly balances the p.d. from the accumulator, as indicated by a zero reading on the galvanometer G. If the length AS is then l_1, the value of E_1 is given by $E_1/E_2 = l_1/l_2$, where l_2 is the length AS when the standard cell is used as the cell C.

pound The unit of mass in the *f.p.s. system of units defined as 0.453 592 37 kilogram. Before 1963 it was defined in terms of a platinum cylinder called the Imperial Standard Pound.

poundal The unit of force in the *f.p.s. system of units equal to the force required to impart to a mass of one pound an acceleration of one foot per second per second.

powder metallurgy A process in which powdered metals or alloys are pressed into a variety of shapes at high temperatures. The process started with the pressing of powdered tungsten into incandescent lamp filaments in the first decade of this century and is now widely used for making self-lubricating bearings and cemented tungsten carbide cutting tools.

The powders are produced by atomization of molten metals, chemical decomposition of a compound of the metal, or crushing and grinding of the metal or alloy. The parts are pressed into moulds at pressures ranging from 140×10^6 Pa to 830×10^6 Pa after which they are heated in a controlled atmosphere to bond the particles together (*see* sintering).

power 1. (in physics) Symbol P. The rate at which work is done or energy is transferred. In SI units it is measured in watts (joules per second). *See also* horsepower. **2.** (in mathematics)

218

The number of times a quantity is multiplied; e.g. x^5 is the fifth power of x. A *power series* is one in which the power of the variable increases with each term, e.g. $a_0 + a_1x + a_2x^2 + a_3x^3 + \ldots + a_nx^n$.

power factor *See* electric power.

power reactor A *nuclear reactor designed to produce electrical power.

preamplifier An *amplifier in a radio, record player, etc., providing a first stage of amplification. It is usually located close to the signal source (i.e. the aerial or pick-up) and the signal is then transmitted by cable to the main amplifier. Preamplification at this early stage improves the signal-to-noise ratio of the whole system.

precessional motion A form of motion that occurs when a torque is applied to a rotating body in such a way that it tends to change the direction of its axis of rotation. It arises because the resultant of the angular velocity of rotation and the increment of angular velocity produced by the torque is an angular velocity about a new direction; this commonly changes the axis of the applied torque and leads to sustained rotation of the original axis of rotation.

A spinning top, the axis of which is not exactly vertical, has a torque acting on it as a result of gravity. Instead of falling over, the top precesses about a vertical line through the pivot. The earth also experiences a torque and undergoes a slow precession, primarily as a result of the gravitational attraction of the sun and the moon on its equatorial bulge (*see* precession of the equinoxes).

precession of the equinoxes The slow westward motion of the *equinoxes about the ecliptic as a result of the earth's *precessional motion. The equinoxes move round the ecliptic with a period of 25 800 years.

preons Hypothetical entities that are postulated as being 'building blocks'

of quarks and leptons. There is no experimental evidence for preons but the idea has considerable theoretical appeal. It is expected that evidence for preons would only be obtained at much higher energies than are available from present accelerators.

presbyopia A loss of accommodation that normally develops in human eyes over the age of 45–50 years. Vision of distant objects remains unchanged but accommodation of the eye to near objects is reduced as a result of loss of elasticity in the lens of the eye. The defect is corrected by reading glasses using weak converging lenses.

pressure The force acting normally on unit area of a surface or the ratio of force to area. It is measured in *pascals in SI units. *Absolute pressure* is pressure measured on a gauge that reads zero at zero pressure rather than at atmospheric pressure. *Gauge pressure* is measured on a gauge that reads zero at atmospheric pressure.

pressure gauge Any device used to measure pressure. Three basic types are in use: the liquid-column gauge (e.g. the mercury *barometer and the *manometer), the expanding-element gauge (e.g. the *Bourdon gauge and the aneroid *barometer), and the electrical transducer. In the last category the *strain gauge is an example. Capacitor pressure gauges also come into this category. In these devices, the pressure to be measured displaces one plate of a capacitor and thus alters its capacitance.

pressurized-water reactor *See* nuclear reactor.

Prévost's theory of exchanges A body emits and absorbs radiant energy at equal rates when it is in equilibrium with its surroundings. Its temperature then remains constant. If the body is not at the same temperature as its surroundings there is a net flow of energy between the surroundings and the body because of unequal

emission and absorption. The theory was proposed by Pierre Prévost (1751–1839) in 1791.

primary cell A *voltaic cell in which the chemical reaction producing the e.m.f. is not satisfactorily reversible and the cell cannot therefore be recharged by the application of a charging current. *See* Daniell cell; Leclanché cell; Weston cell; mercury cell. *Compare* secondary cell.

primary colour Any one of a set of three coloured lights that can be mixed together to give the sensation of white light as well as approximating all the other colours of the spectrum. An infinite number of such sets exists, the condition being that none of the individual colours of a set should be able to be matched by mixing the other two; however, unless the colours are both intense and very different the range that they can match well will be limited. The set of primary colours most frequently used is red, green, and blue. *See also* colour.

primary winding The winding on the input side of a *transformer or *induction coil. *Compare* secondary winding.

principal axis *See* optical axis.

principal focus A point through which rays close to and parallel to the axis of a lens or spherical mirror pass, or appear to pass, after refraction or reflection. A mirror has one principal focus, a lens has a principal focus on both sides.

principal plane The plane that is perpendicular to the optical axis of a lens and that passes through the optical centre. A thick lens has two principal planes, each passing through a *principal point.

principal point Either of two points on the principal axis of a thick lens from which simply related distances can be measured, as from the optical centre of a thin lens.

principle of superposition The resultant displacement at any point in a region through which two waves of the same type pass is the algebraic sum of the displacements that the two would separately produce at that point. Both waves leave the region of superposition unaltered.

printed circuit An electronic circuit consisting of a conducting material deposited (printed) onto the surface of an insulating sheet. These devices are now common in all types of electronic equipment, facilitating batch production and eliminating the unreliability of the hand-soldered joint.

prism 1. (in mathematics) A polyhedron with two parallel congruent polygons as bases and parallelograms for all other faces. A *triangular prism* has triangular bases. **2.** (in optics) A block of glass or other transparent material, usually having triangular bases. Prisms have several uses in optical systems: they can be used to deviate a ray, to disperse white light into the visible spectrum, or to erect an inverted image (*see* binoculars). Prisms of other materials are used for different kinds of radiation. *See also* Nicol prism; Wollaston prism.

probability The likelihood of a particular event occurring. If there are n equally likely outcomes of some experiment, and a ways in which event E could occur, then the probability of event E is a/n. For instance, if a die is thrown there are 6 possible outcomes and 3 ways in which an odd number may occur. The probability of throwing an odd number is $3/6 = 1/2$.

program *See* computer.

progressive wave *See* wave.

projectile Any body that is thrown or projected. If the projectile is discharged on the surface of the earth at an angle θ to the horizontal it will describe a parabolic flight path (if $\theta < 90°$ and the initial velocity < the

*escape velocity). Neglecting air resistance, the maximum height of this flight path will be $(v^2\sin^2\theta)/2g$, where v is the velocity of discharge and g is the acceleration of free fall. The horizontal distance covered will be $(v^2\sin2\theta)/g$ and the time of the flight will be $(2v\sin\theta)/g$.

projector An optical device for throwing a large image of a two-dimensional object onto a screen. In an *episcope*, light is reflected from the surface of an opaque two-dimensional object (such as a diagram or photographic print) and an enlarged image is thrown onto a distant screen by means of a system of mirrors and lenses. The *diascope* passes light through the two-dimensional object (such as a photographic transparency, slide, or film) and uses a converging projection lens to form an enlarged image on a distant screen. An *epidiascope* is a device that can be used as both episcope and diascope. An *overhead projector* is a form of diascope that throws its image on a wall or screen behind and above the operator. In a *motion-picture projector* (or *ciné projector*) the film, consisting of a long sequence of transparent pictures, is driven by a motor past the light source in such a way that each picture comes to rest for a brief period in front of the light source. The illusion of motion is created as each image on the screen is replaced by the next; during the picture change the light is interrupted.

prompt neutrons The neutrons emitted during a nuclear fission process within less than a microsecond of fission. *Compare* delayed neutrons.

proper motion The apparent angular motion of a star on the *celestial sphere. This is motion in a direction that is perpendicular to the line of sight.

proportional counter A type of detector for *ionizing radiation in which the size of the output pulse is proportional to the number of ions formed in the initial ionizing event. It operates in a voltage region, called the *proportional region*, intermediate between that of an *ionization chamber and a *Geiger counter, avalanche ionization being limited to the immediate vicinity of the primary ionization rather than the entire length of the central wire electrode.

proportional limit *See* elasticity.

protactinium Symbol Pa. A radioactive metallic element belonging to the actinoids; a.n. 91; r.a.m. 231.036; r.d. 15.37 (calculated); m.p. <1600°C (estimated). The most stable isotope, protactinium–231, has a half-life of 3.43×10^4 years; at least ten other radioisotopes are known. Protactinium–231 occurs in all uranium ores as it is derived from uranium–235. Protactinium has no practical applications; it was discovered by Lise Meitner and Otto Hahn in 1917.

proton An *elementary particle that is stable, bears a positive charge equal in magnitude to that of the *electron, and has a mass of $1.672\,614 \times 10^{-27}$ kg, which is 1836.12 times that of the electron. The proton occurs in all atomic nuclei (the hydrogen nucleus consists of a single proton).

proton decay A process of the type
$$p \rightarrow e^+ + \pi^0$$
where a proton decays into a positron and a pion, predicted to occur in *grand unified theories (GUTs) because baryon number is no longer conserved. The lifetime depends on the theory used and is typically 10^{35} years, but a combination of GUTs and *supersymmetry gives a lifetime of about 10^{45} years. Considerable experimental effort has been spent in looking for proton decay, so far with no success.

proton number *See* atomic number.

protostar *See* stellar evolution.

221

psi particle

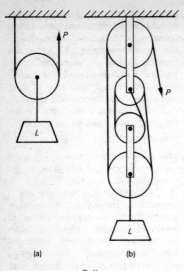

(a)   (b)

Pulleys

psi particle (J particle) A *meson discovered in 1974, which led to the extension of the quark model and the hypothesis that a fourth quark existed with the property of charm (see elementary particles). The psi particle is believed to consist of a charmed quark and its antiquark.

psychrometer See hygrometer.

Ptolemaic astronomy The system of astronomy originally proposed by Apollonius of Perga in the third century BC and completed by Claudius Ptolemaeus of Alexandria (100–178 AD). It assumed that the earth was at the centre of the universe and that each known planet, the moon, and the sun moved round it in a circular orbit, called the deferent. In addition to this motion the orbiting bodies also described epicycles, small circles about points on the deferent. The system gave moderately good predictions, but was completely replaced by the heliocentric astronomy of Copernicus in the 16th century. The Ptolemaic system was published by Ptolemaeus in the work known by its Arabic name, the *Almagest*.

p-type conductivity See semiconductor; transistor.

pulley A simple machine consisting of a wheel with a flat, crowned, or grooved rim to take a belt, rope, or chain with which a load can be raised.

In fig (a), assuming the system is frictionless, the force P in any part of the rope is constant, therefore $2P = L$, where L is the load. In general, $nP = L$, where n is the number of supporting ropes. In fig (b), the number of supporting ropes is 4. The mechanical advantage of a pulley system is the ratio of the load, L, to the effort applied to the free end of the rope, P, i.e. mechanical advantage = $L/P = L(L/n)^{-1} = n$. Thus in fig (b) the mechanical advantage is 4. A combination of ropes and pulleys as in fig (b) is called a *block and tackle*.

pulsar A celestial source of radiation emitted in brief (0.03 second to 4 seconds) regular pulses. First discovered in 1968, pulsars are believed to be rotating *neutron stars. The strong magnetic field of the neutron star concentrates charged particles in two regions and the radiation is emitted in two directional beams. The pulsing effect occurs as the beams rotate. Most pulsars are radio sources (emit electromagnetic radiation of radio frequencies) but a few that emit light or X-rays have been detected. Over 300 pulsars are now known in our Galaxy.

pulsatance See angular frequency.

pulse a. A brief variation in a quantity, usually for a finite time, especially in a quantity that is normally constant. **b.** A series of such variations having a regular waveform in which the variable quantity rises sharply from a base value to a maximum value and then falls back to the base value in a relatively short time.

pulse jet A type of ramjet (*see* jet propulsion) in which a louvred valve at the front of the projectile is blown open by the ram effect of the moving projectile and remains open until pressure has built up in the combustion chamber. Fuel is then admitted and the mixture exploded by spark ignition. This closes the louvred valve and produces thrust at the open rear end of the projectile. The German flying bombs of World War II were powered by pulse jets.

pulse modulation *See* modulation.

pump A device that imparts energy to a fluid in order to move it from one place or level to another or to raise its pressure (*compare* vacuum pump). *Centrifugal pumps* and *turbines have rotating impellers, which increase the velocity of the fluid, part of the energy so acquired by the fluid then being converted to pressure energy. Displacement pumps act directly on the fluid, forcing it to flow against a pressure. They include piston, plunger, gear, screw, and cam pumps. *See also* electromagnetic pump.

pyramid A solid having a polygonal base with n sides, each side forming the base of a triangle. The n triangles so formed have a common vertex. The *axis* of the pyramid is a line joining the vertex to the centre of symmetry of the base. If the axis is perpendicular to the base the solid is a *right pyramid*. A *square pyramid* has a square base and a *triangular pyramid* has a triangular base (*see* tetrahedron). The volume of a pyramid is one third of the base area multiplied by the height.

pyroelectricity The property of certain crystals, such as tourmaline, of acquiring opposite electrical charges on opposite faces when heated. In tourmaline a rise in temperature of 1 K at room temperature produces a polarization of some 10^{-5} C m^{-2}.

pyrometric cones *See* Seger cones.

pyrometry The measurement of high temperatures from the amount of radiation emitted, using a *pyrometer*. Modern *narrow-band* or *spectral* pyrometers use infrared-sensitive *photoelectric cells behind filters that exclude visible light. In the *optical pyrometer* (or disappearing filament pyrometer) the image of the incandescent source is focused in the plane of a tungsten filament that is heated electrically. A variable resistor is used to adjust the current through the filament until it blends into the image of the source, when viewed through a red filter and an eyepiece. The temperature is then read from a calibrated ammeter or a calibrated dial on the variable resistor. In the *total-radiation pyrometer* radiation emitted by the source is focused by a concave mirror onto a blackened foil to which a thermopile is attached. From the e.m.f. produced by the thermopile the temperature of the source can be calculated.

pyrophoric Igniting spontaneously in air. *Pyrophoric alloys* are alloys that give sparks when struck. *See* misch metal.

Q

QCD *See* quantum chromodynamics.

QED *See* quantum electrodynamics.

QFD Quantum flavourdynamics. *See* electroweak theory.

QSG *See* quasars.

QSO *See* quasars.

QSS *See* quasars.

quadratic equation An equation of the second degree having the form $ax^2 + bx + c = 0$. Its roots are:
$$x = [-b \pm \sqrt{(b^2 - 4ac)}]/2a.$$

quadrature The position of the moon or an outer planet when the line joining it to the earth makes a right

angle with a line joining the earth to the sun.

quality of sound (timbre) The quality a musical note has as a result of the presence of *harmonics. A pure note consists only of the *fundamental; however, a note from a musical instrument will have several harmonics present, depending on the type of instrument and the way in which it is played. For example, a plucked string (as in a guitar) produces a series of harmonics of diminishing intensity, whereas a struck string (as in a piano) produces a series of harmonics of more nearly equal intensity.

quantum The minimum amount by which certain properties, such as energy or angular momentum, of a system can change. Such properties do not, therefore, vary continuously, but in integral multiples of the relevant quantum. This concept forms the basis of the *quantum theory. In waves and fields the quantum can be regarded as an excitation, giving a particle-like interpretation to the wave or field. Thus, the quantum of the electromagnetic field is the *photon and the *graviton is the quantum of the gravitational field. *See* quantum mechanics.

quantum chromodynamics (QCD) A *gauge theory that describes the strong interaction in terms of quarks and antiquarks and the exchange of massless gluons between them (*see also* elementary particles). Quantum chromodynamics is similar to quantum electrodynamics (QED), with colour being analogous to electric charge and the gluon being the analogue of the photon. The gauge group of QCD is non-Abelian and the theory is much more complicated than quantum electrodynamics; the gauge symmetry in QCD is not a *broken symmetry.

QCD has the important property of *asymptotic freedom – that at very high energies (and, hence, short dis-

tances) the interactions between quarks tend to zero as the distance between them tends to zero. Because of asymptotic freedom, perturbation theory may be used to calculate the high energy aspects of strong interactions, such as those described by the *parton model.

quantum electrodynamics (QED) The study of the properties of electromagnetic radiation and the way in which it interacts with charged matter in terms of *quantum mechanics. The collision of a moving electron with a proton, in this theory, can be visualized by a space–time diagram (*Feynman diagram*) in which photons are exchanged (see illustration).

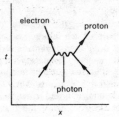

electron

proton

t

photon

x

An electron-proton collision

*Perturbation-theory calculations using Feynman diagrams enable an agreement between theory and experiment to a greater accuracy than one part in 10^9 to be obtained. Because of this, QED is the most accurate theory known in physical science. Although many of the effects calculated in QED are very small (about 4×10^{-6} eV), such as *energy level splitting in the spectra of *atoms, they are of great significance for demonstrating the physical reality of fluctuations and polarization in the vacuum state. QED is a *gauge theory for which the gauge *group is Abelian.

quantum field theory A quantum-mechanical theory applied to systems that have an infinite number of degrees of freedom. In quantum field theories, particles are represented by

fields that have quantized normal modes of oscillation. For instance, *quantum electrodynamics is a quantum field theory in which the photon is emitted or absorbed by particles; the photon is the quantum of the electromagnetic field. *Relativistic quantum field theories* are used to describe fundamental interactions between elementary particles. They predict the existence of *antiparticles and also show the connection between spin and statistics that leads to the Pauli exclusion principle (*see* spin–statistics theorem). In spite of their success, it is not clear whether a quantum field theory can give a completely unified description of all interactions (including the gravitational interaction).

quantum flavourdynamics (QFD) *See* electroweak theory.

quantum Hall effect A quantum mechanical version of the *Hall effect found at very low temperatures, in which the Hall coefficient R_H is proportional to h/e^2, where h is the Planck constant and e is the charge of the electron. Thus, the Hall coefficient is quantized. There are two types of quantum Hall effect. The *integer quantum Hall effect* has R_H given as an integer with great precision. It can be used for precision measurements of constants such as e and h. In the *fractional quantum Hall effect*, R_H has fractional values.

The integer quantum Hall effect can be understood in terms of noninteracting electrons, whereas the fractional effect is thought to result from many-electron interactions in two-dimensional systems, and be an example of anyons (*see* quantum statistics).

quantum jump A change in a system (e.g. an atom or molecule) from one quantum state to another.

quantum mechanics A system of mechanics that was developed from *quantum theory and is used to explain the properties of atoms and

molecules. Using the energy *quantum as a starting point it incorporates Heisenberg's *uncertainty principle and the *de Broglie wavelength to establish the wave–particle duality (*see* complementarity) on which *Schrödinger's equation is based. This form of quantum mechanics is called *wave mechanics*. An alternative but equivalent formalism, *matrix mechanics*, is based on mathematical operators.

quantum number *See* atom; spin.

quantum state The state of a quantized system as described by its quantum numbers. For instance, the state of a hydrogen *atom is described by the four quantum numbers n, l, m, m_s. In the ground state they have values 1, 0, 0, and ½ respectively.

quantum statistics A statistical description of a system of particles that obeys the rules of *quantum mechanics rather than classical mechanics. In quantum statistics, energy states are considered to be quantized. *Bose–Einstein statistics* apply if any number of particles can occupy a given quantum state. Such particles are called *bosons*. Bosons have an angular momentum $nh/2\pi$, where n is zero or an integer and h is the Planck constant. For identical bosons the *wave function is always symmetric. If only one particle may occupy each quantum state, *Fermi–Dirac statistics* apply and the particles are called *fermions*. Fermions have a total angular momentum $(n + ½)h$ and any wave function that involves identical fermions is always antisymmetric.

The relation between the spin and statistics of particles is given by the *spin–statistics theorem.

In two-space dimensions, it is possible that there are particles (or *quasiparticles) that have statistics intermediate between bosons and fermions. These particles are known as *anyons*; for identical anyons the

quantum theory

wave function is not symmetric (a
phase sign of +1) or antisymmetric
(a phase sign of –1), but interpolates
continuously between +1 and –1.
Anyons may be involved in the fractional *quantum Hall effect and have
been suggested as a mechanism for
high-temperature *superconductivity.

quantum theory The theory devised
by Max Planck (1858–1947) in 1900
to account for the emission of the
black-body radiation from hot bodies.
According to this theory energy is
emitted in quanta (see quantum), each
of which has an energy equal to $h\nu$,
where h is the *Planck constant and ν
is the frequency of the radiation. This
theory led to the modern theory of
the interaction between matter and
radiation known as *quantum
mechanics, which generalizes and
replaces classical mechanics and Maxwell's electromagnetic theory. In
nonrelativistic quantum theory particles
are assumed to be neither created nor
destroyed, to move slowly relative to
the speed of light, and to have a
mass that does not change with velocity. These assumptions apply to
atomic and molecular phenomena and
to some aspects of nuclear physics.
Relativistic quantum theory applies to
particles that travel at or near the
speed of light.

quark See elementary particles.

quark confinement The hypothesis
that free quarks can never be seen in
isolation. It is a result of *quantum
chromodynamics, in which the property of *asymptotic freedom means
that the interactions between quarks
get weaker as the distance between
them gets smaller, and tends to zero
as the distance between them tends to
zero. Conversely, the attractive interactions between quarks get stronger
as the distance between them gets
greater, and the quark-confinement
hypothesis is that the quarks cannot
escape from one another. It is possible that at very high temperatures,

such as those in the *early universe,
quarks may become free. The temperature at which this occurs is called
the *deconfinement temperature*.

quarter-wave plate See retardation
plate.

quartz The most abundant and common mineral, consisting of crystalline
silica (silicon dioxide, SiO_2), crystalliz-
ing in the trigonal system. It has a
hardness of 7 on the Mohs' scale.
The mineral has the property of being
piezoelectric and hence is used to
make oscillators for clocks (see quartz
clock), radios, and radar instruments.
It is also used in optical instruments
and in glass, glaze, and abrasives.

quartz clock A clock based on a
*piezoelectric crystal of quartz. Each
quartz crystal has a natural frequency
of vibration, which depends on its
size and shape. If such a crystal is
introduced into an oscillating electronic circuit that resonates at a frequency very close to that of the natural frequency of the crystal, the whole
circuit (including the crystal) will
oscillate at the crystal's natural frequency and the frequency will remain
constant over considerable periods (a
good crystal will maintain oscillation
for a year with an accumulated error
of less than 0.1 second). In a quartz
clock or watch the alternating current
from the oscillating circuit containing
such a crystal is amplified and the
frequency subdivided until it is suitable to drive a synchronous motor,
which in turn drives a gear train to
operate hands. Alternatively it is used
to activate a digital display.

quasars A class of astronomical
objects that appear on optical
photographs as starlike but have large
*redshifts quite unlike those of stars.
They were first observed in 1961
when it was found that strong radio
emission was emanating from many
of these starlike bodies. Over 600
such objects are now known and their
redshifts can be as high as 4. The

redshifts are characteristic of the *expansion of the universe. This *cosmological redshift* is the explanation of the high observed redshifts of quasars favoured by most astronomers. (A few, however, maintain that the redshift could be a local Doppler effect, characteristic of movement relative to the earth and sun of nearby objects in the Galaxy, or a gravitational effect.) If the redshifts are cosmological, quasars are the most distant objects in the universe, some being up to 10^{10} light-years away. The exact nature of quasars is unknown but it is believed that they are the nuclei of galaxies in which there is violent activity. The luminosity of the nucleus is so much greater than that of the rest of the galaxy that the source appears pointlike. It has been proposed that the power source in a quasar is a supermassive *black hole accreting material from the stars and gas in the surrounding galaxy.

The name *quasar* is a contraction of quasistellar object (*QSO*) or quasistellar galaxy (*QSG*). Quasars that are also radio sources are sometimes called quasistellar radio sources (*QSS*).

quasiparticle A long-lived single-particle *excitation in the quantum theory of many-body systems, in which the excitations of the individual particles are modified by their interactions with the surrounding medium.

quenching 1. The rapid cooling of a metal by immersing it in a bath of liquid in order to improve its properties. Steels are quenched to make them harder but some nonferrous metals are quenched for other reasons (copper, for example, is made softer by quenching). **2.** The process of inhibiting a continuous discharge in a *Geiger counter so that the incidence of further ionizing radiation can cause a new discharge. This is achieved by introducing a quenching vapour, such as methane mixed with argon or neon into the tube.

R

racemic mixture (racemate) A mixture of equal quantities of the (+)- or *d*- and (–)- or *l*- forms of an optically active compound. Racemic mixtures are denoted by the prefix (±)- or *dl*- (e.g. (±)-lactic acid). A racemic mixture shows no *optical activity.

rad *See* radiation units.

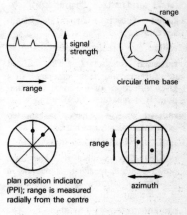

plan position indicator (PPI); range is measured radially from the centre

Types of cathode ray tube radar displays

radar (radio detection and ranging) A method of detecting the presence, position, and direction of motion of distant objects (such as ships and aircraft) by means of their ability to reflect a beam of electromagnetic radiation of centimetric wavelengths. It is also used for navigation and guidance. It consists of a transmitter producing radio-frequency radiation, often pulsed, which is fed to a movable aerial from which it is transmitted as a beam. If the beam is interrupted by a solid object, a part of the energy of the radiation is reflected back to the aerial. Signals received by the aerial are passed to the receiver, where they are amplified and detected. An echo from a reflec-

tion of a solid object is indicated by a sudden rise in the detector output. The time taken for a pulse to reach the object and be reflected back (t) enables the distance away (d) of the target to be calculated from the equation $d = ct/2$, where c is the speed of light. In some systems the speed of the object can be measured using the *Doppler effect. The output of the detector is usually displayed on a cathode-ray tube in a variety of different formats (see illustration).

radial velocity *See* line-of-sight velocity.

radian *See* circular measure.

radiance Symbol L_e. The radiant intensity per unit transverse area, in a given direction, of a source of radiation. It is measured in $W\ sr^{-1}\ m^{-2}$.

radiant energy Energy transmitted as electromagnetic radiation.

radiant exitance *See* exitance.

radiant flux Symbol Φ_e. The total power emitted, received, or passing in the form of electromagnetic radiation. It is measured in watts.

radiant intensity Symbol I_e. The *radiant flux per unit solid angle emitted by a point source. It is measured in watts per steradian.

radiation 1. Energy travelling in the form of electromagnetic waves or photons. **2.** A stream of particles, especially alpha-or beta-particles from a radioactive source or neutrons from a nuclear reactor.

radiation belts *See* Van Allen belts.

radiation damage Harmful changes that occur to inanimate materials and living organisms as a result of exposure to energetic electrons, nucleons, fission fragments, or high-energy electromagnetic radiation. In inanimate materials the damage may be caused by electronic excitation, ionization, transmutation, or displacement of atoms. In organisms, these mechanisms can cause changes to cells that alter their genetic structure, interfere with their division, or kill them. In humans, these changes can lead to *radiation sickness*, *radiation burns* (from large doses of radiation), or to long-term damage of several kinds, the most serious of which result in various forms of cancer (especially leukaemia).

radiation pressure The pressure exerted on a surface by electromagnetic radiation. As radiation carries momentum as well as energy it exerts a force when it meets a surface, i.e. the *photons transfer momentum when they strike the surface. The pressure is usually negligible on large bodies, for example, the pressure of radiation from the sun on the surface of the earth is of the order of 10^{-5} pascal, but on small bodies it can have a considerable effect, driving them away from the radiation source. Radiation pressure is also important in the interiors of stars of very high mass.

radiation temperature The surface temperature of a celestial body as calculated by *Stefan's law, assuming that the body behaves as a *black body. The radiation temperature is usually measured over a narrow portion of the electromagnetic spectrum, such as the visible range (which gives the *optical temperature*).

radiation units Units of measurement used to express the *activity of a radionuclide and the *dose of ionizing radiation. The units *curie*, *roentgen*, *rad*, and *rem* are not coherent with SI units but their temporary use with SI units has been approved while the derived SI units *becquerel*, *gray*, and *sievert* become familiar.

The becquerel (Bq), the SI unit of activity, is the activity of a radionuclide decaying at a rate, on average, of one spontaneous nuclear transition per second. Thus $1\ Bq = 1\ s^{-1}$. The former unit, the curie (Ci), is equal to 3.7×10^{10} Bq. The curie was origi-

nally chosen to approximate the activity of 1 gram of radium–226.

The gray (Gy), the SI unit of absorbed dose, is the absorbed dose when the energy per unit mass imparted to matter by ionizing radiation is 1 joule per kilogram. The former unit, the rad (rd), is equal to 10^{-2} Gy.

The sievert (Sv), the SI unit of dose equivalent, is the dose equivalent when the absorbed dose of ionizing radiation multiplied by the stipulated dimensionless factors is 1 $J\,kg^{-1}$. As different types of radiation cause different effects in biological tissue a weighted absorbed dose, called the *dose equivalent*, is used in which the absorbed dose is modified by multiplying it by dimensionless factors stipulated by the International Commission on Radiological Protection. The former unit of dose equivalent, the rem (originally an acronym for *r*oentgen equivalent *m*an), is equal to 10^{-2} Sv.

In SI units, exposure to ionizing radiation is expressed in coulombs per kilogram, the quantity of X- or gamma-radiation that produces ion pairs carrying 1 coulomb of charge of either sign in 1 kilogram of pure dry air. The former unit, the roentgen (R), is equal to 2.58 × 10^{-4} $C\,kg^{-1}$.

radiative collision A collision between charged particles in which part of the kinetic energy is radiated in the form of photons.

radical A root of a number or a quantity. The symbol $\sqrt{}$ is called the *radical sign*.

radio A means of transmitting information in which the transmission medium consists of electromagnetic radiation. Information is transmitted by means of the *modulation of a *carrier wave in a transmitter; the modulated carrier wave is fed to a transmitting aerial from which it is broadcast through the atmosphere or through space. A receiving aerial forms part of a *resonant circuit, which can be tuned to the frequency of the carrier wave, enabling the receiver that it feeds selectively to amplify and then to demodulate the transmitted signal. A replica of the original information is thus produced by the receiver. *See also* radio transmission.

radioactive age The age of an archaeological or geological specimen as determined by a process that depends on a radioactive decay. *See* carbon dating; fission-track dating; potassium–argon dating; rubidium–strontium dating; uranium–lead dating.

radioactive series A series of radioactive nuclides in which each member of the series is formed by the decay of the nuclide before it. The series ends with a stable nuclide. Three radioactive series occur naturally, those headed by thorium–232 (*thorium series*), uranium–235 (*actinium series*), and uranium–238 (*uranium series*). All three series end with an isotope of lead. The neptunium series starts with the artificial isotope plutonium–241, which decays to neptunium–237, and ends with bismuth–209.

radioactive tracing *See* labelling.

radioactive waste (nuclear waste) Any waste material that contains *radionuclides. These wastes are produced in the mining of radioactive ores, the normal running of nuclear power stations and other reactors, the manufacture of nuclear weapons, and in research laboratories. Because high-level radioactive wastes can be extremely dangerous to all living matter and because they may contain radionuclides having half-lives of many thousands of years, their disposal has to be controlled with great stringency.

The first stage in disposal involves extensive reprocessing to retrieve usable material and reduce the activ-

ity of the waste. Subsequent final disposal, usually of solid material in strong metal canisters, involves burial of the material. The two currently favoured categories of sites for burial are deep (600 metres) mined cavities in stable geological formations on land and in red clay some 50–100 metres below the seabed away from tectonic plate margins and where the currents at the bottom of the sea are weak.

radioactivity The spontaneous disintegration of certain atomic nuclei accompanied by the emission of alpha-particles (helium nuclei), beta-particles (electrons), or gamma-radiation (short-wave electromagnetic waves).

Natural radioactivity is the result of the spontaneous disintegration of naturally occurring radioisotopes. Many radioisotopes can be arranged in three *radioactive series. The rate of disintegration is uninfluenced by chemical changes or any normal changes in their environment. However, radioactivity can be induced in many nuclides by bombarding them with neutrons or other particles. *See also* half-life; ionizing radiation; radiation units.

radio astronomy The study of the radio-frequency radiation emitted by celestial bodies. This branch of astronomy began in 1932 when a US engineer, Karl Jansky (1905–40), first detected radio waves from outside the earth's atmosphere. *See* radio source; radio telescope; radio window.

radiobiology The branch of biology concerned with the effects of radioactive substances on living organisms and the use of radioactive tracers to study metabolic processes (*see* labelling).

radiocarbon dating *See* carbon dating.

radiochemistry The branch of chemistry concerned with radioactive compounds and with ionization. It includes the study of compounds of radioactive elements and the preparation and use of compounds containing radioactive atoms. *See* labelling; radiolysis.

radio frequencies The range of frequencies, between about 3 kilohertz and 300 gigahertz, over which electromagnetic radiation is used in radio transmission. It is subdivided into eight equal bands, known as very low frequency, low frequency, medium frequency, high frequency, very high frequency, and extremely high frequency.

radio galaxies A *radio source outside the Galaxy that has been identified with an optically visible galaxy. These radio galaxies are distinguished from normal galaxies by having a radio power output some 10^6 times greater (i.e. up to 10^{38} watts rather than 10^{32} W). The source of the radio-frequency energy is associated with violent activity, involving the ejection of relativistic jets of particles from the nucleus of the galaxy. It has been suggested that the sources are powered by supermassive *black holes in the nucleus.

radiography The process or technique of producing images of an opaque object on photographic film or on a fluorescent screen by means of radiation (either particles or electromagnetic waves of short wavelength, such as X-rays and gamma-rays). The photograph produced is called a *radiograph*. The process is widely used in diagnostic *radiology, using X-rays, and in flaw detection in industrial products, using high-energy X-rays, gamma-radiations, neutron beams, and (more recently) beams of charged particles.

radio interferometry *See* radio telescope.

radioisotope (radioactive isotope) An isotope of an element that is radioactive. *See* labelling.

radiolocation The location of distant objects by means of *radar.

radiology The study and use of X-rays, radioactive materials, and other ionizing radiations for medical purposes, especially for diagnosis (*diagnostic radiology*) and the treatment of cancer and allied diseases (*radiotherapy*).

radiolysis The use of ionizing radiation to produce chemical reactions. The radiation used includes alpha particles, electrons, neutrons, X-rays, and gamma rays from radioactive materials or from accelerators. Energy transfer produces ions and excited species, which undergo further reaction. A particular feature of radiolysis is the formation of short-lived solvated electrons in water and other polar solvents.

radiometric dating (radioactive dating) *See* dating techniques; radioactive age.

radionuclide (radioactive nuclide) A *nuclide that is radioactive.

radio-opaque *See* opacity.

radiosonde A meteorological instrument that measures temperature, pressure, humidity, and winds in the upper atmosphere. It consists of a package of instruments and a radio transmitter attached to a balloon. The data is relayed back to earth by the transmitter. The position of the balloon can be found by radar and from its changes in position the wind velocities can be calculated.

radio source An astronomical object that has been observed with a *radio telescope to emit radio-frequency electromagnetic radiation. Radio sources within the Galaxy include Jupiter, the sun, pulsars, and background radiation arising from *synchrotron radiation. Sources outside the Galaxy include spiral galaxies, *radio galaxies, and *quasars. Radio sources were formerly known as *radio stars*.

radio star *See* radio source.

radio telescope An instrument for detecting and measuring electromagnetic radiation of radio frequencies that have passed through the *radio window in the earth's atmosphere and reached the surface of the earth. There are a great diversity of *radio sources within the universe and radio telescopes are required to detect both continuous emissions and specific spectral lines. They therefore require the highest possible angular resolution so that the details of radio sources can be studied and they should be able to pick up weak signals. The simplest radio telescope consists of a paraboloidal steerable-dish aerial together with ancillary amplifiers. The paraboloidal reflecting dish surface reflects the incoming signal to the principal focus of the reflector. At this point the radio-frequency signals are amplified up to 1000 times and converted to a lower, intermediate, frequency before transmission by cable to the control building. Here the intermediate frequency is amplified again and passed to the detector and display unit. As the radio waves arriving from the surface of the reflector at the focus must be in phase, the surface of the dish must be very accurately constructed; for example, a 100-metre-diameter dish must be accurate to the nearest millimetre, when receiving radiation of 1 cm wavelength. To overcome the problem of constructing large dishes to such a high accuracy, the technique of *radio interferometry* has been developed. In this technique an array of small aerials connected by cable is used to simulate a large dish aerial. In earth-rotation *aperture synthesis*, the individual positions and displacements of an array of only a few such small aerials can be made to simulate an enormous dish aerial as the earth rotates. All but the smallest steerable dishes are constructed from metal mesh so that wind can pass through them. A few very large fixed dishes

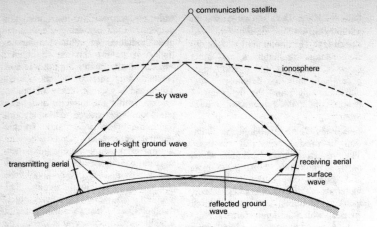

Radio transmission

have been built into the earth's surface.

radiotherapy *See* radiology.

radio transmission The transmission of radio waves from a transmitting aerial to a receiving aerial. The radiation may take several paths (see illustration). The sum of the line-of-sight ground wave, the reflected ground wave, and the surface wave is called the *ground wave* (or *tropospheric wave*). *Sky waves* (or *ionospheric waves*) are reflected by the *ionosphere and enable long-distance transmissions to be made. The ionization of atoms and molecules in the ionosphere is caused largely by solar ultraviolet and X-radiation and therefore conditions differ between night and day. Ionization in the lower E-region of the ionosphere falls off at night in the absence of sunlight and ions and electrons tend to recombine. However, in the less dense (higher) F-region there are fewer collisions between ions and electrons and therefore fewer recombinations at night. The F-region is therefore a more effective reflector at night.

The UHF and VHF waves used in television broadcasting penetrate the ionosphere with little reflection. Therefore TV broadcasts can only be made over long distances by means of artificial satellites. *See also* radio.

radiotransparent Transparent to radiation, especially to X-rays and gamma-rays.

radio window A region of the electromagnetic spectrum in the radio-frequency band within which radio waves can be transmitted through the earth's atmosphere without significant reflection or attenuation by constituents of the atmosphere. It extends from about 10 megahertz to 100 gigahertz and enables radiation in this range from celestial radio sources to be picked up by *radio telescopes on the earth's surface. Below 100 MHz incoming radio waves are reflected by the *ionosphere and those above 100 GHz are increasingly affected by molecular absorption.

radium Symbol Ra. A radioactive metallic element; a.n. 88; r.a.m. 226.0254; r.d. ~5; m.p. 700°C; b.p. 1140°C. It occurs in uranium ores (e.g. pitchblende). The most stable isotope is radium–226 (half-life 1602 years), which decays to radon. It is used as a radioactive source in

research and, to some extent, in radiotherapy. The element was isolated from pitchblende in 1898 by Marie and Pierre Curie.

radius of curvature *See* centre of curvature.

radius of gyration Symbol k. The square root of the ratio of the *moment of inertia of a rigid body about an axis to the body's mass, i.e. $k^2 = I/m$, where I is the body's moment of inertia and m is its mass. If a rigid body has a moment of inertia I about an axis and mass m it behaves as if all its mass is rotating at a distance k from the axis.

radius vector *See* polar coordinates.

radon Symbol Rn. A colourless radioactive gaseous element; a.n. 86; r.a.m. 222; d. 9.73 g dm^{-3}; m.p. $-71°C$; b.p. $-61.8°C$. At least 20 isotopes are known, the most stable being radon–222 (half-life 3.8 days). It is formed by decay of radium–226 and undergoes alpha decay. It is used in radiotherapy. It was first isolated by Ramsey and Gray in 1908.

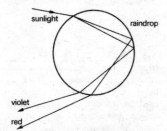

Primary rainbow (one internal reflection)

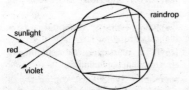

Secondary rainbow (two internal reflections)

rainbow An optical phenomenon that appears as an arc of the colours of the spectrum across the sky when falling water droplets are illuminated by sunlight from behind the observer. The colours are produced by the refraction and internal reflection of the sunlight by the water drops. Two bows may be visible, the inner ring being known as the primary bow and the outer, in which the colours are reversed, as the secondary bow (see illustration).

r.a.m. *See* relative atomic mass.

Raman effect A type of *scattering of electromagnetic radiation in which light suffers a change in frequency and a change in phase as it passes through a material medium. The intensity of Raman scattering is about one-thousandth of that in Rayleigh scattering in liquids; for this reason it was not discovered until 1928. However, it was not until the development of the laser that the effect was put to use.

In *Raman spectroscopy* light from a laser is passed through a substance and the scattering is analysed spectroscopically. The new frequencies in the *Raman spectrum* of monochromatic light scattered by a substance are characteristic of the substance. Both inelastic and superelastic scattering occurs. The technique is used as a means of determining molecular structure and as a tool in chemical analysis. The effect was discovered by the Indian scientist Sir C. V. Raman (1888–1970).

ramjet *See* jet propulsion.

Ramsden eyepiece An eyepiece for optical instruments consisting of two identical plano-convex lenses with their convex faces pointing towards each other. They are separated by a distance of two thirds of the focal length of either lens.

Rankine cycle A cycle of operations in a heat engine. The Rankine cycle more closely approximates to the

Rankine temperature scale

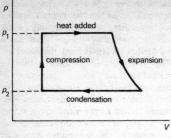

Rankine cycle

cycle of a real steam engine that does the *Carnot cycle. It therefore predicts a lower ideal thermal efficiency than the Carnot cycle. In the Rankine cycle (see illustration), heat is added at constant pressure p_1, at which water is converted in a boiler to superheated steam; the steam expands at constant entropy to a pressure p_2 in the cylinder; heat is rejected at constant pressure p_2 in a condenser; the water so formed is compressed at constant entropy to pressure p_1 by a feed pump. The cycle was devised by W. J. M. Rankine (1820–70).

Rankine temperature scale An absolute temperature scale based on the Fahrenheit scale. Absolute zero on this scale, $0°R$, is equivalent to $-459.67°F$ and the melting point of ice ($32°F$) is therefore ($459.67 + 32 = 491.67)°R$. The scale was devised by W. J. M. Rankine (1820–70).

Raoult's law The partial vapour pressure of a solvent is proportional to its mole fraction. If p is the vapour pressure of the solvent (with a substance dissolved in it) and X the mole fraction of solvent (number of moles of solvent divided by total number of moles) then $p = p_0X$, where p_0 is the vapour pressure of the pure solvent. A solution that obeys Raoult's law is said to be an *ideal solution*. In general the law holds only for dilute solutions, although some mixtures of liquids obey it over a whole range of concentrations. Such solutions are *perfect solutions* and occur when the intermolecular forces between molecules of the pure substances are similar to the forces between molecules of one and molecules of the other. Deviations in Raoult's law for mixtures of liquids cause the formation of *azeotropes. The law was discovered by the French chemist François Raoult (1830–1901).

rarefaction A reduction in the pressure of a fluid and therefore of its density.

raster The pattern of scanning lines on the screen of the cathode-ray tube in a television receiver or other device that provides a visual display.

rationalized units A system of units in which the defining equations have been made to conform to the geometry of the system in a logical way. Thus equations that involve circular symmetry contain the factor 2π, while those involving spherical symmetry contain the factor 4π. *SI and *Heaviside–Lorentz units are rationalized; *Gaussian units are unrationalized.

rational number Any number that can be expressed as the ratio of two integers. For example, $0.3333\ldots$ is rational because it can be written as $1/3$. $\sqrt{2}$, however, is *irrational.

ray A narrow beam of radiation or an idealized representation of such a beam on a *ray diagram*, which can be used to indicate the positions of the object and image in a system of lenses or mirrors.

Rayleigh criterion *See* resolving power.

Rayleigh–Jeans formula *See* Planck's radiation law.

Rayleigh scattering *See* scattering of electromagnetic radiation.

reactance Symbol X. A property of a circuit containing inductance or capacitance that together with any

234

resistance makes up its *impedance. The impedance Z is given by $Z^2 = R^2 + X^2$, where R is the resistance. For a pure capacitance C, the reactance is given by $X_C = 1/2\pi fC$, where f is the frequency of the *alternating current; for a pure inductance L, $X_L = 2\pi fL$. If the resistance, inductance, and capacitance are in series the impedance $Z = \sqrt{[R^2 + (X_L - X_C)^2]}$. Reactance is measured in ohms.

reaction A force that is equal in magnitude but opposite in direction to some other force, in accordance with Newton's third law of motion. If a body A exerts a force on body B, then B exerts an equal and opposite force on A. Thus, every force could be described as 'a reaction', and the term is better avoided, although it is still used in such terms as 'reaction propulsion'.

reaction propulsion See jet propulsion.

reactor 1. See nuclear reactor. 2. Any device, such as an inductor or capacitor, that introduces *reactance into an electrical circuit.

real gas A gas that does not have the properties assigned to an *ideal gas. Its molecules have a finite size and there are forces between them (see equation of state).

real image See image.

real-is-positive convention (real-positive convention) A convention used in optical formulae relating to lenses and mirrors. In this convention, distances from optical components to real objects, images, and foci are taken as positive, whereas distances to virtual points are taken as negative.

Réaumur temperature scale A temperature scale in which the melting point of ice is taken as 0°R and the boiling point of water as 80°R. It was devised by René Antoine Réaumur (1683–1757).

recombination process The process in which a neutral atom or molecule is formed by the combination of a positive ion and a negative ion or electron; i.e. a process of the type:
$$A^+ + B^- \rightarrow AB$$
or
$$A^+ + e^- \rightarrow A$$
In recombination, the neutral species formed is usually in an excited state, from which it can decay with emission of light or other electromagnetic radiation.

rectification 1. (in physics) The process of obtaining a direct current from an alternating electrical supply. See rectifier. 2. (in chemistry) The process of purifying a liquid by distillation.

rectifier An electrical device that allows more current to flow in one direction than the other, thus enabling alternating e.m.f.s to drive only direct current. The device most commonly used for rectification is the semiconductor *diode. In half-wave rectification, achieved with one diode, a pulsating current is produced. In full-wave rectification two diodes are used, one pair conducting during the first half cycle and the other conducting during the second half (see illustration). The full-wave rectified signal can be smoothed using a capacitor or an inductor.

red giant A *giant star thought to be in the later stages of *stellar evolution. It has a surface temperature in the range 2000–3000 K and a diameter 10–100 times that of the sun. See also Hertzsprung–Russell diagram.

redshift 1. **(Doppler redshift)** A displacement of the lines in the spectra of certain galaxies towards the red end of the visible spectrum (i.e. towards longer wavelengths). It is usually interpreted as a *Doppler effect resulting from the recession of the galaxies along the line of sight (see expansion of the universe). The redshift is usually expressed as $\Delta\lambda/\lambda$,

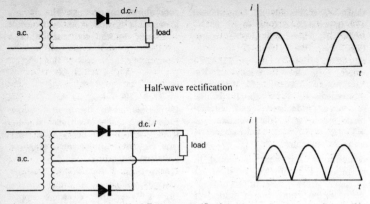

Half-wave rectification

Full-wave rectification

where $\Delta\lambda$ is the shift in wavelength of radiation of wavelength λ. For relatively low velocities of recession this is equivalent to v/c, where v is the relative velocity of recession and c is the speed of light. If very high velocities of recession are involved, a relativistic version of v/c is required (*see* relativistic velocity). The redshift of spectral lines occurs in all regions of the electromagnetic spectrum; ultraviolet can be shifted into the visible region and visible radiation can be shifted into the infrared region. **2. (gravitational** *or* **Einstein redshift)** A similar displacement of spectral lines towards the red caused not by a Doppler effect but by a high gravitational field. This type of redshift was predicted by Einstein and some astronomers believe that this is the cause of the large redshifts of *quasars, which can be as high as 3.35.

reflectance The ratio of the radiant flux reflected by a surface to that falling on it. This quantity is also known as the *radiant reflectance*. The radiant reflectance measured for a specified wavelength of the incident radiant flux is called the *spectral reflectance*.

reflecting telescope (reflector) *See* telescope.

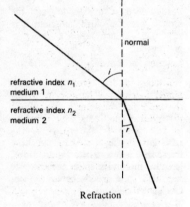

Refraction

reflection The return of all or part of a beam of particles or waves when it encounters the boundary between two media. The *laws of reflection* state: (1) that the incident ray, the reflected ray, and the normal to the reflecting interface at the point of incidence are all in the same plane; (2) that the angle of incidence equals the angle of reflection. *See also* mirror; reflectance; total internal reflection.

refracting telescope (refractor) *See* telescope.

refraction The change of direction suffered by wavefront as it passes obliquely from one medium to another in which its speed of propagation is altered. The phenomenon occurs with all types of waves, but is most familiar with light waves. In optics the direction is changed in accordance with *Snell's law*, i.e. $n_1 \sin i = n_2 \sin r$, where i and r are the angles made by the incident beam of radiation and the refracted beam to the normal (an imaginary line perpendicular to the interface between the two media); n_1 and n_2 are the *refractive indices of the two media. This law is also known as one of the *laws of refraction*. The other law of refraction is that the incident ray, the refracted ray, and the normal at the point of incidence lie in the same plane. The change of direction results from a change in the speed of propagation and the consequent change in wavelength (see illustration).

refractive index (refractive constant) Symbol n. The *absolute refractive index* of a medium is the ratio of the speed of electromagnetic radiation in free space to the speed of the radiation in that medium. As the refractive index varies with wavelength, the wavelength should be specified. It is usually given for yellow light (sodium D-lines; wavelength 589.3 nm). The *relative refractive index* is the ratio of the speed of light in one medium to that in an adjacent medium. See also refraction.

refractivity A measure of the extent to which a medium will deviate a ray of light entering its surface. In some contexts it is equal to $(n − 1)$, where n is the *refractive index.

refractometer Any of various instruments for measuring the *refractive index of a substance or medium. An example is the *Pulfrich refractometer*, which is a glass block with a polished top, with a small cell on top of the block for liquid samples. A telescope rotating on a vertical circular scale is used to find the angle (α) between the top of the block and the direction in which the limiting ray (from incident light parallel to the top face) leaves the side of the block. If the refractive index of the block (n_g) is known, that of the liquid can be calculated using $n = \sqrt{(n_g^2 - \sin^2\alpha)}$.

refractory 1. Having a high melting point. Metal oxides, carbides, and silicides tend to be refractory materials, and are extensively used for lining furnaces, etc. **2.** A refractory material.

refrigerant See refrigeration.

refrigeration The process of cooling a substance and of maintaining it at a temperature below that of its surroundings. Most commercial refrigerators use a cycle of operations equivalent to those of a *heat pump (see illustrations). In the *vapour-compression cycle* a volatile liquid (the *refrigerant*) passes to an evaporator where it boils, extracting heat from the refrigerator chamber as it does so. The vapour is then compressed by a compressor, where its temperature and pressure are raised. The compressed vapour then passes to a condenser, where the refrigerant discharges its heat to the surroundings.

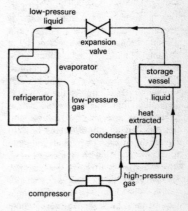

Refrigerator: vapour–compression cycle

Regnault's method

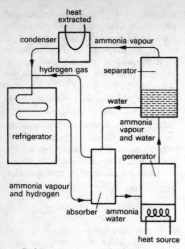

Refrigerator: vapour–absorption cycle

The liquid so formed then passes to a storage vessel and finally to an expansion valve, through which the high-pressure liquid expands to a low-pressure before entering the evaporator again. The refrigerant used is ammonia, sulphur dioxide, or a haloalkane.

In the *vapour-absorption cycle*, there are no moving parts and energy is supplied as heat, either an electric heater or a gas burner. The refrigerant is usually ammonia, which is liberated from a water solution and moved through the evaporator by a stream of hydrogen gas under pressure. Heat is applied to the generator, raising the ammonia and water vapour to the separator; the ammonia separates from the water and passes to the condenser, where it cools and liquefies, giving off its latent heat to the surroundings. The liquid ammonia is then mixed with hydrogen gas, which carries it through the evaporator and helps in the process of evaporation. The hydrogen and ammonia vapour then enter the absorber, where the water returned from the separator dissolves the ammonia before returning to the generator.

Small-scale refrigeration is sometimes achieved by means of the *Seebeck effect and the *Peltier effect at junctions of *n*- and *p*-type semiconductors.

Regnault's method A technique for measuring gas density by evacuating and weighing a glass bulb of known volume, admitting gas at known pressure, and reweighing. The determination must be carried out at constant known temperature and the result corrected to standard temperature and pressure. The method is named after the French chemist Henri Victor Regnault (1810–78).

relative aperture *See* aperture.

relative atomic mass (atomic weight; r.a.m.) Symbol A_r. The ratio of the average mass per atom of the naturally occurring form of an element to 1/12 of the mass of a carbon–12 atom.

relative density (r.d.) The ratio of the *density of a substance to the density of some reference substance. For liquids or solids it is the ratio of the density (usually at 20°C) to the density of water (at its maximum density). This quantity was formerly called *specific gravity*. Sometimes relative densities of gases are used; for example, relative to dry air, both gases being at s.t.p.

relative humidity *See* humidity.

relative molecular mass (molecular weight) Symbol M_r. The ratio of the average mass per molecule of the naturally occurring form of an element or compound to 1/12 of the mass of a carbon–12 atom. It is equal to the sum of the relative atomic masses of all the atoms that comprise a molecule.

relative permeability *See* permeability.

relative permittivity *See* permittivity.

relativistic mass The mass of a moving body as measured by an observer in the same frame of reference as the body. According to the special theory of *relativity the mass m of a body moving at speed v is given by $m = m_0/\sqrt{(1 - v^2/c^2)}$, where m_0 is its *rest mass and c is the speed of light. The relativistic mass therefore only differs significantly from the rest mass if its speed is a substantial fraction of the speed of light. If $v = c/2$, for example, the relativistic mass is 15% greater than the rest mass.

relativistic mechanics An extension of Newtonian mechanics that takes into account the theory of *relativity.

relativistic quantum theory *See* quantum theory; quantum field theory.

relativistic speed A speed that is sufficiently large to make the mass of a body significantly greater than its *rest mass. It is usually expressed as a proportion of the speed of light. *See* relativity; relativistic mass.

relativity One of several theories concerning motion, designed to account for departures from *Newtonian mechanics that occur with very high-speed relative motion. The theory implied is now usually one of two proposed by Albert Einstein (1879–1955). The *special theory* was proposed in 1905 and referred to inertial (nonaccelerated) frames of reference. It assumes that physical laws are identical in all frames of reference and that the speed of light *in vacuo*, c, is constant throughout the universe and is independent of the speed of the observer. The theory develops a system of mathematics to reconcile these apparently conflicting statements. A conclusion of the theory is that the mass of a body, m, increases with its velocity, v, according to the relationship $m = m_0/\sqrt{(1 - v^2/c^2)}$, where m_0 is the *rest mass of the body. Einstein also concluded that if a body loses energy L, its mass

diminishes by L/c^2. Einstein generalized this conclusion to the far-reaching postulate that the mass of a body is a measure of its energy content, according to the equation $m = E/c^2$ (or $E = mc^2$ in its more familiar form).

In the *general theory* of 1915, Einstein extended his earlier work to include accelerated systems, which led to his analysis of gravitation. He interpreted the universe in terms of a four-dimensional space–time continuum in which the presence of mass curves space in such a way that the gravitational field is created. The small differences between Newton's interpretation of gravitation and Einstein's interpretation have provided a means of testing the two theories. For example, the motion of the planet Mercury, thought to be anomalous in terms of Newtonian mechanics, can be explained by relativity. Moreover, Einstein's prediction that light rays passing close to the sun would be bent by its gravitational field has also been confirmed, at least qualitatively, by experiments performed during solar eclipses. The general theory is one of several current theories of gravitation; most of these have a good deal in common with it.

relaxation oscillator *See* oscillator.

relay An electrical or electronic device in which a variation in the current in one circuit controls the current in a second circuit. These devices are used in an enormous number of different applications in which electrical control is required. The simplest is the electromechanical relay in which the first circuit energizes an electromagnet, which operates a switch in a second circuit. The *thyratron gas-filled relay found many uses in the past but has now been largely replaced by the *thyristor solid-state relay.

reluctance Symbol R. The ratio of the magnetomotive force to the total

magnetic flux in a magnetic circuit or component. It is measured in henries.

reluctivity The reciprocal of magnetic *permeability.

rem *See* radiation units.

remanence (retentivity) The magnetic flux density remaining in a ferromagnetic substance when the saturating field is reduced to zero. *See* hysteresis.

remote sensing The gathering and recording of information concerning the earth's surface by techniques that do not involve actual contact with the object or area under study. These techniques include photography (e.g. aerial photography), multispectral imagery, infrared imagery, and radar. Remote sensing is generally carried out from aircraft and, increasingly, satellites. The techniques are used, for example, in cartography (map making).

renewable energy sources Sources of energy that do not use up the earth's finite mineral resources. Nonrenewable sources are *fossil fuels and fission fuels (*see* nuclear fission). Various renewable energy sources are being used or investigated. *See* geothermal energy; hydroelectric power; nuclear fusion; solar energy; tides; wind power; wave power.

renormalization A procedure used in relativistic *quantum field theory to deal with the fact that in *perturbation theory calculations give rise to infinities beyond the first term. Renormalization was first used in *quantum electrodynamics, where the infinities were removed by taking the observed mass and charge of the electron as 'renormalized' parameters rather than the 'bare' mass and charge.

Theories for which finite results for all perturbation-theory calculations exist, by taking a finite number of parameters from experiment and using renormalization, are called *renormalizable*. Only certain types of quantum field theories are renormalizable. Theories that need an infinite number of parameters are said to be *nonrenormalizable* and are regarded as unacceptable as complete consistent physical theories. The *gauge theories that describe the strong, weak, and electromagnetic interactions are renormalizable. The quantum theory of gravitational interactions is a nonrenormalizable theory, which perhaps indicates that gravity needs to be unified with other fundamental interactions before one can have a consistent quantum theory of gravity.

resistance Symbol R. The ratio of the potential difference across an electrical component to the current passing through it. It is thus a measure of the component's opposition to the flow of electric charge. In general, the resistance of a metallic conductor increases with temperature, whereas the resistance of a *semiconductor decreases with temperature.

resistance thermometer (resistance pyrometer) A *thermometer that relies on the increase of electrical resistance of a metal wire with rising temperature, according to the approximate relationship $R = R_0(1 + aT + bT^2)$, where R is the resistance of the wire at temperature T and R_0 is the resistance of the wire at a reference temperature, usually $0°C$; a and b are constants characteristic of the metal of the wire. The metal most frequently used is platinum and the platinum resistance coil is usually incorporated into one arm of a *Wheatstone bridge. The effect of the temperature change on the leads carrying current to the platinum coil is compensated by including a pair of dummy leads within the casing carrying the coil. *See also* thermistor.

resistivity Symbol ρ. A measure of a material's ability to oppose the flow of an electric current. The resistivity

of a material is given by RA/l, where R is the resistance of a uniform specimen of the material, having a length l and a cross-sectional area A. It is usually given at $0°C$ or $20°C$ and is measured in ohm metres. It was formerly known as *specific resistance*.

resistor A component in an electrical or electronic circuit that is present because of its electrical resistance. For electronic purposes many resistors are either wire-wound or consist of carbon particles in a ceramic binder. The ceramic coating carries a number or colour code indicating the value of the resistance. Some resistors can be varied manually by means of a sliding contact; others are markedly dependent on temperature or illumination.

resolution The separation of a vector quantity into two components, which are usually at right angles to each other. Thus, a force F acting on a body in a vertical plane at an angle θ to the horizontal can be resolved into a horizontal component $F\cos\theta$ and a vertical component $F\sin\theta$, both in the same plane as the original force.

resolving power A measure of the ability of an optical instrument to form separable images of close objects or to separate close wavelengths of radiation. The *chromatic resolving power* for any spectroscopic instrument is equal to $\lambda/\delta\lambda$, where $\delta\lambda$ is the difference in wavelength of two equally strong spectral lines that can barely be separated by the instrument and λ is the average wavelength of these two lines. For a telescope forming images of stars the *angular resolving power* is the smallest angular separation of the images; the *linear resolving power* is the linear separation of the images in the focal plane. In a telescope forming images of two stars, as a result of diffraction by the lens aperture each image consists of a bright central blob surrounded by light and dark rings.

According to the *Rayleigh criterion* for resolution, the central ring of one image should fall on the first dark ring of the other. The angular resolving power in radians is then $1.22\lambda/d$, where d is the diameter of the objective lens in centimetres and λ is the wavelength of the light (usually taken as 560 nanometres). For microscopes, the resolving power is usually taken as the minimum distance between two points that can be separated. In both cases, the smaller the resolving power, the better the resolution; to avoid this apparent paradox the resolving power is now sometimes taken as the reciprocals of the quantities stated above.

resonance 1. An oscillation of a system at its natural frequency of vibration, as determined by the physical parameters of the system. It has the characteristic that large amplitude vibrations will ultimately result from low-power driving of the system. Resonance can occur in atoms and molecules, mechanical systems, and electrical circuits (*see* resonant circuit; resonant cavity). **2.** A very short-lived *elementary particle that can be regarded as an excited state of a more stable particle. Resonances decay by the strong interaction (*see* fundamental interactions) in 10^{-24} second.

resonant cavity (cavity resonator) A closed space within a conductor in which an electromagnetic field can be made to oscillate at frequencies above those at which a *resonant circuit will operate. The resonant frequency of the oscillation will depend on the dimensions and the shape of the cavity. The device is used to produce microwaves (*see* klystron; magnetron).

resonant circuit A reactive circuit (*see* reactance) so arranged that it is capable of *resonance. In a *series resonant circuit* a resistor, inductor, and capacitor are arranged in series. Resonance occurs when the *imped-

ance (Z) is a minimum and the current amplitude therefore a maximum. In a *parallel resonant circuit* the inductance and capacitance are in parallel and resonance (with minimal current amplitude) occurs at maximum impedance. The frequency at which resonance occurs is called the *resonant frequency*. In a series resonant circuit $Z = R + i[\omega L - 1/\omega C]$, where $\omega = 2\pi f$ and f is the frequency, R is the resistance, L is the inductance, and C is the capacitance. At resonance, Z is a minimum and $\omega L = 1/\omega C$, i.e. the circuit behaves as if it is purely resistive. In the parallel circuit, resonance occurs when $R^2 + \omega^2 L^2 = L/C$, which in most cases also approximates to $\omega L = 1/\omega C$. Resonant circuits are widely used in *radio to select one carrier-wave frequency in preference to others.

rest energy The *rest mass of a body expressed in energy terms according to the relationship $E_0 = m_0 c^2$, where m_0 is the rest mass of the body and c is the speed of light.

restitution coefficient Symbol e. A measure of the elasticity of colliding bodies. For two spheres moving in the same straight line, $e = (v_2 - v_1)/(u_1 - u_2)$, where u_1 and u_2 are the velocities of bodies 1 and 2 before collision ($u_1 > u_2$) and v_1 and v_2 are the velocities of 1 and 2 after impact ($v_2 > v_1$). If the collision is perfectly elastic $e = 1$ and the kinetic energy is conserved; for an inelastic collision $e < 1$.

rest mass The mass of a body at rest when measured by an observer who is at rest in the same frame of reference. *Compare* relativistic mass.

resultant A *vector quantity that has the same effect as two or more other vector quantities of the same kind. *See* parallelogram of vectors.

retardation (deceleration) The rate of reduction of speed, velocity, or rate of change.

retardation plate A transparent plate of a birefringent material, such as quartz, cut parallel to the optic axis. Light falling on the plate at 90° to the optic axis is split into an ordinary ray and an extraordinary ray (*see* double refraction), which travel through the plate at different speeds. By cutting the plate to different thicknesses a specific phase difference can be introduced between the transmitted rays. In the *half-wave plate* a phase difference of π radians, equivalent to a path difference of half a wavelength, is introduced. In the *quarter-wave plate* the waves are out of step by one quarter of a wavelength.

retina The light-sensitive membrane that lines the interior of the eye. The retina consists of two layers. The inner layer contains nerve cells, blood vessels, and two types of light-sensitive cells (*rods and *cones). The outer layer is pigmented, which prevents the back reflection of light and consequent decrease in visual acuity. Light passing through the lens stimulates individual rods and cones, which generates nerve impulses that are transmitted through the optic nerve to the brain, where the visual image is formed.

retrograde motion 1. The apparent motion of a planet from east to west as seen from the earth against the background of the stars. **2.** The clockwise rotation of a planet, as seen from its north pole. *Compare* direct motion.

retrorocket A small rocket motor that produces thrust in the opposite direction to a *rocket's main motor or motors in order to decelerate it.

reverberation time The time taken for the energy density of a sound to fall to the threshold of audibility from a value 10^6 times as great; i.e. a fall of 60 decibels. It is an important characteristic of an auditorium. The

optimum value is proportional to the linear dimensions of the auditorium.

reverberatory furnace A metallurgical furnace in which the charge to be heated is kept separate from the fuel. It consists of a shallow hearth on which the charge is heated by flames that pass over it and by radiation reflected onto it from a low roof.

reverse osmosis A method of obtaining pure water from water containing a salt, as in desalination. Pure water and the salt water are separated by a semipermeable membrane and the pressure of the salt water is raised above the osmotic pressure, causing water from the brine to pass through the membrane into the pure water. This process requires a pressure of some 25 atmospheres, which makes it difficult to apply on a large scale.

reversible process Any process in which the variables that define the state of the system can be made to change in such a way that they pass through the same values in the reverse order when the process is reversed. It is also a condition of a reversible process that any exchanges of energy, work, or matter with the surroundings should be reversed in direction and order when the process is reversed. Any process that does not comply with these conditions when it is reversed is said to be an *irreversible process*. All natural processes are irreversible, although some processes can be made to approach closely to a reversible process.

Reynolds number Symbol *Re*. A dimensionless number used in fluid dynamics to determine the type of flow of a fluid through a pipe, to design prototypes from small-scale models, etc. It is the ratio $v\rho l/\eta$, where v is the flow velocity, ρ is the fluid density, l is a characteristic linear dimension, such as the diameter of a pipe, and η is the fluid viscosity. In a smooth straight uniform pipe, laminar flow usually occurs if *Re* <

2000 and turbulent flow is established if *Re* > 3000.

rhe A unit of fluidity equal to the reciprocal of the *poise.

rheology The study of the deformation and flow of matter.

rheopexy The process by which certain thixotropic substances set more rapidly when they are stirred, shaken, or tapped. Gypsum in water is such a *rheopectic substance*.

rheostat A variable *resistor, the value of which can be changed without interrupting the current flow. In the common wire-wound rheostat, a sliding contact moves along the length of the coil of wire.

Richardson (Richardson–Dushman) equation *See* thermionic emission.

Richter scale A logarithmic scale devised in 1935 by C. F. Richter (1900–85) to compare the magnitude of earthquakes. The scale ranges from 0 to 10 and the Richter scale value is related to the logarithm of the amplitude of the ground motion divided by the period of the dominant wave, subject to certain corrections. On this scale a value of 2 can just be felt as a tremor and damage to buildings occurs for values in excess of 6. The largest shock recorded had a magnitude of 8.9.

rigidity modulus *See* elastic modulus.

RMS value *See* root-mean-square value.

Rochelle salt Potassium sodium tartrate tetrahydrate, $KNaC_4H_4O_6.4H_2O$. A colourless crystalline salt used for its piezoelectric properties.

Rochon prism An optical device consisting of two quartz prisms; the first, cut parallel to the optic axis, receives the light; the second, with the optic axis at right angles, transmits the ordinary ray without deviation but the extraordinary ray is

deflected and can be absorbed by a screen. The device can be used to produce plane-polarized light and it can also be used with ultraviolet radiation.

rock crystal *See* quartz.

rocket A space vehicle or projectile that is forced through space or the atmosphere by *jet propulsion and that carries its own propellants and oxidizers. It is therefore independent of the earth's atmosphere for lift, thrust, or oxygen and is the only known vehicle for travel outside the earth's atmosphere. Rocket motors (or rocket engines) are currently driven by solid or liquid chemical propellants, which burn in an oxidizer carried within the rocket. Typical liquid bipropellant combinations include hydrazine fuel with dinitrogen tetroxide oxidizer and kerosine fuel with nitric acid oxidizer. Experimental rocket motors have also been tested using ionized gases and plasmas to provide thrust (*see also* ion engine). The measure of a rocket motor's performance is its *specific impulse.

rod A type of light-sensitive receptor cell present in the retinas of vertebrates. Rods contain the pigment rhodopsin and are essential for vision in dim light. *Compare* cone.

roentgen The former unit of dose equivalent (*see* radiation units). It is named after the discoverer of X-rays, W. K. Roentgen (1845–1923).

rolling friction *Friction between a rolling wheel and the plane surface on which it is rotating. As a result of any small distortions of the two surfaces, there is a frictional force with a component, F_1, that opposes the motion. If N is the normal force, $F_r = N\mu_r$, where μ_r is called the *coefficient of rolling friction*.

root-mean-square value (RMS value) 1. (in statistics) A typical value of a number (n) of values of a quantity ($x_1, x_2, x_3 \ldots$) equal to the square root of the sum of the squares of the values divided by n, i.e.

RMS value = $[\sqrt{(x_1^2 + x_2^2 + x_3^2 \ldots)/n}]$

2. (in physics) A typical value of a continuously varying quantity, such as an alternating electric current, obtained similarly from many samples taken at regular time intervals during a cycle. Theoretically this can be shown to be the *effective value*, i.e. the value of the equivalent direct current that would produce the same power dissipation in a given resistor. For a sinusoidal current this is equal to $I_m/\sqrt{2}$, where I_m is the maximum value of the current.

Rose's metal An alloy of low melting point (about 100°C) consisting of 50% bismuth, 25–28% lead, and 22–25% tin.

rot *See* curl.

rotary converter A device for converting direct current to alternating current or one d.c. voltage to another. It consists of an electric motor coupled to a generator.

rotational motion The laws relating to the rotation of a body about an axis are analogous to those describing linear motion. The *angular displacement* (θ) of a body is the angle in radians through which a point or line has been rotated in a specified sense about a specified axis. The *angular velocity* (ω) is the rate of change of angular displacement with time, i.e. $\omega = d\theta/dt$, and the *angular acceleration* (α) is the rate of change of angular velocity, i.e. $\alpha = d\omega/dt = d^2\theta/dt^2$. The equations of linear motion have analogous rotational equivalents, e.g.:

$$\omega_2 = \omega_1 + \alpha t$$
$$\theta = \omega_1 t + \alpha t^2/2$$
$$\omega_2^2 = \omega_1^2 + 2\theta\alpha$$

The counterpart of Newton's second law of motion is $T = I\alpha$, where T is the *torque causing the angular acceleration and I is the *moment of inertia of the rotating body.

rotor The rotating part of an electric motor, electric generator, turbine, etc. *Compare* stator.

rubidium–strontium dating A method of dating geological specimens based on the decay of the radioisotope rubidium–87 into the stable isotope strontium–87. Natural rubidium contains 27.85% of rubidium–87, which has a half-life of 4.7 $\times$ 10^{10} years. The ratio ^{87}Rb/^{87}Sr in a specimen gives an estimate of its age (up to several thousand million years).

Rydberg constant Symbol R. A constant that occurs in the formulae for atomic spectra and is related to the binding energy between an electron and an atomic nucleus. It is connected to other constants by the relationship $R = \mu_0^2 me^4c^3/8h^3$, where μ_0 is the magnetic constant (*see* permeability), m and e are the mass and charge of an electron, c is the speed of light, and h is the *Planck constant. It has the value 1.097 $\times$ 10^7 m^{-1}.

Rydberg spectrum An absorption spectrum of a gas in the ultraviolet region, consisting of a series of lines that become closer together towards shorter wavelengths, merging into a continuous absorption region. The absorption lines correspond to electronic transitions to successively higher energy levels. The onset of the continuum corresponds to photoionization of the atom or molecule, and can thus be used to determine the ionization potential.

S

sampling The selection of small groups of entities to represent a large number of entities in *statistics. In *random sampling* each individual of a population has an equal chance of being selected as part of the sample. In *stratified random sampling*, the population is divided into strata, each of which is randomly sampled and the samples from the different strata are pooled. In *systematic sampling*, individuals are chosen at fixed intervals; for example, every hundredth article on a production line. In *sampling with replacement*, each individual chosen is replaced before the next selection is made.

satellite 1. (*or* **natural satellite**) A relatively small natural body that orbits a planet. For example, the earth's only natural satellite is the moon. **2.** (*or* **artificial satellite**) A man-made spacecraft that orbits the earth, moon, sun, or a planet. Artificial satellites are used for a variety of purposes. *Communication satellites* are used for relaying telephone, radio, and television signals round the curved surface of the earth (*see* synchronous orbit). They are of two types: *passive satellites* reflect signals from one point on the earth's surface to another; *active satellites* are able to amplify and retransmit the signals that they pick up. *Astronomical satellites* are equipped to gather and transmit to earth astronomical information from space, including conditions in the earth's atmosphere, which is of great value in weather forecasting.

saturated 1. (of a ferromagnetic material) Unable to be magnetized more strongly as all the domains are orientated in the direction of the field. **2.** (of a solution) Containing the maximum equilibrium amount of solute at a given temperature. In a saturated solution the dissolved substance is in equilibrium with undissolved substance; i.e. the rate at which solute particles leave the solution is exactly balanced by the rate at which they dissolve. A solution containing less than the equilibrium amount is said to be *unsaturated*. One containing more than the equilibrium

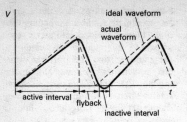

Sawtooth waveform

amount is *supersaturated*. Supersaturated solutions can be made by slowly cooling a saturated solution. Such solutions are metastable; if a small crystal seed is added the excess solute crystallizes out of solution. **3.** (of a vapour) *See* vapour pressure.

saturation **1.** *See* colour. **2.** *See* supersaturation.

sawtooth waveform A waveform in which the variable increases uniformly with time for a fixed period, drops sharply to its initial value, and then repeats the sequence periodically. The illustration shows the ideal waveform and the waveform generated by practical electrical circuits. Sawtooth generators are frequently used to provide a time base for electronic circuits, as in the *cathode-ray oscilloscope.

scalar product (dot product) The product of two vectors U and V, with components U_1, U_2, U_3 and V_1, V_2, V_3, respectively, given by:
$$U.V = U_1V_1 + U_2V_2 + U_3V_3.$$
It can also be written as $UV\cos\theta$, where U and V are the lengths of U and V, respectively, and θ is the angle between them. *Compare* vector product.

scalar quantity A quantity in which direction is either not applicable (as in temperature) or not specified (as in speed). *Compare* vector quantity.

scalene Denoting a triangle having three unequal sides.

scaler (scaling circuit) An electronic counting circuit that provides an output when it has been activated by a prescribed number of input pulses. A *decade scaler* produces an output pulse when it has received ten or a multiple of ten input pulses; a *binary scaler* produces its output after two input pulses.

scanning The process of repeatedly crossing a surface or volume with a beam, aerial, or moving detector in order to bring about some change to the surface or volume, to measure some activity, or to detect some object. The fluorescent screen of a television picture tube is scanned by an electron beam in order to produce the picture; an area of the sky may be scanned by the movable dish aerial of a radio telescope in order to detect celestial bodies, etc.

scanning electron microscope *See* electron microscope.

scanning tunnelling microscope (STM) A type of microscope in which a fine conducting probe is held close to the surface of a sample. Electrons tunnel between the sample and the probe, producing an electrical signal. The probe is slowly moved across the surface and raised and lowered so as to keep the signal constant. A profile of the surface is produced, and a computer-generated contour map of the surface is produced. The technique is capable of resolving individual atoms, but works better with conducting materials. *See also* atomic force microscope.

scattering of electromagnetic radiation The process in which electromagnetic radiation is deflected by particles in the matter through which it passes. In *elastic scattering* the photons of the radiation are reflected; i.e. they bounce off the atoms and molecules without any change of energy. In this type of scattering, known as *Rayleigh scattering* (after Lord Rayleigh; 1842–1919), there is a change of phase but no frequency change. In *inelastic scattering* and

superelastic scattering, there is interchange of energy between the photons and the particles. Consequently, the scattered photons have a different wavelength as well as a different phase. Examples include the *Raman effect and the *Compton effect. *See also* Tyndall effect.

schlieren photography A technique that enables density differences in a moving fluid to be photographed. In the turbulent flow of a fluid, for example, short-lived localized differences in density create differences of refractive index, which show up on photographs taken by short flashes of light as streaks (German: Schliere). Schlieren photography is used in wind-tunnel studies to show the density gradients created by turbulence and the shock waves around a stationary model.

Schmidt camera *See* telescope.

Schottky defect *See* defect.

Schrödinger equation An equation used in wave mechanics (*see* quantum mechanics) for the wave function of a particle. The time-independent Schrödinger equation is:

$$\nabla^2\psi + 8\pi^2 m(E - U)\psi/h^2 = 0$$

where ψ is the wave function; ∇^2 the Laplace operator (*see* Laplace equation), h the Planck constant, m the particle's mass, E its total energy, and U its potential energy.

Schwartzchild radius A critical radius of a body of given mass that must be exceeded if light is to escape from that body. It is equal to $2GM/c^2$, where G is the gravitational constant, c is the speed of light, and M is the mass of the body. If the body collapses to such an extent that its radius is less than the Schwartzchild radius the escape velocity becomes equal to the speed of light and the object becomes a *black hole. The Schwartzchild radius is then the radius of the hole's event horizon.

scintillation counter A type of particle or radiation counter that makes use of the flash of light (scintillation) emitted by an excited atom falling back to its ground state after having been excited by a passing photon or particle. The scintillating medium is usually either solid or liquid and is used in connection with a *photomultiplier, which produces a pulse of current for each scintillation. The pulses are counted with a *scaler. In certain cases, a pulse-height analyser can be used to give an energy spectrum of the incident radiation.

scintillator *See* phosphor.

sclerometer A device for measuring the hardness of a material by determining the pressure on a standard point that is required to scratch it or by determining the height to which a standard ball will rebound from it when dropped from a fixed height. The rebound type is sometimes called a *scleroscope*.

scotopic vision The type of vision that occurs when the *rods in the eye are the principal receptors, i.e. when the level of illumination is low. With scotopic vision colours cannot be identified. *Compare* photopic vision.

screen grid A wire grid in a tetrode or pentode *thermionic valve, placed between the anode and the *control grid to reduce the grid–anode capacitance. *See also* suppressor grid.

screw A simple *machine effectively consisting of an inclined plane wrapped around a cylinder. The mechanical advantage of a screw is $2\pi r/p$, where r is the radius of the thread and p is the *pitch*, i.e. the distance between adjacent threads of the screw measured parallel to its axis.

S-drop *See* strange matter.

search coil A small coil in which a current can be induced to detect and measure a magnetic field. It is used in conjunction with a *fluxmeter.

Searle's bar An apparatus for determining the thermal conductivity of a bar of material. The bar is lagged and one end is heated while the other end is cooled, by steam and cold water respectively. At two points *d* apart along the length of the bar the temperature is measured using a thermometer or thermocouple. The conductivity can then be calculated from the measured temperature gradient.

second 1. Symbol s. The SI unit of time equal to the duration of 9 192 631 770 periods of the radiation corresponding to the transition between two hyperfine levels of the ground state of the caesium−133 atom. **2.** Symbol ″. A unit of angle equal to 1/3600 of a degree or 1/60 of a minute.

secondary cell A *voltaic cell in which the chemical reaction producing the e.m.f. is reversible and the cell can therefore be charged by passing a current through it. *See* accumulator. *Compare* primary cell.

secondary colour Any colour that can be obtained by mixing two *primary colours. For example, if beams of red light and green light are made to overlap, the secondary colour, yellow, will be formed. Secondary colours of light are sometimes referred to as the pigmentary primary colours. For example, if transparent yellow and magenta pigments are overlapped in white light, red will be observed. In this case the red is a pigmentary secondary although it is a primary colour of light.

secondary emission The emission of electrons from a surface as a result of the impact of other charged particles, especially as a result of bombardment with (primary) electrons. As the number of secondary electrons can exceed the number of primary electrons, the process is important in *photomultipliers. *See also* Auger effect.

secondary winding The winding on the output side of a *transformer or *induction coil. *Compare* primary winding.

secular magnetic variation *See* geomagnetism.

sedimentation The settling of the solid particles through a liquid either to produce a concentrated slurry from a dilute suspension or to clarify a liquid containing solid particles. Usually this relies on the force of gravity, but if the particles are too small or the difference in density between the solid and liquid phases is too small, a *centrifuge may be used. In the simplest case the rate of sedimentation is determined by *Stokes's law, but in practice the predicted rate is rarely reached. Measurement of the rate of sedimentation in an *ultracentrifuge can be used to estimate the size of macromolecules.

Seebeck effect (thermoelectric effect) The generation of an e.m.f. in a circuit containing two different metals or semiconductors, when the junctions between the two are maintained at different temperatures. The magnitude of the e.m.f. depends on the nature of the metals and the difference in temperature. The Seebeck effect is the basis of the *thermocouple. It was named after T. J. Seebeck (1770–1831), who actually found that a magnetic field surrounded a circuit consisting of two metal conductors only if the junctions between the metals were maintained at different temperatures. He wrongly assumed that the conductors were magnetized directly by the temperature difference. *Compare* Peltier effect.

Seger cones (pyrometric cones) A series of cones used to indicate the temperature inside a furnace or kiln. The cones are made from different mixtures of clay, limestone, feldspars, etc., and each one softens at a different temperature. The drooping of the vertex is an indication that the known

softening temperature has been reached and thus the furnace temperature can be estimated.

seismograph An instrument that records ground oscillations, e.g. those caused by earthquakes, volcanic activity, and explosions. Most modern seismographs are based on the inertia of a delicately suspended mass and depend on the measurement of the displacement between the mass and a point fixed to the earth. Others measure the relative displacement between two points on earth. The record made by a seismograph is known as a *seismogram*.

seismology The branch of geology concerned with the study of earthquakes.

selectron *See* supersymmetry.

selenium cell Either of two types of *photoelectric cell; one type relies on the photoconductive effect, the other on the photovoltaic effect (*see* photoelectric effect). In the photoconductive selenium cell an external e.m.f. must be applied; as the selenium changes its resistance on exposure to light, the current produced is a measure of the light energy falling on the selenium. In the photovoltaic selenium cell, the e.m.f. is generated within the cell. In this type of cell, a thin film of vitreous or metallic selenium is applied to a metal surface, a transparent film of another metal, usually gold or platinum, being placed over the selenium. Both types of cell are used as light meters in photography.

selenology The branch of astronomy concerned with the scientific study of the *moon.

self-exciting generator A type of electrical generator in which the magnets are excited by current from the generator output.

self inductance *See* inductance.

semiconductor A crystalline solid, such as silicon or germanium, with an electrical conductivity (typically 10^5–10^{-7} siemens per metre) intermediate between that of a conductor (up to 10^9 S m^{-1}) and that of an insulator (as low as 10^{-15} S m^{-1}). As the atoms in a crystalline solid are close together, the orbitals of their electrons overlap and their individual *energy levels are spread out into *energy bands. Conduction occurs in semiconductors as the result of a net movement, under the influence of an electric field, of electrons in the conduction band and empty states, called *holes*, in the valence band. A hole behaves as if it was an electron with a positive charge. Electrons and holes are known as the *charge carriers* in a semiconductor. The type of charge carrier that predominates in a particular region or material is called the *majority carrier* and that with the lower concentration is the *minority carrier*. An *intrinsic semiconductor* is one in which the concentration of charge carriers is a characteristic of the material itself; electrons jump to the conduction band from the valence band as a result of thermal excitation, each electron that makes the jump leaving behind a hole in the valence band. Therefore, in an intrinsic semiconductor the charge carriers are equally divided between electrons and holes. In *extrinsic semiconductors* the type of conduction that predominates depends on the number and valence of the impurity atoms present. Germanium and silicon atoms have a valence of four. If impurity atoms with a valence of five, such as arsenic, antimony, or phosphorus, are added to the lattice, there will be an extra electron per atom available for conduction, i.e. one that is not required to pair with the four valence electrons of the germanium or silicon. Thus extrinsic semiconductors doped with atoms of valence five give rise to crystals with electrons as majority carriers, the so-called *n-type conductors*. Similarly, if the impurity atoms have a valence of three, such

semiconductor diode

as boron, aluminium, indium, or gallium, one hole per atom is created by an unsatisfied bond. The majority carriers are therefore holes, i.e. *p-type conductors*.

Semiconductor devices have virtually replaced thermionic devices, because they are several orders of magnitude smaller, cheaper in energy consumption, and more reliable. The basic structure for electronic semiconductor devices is the *semiconductor diode* (*see also* transistor). This consists of a silicon crystal doped in such a way that half is *p*-type and half is *n*-type. At the junction between the two halves there is a depletion layer in which electrons from the *n*-type have filled holes from the *p*-type. This sets up a potential barrier, which tends to keep the remaining electrons in the *n*-region and the remaining holes in the *p*-region. However, if the *p*-region is biased with a positive potential, the height of the barrier is reduced; the diode is said to be forward biased, because the majority holes in the *p*-region can then flow to the *n*-region and majority electrons in the *n*-region flow to the *p*-region. When forward biased there is a good current flow across the barrier. On the other hand if the *p*-region is negatively biased, the height of the potential barrier is increased and there is only a small leakage current of minority electrons from the *p*-region able to flow to the *n*-region. Thus the *p–n* junction acts as an efficient rectifier, for which purpose it is widely used.

semiconductor diode *See* diode; semiconductor.

semipermeable membrane A membrane that is permeable to molecules of the solvent but not the solute in *osmosis. Semipermeable membranes can be made by supporting a film of material (e.g. cellulose) on a wire gauze or porous pot.

series A sequence of terms each of which can be written in a form that

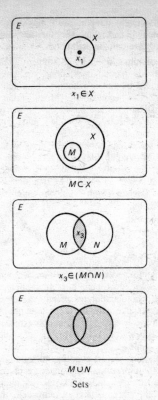

$x_1 \in X$

$M \subset X$

$x_3 \in (M \cap N)$

$M \cup N$

Sets

is an algebraic function of its position in the series. For example, the *exponential series $1 + x + x^2/2! + x^3/3!$ has an *n*th term $x^n/n!$. The sum of all the terms from $n = 0$ to $n = \infty$ is written:

$$\sum_{n=0}^{\infty} x^n/n!$$

This series has an infinite number of terms and is therefore called an *infinite series*. A *finite series* has a fixed number of terms. *See also* asymptotic series; convergent series; divergent series.

series circuit A circuit in which the circuit elements are arranged in sequence so that the same current flows through each of them in turn. For resistances in series, the total resistance is the sum of the individual

resistances. For capacitors in series, the total capacitance, C, is given by $1/C = 1/C_1 + 1/C_2 + 1/C_3 \ldots$

series-wound machine *See* shunt.

sets Collections of objects or elements that have at least one characteristic in common. For example, the set X may consist of all the elements x_1, x_2, x_3, etc. This is written $\{x_1, x_2, x_3, \ldots\} = X$. A specific element in a set is characterized by $x_1 \in X$, meaning x_1 is a member of set X. A *subset* of set X, say M, would be written $M \subset X$, i.e. M is contained in X. If x_3 is a member of both subsets M and N, then $x_3 \in (M \cap N)$, i.e. x_3 belongs to the *intersection* of M and N. $M \cup N$ means the *union* of M and N. For example, if M consists of $\{1, 4, 5, 8\}$ and N consists of $\{2, 3, 4, 5\}$ then $M \cap N = \{4, 5\}$ and $M \cup N = \{1, 2, 3, 4, 5, 8\}$. In the diagram, the rectangle represents the universal set E, circles represent sets or subsets. These diagrams are called *Venn diagrams*, after John Venn (1834–1923), who invented them.

sextant An instrument used in navigation to measure the altitude of a celestial body. Originally it had an arc of 60° (one sixth of a circle, hence its name) but modern instruments have various angles. The sextant uses two mirrors: the horizon glass, in which only the lower half is

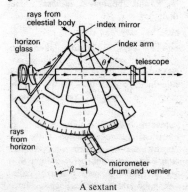

A sextant

silvered, and the index mirror, which can be rotated about an axis perpendicular to the plane of the instrument (see illustration). An arm attached to the index glass sweeps round the calibrated arc, from which angles are read. The instrument is aimed at the horizon and the index mirror rotated until the celestial object can also be seen through the telescope. After careful adjustment to make the image of the celestial body just touch the horizon, the angle is read off the graduated scale.

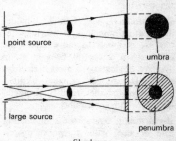

Shadows

shadow An area of darkness formed on a surface when an object intercepts the light falling on the surface from a source. In the case of a point source the shadow has a sharply defined outline. If the source has an appreciable size the shadow has two distinct regions; one of full-shadow, called the *umbra*, the other of half-shadow, called the *penumbra* (see illustration).

shearing force A force that acts parallel to a plane rather than perpendicularly, as with a tensile or compressive force. A *shear stress* requires a combination of four forces acting over (most simply) four sides of a plane and produces two equal and opposite couples. It is measured as the ratio of one shearing force to the area over which it acts, $F/(ab)$ in the diagram. The shear strain is the angular deformation, θ, in circular measure. The *shear modulus* is the

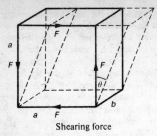

Shearing force

ratio of the shear stress to the shear strain (*see also* elastic modulus).

shear modulus *See* elastic modulus; shearing force.

shell model 1. *See* atom. **2.** A model of the atomic nucleus in which nucleons are assumed to move under the influence of a central field in shells that are analogous to atomic electron shells. The model provides a good explanation of the stability of nuclei that have *magic numbers.

sherardizing The process of coating iron or steel with a zinc corrosion-resistant layer by heating the iron or steel in contact with zinc dust to a temperature slightly below the melting point of zinc. At a temperature of about 371°C the two metals amalgamate to form internal layers of zinc–iron alloys and an external layer of pure zinc. The process was invented by Sherard Cowper-Coles (d. 1935).

shielding 1. A barrier surrounding a region to exclude it from the influence of an energy field. For example, to protect a region from an electric field an earthed barrier is required; to protect it from a magnetic field a shield of high magnetic permeability is needed. **2.** A barrier used to surround a source of harmful or unwanted radiations. For example, the core of a *nuclear reactor is surrounded by a cement or lead shield to absorb neutrons and other dangerous radiation.

SHM *See* simple harmonic motion.

shock wave A very narrow region of high pressure and temperature formed in a fluid when the fluid flows supersonically over a stationary object or a projectile flying supersonically passes through a stationary fluid. A shock wave may also be generated by violent disturbances in a fluid, such as a lightning stroke or a bomb blast.

short-sightedness *See* myopia.

shower *See* cosmic radiation.

shunt An electrical resistor or other element connected in parallel with some other circuit or device, to take part of the current passing through it. For example, a shunt is used across the terminals of a galvanometer to increase the current that can pass through the system. A *shunt-wound* electric generator or motor is one in which the field winding is in parallel with the armature circuit. In a *series-wound* electrical machine the field coils and the armature circuit are in series.

sideband The band of frequencies above or below the frequency of the carrier wave in a telecommunications system within which the frequency components of the wave produced by *modulation fall. For example, if a carrier wave of frequency f is modulated by a signal of frequency x, the *upper sideband* will have a frequency $f + x$ and the *lower sideband* a frequency $f - x$.

sidereal day *See* day.

sidereal period The time taken for a planet or satellite to complete one revolution of its orbit measured with reference to the background of the stars. *See also* day; synodic period; year.

siemens Symbol S. The SI unit of electrical conductance equal to the conductance of a circuit or element that has a resistance of 1 ohm. $1 S = 10^{-1} \Omega$. The unit was formerly called the mho or reciprocal ohm. It is

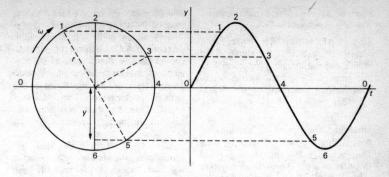

Simple harmonic motion

named after Ernst Werner von Siemens (1816–92).

sievert The SI unit of dose equivalent (*see* radiation units).

signal The variable parameter that contains information and by which information is transmitted in an electronic system or circuit. The signal is created by the *signal generator*, often a voltage source in which the amplitude, frequency, and waveform can be varied.

sign convention A set of rules determined by convention for giving plus or minus signs to distances in the formulae involving lenses and mirrors. The *real-is-positive is the convention now usually adopted. The *New Cartesian convention* is now not widely used. In this convention distances to the right of the pole are treated as positive, those to the left as negative. This system has the advantage of conforming to the sign convention used with Cartesian coordinates in mathematics and is therefore preferred by some for the more complicated calculations.

significant figures The number of digits used in a number to specify its accuracy. The number 6.532 is a value taken to be accurate to four significant figures. The number 7.3 × 10^3 is accurate only to three signifi-

cant figures. Similarly 0.0732 is also only accurate to three significant figures. In these cases the zeros only indicate the order of magnitude of the number, whereas 7.065 is accurate to four significant figures as the zero in this case is significant in expressing the value of the number.

silicon chip A single crystal of a semiconducting silicon material, typically having millimetre dimensions, fabricated in such a way that it can perform a large number of independent electronic functions (*see* integrated circuit).

simple harmonic motion (SHM) A form of periodic motion in which a point or body oscillates along a line about a central point in such a way that it ranges an equal distance on either side of the central point and that its acceleration towards the central point is always proportional to its distance from it. One way of visualizing SHM is to imagine a point rotating around a circle of radius r at a constant angular velocity ω. If the distance from the centre of the circle to the projection of this point on a vertical diameter is y at time t, this projection of the point will move about the centre of the circle with simple harmonic motion. A graph of y against t will be a sine wave, whose

equation is $y = r\sin\omega t$ (see diagram). *See also* pendulum.

sine wave (sinusoidal wave) Any waveform that has an equation in which one variable is proportional to the sine of the other. Such a waveform can be generated by an oscillator that executes *simple harmonic motion.

sintering The process of heating and compacting a powdered material at a temperature below its melting point in order to weld the particles together into a single rigid shape. Materials commonly sintered include metals and alloys, glass, and ceramic oxides. Sintered magnetic materials, cooled in a magnetic field, make especially retentive permanent magnets.

sinusoidal oscillator *See* oscillator.

sinusoidal wave *See* sine wave.

siphon An inverted U-tube with one limb longer than the other. Liquid will be transferred from a reservoir at the base of the shorter limb to the end of the longer limb, provided that the U-tube is filled with liquid (see illustration). The device is useful for emptying an inaccessible container, such as a car's petrol tank.

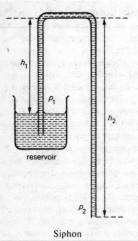

Siphon

The pressure (p_1) on the liquid at the base of the short limb (length h_1) is $p - h_1k$, where p is the atmospheric pressure and k is a constant equal to the product of the density of the liquid and the acceleration of free fall. The pressure (p_2) on the liquid at the base of the long limb (length h_2) is $p - h_2k$. Thus for fluid flow to occur through the tube, from short limb to long limb, $p_1 > p_2$, and for this to occur $h_2 > h_1$. Thus if the limbs are of equal length no flow will occur; it will only occur if the limb dipping into the reservoir is shorter than the delivering limb.

SI units Système International d'Unités: the international system of units now recommended for most scientific purposes. A coherent and rationalized system of units derived from the *m.k.s. units, SI units have now replaced *c.g.s. units and *Imperial units for many purposes. The system has seven *base units* and two *supplementary units* (see Appendix), all other units being derived from these nine units. There are 18 derived units with special names. Each unit has an agreed symbol (a capital letter or an initial capital letter if it is named after a scientist, otherwise the symbol consists of one or two lower-case letters). Decimal multiples of the units are indicated by a set of prefixes; whenever possible a prefix representing 10 raised to a power that is a multiple of three should be used. *See also* Gaussian units; Heaviside–Lorentz units.

skip distance The minimum distance from the transmitter of a radio wave at which reception is possible by means of a sky wave (*see* radio transmission). If a radio wave strikes the ionosphere at a small angle of incidence the wave passes through it and is not reflected. There is therefore a minimum angle of incidence at which reflection occurs for a given frequency. This leads to a region around

a transmitter in which sky waves cannot be received. As the frequency of the transmission increases the minimum angle of incidence at which ionospheric reflection occurs becomes greater. Above about 4 megahertz there may be a region of several hundred kilometres around a transmitter, which is within the skip distance and in which ground waves are too attenuated to be effectively received. In this region no reception is possible.

sky wave *See* radio transmission.

slepton *See* supersymmetry.

slow neutron A neutron with a kinetic energy of less than 10^2 eV (10^{-17} joule). *See also* fast neutron; thermalization.

slug An f.p.s. unit of mass equal to the mass that will acquire an acceleration of 1 ft sec^{-2} when acted on by a force of one pound-force.

smectic *See* liquid crystal.

smelting The process of separating a metal from its ore by heating the ore to a high temperature in a suitable furnace in the presence of a reducing agent, such as carbon, and a fluxing agent, such as limestone. Iron ore is smelted in this way so that the metal melts and, being denser than the molten slag, sinks below the slag, enabling it to be removed from the furnace separately.

smoke A fine suspension of solid particles in a gas.

Snell's law *See* refraction.

sodium-vapour lamp A form of *electric lighting that gives a yellow light as a result of the luminous discharge obtained by the passage of a stream of electrons between tungsten electrodes in a tube containing sodium vapour. To facilitate starting, the tube also contains some neon; for this reason, until the lamp is warm the neon emits a characteristic pink glow. As the sodium vaporizes, the yellow light predominates. Sodium-vapour lamps are widely used as

street lights because of their high luminous efficiency and because the yellow light is less absorbed than white light by fog and mist. Low-pressure sodium lamps emit a characteristic yellow light; in high-pressure lamps the atoms are sufficiently close to each other to interact and broaden the spectral lines into the orange and green regions.

soft iron A form of iron that contains little carbon, has high relative permeability, is easily magnetized and demagnetized, and has a small hysteresis loss. Soft iron and other *soft ferromagnetic materials*, such as silicon steel, are used in making parts exposed to rapid changes of magnetic flux, such as the cores of electromagnets, motors, generators, and transformers.

By comparison, *hard ferromagnetic materials*, such as cobalt steel and various alloys of nickel, aluminium, and cobalt, have low relative permeability, are difficult to magnetize, and have a high hysteresis loss. They are used in making permanent magnets.

soft radiation Ionizing radiation of low penetrating power, usually used with reference to X-rays of long wavelength. *Compare* hard radiation.

software *See* computer.

sol A *colloid in which small solid particles are dispersed in a liquid continuous phase.

solar cell An electric cell that uses the sun's radiation to produce usable electric current. Most solar cells consist of a single-crystal silicon *p–n* junction. When photons of light energy from the sun fall on or near the *semiconductor junction the electron–hole pairs created are forced by the electric field at the junction to separate so that the holes pass to the *p*-region and the electrons pass to the *n*-region. This displacement of free charge creates an electric current when a load is connected across the terminals of the device (see illustra-

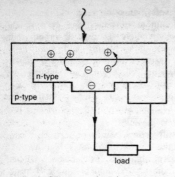

Silicon p–n junction

tion). Individual silicon solar cells cannot be made with a surface area much in excess of 4000 mm^2 and the maximum power delivered by such a cell is approximately 0.6 W at about 0.5 V in full sun. The efficiency of such devices is about 15%. For practical use, therefore, solar cells have to be assembled in arrays. Panels of solar cells have been the exclusive source of power for satellites and space capsules. Their use on earth has been largely limited by their high cost, a reduction in the cost by a factor of 10 being required to make them competitive with other energy sources at present.

solar constant The rate at which solar energy is received per unit area at the outer limit of the earth's atmosphere at the mean distance between the earth and the sun. The value is 1.353 kW m^{-2}.

solar day *See* day.

solar energy The electromagnetic energy radiated from the sun. The tiny proportion (about 5×10^{-10} of the total) that falls on the earth is indicated by the *solar constant. The total quantity of solar energy falling on the earth in one year is about 4×10^{18} J, whereas the total annual energy consumption of the earth's inhabitants is only some 3×10^{14} J. The sun, therefore, could provide all the energy needed. The direct ways of making use of solar energy can be divided into thermal methods (*see* solar heating) and nonthermal methods (*see* solar cell).

solar heating A form of domestic or industrial heating that relies on the direct use of solar energy. The basic form of *solar heater* is a thermal device in which a fluid is heated by the sun's rays in a collector (see illustration) and pumped or allowed to flow round a circuit that provides some form of heat storage and some form of auxiliary heat source for use when the sun is not shining. More complicated systems are combined heating-and-cooling devices, providing heat in the winter and air-conditioning in the summer. The simplest form of solar collector is the flat-plate collector, in which a blackened receiving

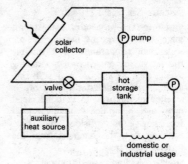

Typical solar heating system

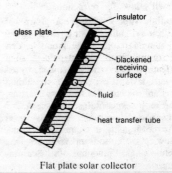

Flat plate solar collector

surface is covered by one or more glass plates that acts like a greenhouse (see greenhouse effect) and traps the maximum amount of solar energy. Tubes attached to the receiving surface carry air, water, or some other fluid to which the absorbed heat is transferred. The whole panel is insulated at the back and can thus form part of the roof of a building. More sophisticated collectors focus the sun's rays using reflectors. See also solar cell.

solar parallax The angle subtended by the earth's equatorial radius at the centre of the sun at the mean distance between the earth and the sun (i.e. at 1 astronomical unit). It has the value 8.794 148 arc seconds.

solar prominence A cloud of gas that forms temporarily in the upper *chromosphere or inner *corona of the sun. It has a lower temperature but higher density than its surroundings and is observed as a bright projection.

solar system The sun, the nine major planets (Mercury, Venus, Earth, Mars, Jupiter, Saturn, Uranus, Neptune, and Pluto) and their natural satellites, the asteroids, the comets, and meteoroids. Over 99% of the mass of the system is concentrated in the sun. The solar system as a whole moves in an approximately circular orbit about the centre of the Galaxy, taking about 2.2×10^8 years to complete its orbit.

solar wind A continuous outward flow of charged particles, mostly protons and electrons, from the sun's *corona into interplanetary space. The particles are controlled by the sun's magnetic field and are able to escape from the sun's gravitational field because of their high thermal energy. The average velocity of the particles in the vicinity of the earth is about 450 km s^{-1} and their density at this range is about 8×10^6 protons per cubic metre.

solar year See year.

solder An alloy used to join metal surfaces. A soft solder melts at a temperature in the range 200–300°C and consists of a tin–lead alloy. The tin content varies between 80% for the lower end of the melting range and 31% for the higher end. Hard solders contain substantial quantities of silver in the alloy. Brazing solders are usually alloys of copper and zinc, which melt at over 800°C.

solenoid A coil of wire wound on a cylindrical former in which the length of the former is greater than its diameter. When a current is passed through the coil a magnetic field is produced inside the coil parallel to its axis. This field can be made to operate a plunger inside the former so that the solenoid can be used to operate a circuit breaker, valve, or other electromechanical device.

solid A state of matter in which there is a three-dimensional regularity of structure, resulting from the proximity of the component atoms, ions, or molecules and the strength of the forces between them. Solids can be crystalline or *amorphous. If a crystalline solid is heated, the kinetic energy of the components increases. At a specific temperature, called the melting point, the forces between the components become unable to contain them within the crystal structure. At this temperature, the lattice breaks down and the solid becomes a liquid.

solid angle Symbol Ω. The three-dimensional 'angle' formed by the vertex of a cone. When this vertex is the centre of a sphere of radius r and the base of the cone cuts out an area s on the surface of the sphere, the solid angle in *steradians is defined as s/r^2.

solid solution A crystalline material that is a mixture of two or more components, with ions, atoms, or molecules of one component replacing some of the ions, atoms, or molecules

of the other component in its normal crystal lattice. Solid solutions are found in certain alloys. For example, gold and copper form solid solutions in which some of the copper atoms in the lattice are replaced by gold atoms. In general, the gold atoms are distributed at random, and a range of gold–copper compositions is possible. At a certain composition, the gold and copper atoms can each form regular individual lattices (referred to as *superlattices*). Mixed crystals of double salts (such as alums) are also examples of solid solutions. Compounds can form solid solutions if they are isomorphous (*see* isomorphism).

solid-state detector *See* junction detector.

solid-state physics The study of the physical properties of solids, with special emphasis on the electrical properties of semiconducting materials in relation to their electronic structure. *Solid-state devices* are electronic components consisting entirely of solids (e.g. semiconductors, transistors, etc.) without heating elements, as in thermionic valves.

Recently the term *condensed-matter physics* has been introduced to include the study of crystalline solids, amorphous solids, and liquids.

soliton A stable particle-like solitary wave state that is a solution of certain equations for propagation. Solitons are thought to occur in many areas of physics and applied mathematics, such as plasmas, fluid mechanics, lasers, optics, solid-state physics, and elementary-particle physics.

solstice 1. Either of the two points on the *ecliptic midway between the *equinoxes, at which the sun is at its greatest angular distance north (*summer solstice*) or south (*winter solstice*) of the celestial equator. **2.** The time at which the sun reaches either of these points. The summer solstice occurs on June 21 and the winter solstice on December 21 in the northern hemisphere; the dates are reversed in the southern hemisphere.

solubility The quantity of solute that dissolves in a given quantity of solvent to form a saturated solution. Solubility is measured in kilograms per metre cubed, moles per kilogram of solvent, etc. The solubility of a substance in a given solvent depends on the temperature. Generally, for a solid in a liquid, solubility increases with temperature; for a gas, solubility decreases. *See also* concentration.

solubility product Symbol K_s. The product of the concentrations of ions in a saturated solution. For instance, if a compound A_xB_y is in equilibrium with its solution

$$A_xB_y(s) \leftrightarrows xA^+(aq) + yB^-(aq)$$

the equilibrium constant is

$$K_c = [A^+]^x[B^-]^y/[A_xB_y]$$

Since the concentration of the undissolved solid can be put equal to 1, the solubility product is given by

$$K_s = [A^+]^x[B^-]^y$$

The expression is only true for sparingly soluble salts. If the product of ionic concentrations in a solution exceeds the solubility product, then precipitation occurs.

solute The substance dissolved in a solvent in forming a *solution.

solution A homogeneous mixture of a liquid (the *solvent) with a gas or solid (the *solute*). In a solution, the molecules of the solute are discrete and mixed with the molecules of solvent. There is usually some interaction between the solvent and solute molecules (*see* soivation). Two liquids that can mix on the molecular level are said to be *miscible*. In this case, the solvent is the major component and the solute the minor component. *See also* solid solution.

solvent A liquid that dissolves another substance or substances to form a *solution. *Polar solvents* are compounds such as water and liquid

ammonia, which have dipole moments and consequently high dielectric constants. These solvents are capable of dissolving ionic compounds or covalent compounds that ionize (*see* solvation). *Nonpolar solvents* are compounds such as ethoxyethane and benzene, which do not have permanent dipole moments. These do not dissolve ionic compounds but will dissolve nonpolar covalent compounds.

sonar *See* echo.

sonic boom A strong *shock wave generated by an aircraft when it is flying in the earth's atmosphere at supersonic speeds. This shock wave is radiated from the aircraft and where it intercepts the surface of the earth a loud booming sound is heard. The loudness depends on the speed and altitude of the aircraft and is lower in level flight than when the aircraft is undertaking a manoeuvre. The maximum increase of pressure in the shock wave during a transoceanic flight of a commercial supersonic transport (SST) is 120 Pa, equivalent to 136 decibels.

sonometer A device consisting essentially of a hollow sounding box with two bridges attached to its top. The string, fixed to the box at one end, is stretched between the two bridges so that the free end can run over a pulley and support a measured load. When the string is plucked the frequency of the note can be matched with that of another sound source, such as a tuning fork. It can be used to verify that the frequency (f) of a stretched string is given by $f = (1/2l)\sqrt{(T/m)}$, where l is the length of the string, m is its mass per unit length, and T is its tension. Originally called the *monochord*, the sonometer was widely used as a tuning aid, but is now used only in teaching laboratories.

sorption *Absorption of a gas by a solid.

sorption pump A type of vacuum pump in which gas is removed from a system by absorption on a solid (e.g. activated charcoal or a zeolite) at low temperature.

sound A vibration in an elastic medium at a frequency and intensity that is capable of being heard by the human ear. The frequency of sounds lie in the range 20–20 000 Hz, but the ability to hear sounds in the upper part of the frequency range declines with age (*see also* pitch). Vibrations that have a lower frequency than sound are called *infrasounds* and those with a higher frequency are called *ultrasounds*.

Sound is propagated through an elastic fluid as a longitudinal *sound wave*, in which a region of high pressure travels through the fluid at the *speed of sound in that medium. At a frequency of about 10 kilohertz the maximum excess pressure of a sound wave in air lies between 10^{-4} Pa and 10^3 Pa. Sound travels through solids as either longitudinal or transverse waves.

source The electrode in a field-effect *transistor from which electrons or holes enter the interelectrode space.

space 1. A property of the universe that enables physical phenomena to be extended into three mutually perpendicular directions. In Newtonian physics, space, time, and matter are treated as quite separate entities. In Einsteinian physics, space and time are combined into a four-dimensional continuum (*see* space–time) and in the general theory of *relativity matter is regarded as having an effect on space, causing it to curve. **2.** (*or* **outer space**) The part of the universe that lies outside the earth's atmosphere.

space probe An unmanned spacecraft that investigates features within the solar system. A *planetary probe* examines the conditions on or in the vicinity of one or more planets and a *lunar probe* is designed to obtain

information about the moon. Probes are propelled by rocket motors and once out of the earth's gravitational field use their propulsion systems for course changes. Many are powered by panels of *solar cells, for both internal operation and radio communications.

space-reflection symmetry *See* parity.

space–time (space–time continuum) A geometry that includes the three dimensions and a *fourth dimension* of time. In Newtonian physics, space and time are considered as separate entities and whether or not events are simultaneous is a matter that is regarded as obvious to any competent observer. In Einstein's concept of the physical universe, based on a system of geometry devised by H. Minkowski (1864–1909), space and time are regarded as entwined, so that two observers in relative motion could disagree regarding the simultaneity of distant events. In Minkowski's geometry, an event is identified by a *world point* in a four-dimensional continuum.

spallation A type of nuclear reaction in which the interacting nuclei disintegrate into a large number of protons, neutrons, and other light particles, rather than exchanging nucleons between them.

spark *See* electric spark.

spark chamber A device for detecting charged particles. It consists of a chamber, filled with helium and neon at atmospheric pressure, in which a stack of 20 to 100 plates are placed; the plates are connected alternately to the positive and negative terminals of a source of high potential (10 000 V or more). An incoming particle creates ion pairs in its track, causing the gas to become conducting and sparks to jump between the plates. The light from the sparks is focused to obtain stereoscopic photographs of the particles' tracks. It can also func-tion as a counter (called a *spark counter*) when connected to suitable counting circuits. Some versions use crossed sets of parallel wires rather than plates; simple patterns may have a single wire near a plate, in the open atmosphere.

spark counter *See* spark chamber.

special theory of relativity *See* relativity.

specific 1. Denoting that an extensive physical quantity so described is expressed per unit mass. For example, the *specific latent heat* of a body is its latent heat per unit mass. When the extensive physical quantity is denoted by a capital letter (e.g. L for latent heat), the specific quantity is denoted by the corresponding lower-case letter (e.g. l for specific latent heat). **2.** In some older physical quantities the adjective 'specific' was added for other reasons (e.g. specific gravity, specific resistance). These names are now no longer used.

specific activity *See* activity.

specific charge The ratio of the charge of an *elementary particle or other charged body to its mass.

specific gravity *See* relative density; specific.

specific heat capacity *See* heat capacity.

specific humidity *See* humidity.

specific impulse A measure of the thrust available from a rocket propellant. It is the ratio of the thrust produced to the fuel consumption.

specific intensity *See* Planck's radiation law.

specific latent heat *See* latent heat.

specific resistance *See* resistivity; specific.

specific surface The surface area of a particular substance per unit mass, expressed in $m^2\ kg^{-1}$. It provides a measure of the surface area available for a process, such as adsorption, for

a given mass of a powder or porous substance.

specific volume The volume of a substance per unit mass. The reciprocal of density, it has the units $m^3 kg^{-1}$.

spectral class (spectral type) A form of classification used for stars, based on their spectra. The *Harvard classification*, introduced in 1890 and modified in the 1920s, is based on the seven star types known as O, B, A, F, G, K, M:

O hottest blue stars; ionized helium lines dominant

B hot blue stars; neutral helium lines dominant, no ionized helium

A blue blue-white stars; hydrogen lines dominant

F white stars; metallic lines strengthen, hydrogen lines weaken

G yellow stars; ionized calcium lines dominant

K orange-red stars; neutral metallic lines dominant, some molecular bands

M coolest red stars; molecular bands dominant

spectrograph *See* spectroscope.

spectrometer Any of various instruments for producing a spectrum and measuring the wavelengths, energies, etc., involved. A simple type, for visible radiation, is a spectroscope equipped with a calibrated scale allowing wavelengths to be read off or calculated. In the X-ray to infrared region of the electromagnetic spectrum, the spectrum is produced by dispersing the radiation with a prism or diffraction grating (or crystal, in the case of hard X-rays). Some form of photoelectric detector is used, and the spectrum can be obtained as a graphical plot, which shows how the intensity of the radiation varies with wavelength. Such instruments are also called *spectrophotometers*. Spectrometers also exist for investigating the gamma-ray region and the microwave and radio-wave regions of the spectrum (*see* electron-spin resonance;

nuclear magnetic resonance). Instruments for obtaining spectra of particle beams are also called spectrometers (*see* spectrum; photoelectron spectroscopy).

spectrophotometer *See* spectrometer.

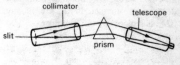

Spectroscope

spectroscope An optical instrument that produces a *spectrum for visual observation. The first such instrument was made by R. W. Bunsen; in its simplest form it consists of a hollow tube with a slit at one end by which the light enters and a collimating lens at the other end to produce a parallel beam, a prism to disperse the light, and a telescope for viewing the spectrum (see illustration). In the *spectrograph*, the spectroscope is provided with a camera to record the spectrum. For a broad range of spectroscopic work, from the ultraviolet to the infrared, a diffraction grating is used instead of a prism. *See also* spectrometer.

spectroscopic binary *See* binary stars.

spectroscopy The study of methods of producing and analysing *spectra using *spectroscopes, *spectrometers, spectrographs, and spectrophotometers. The interpretations of the spectra so produced can be used for chemical analysis, examining atomic and molecular energy levels and molecular structures, and for determining the composition and motions of celestial bodies (*see* redshift).

spectrum 1. A distribution of entities or properties arrayed in order of increasing or decreasing magnitude. For example, a beam of ions passed through a mass spectrograph, in which they are deflected according to

their charge-to-mass ratios, will have a range of masses called a *mass spectrum*. A *sound spectrum* is the distribution of energy over a range of frequencies of a particular source. **2.** A range of electromagnetic energies arrayed in order of increasing or decreasing wavelength or frequency (*see* electromagnetic spectrum). The *emission spectrum* of a body or substance is the characteristic range of radiations it emits when it is heated, bombarded by electrons or ions, or absorbs photons. The *absorption spectrum* of a substance is produced by examining, through the substance and through a spectroscope, a continuous spectrum of radiation. The energies removed from the continuous spectrum by the absorbing medium show up as black lines or bands. With a substance capable of emitting a spectrum, these are in exactly the same positions in the spectrum as some of the lines and bands in the emission spectrum.

Emission and absorption spectra may show a *continuous spectrum*, a *line spectrum*, or a *band spectrum*. A continuous spectrum contains an unbroken sequence of frequencies over a relatively wide range; it is produced by incandescent solids, liquids, and compressed gases. Line spectra are discontinuous lines produced by excited atoms and ions as they fall back to a lower energy level. Band spectra (closely grouped bands of lines) are characteristic of molecular gases or chemical compounds. *See also* spectroscopy.

speculum An alloy of copper and tin formerly used in reflecting *telescopes to make the main mirror as it could be cast, ground, and polished to make a highly reflective surface. It has now been largely replaced by silvered glass for this purpose.

speed The ratio of a distance covered by a body to the time taken. Speed is a *scalar quantity, i.e. no direction is given. Velocity is a *vector quantity, i.e. both the rate of travel and the direction are specified.

speed of light Symbol c. The speed at which electromagnetic radiation travels. The speed of light in a vacuum is $2.997\,924\,58 \times 10^8$ m s^{-1}. When light passes through any material medium its speed is reduced (*see* refractive index). The speed of light in a vacuum is the highest speed attainable in the universe (*see* relativity; Cerenkov radiation). It is a universal constant and is independent of the speed of the observer. Since October 1983 it has formed the basis of the definition of the *metre.

speed of sound Symbol c or c_s. The speed at which sound waves are propagated through a material medium. In air at 20°C sound travels at 344 m s^{-1}, in water at 20°C it travels at 1461 m s^{-1}, and in steel at 20°C at 5000 m s^{-1}. The speed of sound in a medium depends on the medium's modulus of elasticity (E) and its density (ρ) according to the relationship $c = \sqrt{(E/\rho)}$. For longitudinal waves in a narrow solid specimen, E is the Young modulus; for a liquid E is the bulk modulus (*see* elastic modulus); and for a gas $E = \gamma p$, where γ is the ratio of the principal specific *heat capacities and p is the pressure of the gas. For an ideal gas the relationship takes the form $c = \sqrt{(\gamma r T)}$, where r is the gas constant per unit mass and T is the thermodynamic temperature. This equation shows how the speed of sound in a gas is related to its temperature. This relationship can be written $c = c_0\sqrt{(1 + t/273)}$, where c_0 is the speed of sound in a particular gas at 0°C and t is the temperature in °C.

sphere The figure generated when a circle is rotated about a diameter. The volume of a sphere is $4\pi r^3/3$ and its surface area is $4\pi r^2$, where r is its radius. In Cartesian coordinates the

equation of a sphere centred at the origin is $x^2 + y^2 + z^2 = r^2$.

spherical aberration *See* aberration.

spherical mirror *See* mirror.

spherical polar coordinates *See* polar coordinates.

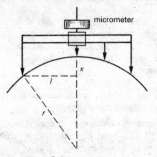

Spherometer

spherometer An instrument for measuring the curvature of a surface. The usual instrument for this purpose consists of a tripod, the pointed legs of which rest on the spherical surface at the corners of an equilateral triangle. In the centre of this triangle is a fourth point, the height of which is adjusted by means of a micrometer screw (see illustration). If the distance between each leg and the axis through the micrometer screw is l, and the height of the micrometer point above (or below) a flat surface is x, the radius (r) of the sphere is given by $r = (l^2 + x^2)/2x$.

spiegel (spiegeleisen) A form of *pig iron containing 15–30% of manganese and 4–5% of carbon. It is added to steel in a Bessemer converter as a deoxidizing agent and to raise the manganese content of steel.

spin (intrinsic angular momentum) Symbol s. The part of the total angular momentum of a particle, atom, nucleus, etc., that is distinct from its orbital angular momentum. A molecule, atom, or nucleus in a specified energy level, or a particular elementary particle, has a particular spin,

just as it has a particular charge or mass. According to *quantum theory, this is quantized and is restricted to multiples of $h/2\pi$, where h is the *Planck constant. Spin is characterized by a quantum number s. For example, for an electron $s = \pm\frac{1}{2}$, implying a spin of $+ h/4\pi$ when it is spinning in one direction and $-h/4\pi$ when it is spinning in the other. Because of their spin, particles also have their own intrinsic *magnetic moments and in a magnetic field the spin of the particles lines up at an angle to the direction of the field, precessing around this direction. *See* nuclear magnetic resonance.

spin glass An alloy of a small amount of a magnetic metal (0.1–10%) with a nonmagnetic metal, in which the atoms of the magnetic element are randomly distributed through the crystal lattice of the nonmagnetic element. Examples are AuFe and CuMn. Theories of the magnetic and other properties of spin glasses are complicated by the random distribution of the magnetic atoms.

spin–statistics theorem A fundamental theorem of relativistic *quantum field theory that states that half-integer *spins can only be quantized consistently if they obey Fermi–Dirac statistics and even-integer spins can only be quantized consistently if they obey Bose–Einstein statistics (*see* quantum statistics). This theorem enables one to understand the result of quantum statistics that wave functions for bosons are symmetric and wave functions for fermions are antisymmetric. It also provides the foundation for the *Pauli exclusion principle. It was first proved by Pauli in 1940.

spin wave (magnon) A *collective excitation associated with magnetic systems. Spin waves occur in both ferromagnetic and antiferromagnetic systems (*see* magnetism).

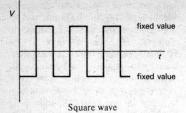

Square wave

spiral galaxy *See* galaxy.

spring balance A simple form of *balance in which a force is measured by the extension it produces in a helical spring. The extension, which is read off a scale, is directly proportional to the force, provided that the spring is not overstretched. The device is often used to measure the weight of a body approximately.

sputtering The process by which some of the atoms of an electrode (usually a cathode) are ejected as a result of bombardment by heavy positive ions. Although the process is generally unwanted, it can be used to produce a clean surface or to deposit a uniform film of a metal on an object in an evacuated enclosure.

square wave A train of rectangular voltage pulses that alternate between two fixed values for equal lengths of time. The time of transition between each fixed value is negligible compared to the duration of the fixed value. See diagram.

squark *See* supersymmetry.

stable equilibrium *See* equilibrium.

stainless steel A form of *steel containing at least 11–12% of chromium, a low percentage of carbon, and often some other elements, notably nickel and molybdenum. Stainless steel does not rust or stain and therefore has a wide variety of uses in industrial, chemical, and domestic environments. A particularly successful alloy is the steel known as 18–8, which contains 18% Cr, 8% Ni, and 0.08% C.

standard cell A *voltaic cell, such as a *Clark cell, or *Weston cell, used as a standard of e.m.f.

standard deviation A measure of the dispersion of data in statistics. For a set of values a_1, a_2, a_3, ... a_n, the mean m is given by $(a_1 + a_2 + ... + a_n)/n$. The *deviation* of each value is absolute value of the difference from the mean $|m - a_1|$, etc. The standard deviation is the square root of the mean of the squares of these values, i.e.

$$\sqrt{[(|m - a_1|^2 + ... |m - a_n|^2)/n]}$$

When the data is continuous the sum is replaced by an integral.

standard electrode An electrode (a half cell) used in measuring electrode potential. *See* hydrogen half cell.

standard electrode potential *See* electrode potential.

standard form A way of writing a number, especially a large or small number, in which only one integer appears before the decimal point, the value being adjusted by multiplying by the appropriate power of 10. For example, 236,214 would be written in the standard form as $2.362\ 14 \times 10^5$; likewise 0.006821047 would be written $6.821\ 047 \times 10^{-3}$. Note that in the standard form, commas are not used, the digits are grouped into threes and a space is left between groups.

standard model The combination of *quantum chromodynamics to describe strong interactions, *electroweak theory to give a unified description of the electromagnetic interaction and the weak interaction, and the general theory of *relativity to describe classical gravitational interactions. Although the standard model, in principle, gives a complete description of all known phenomena, it is regarded by most physicists as being incomplete since it has many arbitrary features.

standard state A state of a system used as a reference value in thermo-

dynamic measurements. Standard states involve a reference value of pressure (usually one atmosphere, 101.325 kPa) or concentration (usually 1 M). Thermodynamic functions are designated as 'standard' when they refer to changes in which reactants and products are all in their standard and their normal physical state. For example, the standard molar enthalpy of formation of water at 298 K is the enthalpy change for the reaction

$$H_2(g) + \tfrac{1}{2}O_2(g) \rightarrow H_2O(l)$$

$\Delta H^{\ominus}_{298} = -285.83$ kJ mol^{-1}. Note the superscript $\ominus$ is used to denote standard state and the temperature should be indicated.

standard temperature and pressure See s.t.p.

standing wave See stationary wave.

star A self-luminous celestial body, such as the *sun, that generates nuclear energy within its core. Stars are not distributed uniformly throughout the universe, but are collected together in *galaxies. The age and lifetime of a star are related to its mass (see stellar evolution; Hertzsprung–Russell diagram).

star cluster A group of stars that are sufficiently close to each other for them to be physically associated. Stars belonging to the cluster are formed together from the same cloud of interstellar gas and have approximately the same age and initial chemical composition. Because of this, and since the stars in a given cluster are at roughly the same distance from earth, observations of star clusters are of great importance in studies of stellar evolution.

There are two types of star cluster. Open (or galactic) clusters are fairly loose systems of between a few hundred and a few thousand members. The stars in open clusters are quite young by astronomical standards (some as young as a few million years) and have relatively high abundances of heavy elements. Globu-lar clusters are approximately spherical collections of between ten thousand and a million stars. These are very old (of order 10^{10} years) and have low heavy-element abundances.

stat- A prefix attached to the name of a practical electrical unit to provide a name for a unit in the electrostatic system of units, e.g. statcoulomb, statvolt. Compare ab-. In modern practice both absolute and electrostatic units have been replaced by *SI units.

state of matter One of the three physical states in which matter can exist, i.e. *solid, *liquid, or *gas. *Plasma is sometimes regarded as the fourth state of matter.

static electricity The effects produced by electric charges at rest, including the forces between charged bodies (see Coulomb's law) and the field they produce (see electric field).

statics The branch of mechanics concerned with bodies that are acted upon by balanced forces and couples so that they remain at rest or in unaccelerated motion. Compare dynamics.

stationary orbit See synchronous orbit.

stationary state A state of a system when it has an energy level permitted by *quantum mechanics. Transitions from one stationary state to another can only occur by the emission or absorption of an appropriate quanta of energy (e.g. in the form of photons).

stationary wave (standing wave) A form of *wave in which the profile of the wave does not move through the medium but remains stationary. This is in contrast to a travelling (or progressive) wave, in which the profile moves through the medium at the speed of the wave. A stationary wave results when a travelling wave is reflected back along its own path. In a stationary wave there are points at

which the displacement is zero; these are called *nodes*. Points of maximum displacement are called *antinodes*. The distance between a node and its neighbouring antinode is one quarter of a wavelength. In a stationary wave all the points along the wave have different amplitudes and the points between successive nodes are in phase; in a travelling wave every point vibrates with the same amplitude and the phase of vibration changes for different points along its path.

statistical mechanics The branch of physics in which statistical methods are applied to the microscopic constituents of a system in order to predict its macroscopic properties. The earliest application of this method was Boltzmann's attempt to explain the thermodynamic properties of gases on the basis of the statistical properties of large assemblies of molecules.

In classical statistical mechanics, each particle is regarded as occupying a point in *phase space, i.e. to have an exact position and momentum at any particular instant. The probability that this point will occupy any small volume of the phase space is taken to be proportional to the volume. The Maxwell–Boltzmann law gives the most probable distribution of the particles in phase space.

With the advent of quantum theory, the exactness of these premises was disturbed (by the Heisenberg uncertainty principle). In the *quantum statistics that evolved as a result, the phase space is divided into cells, each having a volume h^f, where h is the Planck constant and f is the number of degrees of freedom of the particles. This new concept led to Bose–Einstein statistics, and for particles obeying the Pauli exclusion principle, to Fermi–Dirac statistics.

statistics The branch of mathematics concerned with the inferences that

can be drawn from numerical data on the basis of probability. A *statistical inference* is a conclusion drawn about a population as a result of an analysis of a representative sample. *See* sampling.

stator The stationary electromagnetic structure of an electric motor or electric generator. *Compare* rotor.

steady-state theory The cosmological theory that the universe has always existed in a steady state, that it had no beginning, will have no end, and has a constant mean density. To compensate for the observed *expansion of the universe this theory postulates that matter is created throughout the universe at a rate of about 10^{-10} nucleon per metre cubed per year as a property of space. Because it has failed to account for the *microwave background radiation or the evidence of evolution in the universe it has lost favour to the *big-bang theory. It was first proposed by Hermann Bondi (1919–), Thomas Gold (1920–), and Fred Hoyle (1915–) in 1948.

steam distillation A method of distilling liquids that are immiscible with water by bubbling steam through them. It depends on the fact that the vapour pressure (and hence the boiling point) of a mixture of two immiscible liquids is lower than the vapour pressure of either pure liquid.

steam engine A *heat engine in which the thermal energy of steam is converted into mechanical energy. It consists of a cylinder fitted with a piston and valve gear to enable the high-pressure steam to be admitted to the cylinder when the piston is near the top of its stroke. The steam forces the piston to the bottom of its stroke and is then exhausted from the cylinder usually into a condenser. The reciprocating motion of the piston is converted to rotary motion of the flywheel by means of a connecting rod, crosshead, and crank. The steam

engine reached its zenith at the end of the 19th century, since when it has been replaced by the steam turbine and the internal-combustion engine. *See also* Rankine cycle.

steam point The temperature at which the maximum vapour pressure of water is equal to the standard atmospheric pressure (101 325 Pa). On the Celsius scale it has the value 100°C.

steel Any of a number of alloys consisting predominantly of iron with varying proportions of carbon (up to 1.7%) and, in some cases, small quantities of other elements (*alloy steels*), such as manganese, silicon, chromium, molybdenum, and nickel. Steels containing over 11–12% of chromium are known as *stainless steels.

Carbon steels exist in three stable crystalline phases: *ferrite* has a body-centred cubic crystal, *austenite* has a face-centred cubic crystal, and *cementite* has an orthorhombic crystal. *Pearlite* is a mixture of ferrite and cementite arranged in parallel plates. The phase diagram shows how the phases form at different temperatures and compositions.

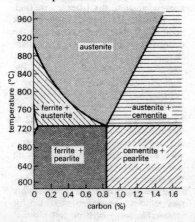

Phase diagram for steel

Steels are made by the *basic-oxygen process (L–D process), which has largely replaced the *Bessemer process and the *open-hearth process, or in electrical furnaces.

Stefan's law (Stefan–Boltzmann law) The total energy radiated per unit surface area of a *black body in unit time is proportional to the fourth power of its thermodynamic temperature. The constant of proportionality, the *Stefan constant* (or *Stefan–Boltzmann constant*) has the value $5.6697 \times 10^{-8} \ J s^{-1} m^{-2} K^{-4}$. The law was discovered by Joseph Stefan (1853–93) and theoretically derived by Ludwig Boltzmann (1844–1906).

stellar evolution The changes that occur to a *star during its lifetime, from birth to final extinction. A star is believed to form from a condensation of interstellar matter, which collects either by chance or for unexplained reasons, and grows by attracting other matter towards itself as a result of its gravitational field. This initial cloud of cold contracting matter, called a *protostar*, builds up an internal pressure as a result of its gravitational contraction. The pressure raises the temperature until it reaches $5–10 \times 10^6$ K, at which temperature the thermonuclear conversion of hydrogen to helium begins. In our *sun, a typical star, hydrogen is converted at a rate of some 10^{11} kg s^{-1} with the evolution of some 6×10^{25} J s^{-1} of energy. It is estimated that the sun contains sufficient hydrogen to burn at this rate for 10^{10} years and that it still has half its life to live as a main-sequence star (*see* Hertzsprung–Russell diagram). Eventually, however, this period of stability comes to an end, because the thermonuclear energy generated in the interior is no longer sufficient to counterbalance the gravitational contraction. The core, which is now mostly helium, collapses until a sufficiently high temperature is reached in a shell

of unburnt hydrogen round the core to start a new phase of thermonuclear reaction. This burning of the shell causes the star's outer envelope to expand and cool, the temperature drop changes the colour from white to red and the star becomes a *red giant* or a *supergiant* if the original star was very large. The core now contracts, reaching a temperature of 10^8 K, and the helium in the core acts as the thermonuclear energy source. This reaction produces carbon, but a star of low mass relatively soon runs out of helium and the core collapses into a *white dwarf, while the outer regions drift away into space, possibly forming a *planetary nebula*. Larger stars (several times larger than the sun) have sufficient helium for the process to continue so that heavier elements, up to iron, are formed. But iron is the heaviest element that can be formed with the production of energy and when the helium has all been consumed there is a catastrophic collapse of the core, resulting in a *supernova explosion, blowing the outer layers away. The current theory suggests that thereafter the collapsed core becomes a *neutron star or a *black hole.

steradian Symbol sr. The supplementary *SI unit of solid angle equal to the *solid angle that encloses a surface on a sphere equal to the square of the radius of the sphere.

stere A unit of volume equal to 1 m³. It is not now used for scientific purposes.

stimulated emission *See* laser.

STM *See* scanning tunnelling microscope.

stochastic process Any process in which there is a random variable.

stokes Symbol St. A c.g.s. unit of kinematic viscosity equal to the ratio of the viscosity of a fluid in poises to its density in grams per cubic centimetre. 1 stokes = 10^{-4} m² s⁻¹. It is

named after Sir George Stokes (1819–1903).

Stokes' law A law that predicts the frictional force F on a spherical ball moving through a viscous medium. According to this law $F = 6\pi r \eta v$, where r is the radius of the ball, v is its velocity, and η is the viscosity of the medium. The sphere accelerates until it reaches a steady terminal speed. For a falling ball, F is equal to the gravitational force on the sphere, less any upthrust. The law was discovered by Sir George Stokes (1819–1903).

stop A circular aperture that limits the effective size of a lens in an optical system. It may be adjustable, as the iris diaphragm in a camera, or have a fixed diameter, as the disc used in some telescopes.

stopping power A measure of the ability of matter to reduce the kinetic energy of a particle passing through it. The *linear stopping power*, $-dE/dx$, is energy loss of a particle per unit distance. The *mass stopping power*, $(1/\rho)dE/dx$, is linear stopping power divided by the density (ρ) of the substance. The *atomic stopping power*, $(1/n)dE/dx = (A/\rho N)dE/dx$, is the energy loss per atom per unit area perpendicular to the particle's motion, i.e. n is the number of atoms in unit volume of the substance, N is the Avogadro number, and A is the relative atomic mass of the substance. The relative stopping power is the ratio of the stopping power of a substance to that of a standard substance, usually aluminium, oxygen, or air.

storage ring A large evacuated toroidal ring forming a part of some particle accelerators. The rings are designed like *synchrotrons, except that they do not accelerate the particles circling within them but supply just sufficient energy to make up for losses (mainly *synchrotron radiation). The storage rings are usually

built tangentially to the associated accelerator so that particles can be transferred accurately between them. At *CERN in Geneva, two interlaced storage rings are used, containing protons rotating in opposite directions. At the intersections very high collision energies (up to 1700 GeV) can be achieved.

s.t.p. Standard temperature and pressure, formerly known as *N.T.P.* (normal temperature and pressure). The standard conditions used as a basis for calculations involving quantities that vary with temperature and pressure. These conditions are used when comparing the properties of gases. They are 273.15 K (or 0°C) and 101 325 Pa (or 760.0 mmHg).

strain A measure of the extent to which a body is deformed when it is subjected to a *stress. The *linear strain* or *tensile strain* is the ratio of the change in length to the original length. The *bulk strain* or *volume strain* is the ratio of the change in volume to the original volume. The *shear strain* is the angular distortion in radians of a body subjected to a *shearing force. *See also* elasticity; elastic modulus.

strain gauge A device used to measure a small mechanical deformation in a body (*see* strain). The most widely used devices are metal wires or foils or semiconductor materials, such as a single silicon crystal, which are attached to structural members; when the members are stretched under tensile *stress the resistance of the metal or semiconductor element increases. By making the resistance a component in a *Wheatstone-bridge circuit an estimate of the strain can be made by noting the change in resistance. Other types of strain gauge rely on changes of capacitance or the magnetic induction between two coils, one of which is attached to the stressed member.

strain hardening (work hardening) An increase in the resistance to the further plastic deformation of a body as a result of a rearrangement of its internal structure when it is strained, particularly by repeated stress. *See also* elasticity.

strange attractor *See* attractor.

strange matter Matter composed of up, down, and strange quarks (rather than the up and down quarks found in normal nucleons). It has been suggested that strange matter may have been formed in the *early universe, and that pieces of this matter (called *S-drops*) may still exist.

strangeness Symbol *s*. A property of certain elementary particles called hadrons (K-mesons and hyperons) that decay more slowly than would have been expected from the large amount of energy released in the process. These particles were assigned the quantum number *s* to account for this behaviour. For nucleons and other nonstrange particles $s = 0$; for strange particles *s* does not equal zero but has an integral value. In quark theory (*see* elementary particles) hadrons with the property of strangeness contain a strange quark or its antiquark.

stratosphere *See* earth's atmosphere.

streamline flow A type of fluid flow in which no *turbulence occurs and the particles of the fluid follow continuous paths, either at constant velocity or at a velocity that alters in a predictable and regular way (*see also* laminar flow).

stress The force per unit area on a body that tends to cause it to deform (*see* strain). It is a measure of the internal forces in a body between particles of the material of which it consists as they resist separation, compression, or sliding in response to externally applied forces. *Tensile stress* and *compressive stress* are axial forces per unit area applied to a body

that tend either to extend it or compress it linearly. *Shear stress* is a tangential force per unit area that tends to shear a body. *See also* elasticity; elastic modulus.

string A one-dimensional object used in theories of elementary particles and in cosmology (*cosmic string*). *String theory* replaces the idea of a pointlike elementary particle (used in quantum field theory) by a line or loop (a closed string). States of a particle may be produced by standing waves along this string. The combination of string theory with supersymmetry leads to *superstring theory.

stroboscope A device for making a moving body intermittently visible in order to make it appear stationary. It may consist of a lamp flashing at regular intervals or a shutter that enables it to be seen intermittently. *Stroboscopic photography* is the taking of very short-exposure pictures of moving objects using an electronically controlled flash lamp.

strong interaction *See* fundamental interactions.

subatomic particle *See* elementary particles.

subcritical *See* critical mass; critical reaction; multiplication factor.

sublimate A solid formed by sublimation.

sublimation A direct change of state from solid to gas.

subshell *See* atom.

subsonic speed A speed that is less than *Mach 1.

subtractive process *See* colour.

sun The *star at the centre of the *solar system. A typical main-sequence dwarf star (*see* Hertzsprung–Russell diagram; stellar evolution), the sun is some 149 600 000 km from earth. It has a diameter of about 1 392 000 km and a mass of 1.9 $\times$ 10^{30} kg. Hydrogen and helium are the primary constituents (about 75%

hydrogen, 25% helium), with less than 1% of heavier elements. In the central core, some 400 000 km in diameter, hydrogen is converted into helium by thermonuclear reactions, which generate vast quantities of energy. This energy is radiated into space and provides the earth with all the light and heat necessary to have created and maintained life (*see* solar constant). The surface of the sun, the *photosphere, forms the boundary between its opaque interior and its transparent atmosphere. It is here that *sunspots occur. Above the photosphere is the *chromosphere and above this the *corona, which extends tenuously into interplanetary space. *See also* solar wind.

sunspot A dark patch in the sun's *photosphere resulting from a localized fall in temperature to about 4000 K. Most spots have a central very dark umbra surrounded by a lighter penumbra. Sunspots tend to occur in clusters and to last about two weeks. The number of sunspots visible fluctuates over an eleven-year cycle – often called the *sunspot cycle*. The cause is thought to be the presence of intense localized magnetic fields, which suppress the convection currents that bring hot gases to the photosphere.

supercluster *See* galaxy cluster.

superconductivity The absence of measurable electrical resistance in certain substances at temperatures close to 0 K. First discovered in 1911 in mercury, superconductivity is now known to occur in some 26 metallic elements and many compounds and alloys. The temperature below which a substance becomes superconducting is called the *transition temperature* (or *critical temperature*). Compounds are now known that show superconductivity at liquid-nitrogen temperatures. The theoretical explanation of the phenomenon was given by J. Bardeen (1908–), L. N. Cooper (1930–),

and J. R. Schrieffer (1931–) in 1957 and is known as the *BCS theory*. According to this theory an electron moving through an elastic crystal lattice creates a slight distortion of the lattice as a result of Coulomb forces between the positively charged lattice and the negatively charged electron. If this distortion persists for a finite time it can affect a second passing electron. In 1956 Cooper showed that the effect of this phenomenon is for the current to be carried in superconductors not by individual electrons but by bound pairs of electrons, the *Cooper pairs*. The BCS theory is based on a *wave function in which all the electrons are paired. Because the total momentum of a Cooper pair is unchanged by the interaction between one of its electrons and the lattice, the flow of electrons continues indefinitely.

Superconducting coils in which large currents can circulate indefinitely can be used to create powerful magnetic fields and are used for this purpose in some particle accelerators and in other devices.

Superconductivity can also occur by a slightly more complicated mechanism than BCS theory in *heavy-fermion systems. In 1986, Bednorz and Müller found an apparently completely different type of superconductivity. This is called *high-temperature superconductivity*, since the critical temperature is very much higher than for BCS superconductors; some high-temperature superconductors have critical temperatures greater than 100 K. A typical high-temperature superconductor is $YBa_2Cu_3O_{1-7}$.

At the present time a theory of high-temperature superconductivity has not been established in spite of a great deal of effort, which is still going on. The BCS mechanism, and minor modifications of it, almost certainly do not apply. One model for high-temperature superconductivity uses the concept of anyons, but at present

there is no evidence for this mechanism.

supercooling 1. The cooling of a liquid to below its freezing point without a change from the liquid to solid state taking place. In this metastable state the particles of the liquid lose energy but do not fall into place in the lattice of the solid crystal. If the liquid is seeded with a small crystal, crystallization usually takes place and the temperature returns to the freezing point. This is a common occurrence in the atmosphere where water droplets frequently remain unfrozen at temperatures well below 0°C until disturbed, following which they rapidly freeze. The supercooled droplets, for example, rapidly freeze on passing aircraft forming 'icing', which can be a hazard. **2.** The analogous cooling of a vapour to make it supersaturated until a disturbance causes condensation to occur, as in the Wilson *cloud chamber.

supercritical *See* critical mass; critical reaction; multiplication factor.

superficial expansivity *See* expansivity.

superfluidity The property of liquid helium at very low temperatures that enables it to flow without friction. Both helium isotopes possess this property, but ^4He becomes superfluid at 2.172 K, whereas ^3He does not become superfluid until a temperature of 0.00093 K is reached. There is a basic connection between superfluidity and *superconductivity, so that sometimes a superconductor is called a charged superfluid.

supergiant The largest and most luminous type of star. They are formed from the most massive stars and are therefore very rare. They lie above the giants on the *Hertzsprung–Russell diagram. *See also* stellar evolution.

supergravity A *unified-field theory for all the known fundamental inter-

actions that involves *supersymmetry. Supergravity is most naturally formulated as a *Kaluza–Klein theory in eleven dimensions. The theory contains particles of spin 2, spin 3/2, spin 1, spin 1/2, and spin 0. Although supersymmetry means that the infinities in the calculations are less severe than in other attempts to construct a quantum theory of gravity, it is probable that supergravity still contains infinities that cannot be removed by the process of *renormalization. It is thought by many physicists that to obtain a consistent quantum theory of gravity one has to abandon *quantum field theories, since they deal with point objects, and move to theories based on extended objects, such as *superstrings and *supermembranes, and therefore that supergravity is not a complete theory of the fundamental interactions.

superheterodyne receiver A widely used type of radio receiver in which the incoming radio-frequency signal is mixed with an internally generated signal from a local oscillator. The output of the mixer has a carrier frequency equal to the difference between the transmitted carrier frequency and the locally generated frequency, still retains the transmitted modulation, and is called the *intermediate frequency* (IF). The IF signal is amplified before being passed to the audio-frequency amplifier. This system enables the IF signal to be amplified with less distortion, greater gain, better selectivity, and easier elimination of noise than can be achieved by amplifying the radio-frequency signal.

super high frequency (SHF) A radio frequency in the range 3–30 gigahertz.

superlattice *See* solid solution.

supermembrane theory A unified theory of the *fundamental interactions involving *supersymmetry, in which the basic entities are two-dimensional extended objects (*supermembranes*). They are thought to have about the same length scale as *superstrings, i.e. 10^{-35} m. At the present time there is no experimental evidence for supermembranes.

supernova An explosive brightening of a star in which the energy radiated by it increases by a factor of 10^{10}. It takes several years to fade and while it lasts dominates the whole galaxy in which it lies. It is estimated that there could be a supernova explosion in the Milky Way every 30 years, although only six have actually been observed in the last 1000 years. A supernova explosion occurs when a star has burnt up all its available nuclear fuel and the core collapses catastrophically (*see* stellar evolution). *Compare* nova.

superplasticity The ability of some metals and alloys to stretch uniformly by several thousand percent at high temperatures, unlike normal alloys, which fail after being stretched 100% or less. Since 1962, when this property was discovered in an alloy of zinc and aluminium (22%), many alloys and ceramics have been shown to possess this property. For superplasticity to occur, the metal grain must be small and rounded and the alloy must have a slow rate of deformation.

supersaturated solution *See* saturated.

supersaturation 1. The state of the atmosphere in which the relative humidity is over 100%. This occurs in pure air where no condensation nuclei are available. Supersaturation is usually prevented in the atmosphere by the abundance of condensation nuclei (e.g. dust, sea salt, and smoke particles). 2. The state of any vapour whose pressure exceeds that at which condensation usually occurs (at the prevailing temperature).

supersonic *See* Mach number.

superstring theory A unified theory of the *fundamental interactions involving supersymmetry, in which the basic objects are one-dimensional objects (*superstrings*). Superstrings are thought to have a length scale of about 10^{-35} m and, since very short distances are associated with very high energies, they should have energy scales of about 10^{19} GeV, which is far beyond the energy of any accelerator that can be envisaged.

Strings associated with bosons are only consistent as quantum theories in a 26-dimensional *space–time; those associated with fermions are only consistent as quantum theories in 10-dimensional space–time. It is thought that four macroscopic dimensions arise by a Kaluza–Klein mechanism, with the remaining dimensions being 'curled up' to become very small.

One of the most attractive features of the theory of superstrings is that it leads to spin 2 particles, which are identified as *gravitons. Thus, a superstring theory automatically contains a quantum theory of the gravitational interaction. It is thought that superstrings are free of the infinities that cannot be removed by *renormalization, which plague attempts to construct a quantum field theory incorporating gravity. There is some evidence that superstring theory is free of infinities but not a complete proof yet.

Although there is no direct evidence for superstrings, some features of superstrings are compatible with the experimental facts of *elementary particles, such as the possibility of particles that do not respect *parity, as found in the weak interactions. Another attractive aspect of the theory is that it reveals the existence of particles that do not conserve parity, as in the weak interaction.

supersymmetry A *symmetry that can be applied to elementary particles

so as to include both bosons and fermions. In the simplest supersymmetry theories, every boson has a corresponding fermion partner and every fermion has a corresponding boson partner. The boson partners of existing fermions have names formed by adding 's' to the beginning of the name of the fermion, e.g. *selectron*, *squark*, and *slepton*. The fermion partners of existing bosons have names formed by replacing '-on' at the end of the boson's name by '-ino' or by adding '-ino', e.g. *gluino*, *photino*, *wino*, and *zino*.

The infinities that cause problems in relativistic quantum field theories (*see* renormalization) are less severe in supersymmetry theories because infinities of bosons and fermions can cancel one another out.

If supersymmetry is relevant to observed elementary particles then it must be a *broken symmetry, although there is no convincing evidence at present to show at what energy it would be broken. There is, in fact, no experimental evidence for the theory, although it is thought that it may form part of a unified theory of interactions. This would not necessarily be a *unified-field theory; the idea of strings with supersymmetry may be the best approach to unifying the four fundamental interactions (*see* superstring theory).

supplementary units *See* SI units.

suppressor grid A wire grid in a pentode *thermionic valve placed between the *screen grid and the anode to prevent electrons produced by *secondary emission from the anode from reaching the screen grid.

surd A quantity that cannot be expressed as a *rational number. It consists of the root of an arithmetic member (e.g. $\sqrt{3}$), which cannot be exactly determined, or the sum or difference of such roots.

surface tension Symbol γ. The property of a liquid that makes it behave

surfactant

as if its surface is enclosed in an elastic skin. The property results from intermolecular forces: a molecule in the interior of a liquid experiences interactions with other molecules equally from all sides, whereas a molecule at the surface is only affected by molecules below it in the liquid. The surface tension is defined as the force acting over the surface per unit length of surface perpendicular to the force. It is measured in newtons per metre. It can equally be defined as the energy required to increase the surface area isothermally by one square metre, i.e. it can be measured in joules per metre squared (which is equivalent to $N\,m^{-1}$).

The property of surface tension is responsible for the formation of liquid drops, soap bubbles, and meniscuses, as well as the rise of liquids in a capillary tube (*capillarity*), the absorption of liquids by porous substances, and the ability of liquids to wet a surface.

surfactant (surface active agent) A substance, such as a *detergent, added to a liquid to increase its spreading or wetting properties by reducing its *surface tension.

susceptance Symbol B. The reciprocal of the *reactance of a circuit and thus the imaginary part of its *admittance. It is measured in siemens.

susceptibility 1. (*or* **magnetic susceptibility)** Symbol χ_m. The dimensionless quantity describing the contribution made by a substance when subjected to a magnetic field to the total magnetic flux density present. It is equal to $\mu_r - 1$, where μ_r is the relative *permeability of the material. Diamagnetic materials have a low negative susceptibility, paramagnetic materials have a low positive susceptibility, and ferromagnetic materials have a high positive value. **2. (***or* **electric susceptibility)** Symbol χ_e. The dimensionless quantity referring to a *dielectric equal to $P/\varepsilon_0 E$, where P is the electric polarization, E is the electric intensity producing it, and ε_0 is the electric constant. The electric susceptibility is also equal to $\varepsilon_r - 1$, where ε_r is the relative *permittivity of the dielectric.

suspension A mixture in which small solid or liquid particles are suspended in a liquid or gas.

symmetry The set of invariances of a system. Upon application of a symmetry operation on a system, the system is unchanged. Symmetry is studied mathematically using *group theory. Some of the symmetries are directly physical. Examples include reflections and rotation for molecules and translation in crystal lattices. Symmetries can be *discrete* (i.e. have a finite number), such as the set of rotations for an octahedral molecule, or *continuous* (i.e. do not have a finite number), such as the set of rotations for atoms or nuclei. More general and abstract symmetries can occur, as in CPT invariance and in the symmetries associated with *gauge theories. *See also* broken symmetry; supersymmetry.

synchrocyclotron A form of *cyclotron in which the frequency of the accelerating potential is synchronized with the increasing period of revolution of a group of the accelerated particles, resulting from their relativistic increase in mass as they reach *relativistic speeds. The accelerator is used with protons, deuterons, and alpha-particles.

synchronous motor *See* electric motor.

synchronous orbit (geosynchronous orbit) An orbit of the earth made by an artificial *satellite with a period exactly equal to the earth's period of rotation on its axis, i.e. 23 hours 56 minutes 4.1 seconds. If the orbit is inclined to the equatorial plane the satellite will appear from the earth to trace out a figure-of-eight track once every 24 hours. If the

orbit lies in the equatorial plane and is circular, the satellite will appear to be stationary. This is called a *stationary orbit* (or *geostationary orbit*) and it occurs at an altitude of 35 900 km. Most communication satellites are in stationary orbits, with three or more spaced round the orbit to give world-wide coverage.

synchronous rotation The rotation of a natural satellite in which the period of rotation is equal to its orbital period. The moon, for example, is in synchronous rotation about the earth.

synchrotron A particle accelerator used to impart energy to electrons and protons in order to carry out experiments in particle physics and in some cases to make use of the *synchrotron radiation produced. The particles are accelerated in closed orbits (often circular) by radio-frequency fields. Magnets are spaced round the orbit to bend the trajectory of the particles and separate focusing magnets are used to keep the particles in a narrow beam. The radio-frequency accelerating cavities are interspersed between the magnets. The motion of the particles is automatically synchronized with the rising magnetic field, as the field strength has to increase as the particle energy increases; the frequency of the accelerating field also has to increase synchronously.

synchrotron radiation (magneto-bremsstrahlung) Electromagnetic radiation that is emitted by charged particles moving at relativistic speeds in circular orbits in a magnetic field. The rate of emission is inversely proportional to the product of the radius of curvature of the orbit and the fourth power of the mass of the particles. For this reason, synchrotron radiation is not a problem in the design of proton *synchrotrons but it

is significant in electron synchrotrons. The greater the circumference of a synchrotron, the less important is the loss of energy by synchrotron radiation. In *storage rings, synchrotron radiation is the principal cause of energy loss.

However, since the 1950s it has been realized that synchrotron radiation is itself a very useful tool and many accelerator laboratories have research projects making use of the radiation on a secondary basis to the main high-energy research. The radiation used for these purposes is primarily in the ultraviolet and X-ray frequencies.

Much of the microwave radiation from celestial radio sources outside the Galaxy is believed to originate from electrons moving in curved paths in celestial magnetic fields; it is also called synchrotron radiation as it is analogous to the radiation occurring in a synchrotron.

synodic month (lunation) The interval between new *moons. It is equal to 29 days, 12 hours, and 44 minutes.

synodic period The mean time taken by any object in the solar system to move between successive returns to the same position, relative to the sun as seen from the earth. Since a planet is best observed at opposition the synodic period of a planet, S, is easier to measure than its *sidereal period, P. For inferior planets $1/S = 1/P - 1/E$; for superior planets $1/S = 1/E - 1/P$, where E is the sidereal period of the earth.

Système International d'Unités *See* SI units.

syzygy The situation that occurs when the sun, the moon (or a planet), and the earth are in a straight line. This occurs when the moon (or planet) is at *conjunction or *opposition.

T

tachometer An instrument for measuring angular speed, especially the number of revolutions made by a rotating shaft in unit time. Various types of instrument are used, including mechanical, electrical, and electronic devices. The widely used electrical-generator tachometer consists of a small generator in which the output voltage is a measure of the rate of rotation of the shaft that drives it.

tachyon A hypothetical particle that has a speed in excess of the *speed of light. According to electromagnetic theory, a charged particle travelling through a medium at a speed in excess of the speed of light in that medium emits *Cerenkov radiation. A charged tachyon would emit Cerenkov radiation even in a vacuum. No such particle has yet been detected. According to the special theory of *relativity, it is impossible to accelerate a particle up to the speed of light because its energy E, given by $E = mc^2/\sqrt{(1 - v^2/c^2)}$, would have to become infinite. The theory, however, does not forbid the existence of particles with $v > c$ (where c is the speed of light). In such cases the expression in the brackets becomes negative and the energy would be imaginary.

tandem generator A type of particle generator, essentially consisting of a *Van de Graaff generator that maintains one electrode at a high positive potential; this electrode is placed between two earthed electrodes. Negative ions are accelerated from earth potential to the positively charged electrode, where surplus electrons are stripped from the ions to produce positive ions, which are accelerated again from the positive electrode back to earth. Thus the ions are accelerated twice over by a single high potential. This tandem arrangement enables energies up to 30 MeV to be achieved.

tangent 1. A line that touches a curve or a plane that touches a surface. **2.** *See* trigonometric functions.

tangent galvanometer A type of galvanometer, now rarely used, in which a small magnetic needle is pivoted horizontally at the centre of a vertical coil that is adjusted to be parallel to the horizontal component of the earth's magnetic field. When a current I is passed through the coil, the needle is deflected so that it makes an angle θ with its equilibrium position parallel to the earth's field. The value of I is given by $I = (2Hr\tan\theta)/n$, where H is the strength of the earth's horizontal component of magnetizing force, r is the radius of the coil, and n is the number of turns in the coil. Although not now used for measuring current, the instrument provides a means of measuring the earth's magnetizing force.

tau particle *See* elementary particles; lepton.

Taylor series The infinite power series of derivatives into which a function f(x) can be expanded, for a fixed value of the variable $x = a$:
$$f(x) = f(a) + f'(a)(x - a) + f''(a)(x - a)^2/2! + \ldots$$
When $a = 0$, the series formed is known as *Maclaurin's series*:
$$f(x) = f(0) + f'(0)x + f''(0)x^2/2! + \ldots$$
The series was discovered by Brook Taylor (1685–1731) and the special case was named after Colin Maclaurin (1698–1746).

tektite A small black, greenish, or yellowish glassy object found in groups on the earth's surface and consisting of a siliceous material unrelated to the geological formations in which it is found. Tektites are believed to have formed on earth as a result of the impact of meteorites.

276

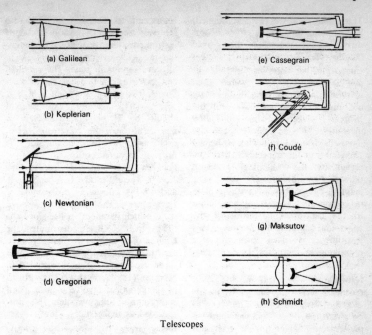

(a) Galilean

(b) Keplerian

(c) Newtonian

(d) Gregorian

(e) Cassegrain

(f) Coudé

(g) Maksutov

(h) Schmidt

Telescopes

telecommunications The study and application of means of transmitting information, either by wires or by electromagnetic radiation.

telescope An instrument that collects radiation from a distant object in order to produce an image of it or enable the radiation to be analysed. An *optical telescope* uses visible radiation (*see also* radio telescope). Optical *astronomical telescopes* fall into two main classes: *refracting telescopes* and *reflecting telescopes*. Refracting telescopes use a converging lens to collect the light and the resulting image is magnified by the eyepiece, a lens of short focal length. This type of instrument was first constructed in 1608 by Hans Lippershey (1587–1619) in Holland and developed in the following year as an astronomical instrument by Galileo, who used a diverging lens as eyepiece (see illustration (a)). The *Galilean telescope* was later

improved by Johannes Kepler (1571–1630), who substituted a converging eyepiece lens, and this form of the instrument is still in use for small astronomical telescopes. For terrestrial telescopes an additional lens is usually inserted in order to provide an upright image (see illustration (b)). However the Galilean design provides an upright image originally, and so is still used for the compact telescopes of opera glasses.

The first reflecting telescope was produced by Newton in 1668. This used a concave mirror to collect and focus the light and a small secondary mirror at an angle of 45° to the main beam to reflect the light into the magnifying eyepiece. The *Gregorian telescope*, designed by James Gregory (1638–75), and the *Cassegrainian telescope*, designed by N. Cassegrain (*fl.* 1670s), use different secondary optical systems (see illustrations (d) and (e)).

The *coudé telescope* (French: angled) is sometimes used with larger instruments as it increases their focal lengths (see illustration (f)).

Catadioptic telescopes use both lenses and mirrors. The most widely used astronomical instruments in this class are the *Maksutov telescope* and the *Schmidt camera*. The Maksutov instrument has a thick spheroidal meniscus lens to introduce spherical aberration to the image, which is corrected by the spheroidal principal mirror (see illustration (g)). The Schmidt camera has a correcting plate of complicated aspherical shape close to the centre of curvature of the spheroidal principal mirror. This instrument is used primarily for photographic purposes (see illustration (h)).

television The transmission and reception of moving images by means of radio waves or cable. The scene to be transmitted is focused onto a photoelectric screen in the television *camera. This screen is scanned by an electron beam. The camera produces an electric current, the instantaneous magnitude of which is proportional to the brightness of the portion of the screen being scanned. In Europe the screen is scanned by 625 lines and 25 such frames are produced every second. In the USA 525 lines and 30 frames per second are used. The picture signal so produced is used to modulate a VHF or UHF carrier wave and is transmitted with an independent sound signal, but with colour information (if any) incorporated into the brief gaps between the picture lines. The signals received by the receiving aerial are demodulated in the receiver; the demodulated picture signal controls the electron beam in a cathode-ray tube, on the screen of which the picture is reconstructed. *See also* colour television.

television tube *See* cathode rays.

temperament The way in which the intervals between notes on keyboard instruments are distributed throughout the scale to ensure that music in all keys sounds in tune. The problem can be illustrated by a piano keyboard. Taking a low C and a high C seven octaves above, the interval should be $2^7 = 128$. However, in passing through the cycle of 12 keys, each using as its fundamental the fifth of its predecessor, the interval between Cs becomes $(3/2)^{12} = 129.75$. The difference between 129.75 and 128 is known as the *comma of Pythagoras*. The *equal-temperament scale*, which has been in use since the time of J. S. Bach, distributes the comma of Pythagoras equally between the 12 intervals of the scale over seven octaves. Thus each fifth becomes $(128)^{1/12} = 1.4983$. All forms of temperament involve a measure of compromise; this system is now regarded as the best.

temperature The property of a body or region of space that determines whether or not there will be a net flow of heat into it or out of it from a neighbouring body or region and in which direction (if any) the heat will flow. If there is no heat flow the bodies or regions are said to be in *thermodynamic equilibrium* and at the same temperature. If there is a flow of heat, the direction of the flow is from the body or region of higher temperature. Broadly, there are two methods of quantifying this property. The empirical method is to take two or more reproducible temperature-dependent events and assign *fixed points* on a scale of values to these events. For example, the Celsius temperature scale uses the freezing point and boiling point of water as the two fixed points, assigns the values 0 and 100 to them, respectively, and divides the scale between them into 100 degrees. This method is serviceable for many practical purposes (*see* tem-

perature scales), but lacking a theoretical basis it is awkward to use in many scientific contexts. In the 19th century, Lord Kelvin proposed a thermodynamic method to specify temperature, based on the measurement of the quantity of heat flowing between bodies at different temperatures. This concept relies on an absolute scale of temperature with an *absolute zero of temperature, at which no body can give up heat. He also used Sadi Carnot's concept of an ideal frictionless perfectly efficient heat engine (see Carnot cycle). This Carnot engine takes in a quantity of heat q_1 at a temperature T, and exhausts heat q_2 at T_2, so that $T_1/T_2 = q_1/q_2$. If T_2 has a value fixed by definition, a Carnot engine can be run between this fixed temperature and any unknown temperature T_1, enabling T_1 to be calculated by measuring the values of q_1 and q_2. This concept remains the basis for defining *thermodynamic temperature*, quite independently of the nature of the working substance. The unit in which thermodynamic temperature is expressed is the *kelvin. In practice thermodynamic temperatures cannot be measured directly; they are usually inferred from measurements with a gas thermometer containing a nearly ideal gas. This is possible because another aspect of thermodynamic temperature is its relationship to the *internal energy of a given amount of substance. This can be shown most simply in the case of an ideal monatomic gas, in which the internal energy per mole (U) is equal to the total kinetic energy of translation of the atoms in one mole of the gas (a monatomic gas has no rotational or vibrational energy). According to *kinetic theory, the thermodynamic temperature of such a gas is given by $T = 2U/3R$, where R is the universal *gas constant.

temperature coefficient A coefficient that determines the rate of change of some physical property with change in temperature. For example, the dependence of the resistance (R) of a material on the Celsius temperature t, is given by $R = R_0 + \alpha t + \beta t^2$, where R_0 is the resistance at 0°C and α and β are constants. If β is negligible, then α is the *temperature coefficient of resistance*.

temperature scales A number of empirical scales of *temperature have been in use: the *Celsius scale is widely used for many purposes and in certain countries the *Fahrenheit scale is still used. These scales both rely on the use of *fixed points*, such as the freezing point and the boiling point of water, and the division of the *fundamental interval* between these two points into units of temperature (100 degrees in the case of the Celsius scale and 180 degrees in the Fahrenheit scale).

However, for scientific purposes the scale in use is the *International Practical Temperature Scale (1968)*, which is designed to conform as closely as possible to thermodynamic temperature and is expressed in the unit of thermodynamic temperature, the *kelvin. The eleven fixed points of the scale are given in the table, with the instruments specified for interpolating between them. Above the freezing point of gold, a radiation pyrometer is used, based on Planck's law of radiation. The scale is expected to be refined in the late 1980s.

tempering The process of increasing the toughness of an alloy, such as steel, by heating it to a predetermined temperature, maintaining it at this temperature for a predetermined time, and cooling it to room temperature at a predetermined rate. In steel, the purpose of the process is to heat the alloy to a temperature that will enable the excess carbide to precipitate out of the supersaturated solid

	T/K	t/°C
triple point of equilibrium hydrogen	13.81	−259.34
temperature of equilibrium hydrogen when its vapour pressure is 25/76 standard atmosphere	17.042	−256.108
b.p. of equilibrium hydrogen	20.28	−252.87
b.p. of neon	27.102	−246.048
triple point of oxygen	54.361	−218.789
b.p. of oxygen	90.188	−182.962
triple point of water	273.16	0.01
b.p. of water	373.15	100
f.p. of zinc	692.73	419.58
f.p. of silver	1235.08	961.93
f.p. of gold	1337.58	1064.43

Temperature scales

solution of *martensite and then to cool the saturated solution fast enough to prevent further precipitation or grain growth. For this reason steel is quenched rapidly by dipping into cold water.

temporary magnetism Magnetism in a body that is present when the body is in a magnetic field but that largely disappears when it is removed from the field.

tensile strength A measure of the resistance that a material offers to tensile *stress. It is defined as the stress, expressed as the force per unit cross-sectional area, required to break it.

tensimeter A form of differential manometer with two sealed bulbs attached to the limbs. It is used to measure the difference in vapour pressure between liquids sealed into the bulbs. If one liquid has a known vapour pressure (often water is used) that of the other can be determined.

tensiometer Any apparatus for measuring *surface tension.

tera- Symbol T. A prefix used in the metric system to denote one million million times. For example, 10^{12} volts = 1 teravolt (TV).

terminal 1. The point at which electrical connection is made to a device or system. **2.** A device at which data is put into a *computer or taken from it.

terminal speed The constant speed finally attained by a body moving through a fluid under gravity when there is a zero resultant force acting on it. See Stokes's law.

terminator The boundary, on the surface of the moon or a planet, between the sunlit area and the dark area.

terrestrial magnetism See geomagnetism.

tertiary colour A colour obtained by mixing two *secondary colours.

tesla Symbol T. The SI unit of magnetic flux density equal to one weber of magnetic flux per square metre, i.e. $1\ T = 1\ Wb\,m^{-2}$. It is named after Nikola Tesla (1870–1943), Croatian-born US electrical engineer.

Tesla coil A device for producing a high-frequency high-voltage current. It consists of a *transformer with a high turns ratio, the primary circuit of which includes a spark gap and a fixed capacitor; the secondary circuit is tuned by means of a variable capacitor to resonate with the pri-

mary. It was devised by Nikola Tesla (1870–1943). Tesla coils are commonly used to excite luminous discharges in glass vacuum apparatus, in order to detect leaks.

tetragonal *See* crystal system.

tetrahedron A polyhedron with four triangular faces. In a *regular tetrahedron* all four triangles are congruent equilateral triangles. It constitutes a regular triangular *pyramid.

tetrode A *thermionic valve with a *screen grid* placed between the anode and the control grid of a *triode to reduce the capacitance between these two electrodes and so improve the valve's performance as an amplifier or oscillator at high frequencies. The screen grid is maintained at a fixed potential.

theodolite An optical surveying instrument for measuring horizontal and vertical angles. It consists of a sighting telescope, with crosshairs in the eyepiece for focusing on the target, which can be rotated in both the horizontal and vertical planes. It is mounted on a tripod and a spirit level is used to indicate when the instrument is horizontal. The angles are read off graduated circles seen through a second eyepiece in the instrument.

therm A practical unit of energy defined as 10^5 British thermal units. 1 therm is equal to 1.055×10^8 joules.

thermal capacity *See* heat capacity.

thermal conductivity *See* conductivity.

thermal diffusion The diffusion that takes place in a fluid as a result of a temperature gradient. If a column of gas is maintained so that the lower end is cooler than the upper end, the heavier molecules in the gas will tend to remain at the lower-temperature end and the lighter molecules will diffuse to the higher-temperature end. This property has been used in the

separation of gaseous isotopes (*see* Clusius column).

thermal equilibrium *See* equilibrium.

thermal expansion *See* expansivity.

thermalization The reduction of the kinetic energy of neutrons in a thermal *nuclear reactor by means of a *moderator; the process of producing thermal neutrons.

thermal neutrons *See* moderator; nuclear reactors; thermalization.

thermal reactor *See* nuclear reactor.

thermionic emission The emission of electrons, usually into a vacuum, from a heated conductor. The emitted current density, J, is given by the *Richardson* (or *Richardson–Dushman*) *equation*, i.e. $J = AT^2\exp(-W/kT)$, where T is the thermodynamic temperature of the emitter, W is its *work function, k is the Boltzmann constant, and A is a constant. Thermionic emission is the basis of the *thermionic valve and the *electron gun in cathode-ray tubes.

thermionics The branch of electronics concerned with the study and design of devices based on the emission of electrons from metal or metal-oxide surfaces as a result of high temperatures. The primary concern of thermionics is the design of *thermionic valves and the electron guns of cathode-ray tubes and other devices.

thermionic valve An electronic valve based on *thermionic emission. In such valves the cathode is either directly heated by passing a current through it or indirectly heated by placing it close to a heated filament. Directly heated cathodes are usually made of tungsten wire, whereas indirectly heated cathodes are usually coated with barium and strontium oxides. Most electronic valves are thermionic vacuum devices, although a few have cold cathodes and some are gas-filled (*see* thyratron). *See* diode; triode; tetrode; pentode.

thermistor A semiconductor electronic device the resistance of which decreases as its temperature increases. It consists of a bead, rod, or disc of various oxides of manganese, nickel, cobalt, copper, iron, or other metals. Thermistors are used as thermometers, often forming one element in a resistance bridge. They are used for this purpose in such applications as bearings, cylinder heads, and transformer cores. They are also used to compensate for the increased resistance of ordinary resistors when hot, and in vacuum gauges, time-delay switches, and voltage regulators.

thermite A stoichiometric powdered mixture of iron(III) oxide and aluminium for the reaction:

$$2Al + Fe_2O_3 \rightarrow Al_2O_3 + 2Fe$$

The reaction is highly exothermic and the increase in temperature is sufficient to melt the iron produced. It has been used for localized welding of steel objects (e.g. railway lines) in the *Thermit process*. Thermite is also used in incendiary bombs.

thermochemistry The branch of physical chemistry concerned with heats of chemical reaction, heats of formation of chemical compounds, etc.

thermocouple A device consisting of two dissimilar metal wires or semiconducting rods welded together at their ends. A thermoelectric e.m.f. is generated in the device when the ends are maintained at different temperatures, the magnitude of the e.m.f. being related to the temperature difference. This enables a thermocouple to be used as a thermometer over a limited temperature range. One of the two junctions, called the *hot* or *measuring junction*, is exposed to the temperature to be measured. The other, the *cold* or *reference junction*, is maintained at a known reference temperature. The e.m.f. generated is measured by a suitable millivoltmeter or potentiometer incorporated into the circuit. *See* Seebeck effect; thermopile.

thermodynamics The study of the laws that govern the conversion of energy from one form to another, the direction in which heat will flow, and the availability of energy to do work. It is based on the concept that in an isolated system anywhere in the universe there is a measurable quantity of energy called the *internal energy (U) of the system. This is the total kinetic and potential energy of the atoms and molecules of the system of all kinds that can be transferred directly as heat; it therefore excludes chemical and nuclear energy. The value of U can only be changed if the system ceases to be isolated. In these circumstances U can change by the transfer of mass to or from the system, the transfer of heat (Q) to or from the system, or by the work (W) being done on or by the system. For an adiabatic ($Q = 0$) system of constant mass, $\Delta U = W$. By convention, W is taken to be positive if work is done on the system and negative if work is done by the system. For nonadiabatic systems of constant mass, $\Delta U = Q + W$. This statement, which is equivalent to the law of conservation of energy, is known as the *first law of thermodynamics*.

All natural processes conform to this law, but not all processes conforming to it can occur in nature. Most natural processes are irreversible, i.e. they will only proceed in one direction (*see* reversible process). The direction that a natural process can take is the subject of the *second law of thermodynamics*, which can be stated in a variety of ways. R. Clausius (1822–88) stated the law in two ways: "heat cannot be transferred from one body to a second body at a higher temperature without producing some other effect" and "the entropy of a closed system increases with time". These statements introduce the ther-

modynamic concepts of *temperature (T) and *entropy (S), both of which are parameters determining the direction in which an irreversible process can go. The temperature of a body or system determines whether heat will flow into it or out of it; its entropy is a measure of the unavailability of its energy to do work. Thus T and S determine the relationship between Q and W in the statement of the first law. This is usually presented by stating the second law in the form $\Delta U = T\Delta S - W$.

The second law is concerned with changes in entropy (ΔS). The *third law of thermodynamics* provides an absolute scale of values for entropy by stating that for changes involving only perfect crystalline solids at *absolute zero, the change of the total entropy is zero. This law enables absolute values to be stated for entropies.

One other law is used in thermodynamics. Because it is fundamental to, and assumed by, the other laws of thermodynamics it is usually known as the *zeroth law of thermodynamics*. This states that if two bodies are each in thermal equilibrium with a third body, then all three bodies are in thermal equilibrium with each other. *See also* enthalpy; free energy.

thermodynamic temperature *See* temperature.

thermoelectricity An electric current generated by temperature difference. There are three interrelated *thermoelectric effects*. *See* Peltier effect; Seebeck effect; Thomson effect.

thermograph 1. A recording thermometer used in meteorology to obtain a continuous record of temperature changes over a period on a graph. **2.** A record so obtained. **3.** A record obtained by the technique of *thermography.

thermography A medical technique that makes use of the infrared radiation from the human skin to detect

an area of elevated skin temperature that could be associated with an underlying cancer. The heat radiated from the body varies according to the local blood flow, thus an area of poor circulation produces less radiation. A tumour, on the other hand, has an abnormally increased blood supply and is revealed on the *thermogram* (or *thermograph*) as a 'hot spot'. The technique is used particularly in mammography, the examination of the infrared radiation emitted by human breasts in order to detect breast cancer.

thermoluminescence *Luminescence produced in a solid when its temperature is raised. It arises when free electrons and *holes, trapped in a solid as a result of exposure to ionizing radiation, unite and emit photons of light. The process is made use of in *thermoluminescent dating*, which assumes that the number of electrons and holes trapped in a sample of pottery is related to the length of time that has elapsed since the pottery was fired. By comparing the luminescence produced by heating a piece of pottery of unknown age with the luminescence produced by heating similar materials of known age, a fairly accurate estimate of the age of an object can be made.

thermoluminescent dating *See* thermoluminescence.

thermometer An instrument used for measuring the *temperature of a substance. A number of techniques and forms are used in thermometers depending on such factors as the degree of accuracy required and the range of temperatures to be measured, but they all measure temperature by making use of some property of a substance that varies with temperature. For example, *liquid-in-glass thermometers* depend on the expansion of a liquid, usually mercury or alcohol coloured with dye. These consist of a liquid-filled glass bulb

attached to a partially filled capillary tube. In the *bimetallic thermometer* the unequal expansion of two dissimilar metals that have been bonded together into a narrow strip and coiled is used to move a pointer round a dial. The *gas thermometer*, which is more accurate than the liquid-in-glass thermometer, measures the variation in the pressure of a gas kept at constant volume. The *resistance thermometer* is based on the change in resistance of conductors or semiconductors with temperature change. Platinum, nickel, and copper are the metals most commonly used in resistance thermometers. *See also* pyrometry; thermistor; thermocouple.

thermonuclear reaction *See* nuclear fusion; thermonuclear reactor.

thermonuclear reactor (fusion reactor) A reactor in which *nuclear fusion takes place with the controlled release of energy. Although thermonuclear reactors do not yet exist, intense research in many parts of the world is being carried out with a view to achieving such a machine. There are two central problems in the creation of a self-sustaining thermonuclear reactor: heating the reacting nuclides to the enormous *ignition temperature (about 40×10^6 K for a deuterium–tritium reaction) and containing the reacting nuclides for long enough for the fusion energy released to exceed the energy required to achieve the ignition temperature (*see* Lawson criterion). The two methods being explored are *magnetic containment* and *pellet fusion*.

In the closed magnetic-containment device the fusion *plasma is contained in a toroidal-shaped reactor, called a *Tokamak*, in which strong magnetic fields guide the charged plasma particles round the toroid without allowing them to contact the container walls. In open-ended magnetic systems the plasma is trapped between magnetic mirrors (strong

magnetic fields) at the two ends of a straight containment vessel.

In pellet fusion the objective is to heat and compress a tiny pellet of the nuclear fuels, by means of a laser or an electron beam, so rapidly that fusion is achieved before the pellet flies apart. Results with this type of equipment have been comparable to those achieved by magnetic confinement.

thermonuclear weapon *See* nuclear weapons.

thermopile A device used to detect and measure the intensity of radiant energy. It consists of a number of *thermocouples connected together in series to achieve greater sensitivity. The hot junctions of the thermocouples are blackened and exposed to the radiation to be detected or measured, while the cold junctions are shielded from the radiation. The thermoelectric e.m.f. generated enables the hot junction excess temperature to be calculated and the radiant intensity to be deduced. They are used in various applications, from a safety device that produces an electric signal if a pilot light blows out to an instrument to measure the heat radiation received from the sun.

thermostat A device that controls the heating or cooling of a substance in order to maintain it at a constant temperature. It consists of a temperature-sensing instrument connected to a switching device. When the temperature reaches a predetermined level the sensor switches the heating or cooling source on or off according to a predetermined program. The sensing thermometer is often a *bimetallic strip that triggers a simple electrical switch. Thermostats are used for space-heating controls, in water heaters and refrigerators, and to maintain the environment of a scientific experiment at a constant temperature.

thixotropy *See* Newtonian fluid.

Thomson effect (Kelvin effect) When an electric current flows through a conductor, the ends of which are maintained at different temperatures, heat is evolved at a rate approximately proportional to the product of the current and the temperature gradient. If either the current or the temperature gradient is reversed heat is absorbed rather than being evolved. It is named after Sir William Thomson (later Lord Kelvin; 1824–1907).

Thomson scattering The scattering of electromagnetic radiation by free charged particles, especially electrons, when the photon energy is small compared with the energy equivalent to the *rest mass of the charged particles. The energy lost by the radiation is accounted for by classical theory as a result of the radiation emitted by the charged particles when they are accelerated in the transverse electric field of the radiation. It is named after Sir J. J. Thomson (1856–1940).

thorium Symbol Th. A grey radioactive metallic element belonging to the actinoids; a.n. 90; r.a.m. 232.038; r.d. 11.5–11.9 (17°C); m.p. 1740–1760°C; b.p. 4780–4800°C. It occurs in monazite sand in Brazil, India, and USA. The isotopes of thorium have mass numbers from 223 to 234 inclusive; the most stable isotope, thorium–232, has a half-life of 1.39×10^{10} years. It can be used as a nuclear fuel for breeder reactors as thorium–232 captures slow neutrons to breed uranium–233. Thorium dioxide (*thoria*, ThO_2) is used on gas mantles and in special refractories. The element was discovered by J. J. Berzelius in 1829.

thorium series *See* radioactive series.

threshold The minimum value of a parameter or variable that will produce a specified effect.

threshold frequency *See* photoelectric effect.

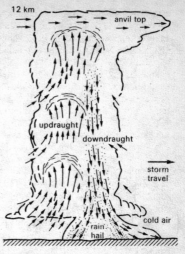

Cross-section through a thunderstorm cell

thrust The propelling force generated by an aircraft engine or rocket. It is usually calculated as the product of the rate of mass discharge and the velocity of the exhaust gases relative to the vehicle.

thunderstorm A convective storm accompanied by *lightning and thunder and a variety of weather conditions, especially heavy rain or hail, high winds, and sudden temperature changes. Thunderstorms originate when intense heating causes a parcel of moist air to rise, leading to instability and the development of cumulonimbus cloud – a towering cloud with a characteristic anvil-shaped top (see illustration). The exact mechanisms of thunderstorms are not fully understood. They occur most frequently in the tropics but are also common in the mid-latitudes.

thyratron A thermionic valve (usually a triode) that functions as a gas-filled relay. A positive pulse fed to a correctly biased thyratron causes a discharge to start and to continue until the anode voltage has been reduced. It has now been replaced by

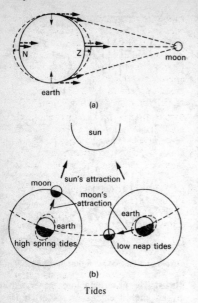

(a)

(b)

Tides

tre. The resultant force when the moon is in zenith (Z in the illustration) is greater than that at nadir (N) because Z is closer to the moon than N and the force is inversely proportional to the square of the distance according to *Newton's law of gravitation. Illustration (b) shows how at full and new moon the sun and moon act together to produce the high-range *spring tides*, while at quarter moon the forces are at right angles to each other causing the low-range *neap tides*.

The use of *tidal energy*, estimated at some 4×10^{18} J per annum at known tidal sites, dates back to medieval tidal mills. Modern tidal power stations use specially designed turbines, operated by tidal waters, to drive generators.

timbre *See* quality of sound.

time A dimension that enables two otherwise identical events that occur at the same point in space to be distinguished (*see* space–time). The interval between two such events forms the basis of time measurement. For general purposes, the earth's rotation on its axis provides the units of the clock (*see* day) and the earth's orbit round the sun (*see* year) provides the units of the calendar. For scientific purposes, intervals of time are now defined in terms of the frequency of a specified electromagnetic radiation (*see* second). *See also* time dilation; time reversal.

time dilation (time dilatation) The principle, predicted by Einstein's special theory of *relativity, that intervals of time are not absolute but are relative to the motion of the observers. If two identical clocks are synchronized and placed side by side in an inertial frame of reference they will read the same time for as long as they both remain side by side. However, if one of the clocks has a velocity relative to the other, which remains beside a stationary observer,

its solid-state counterpart, the silicon-controlled rectifier.

thyristor A silicon-controlled rectifier whose anode–cathode current is controlled by a signal applied to a third electrode (the gate) in much the same way as in a thyratron valve. It consists usually of a four-layer chip comprising three *p–n* junctions.

tidal energy *See* tides.

tides The regular rise and fall of the water level in the earth's oceans as a result of the gravitational forces between the earth, moon, and sun. The forces involved are complex, but the moon is approximately twice as effective as the sun in causing tides. In illustration (a) the resultant gravitational forces between the moon and various points on the earth (solid lines) are shown as the vector sums of the tide-generating forces (broken lines) and a constant force (dotted lines) that is the same at all points on the earth and is equal to the moon's attraction on the earth's cen-

the travelling clock will show, to that observer, that less time has elapsed than the stationary clock. In general, the travelling clock goes more slowly by a factor $\sqrt{(1 - v^2/c^2)}$, when measured in a frame of reference travelling at a velocity v relative to another frame of reference; c is the speed of light. The principle has been verified in a number of ways; for example, by comparing the lifetimes of fast muons, which increase with the speed of the particles to an extent predicted by this factor.

time-lapse photography A form of ciné photography used to record a slow process, such as plant growth. A series of single exposures of the object is made on ciné film at predetermined regular intervals. The film produced is then projected at normal speeds and the process appears to be taking place at an extremely high rate.

time reversal Symbol T. The operation of replacing time t by time $-t$. The *symmetry of time reversal is known as *T invariance*. As with CP violation, *T violation* occurs in weak interactions of kaon decays. *See also* CP invariance; CPT theorem.

T invariance *See* time reversal.

Titan *See* Saturn.

Tokamak *See* thermonuclear reactor.

tomography The use of X-rays to photograph a selected plane of a human body with other planes eliminated. The *CT* (*computerized tomography*) *scanner* is a ring-shaped X-ray machine that rotates through 180° around the horizontal patient, making numerous X-ray measurements every few degrees. The vast amount of information acquired is built into a three-dimensional image of the tissues under examination by the scanner's own computer. The patient is exposed to a dose of X-rays only some 20% of that used in a normal diagnostic X-ray.

topology The branch of geometry concerned with the properties of geometrical objects that are unchanged by continuous deformations, such as twisting or stretching. Mathematical approaches employing topology are of great importance in modern theories of the *fundamental interactions.

torque (moment of a force or couple) The product of a force and its perpendicular distance from a point about which it causes rotation or *torsion. The unit of torque is the newton metre, a vector product, unlike the joule, also equal to a newton metre, which is a scalar product. A turbine produces a torque on its central rotating shaft. *See also* couple.

torr A unit of pressure, used in high-vacuum technology, defined as 1 mmHg. 1 torr is equal to 133.322 pascals. The unit is named after Evangelista Torricelli (1609–47).

Torricellian vacuum The vacuum formed when a long tube, closed at one end and filled with mercury, is inverted into a mercury reservoir so that the open end of the tube is below the surface of the mercury. The pressure inside the Torricellian vacuum is the vapour pressure of mercury, about 10^{-3} torr.

torsion A twisting deformation produced by a *torque or *couple. A *torsion bar* is a form of spring in which one end of a bar is fixed and a torque is applied to the other end. Torsion bars are used in the suspension systems of motor vehicles.

torsion balance An instrument for measuring very weak forces. It consists of a horizontal rod fixed to the end of a vertical wire or fibre or to the centre of a taut horizontal wire. The forces to be measured are applied to the end or ends of the rod. The turning of the rod may be measured by the displacement of a beam of light reflected from a plane mirror attached to it. The best-known form is that used by Henry Cavendish

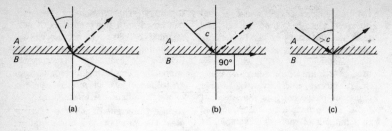

(a)   (b)   (c)

(1731–1810) and later by Sir Charles Boys (1855–1944) to determine the *gravitational constant; in this form the balance is calibrated by determining the torsional coefficient of the suspension by treating the device as a torsional pendulum.

torus A solid generated by rotating a circle about an external line in its plane, also called an *anchor ring*. It has the shape of the inner tube of a tyre. If r is the radius of the rotating circle and R the distance between the centre of the circle and the axis of rotation, the volume of the torus is $2\pi^2 R r^2$ and the surface area is $4\pi^2 R r$. In Cartesian coordinates, if the z-axis is the axis of rotation, the equation of the torus is $[\sqrt{(x^2 + y^2)} - R]^2 + z^2 = r^2$.

total internal reflection The total reflection of a beam of light at the interface of one medium and another medium of lower refractive index, when the angle of incidence to the second medium exceeds a specific *critical angle*.

If a beam of light passing through a medium A (say glass) strikes the boundary to a medium B of lower refractive index (say air) with a small angle of incidence i, part will be refracted, with an angle of refraction r, and part will be reflected (see illustration a). If i is increased it will reach a critical angle c, at which $r = 90°$ (see illustration b). If i is now increased further, no refraction can occur and all the light energy is

reflected by the interface (see illustration c). This total internal reflection occurs when c (given by $n\sin c = 1$) is exceeded (n is the refractive index of A relative to B). The critical angle of optical glass is usually about 40° and total internal reflection is made use of by incorporating prisms in some optical instruments instead of mirrors.

totality The period during a total *eclipse of the sun in which the view of the sun's surface from a point on the earth is totally obscured by the moon. The maximum duration of totality is 7.67 minutes, but it is usually less.

total-radiation pyrometer *See* pyrometry.

tracing (radioactive tracing) *See* labelling.

trajectory *See* phase space.

transcendental number A number that is not algebraic, such as π or e. A *transcendental function* is also nonalgebraic, such as a^x, $\sin x$, or $\log x$.

transducer A device for converting a nonelectrical signal, such as sound, light, heat, etc., into an electrical signal, or vice versa. Thus microphones and loudspeakers are *electroacoustic transducers*. An *active transducer* is one that can itself introduce a power gain and has its own power source. A *passive transducer* has no power source other than the actuating signal and cannot introduce gain.

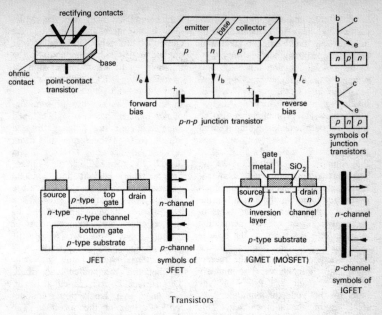

Transistors

transformer A device for transferring electrical energy from one alternating-current circuit to another with a change of voltage, current, phase, or impedance. It consists of a primary winding of N_p turns magnetically linked by a ferromagnetic core or by proximity to the secondary winding of N_s turns. The *turns ratio* (N_s/N_p) is approximately equal to V_s/V_p and to I_p/I_s, where V_p and I_p are the voltage and current fed to the primary winding and V_s and I_s are the voltage and current induced in the secondary winding, assuming that there are no power losses in the core. In practice, however, there are *eddy-current and *hysteresis losses in the core, incomplete magnetic linkage between the coils, and heating losses in the coils themselves. By the use of a *laminated core and careful design, transformers with 98% efficiency can be achieved.

transient A brief disturbance or oscillation in a circuit caused by a sudden rise in the current or e.m.f.

transistor A *semiconductor device capable of amplification in addition to rectification. It is the basic unit in radio, television, and computer circuits, having almost completely replaced the *thermionic valve. The *point-contact transistor*, which is now obsolete, was invented in 1948. It consists of a small germanium crystal with two rectifying point contacts attached to it; a third contact, called the *base*, makes a low-resistance nonrectifying (ohmic) connection with the crystal. Current flowing through the device between the point contacts is modulated by the signal fed to the base. This type of transistor was replaced by the *junction transistor*, which was developed in 1949–50. The *field-effect transistor* (*FET*) was a later invention. *Bipolar transistors*, such as the junction transistor, depend on the

flow of both majority and minority carriers, whereas in *unipolar transistors*, such as the FET, the current is carried by majority carriers only.

In the bipolar junction transistor, two *p*-type semiconductor regions are separated by a thin *n*-type region, making a *p–n–p* structure. Alternatively, an *n–p–n* structure can also be used. In both cases the thin central region is called the base and one outer region of the sandwich is called the *emitter*, the other the *collector*. The emitter–base junction is forward-biased and the collector–base junction is reverse-biased. In the *p–n–p* transistor, the forward bias causes holes in the emitter region to flow across the junction into the base; as the base is thin, the majority of holes are swept right across it (helped by the reverse bias), into the collector. The minority of holes that do not flow from the base to the collector combine with electrons in the *n*-type base. This recombination is balanced by a small electron flow in the base circuit. The diagram illustrates the (conventional) current flow using the *common-base* type of connection. If the emitter, base, and collector currents are I_e, I_b, and I_c, respectively, then $I_e = I_b + I_c$ and the current gain is I_c/I_b.

Field-effect transistors are of two kinds, the *junction FET* (*JFET* or *JUGFET*) and the *insulated-gate FET* (*IGFET*; also known as a *MOSFET*, i.e. metal-oxide-semiconductor FET). Both are unipolar devices and in both the current flows through a narrow *channel* between two electrodes (the *gate*) from one region, called the *source*, to another, called the *drain*. The modulating signal is applied to the gate. In the JFET, the channel consists of a semiconductor material of relatively low conductivity sandwiched between two regions of high conductivity of the opposite polarity. When the junctions between these regions are reverse-biased, *depletion layers form, which narrow

the channel. At high bias the depletion layers meet and pinch-off the channel completely. Thus the voltage applied to the two gates controls the thickness of the channel and thus its conductivity. JFETs are made with both *n*-type and *p*-type channels.

In the IGFET, a wafer of semiconductor material has two highly doped regions of opposite polarity diffused into it, to form the source and drain regions. An insulating layer of silicon dioxide is formed on the surface between these regions and a metal conductor is evaporated on to the top of this layer to form the gate. When a positive voltage is applied to the gate, electrons move along the surface of the *p*-type substrate below the gate, producing a thin surface of *n*-type material, which forms the channel between the source and drain. This surface layer is called an *inversion layer*, as it has opposite conductivity to that of the substrate. The number of induced electrons is directly proportional to the gate voltage, thus the conductivity of the channel increases with gate voltage. IGFETs are also made with both *p*-type and *n*-type channels.

transition point (transition temperature) 1. The temperature at which one crystalline form of a substance changes to another form. **2.** The temperature at which a substance changes phase. **3.** The temperature at which a substance becomes superconducting (*see* superconductivity). **4.** The temperature at which some other change, such as a change of magnetic properties (*see also* Curie temperature), takes place.

translation Motion of a body in which all the points in the body follow parallel paths.

translucent Permitting the passage of radiation but not without some scattering or diffusion. For example, frosted glass allows light to pass through it but an object cannot be

seen clearly through it because the light rays are scattered by it. *Compare* transparent.

transmission coefficient *See* transmittance.

transmission electron microscope *See* electron microscope.

transmittance (transmission coefficient) The ratio of the energy of some form of radiation transmitted through a surface to the energy falling on it. The reciprocal of the transmittance is the *opacity*.

transmitter 1. The equipment used to generate and broadcast radio-frequency electromagnetic waves for communication purposes. It consists of a carrier-wave generator, a device for modulating the carrier wave in accordance with the information to be broadcast, amplifiers, and an aerial system. **2.** The part of a telephone system that converts sound into electrical signals.

transparent Permitting the passage of radiation without significant deviation or absorption. *Compare* translucent. A substance may be transparent to radiation of one wavelength but not to radiation of another wavelength. For example, some forms of glass are transparent to light but not to ultraviolet radiation, while other forms of glass may be transparent to all visible radiation except red light. *See also* radiotransparent.

transport number Symbol *t*. The fraction of the total charge carried by a particular type of ion in the conduction of electricity through electrolytes.

transuranic elements Elements with an atomic number greater than 92, i.e. elements above uranium in the periodic table.

transverse wave *See* wave.

travelling wave *See* wave.

triangle of vectors A triangle constructed so that each of its sides represents one of three coplanar *vectors acting at a point with no resultant. If the triangle is completed, with the sides representing the vectors in both magnitude and direction, so that there are no gaps between the sides, then the vectors are in equilibrium. If the three vectors are forces, the figure is called a *triangle of forces*; if they are velocities, it is a *triangle of velocities*.

triboelectricity *Static electricity produced as a result of friction.

tribology The study of friction, lubrication, and lubricants.

triboluminescence *Luminescence caused by friction; for example, some crystalline substances emit light when they are crushed as a result of static electric charges generated by the friction.

triclinic *See* crystal system.

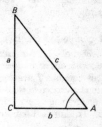

Trigonometric functions

trigonometric functions Functions defined in terms of a right-angled triangle (see diagram) and widely used in the solution of many mathematical problems. They are defined as:

tangent of angle A, written $\tan A = a/b$

sine of angle A, written $\sin A = a/c$

cosine of angle A, written $\cos A = b/c$,

where a is the length of the side opposite the angle A, b is the length of the side opposite the angle B, and c is the hypotenuse of the triangle. The reciprocal functions are:

cotangent of angle A, written cot$A$ = 1/tan$A$ = b/a

secant of angle A, written sec$A$ = 1/cos$A$ = c/b

cosecant of angle A, written cosec$A$ = 1/sin$A$ = c/a

triode A *thermionic valve with three electrodes. Electrons produced by the heated cathode flow to the anode after passing through the negatively biased *control grid. Small voltage fluctuations superimposed on the grid bias cause large fluctuations in the anode current. The triode was thus the first electronic device capable of amplification. Its role has now been taken over by the transistor.

triple point The temperature and pressure at which the vapour, liquid, and solid phases of a substance are in equilibrium. For water the triple point occurs at 273.16 K and 611.2 Pa. This value forms the basis of the definition of the *kelvin and the thermodynamic *temperature scale.

tritiated compound *See* labelling.

tritium Symbol T. An isotope of hydrogen with mass number 3; i.e. the nucleus contains 2 neutrons and 1 proton. It is radioactive (half-life 12.3 years), undergoing beta decay to helium–3. Tritium is used in *labelling.

triton The nucleus of a tritium atom.

tropical year *See* year.

troposphere *See* earth's atmosphere.

tuning fork A metal two-pronged fork that when struck produces an almost pure tone of a predetermined frequency. It is used for tuning musical instruments and in experiments in acoustics.

tunnel diode (Esaki diode) A semiconductor diode, discovered in 1957 by L. Esaki (1925–), based on the *tunnel effect. It consists of a highly doped *p–n* semiconductor junction, which short circuits with negative bias and has negative resistance over part of its range when forward biased. Its fast speed of operation makes it a useful device in many electronic fields.

tunnel effect An effect in which electrons are able to tunnel through a narrow *potential barrier that would constitute a forbidden region if the electrons were treated as classical particles. That there is a finite probability of an electron tunnelling from one classically allowed region to another arises as a consequence of *quantum mechanics. The effect is made use of in the *tunnel diode. Alpha decay (*see* alpha particle) is an example of a tunnelling process.

turbine A machine in which a fluid is used to produce rotational motion. The most widely used turbines are the *steam turbines* and *water turbines* that provide some 95% of the world's electric power (in the form of *turbogenerators) and the *gas turbines* that power all the world's jet-propelled aircraft. In the *impulse turbine* a high-pressure low-velocity fluid is expanded through stationary nozzles, producing low-pressure high-velocity jets, which are directed onto the blades of a rotor. The rotor blades reduce the speed of the jets and thus convert some of the fluid's kinetic energy into rotational kinetic energy of the rotor shaft. In the *reaction turbine* the discharge nozzles are themselves attached to the rotor. The acceleration of the fluid leaving the nozzles produces a force of reaction

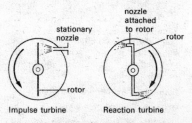

Principle of the turbine

on the pipes, causing the rotor to move in the opposite direction to that of the fluid. (See illustrations.) Many turbines work on a combination of the impulse and reaction principles.

turbogenerator A steam turbine driving an electric generator. This is the normal method of generating electricity in power stations. In a conventional power station the steam is raised by burning a fossil fuel (coal, oil, or natural gas); in a nuclear power station the steam is raised by heat transfer from a nuclear reactor.

turbojet *See* jet propulsion.

turbulence A form of fluid flow in which the particles of the fluid move in a disordered manner in irregular paths, resulting in an exchange of momentum from one portion of a fluid to another. Turbulent flow takes over from *laminar flow when high values of the *Reynolds number are reached.

turns ratio *See* transformer.

T violation *See* time reversal.

tweeter A small loudspeaker capable of reproducing sounds of relatively high frequency, i.e. 5 kilohertz upwards. In high-fidelity equipment a tweeter is used in conjunction with a *woofer.

Tyndall effect The scattering of light as it passes through a medium containing small particles. If a polychromatic beam of light is passed through a medium containing particles with diameters less than about one-twentieth of the wavelength of the light, the scattered light appears blue. This accounts for the blue appearance of tobacco smoke. At higher particle diameters, the scattered light remains polychromatic. It is named after John Tyndall (1820–93). *See also* scattering of electromagnetic radiation.

U

ultracentrifuge A high-speed centrifuge used to measure the rate of sedimentation of colloidal particles or to separate macromolecules, such as proteins or nucleic acids, from solutions. Ultracentrifuges are electrically driven and are capable of speeds up to 60 000 rpm.

ultrahigh frequency (UHF) A radio frequency in the range $3 \times 10^9 – 0.3 \times 10^9$ Hz; i.e. having a wavelength in the range 10 cm to 1 m.

ultramicroscope A form of microscope that uses the *Tyndall effect to reveal the presence of particles that cannot be seen with a normal optical microscope. Colloidal particles, smoke particles, etc., are suspended in a liquid or gas in a cell with a black background and illuminated by an intense cone of light that enters the cell from the side and has its apex in the field of view. The particles then produce diffraction-ring systems, appearing as bright specks on the dark background.

ultrasonics The study and use of pressure waves that have a frequency in excess of 20 000 Hz and are therefore inaudible to the human ear. *Ultrasonic generators* make use of the *piezoelectric effect, *ferroelectric materials, or *magnetostriction to act as transducers in converting electrical energy into mechanical energy. Ultrasonics are used in medical diagnosis, particularly in conditions such as pregnancy, in which X-rays could have a harmful effect. Ultrasonic techniques are also used industrially to test for flaws in metals, to clean surfaces, to test the thickness of parts, and to form colloids.

ultraviolet microscope A *microscope that has quartz lenses and slides and uses *ultraviolet radiation as the illumination. The use of shorter wavelengths than the visible

range enables the instrument to resolve smaller objects and to provide greater magnification than the normal optical microscope. The final image is either photographed or made visible by means of an *image converter.

ultraviolet radiation (UV) Electromagnetic radiation that has wavelengths between that of violet light and long X-rays, i.e. between 400 nanometres and 4 nm. In the range 400–300 nm the radiation is known as the *near ultraviolet*. In the range 300–200 nm it is known as the *far ultraviolet*. Below 200 nm it is known as the *extreme ultraviolet* or the *vacuum ultraviolet*, as absorption by the oxygen in the air makes the use of evacuated apparatus essential. The sun is a strong emitter of UV radiation but only the near UV reaches the surface of the earth as the ozone in the atmosphere absorbs all wavelengths below 290 nm.

Most UV radiation for practical use is produced by various types of *mercury-vapour lamps. Ordinary glass absorbs UV radiation and therefore lenses and prisms for use in the UV are made from quartz.

umbra *See* shadow.

uncertainty principle (Heisenberg uncertainty principle; principle of indeterminism) The principle that it is not possible to know with unlimited accuracy both the position and momentum of a particle. This principle, discovered in 1927 by Werner Heisenberg (1901–76), is usually stated in the form: $\Delta x \Delta p_x \geqslant h/4\pi$, where Δx is the uncertainty in the x-coordinate of the particle, Δp_x is the uncertainty in the x-component of the particle's momentum, and h is the *Planck constant. An explanation of the uncertainty is that in order to locate a particle exactly, an observer must be able to bounce off it a photon of radiation; this act of location itself alters the position of the particle in an unpredictable way. To locate the position accurately, photons of short wavelength would have to be used. The high momenta of such photons would cause a large effect on the position. On the other hand, using photons of lower momenta would have less effect on the particle's position, but would be less accurate because of the longer wavelength.

underdamped *See* damping.

uniaxial crystal A double-refracting crystal (*see* double refraction) having only one *optic axis.

unified-field theory A comprehensive theory that would relate the electromagnetic, gravitational, strong, and weak interactions (*see* fundamental interactions) in one set of equations. In its original context the expression referred only to the unification of general *relativity and classical electromagnetic theory. No such theory has yet been found but some progress has been made in the unification of the electromagnetic and weak interactions (*see* electroweak theory).

Einstein attempted to derive *quantum mechanics from unified-field theory, but it is now thought that any unified-field theory has to start with quantum mechanics. Attempts to construct unified-field theories, such as *supergravity and *Kaluza–Klein theory, have run into great difficulties. At the present time it is not clear whether the framework of relativistic *quantum field theory is adequate to give a unified theory for all the known fundamental interactions and elementary particles, or whether one has to go to extended objects, such as superstrings or supermembranes. Unified-field theories and other fundamental theories, such as *superstring theory and *supermembrane theory, are of great importance in understanding cosmology, particularly the *early universe. In turn cosmology puts constraints on unified-field theories. *See also* grand unified theory.

union *See* set theory.

unit A specified measure of a physical quantity, such as length, mass, time, etc., specified multiples of which are used to express magnitudes of that physical quantity. For many scientific purposes previous systems of units have now been replaced by *SI units.

unit cell The group of particles (atoms, ions, or molecules) in a crystal that is repeated in three dimensions in the *crystal lattice. *See also* crystal system.

unit magnetic pole *See* magnetic poles.

universal constant *See* fundamental constant.

universal motor *See* electric motor.

universe All the matter, energy, and space that exists. *See* cosmology; heat death of the universe.

unstable equilibrium *See* equilibrium.

upper atmosphere The upper part of the *earth's atmosphere above about 300 km. This is the part of the atmosphere that cannot be reached by balloons.

upthrust *See* Archimedes' principle.

uranium Symbol U. A white radioactive metallic element belonging to the actinoids; a.n. 92; r.a.m. 238.03; r.d. 19.05 (20°C); m.p. 1132±1°C; b.p. 3818°C. It occurs as uraninite, from which the metal is extracted by an ion-exchange process. Three isotopes are found in nature: uranium–238 (99.28%), uranium–235 (0.71%), and uranium–234 (0.006%). As uranium–235 undergoes *nuclear fission with slow neutrons it is the fuel used in *nuclear reactors and *nuclear weapons; uranium has therefore assumed enormous technical and political importance since their invention. It was discovered by M. H. Klaproth in 1789.

uranium–lead dating A group of methods of *dating certain rocks that depends on the decay of the radioisotope uranium–238 to lead–206 (half-life 4.5×10^9 years) or the decay of uranium–235 to lead–207 (half-life 7.1×10^8 years). One form of uranium–lead dating depends on measuring the ratio of the amount of helium trapped in the rock to the amount of uranium present (since the decay $^{238}U \rightarrow {}^{206}Pb$ releases eight alpha-particles). Another method of calculating the age of the rocks is to measure the ratio of radiogenic lead (^{206}Pb, ^{207}Pb, and ^{208}Pb) present to nonradiogenic lead (^{204}Pb). These methods give reliable results for ages of the order 10^7–10^9 years.

uranium series *See* radioactive series.

UV *See* ultraviolet radiation.

V

vacancy *See* defect.

vacuum A space in which there is a low pressure of gas, i.e. relatively few atoms or molecules. A *perfect vacuum* would contain no atoms or molecules, but this is unobtainable as all the materials that surround such a space have a finite *vapour pressure. In a *soft* (or *low*) *vacuum* the pressure is reduced to about 10^{-2} pascal, whereas a *hard* (or *high*) vacuum has a pressure of 10^{-2}–10^{-7} pascal. Below 10^{-7} pascal is known as an *ultrahigh vacuum*. *See also* vacuum pump.

vacuum pump A pump used to reduce the gas pressure in a container. The normal laboratory rotary oil-seal pump can maintain a pressure of 10^{-1} Pa. For pressures down to 10^{-7} Pa a *diffusion pump is required. *Ion pumps can achieve a pressure of 10^{-9} Pa and a *cryogenic pump com-

vacuum state

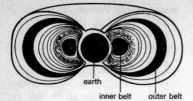

earth

inner belt   outer belt

Van Allen belts

bined with a diffusion pump can reach 10^{-13} Pa.

vacuum state The ground state in a relativistic *quantum field theory. A vacuum state does not mean a state of nothing. Because one is dealing with *quantum mechanics, the vacuum state has a *zero-point energy, which gives rise to *vacuum fluctuations*. The existence of vacuum fluctuations has observable consequences in *quantum electrodynamics.

vacuum tube *See* thermionic valve.

valence band *See* energy bands.

valence electron An electron in one of the outer shells of an atom that takes part in forming chemical bonds.

valency (valence) The combining power of an atom or radical, equal to the number of hydrogen atoms that the atom could combine with or displace in a chemical compound (hydrogen has a valency of 1). It is equal to the ionic charge in ionic compounds; for example, in Na_2S, sodium has a valency of 1 (Na^+) and sulphur a valency of 2 (S^{2-}). In covalent compounds it is equal to the number of bonds formed; in CO_2 both carbon and oxygen have a valency of 2.

valve *See* thermionic valve.

Van Allen belts (radiation belts) Belts that are sources of intense radiation surrounding the earth, consisting of high-energy charged particles trapped in the earth's magnetic field within which they follow roughly helical paths. They were discovered in

1958 by James Van Allen (1914–) as a result of radiation detectors carried by Explorer satellites. The lower belt, extending from 1000 to 5000 km above the equator, contains electrons and protons, while the upper belt, 15 000–25 000 km above the equator, contains mainly electrons (see illustration).

Van de Graaff generator An electrostatic generator used to produce a high voltage, usually in the megavolt range. It consists of a large metal dome-shaped terminal mounted on a hollow insulating support. An endless insulating belt runs through the support from the base to a pulley within the spherical terminal. In the original type, charge is sprayed by point discharge from metal needles, held at a potential of about 10 kV, on to the bottom of the belt. A row of needles near the upper belt pulley removes the charge from the belt and passes it to the outer surface of the spherical terminal. The voltage achieved by the device is proportional to the radius of the spherical terminal. A typical device with a terminal having a radius of 1 m will produce about 1 MV. However, terminals can be made smaller, for a given voltage, by enclosing the apparatus in nitrogen at a pressure of 10–20 atmospheres (1–2 MPa) to reduce sparking. Generators having a positive-ion source are fitted with an evacuated tube through which the particles can be accelerated for research purposes. Machines having an electron source are used for various medical and industrial purposes. The generator was invented by R. J. Van de Graaff (1901–67).

Modern patterns of the generator have a chainlike belt of alternate links of metal and insulator. The metal links are charged by contact with a metal pulley, and discharge to the dome in the same way. This permits much higher current drain that the point discharge.

van der Waals' equation *See* equation of state.

van der Waals' force An attractive force between atoms or molecules, named after J. D. van der Waals (1837–1923). The force accounts for the term a/V^2 in the van der Waals equation (*see* equation of state). These forces are much weaker than those arising from valence bonds and are inversely proportional to the seventh power of the distance between the atoms or molecules. They are the forces responsible for nonideal behaviour of gases and for the lattice energy of molecular crystals. There are three factors causing such forces: (1) dipole–dipole interaction, i.e. electrostatic attractions between two molecules with permanent dipole moments; (2) dipole-induced dipole interactions, in which the dipole of one molecule polarizes a neighbouring molecule; (3) dispersion forces arising because of small instantaneous dipoles in atoms.

van't Hoff factor Symbol *i*. A factor appearing in equations for *colligative properties, equal to the ratio of the number of actual particles present to the number of undissociated particles. It was first suggested by Jacobus van't Hoff (1852–1911).

van't Hoff's isochore An equation for the variation of equilibrium constant with temperature

$$(d \log_e K)/dT = \Delta H/RT^2$$

where T is the thermodynamic temperature and ΔH the enthalpy of the reaction.

vapour density The density of a gas or vapour relative to hydrogen, oxygen, or air. Taking hydrogen as the reference substance, the vapour density is the ratio of the mass of a particular volume of a gas to the mass of an equal volume of hydrogen under identical conditions of pressure and temperature. Taking the density of hydrogen as 1, this ratio is equal to half the relative molecular mass of the gas.

vapour pressure The pressure exerted by a vapour. All solids and liquids give off vapours, consisting of atoms or molecules of the substances that have evaporated from the condensed forms. These atoms or molecules exert a vapour pressure. If the substance is in an enclosed space, the vapour pressure will reach an equilibrium value that depends only on the nature of the substance and the temperature. This maximum value occurs when there is a dynamic equilibrium between the atoms or molecules escaping from the liquid or solid and those that strike the surface of the liquid or solid and return to it. The vapour is then said to be a *saturated vapour* and the pressure it exerts is the *saturated vapour pressure*.

variation *See* geomagnetism.

variometer 1. A variable inductor consisting of two coils connected in series and able to move relative to each other. It can be used to measure inductance. 2. Any of several devices for detecting and measuring changes in the geomagnetic elements (*see* geomagnetism).

vector A quantity in which both the magnitude and the direction must be stated (*compare* scalar quantity). Force, velocity, and field strength are examples of vector quantities. Note that distance and speed are scalar quantities, whereas displacement and velocity are vector quantities. Vector quantities must be treated by *vector algebra*, for example, the resultant of two vectors may be found by a *parallelogram of vectors. A (three-dimensional) vector V may be written in terms of components V_1, V_2, and V_3 along the x, y, and z axes (say) as $V_1\boldsymbol{i} + V_2\boldsymbol{j} + V_3\boldsymbol{k}$, where $\boldsymbol{i}$, $\boldsymbol{j}$, and $\boldsymbol{k}$ are *unit vectors* (i.e. vectors of unit length) along the x, y, and z axes. *See also* triangle of vectors.

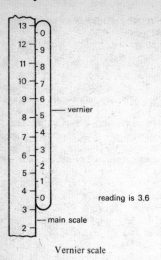

reading is 3.6

Vernier scale

vector product (cross product) The product of two *vectors U and V, with components U_1, U_2, U_3 and V_1, V_2, V_3, respectively, given by:

$$U \times V = (U_2V_3 - U_3V_2)i + (U_3V_1 - U_1V_3)j + (U_1V_2 - U_2V_1)k.$$

It is itself a vector, perpendicular to both U and V, and of length $UV\sin\theta$, where U and V are the lengths of U and V, respectively, and θ is the angle between them. *Compare* scalar product.

velocity Symbol v. The rate of displacement of a body. It is the *speed of a body in a specified direction. Velocity is thus a *vector quantity, whereas speed is a scalar quantity.

velocity modulation *See* klystron.

velocity ratio (distance ratio) The ratio of the distance moved by the point of application effort in a simple *machine to the distance moved by the point of application load in the same time.

Venn diagram *See* set theory.

Venturi tube A device for mixing a fine spray of liquid with a gas or measuring a flow rate of a gas. It consists of two tapered sections of pipe joined by a narrow throat. The fluid velocity in the throat is increased and the pressure is therefore reduced. By attaching manometers to the three sections of the tube, the pressure drop can be measured and the flow rate through the throat can be calculated. In a carburettor, the petrol from the float chamber is made into a fine spray by being drawn through a jet into the low pressure in the throat of a Venturi tube, where it mixes with the air being drawn into the engine. The device was invented by G. B. Venturi (1746–1822).

vernier A short auxiliary scale placed beside the main scale on a measuring instrument to enable subdivisions of the main scale to be read accurately. The vernier scale is usually calibrated so that each of its divisions is 0.9 of the main scale divisions. The zero on the vernier scale is set to the observed measurement on the main scale and by noting which division on the vernier scale is exactly in line with a main scale division, the second decimal place of the measurement is obtained (see illustration). The device was invented by Pierre Vernier (1580–1637) in about 1630.

very high frequency (VHF) A radio frequency in the range $3 \times 10^8 - 0.3 \times 10^8$ Hz, i.e. having a wavelength in the range 1–10 m.

very low frequency (VLF) A radio frequency in the range $3 \times 10^4 - 0.3 \times 10^4$ Hz, i.e. having a wavelength in the range 10–100 km.

Victor Meyer's method A method of measuring vapour density, devised by Victor Meyer (1848–97). A weighed sample in a small tube is dropped into a heated bulb with a long neck. The sample vaporizes and displaces air, which is collected over water and the volume measured. The vapour density can then be calculated.

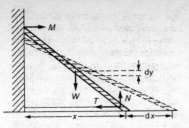

Virtual work

virial equation A gas law that attempts to account for the behaviour of real gases, as opposed to an ideal gas. It takes the form

$$pV = RT + Bp + Cp^2 + Dp^3 + \ldots,$$

where B, C, and D are known as *virial coefficients*.

virtual image *See* image.

virtual state The state of the *virtual particles* that are exchanged between two interacting charged particles. These particles, called *photons, are not in the real state, i.e. directly observable; they are constructs to enable the phenomenon to be explained in terms of *quantum mechanics.

virtual work The imaginary work done when a system is subjected to infinitesimal hypothetical displacements. According to the *principle of virtual work*, the total work done by all the forces acting on a system in equilibrium is zero. This principle can be used to determine the forces acting on a system in equilibrium. For example, the illustration shows a ladder leaning against a wall, with the bottom of the ladder attached to the wall by a horizontal weightless string. The tension, T, in the string can be calculated by assuming that infinitesimal movement dx and dy take place as shown. Then by applying the principle of virtual work, $T\mathrm{d}x + W\mathrm{d}y = 0$. As d$x$ and dy can be calculated from the geometry, T can be found.

viscometer An instrument for measuring the viscosity of a fluid. In the *Ostwald viscometer*, used for liquids, a bulb in a capillary tube is filled with the liquid and the time taken for the meniscus to reach a mark on the capillary, below the bulb, is a measure of the viscosity. The *falling-sphere viscometer*, based on *Stokes' law, enables the speed of fall of a ball falling through a sample of the fluid to be measured. Various other devices are used to measure viscosity.

viscosity A measure of the resistance to flow that a fluid offers when it is subjected to shear stress. For a *Newtonian fluid, the force, F, needed to maintain a velocity gradient, dv/dx, between adjacent planes of a fluid of area A is given by: $F = \eta A(\mathrm{d}v/\mathrm{d}x)$, where η is a constant, the coefficient of viscosity. In *SI units it has the unit pascal second (in the c.g.s. system it is measured in *poise). Non-Newtonian fluids, such as clays, do not conform to this simple model. *See also* kinematic viscosity.

visible spectrum The *spectrum of electromagnetic radiations to which the human eye is sensitive. *See* colour.

visual binary *See* binary stars.

visual-display unit (VDU) The part of a *computer system or word processor on which text or diagrams are displayed. It consists of a *cathode-ray tube and usually has its own input keyboard attached.

volt Symbol V. The SI unit of electric potential, potential difference, or e.m.f. defined as the difference of potential between two points on a conductor carrying a constant current of one ampere when the power dissipated between the points is one watt. It is named after Alessandro Volta (1745–1827).

voltage Symbol V. An e.m.f. or potential difference expressed in volts.

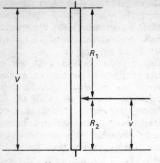

Voltage divider

voltage divider (potential divider; potentiometer) A resistor or a chain of resistors connected in series that can be tapped at one or more points to obtain a known fraction of the total voltage across the whole resistor or chain. In the illustration, V is the total voltage across the divider and v is required voltage, then

$$v/V = R_2/(R_1 + R_2).$$

voltaic cell (galvanic cell) A device that produces an e.m.f. as a result of chemical reactions that take place within it. These reactions occur at the surfaces of two electrodes, each of which dips into an electrolyte. The first voltaic cell, devised by Alessandro Volta (1745–1827), had electrodes of two different metals dipping into brine. *See* primary cell; secondary cell.

voltaic pile An early form of battery, devised by Alessandro Volta, consisting of a number of flat *voltaic cells joined in series. The liquid electrolyte was absorbed into paper or leather discs.

voltameter (coulometer) 1. An electrolytic cell formerly used to measure quantity of electric charge. The increase in mass (m) of the cathode of the cell as a result of the deposition on it of a metal from a solution of its salt enables the charge (Q) to be determined from the relationship $Q = m/z$, where z is the electrochemical equivalent of the metal. **2.** Any other type of electrolytic cell used for measurement.

voltmeter An instrument used to measure voltage. *Moving-coil instruments are widely used for this purpose; generally a galvanometer is used in series with a resistor of high values (sometimes called a *multiplier*). To measure an alternating potential difference a rectifier must be included in the circuit. A moving-iron instrument can be used for either d.c. or a.c. without a rectifier. *Cathode-ray oscilloscopes are also used as voltmeters. The electronic *digital voltmeter* displays the value of the voltage in digits. The input is repeatedly sampled by the voltmeter and the instantaneous values are displayed.

volume Symbol V. The space occupied by a body or mass of fluid.

W

wall effect Any effect resulting from the nature or presence of the inside wall of a container on the system it encloses.

watt Symbol W. The SI unit of power, defined as a power of one joule per second. In electrical contexts it is equal to the rate of energy transformation by an electric current of one ampere flowing through a conductor the ends of which are maintained at a potential difference of one volt. The unit is named after James Watt (1736–1819).

wattmeter An instrument for measuring the power in watts in an alternating-current electric circuit. In a direct-current circuit, power is usually determined by separate measurements of the voltage and the current. The *electrodynamic wattmeter* consists of two coils, one fixed (current) coil

and one movable (potential) coil. The fixed coil carries the load current, and the movable coil carries a current proportional to the voltage applied to the measured circuit. The deflection of the needle attached to the movable coil indicates the power.

wave A periodic disturbance in a medium or in space. In a *travelling wave* (or *progressive wave*) energy is transferred from one place to another by the vibrations (*see also* stationary wave). In a wave passing over the surface of water, for example, the water rises and falls as the wave passes but the particles of water on average do not move forward with the wave. This is called a *transverse wave* because the disturbances are at right angles to the direction of propagation. The water surface moves up and down while the waves travel across the surface of the water. Electromagnetic waves (see diagram) are also of this kind, with electric and magnetic fields varying in a periodic way at right angles to each other and to the direction of propagation. In

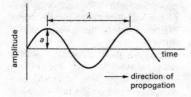

Sine wave

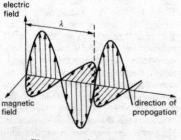

Electromagnetic waves

sound waves, the air is alternately compressed and rarefied by displacements in the direction of propagation. Such waves are called *longitudinal waves*.

The chief characteristics of a wave are its *speed of propagation*, its *frequency*, its *wavelength*, and its *amplitude*. The speed of propagation is the distance covered by the wave in unit time. The frequency is the number of complete disturbances (cycles) in unit time, usually expressed in *hertz. The wavelength is the distance in metres between successive points of equal phase in a wave. The amplitude is the maximum difference of the disturbed quantity from its mean value.

Generally, the amplitude (a) is half the peak-to-peak value. There is a simple relationship between the wavelength (λ) and the frequency (f), i.e. $\lambda = c/f$, where c is the speed of propagation. The energy transferred by a progressive *sine wave (see diagram) is proportional to a^2f^2. *See also* simple harmonic motion.

wave equation A partial differential equation of the form:
$$\nabla^2 u = (1/c^2)\partial^2 u/\partial t^2$$
where
$$\nabla^2 = \partial^2/\partial x^2 + \partial^2/\partial y^2 + \partial^2/\partial z^2$$
is the Laplace operator (*see* Laplace equation). It represents the propagation of a wave, where u is the displacement and c the speed of propagation. *See also* Schrödinger's equation.

wave form The shape of a wave or the pattern representing a vibration. It can be illustrated by drawing a graph of the periodically varying quantity against distance for one complete wavelength. *See also* sine wave.

wavefront A line or surface within a two- or three-dimensional medium through which waves are passing, being the locus of all adjacent points at which the disturbances are in phase. At large distances from a

wave function

small source in a uniform medium, the fronts are small parts of a sphere of very large radius and they can be considered as plane. For example, sunlight reaches the earth with plane wavefronts.

wave function A function $\psi(x,y,z)$ appearing in *Schrödinger's equation in *quantum mechanics. The wave function is a mathematical expression involving the coordinates of a particle in space. If the Schrödinger equation can be solved for a particle in a given system (e.g. an electron in an atom) then, depending on the boundary conditions, the solution is a set of allowed wave functions (*eigenfunctions*) of the particle, each corresponding to an allowed energy level (*eigenvalue*). The physical significance of the wave function is that the square of its absolute value, $|\psi|^2$, at a point is proportional to the probability of finding the particle in a small element of volume, $dxdydz$, at that point. For an electron in an atom, this gives rise to the idea of atomic and molecular *orbitals.

wave guide A hollow tube through which microwave electromagnetic radiation can be transmitted with relatively little attenuation. They often have a rectangular cross section, but some have a circular cross section. In transverse electric (TE) modes the electric vector of the field has no component in the direction of propagation. In transverse magnetic (TM) modes, the magnetic vector has no such component.

wavelength *See* wave.

wave mechanics *See* quantum mechanics.

wavemeter A device for measuring the wavelength of electromagnetic radiation. For frequencies up to about 100 MHz a wavemeter consists of a tuned circuit with a suitable indicator to establish when resonance occurs. Usually the tuned circuit includes a variable capacitor calibrated to read

wavelengths and resonance is indicated by a current-detecting instrument. At higher frequencies a cavity-resonator in a waveguide is often used. The cavity resonator is fitted with a piston, the position of which determines the resonant frequency of the cavity.

wave number Symbol k. The number of cycles of a wave in unit length. It is the reciprocal of the wavelength (*see* wave).

wave–particle duality The concept that waves carrying energy may have a corpuscular aspect and that particles may have a wave aspect; which of the two models is the more appropriate will depend on the properties the model is seeking to explain. For example, waves of electromagnetic radiation need to be visualized as particles, called *photons, to explain the *photoelectric effect while electrons need to be thought of as de Broglie waves in *electron diffraction. *See also* complementarity; de Broglie wavelength; light.

wave power The use of wave motion in the sea to generate energy. The technique used is to anchor a series of bobbing floats offshore; the energy of the motion of the floats is used to turn a generator. It has been estimated that there are enough suitable sites to generate over 100 GW of electricity in the UK.

wave theory *See* light.

W boson (W particle) Either of a pair of elementary particles (W^+ or W^-), classified as *intermediate vector bosons*, that are believed to transmit the weak interaction (*see* fundamental interactions) in much the same way as photons transmit the electromagnetic interaction. They are not, however, massless like photons, and are believed to have a rest mass of the order of 10^{-25} kg (806 GeV). W bosons were discovered at CERN in 1983 with the expected mass. *See also* Z boson.

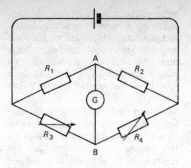

weak interaction *See* fundamental interactions.

weakly interacting massive particle (WIMP) *See* missing mass.

weber Symbol Wb. The SI unit of magnetic flux equal to the flux that, linking a circuit of one turn, produces in it an e.m.f. of one volt as it is reduced to zero at a uniform rate in one second. It is named after Wilhelm Weber (1804–91).

weight The force by which a body is attracted to the earth. *See* mass.

weightlessness A condition of a body when it is an infinite distance from any other body. In practice the appearance of weightlessness occurs in space when the gravitational attraction of the earth on a body in space is equal to the centripetal force required by its orbital motion so that the body is effectively in free fall. Weightlessness can also be simulated for short periods in an aircraft flying a parabolic flight path, so that its occupants are again in free fall.

Weinberg–Salam model (WS model) *See* electroweak theory.

Weston cell (cadmium cell) A type of primary *voltaic cell, which is used as a standard; it produces a constant e.m.f. of 1.0186 volts at 20°C. The cell is usually made in an H-shaped glass vessel with a mercury anode covered with a paste of cadmium sul-

phate and mercury(I) sulphate in one leg and a cadmium amalgam cathode covered with cadmium sulphate in the other leg. The electrolyte, which connects the two electrodes by means of the bar of the H, is a saturated solution of cadmium sulphate. In some cells sulphuric acid is added to prevent the hydrolysis of mercury sulphate.

wet-and-dry bulb hygrometer *See* hygrometer.

Wheatstone bridge An electrical circuit for measuring the value of a resistance. In the illustration, R_1 is a resistance of unknown value, R_2 is a fixed resistance of known value, R_3 and R_4 are variable resistances with known values. When no current flows between A and B the bridge is said to be balanced, the galvanometer registers no deflection, and $R_1/R_2 = R_3/R_4$. R_1 can therefore be calculated. The Wheatstone bridge is used in various forms. In the *metre bridge*, a wire 1 metre long of uniform resistance is attached to the top of a board alongside a metre rule. A sliding contact is run along the wire, which corresponds to R_3 and R_4, until the galvanometer registers zero. Most practical forms use one or more rotary rheostats to provide the variation. The device was popularized though not invented by Sir Charles Wheatstone (1802–75).

white dwarf A compact stellar object that is supported against collapse under self-gravity by the *degeneracy pressure of electrons. White dwarfs are formed as the end products of the evolution of stars of relatively low mass (about that of the sun); high-mass stars may end up as *neutron stars or *black holes (*see* stellar evolution). White dwarfs consist of helium nuclei (and carbon and oxygen nuclei in the more massive cases) and a *degenerate gas of electrons. A typical white-dwarf density is 10^9 kg m^{-3}; white dwarf masses and radii

are in the region of 0.7 solar masses and 10^3 km respectively. There is a maximum mass for white dwarfs, above which they are unstable to gravitational collapse – this is known as the *Chandrasekhar limit and is about 1.4 solar masses.

Wiedemann–Franz law The ratio of the thermal conductivity of any pure metal to its electrical conductivity is approximately constant at a given temperature. The law is fairly well obeyed, except at low temperatures.

Wien formula *See* Planck's radiation law.

Wien's displacement law For a *black body, $\lambda_m T$ = constant, where λ_m is the wavelength corresponding to the maximum radiation of energy and T is the thermodynamic temperature of the body. Thus as the temperature rises the maximum of the spectral energy distribution curve is displaced towards the short-wavelength end of the spectrum. The law was stated by Wilhelm Wien (1864–1928).

Wigner energy Energy stored in a crystalline substance as a result of irradiation. This phenomenon is known as the *Wigner effect*. For example, some of the energy lost by neutrons in a *nuclear reactor is stored by the graphite moderator. As a result, the crystal lattice is changed and there is a consequent change in the physical dimensions of the moderator. It is named after E. P. Wigner (1902–).

Wigner nuclides Pairs of isobars with odd nucleon numbers in which the atomic number and the neutron number differ by one. ^3H and ^3He are examples.

Wilson cloud chamber *See* cloud chamber.

WIMP Weakly interacting massive particle. *See* missing mass.

Wimshurst machine A laboratory electrostatic generator. It consists of two insulating discs to which radial strips of metal foil are attached. After a few strips have been charged individually, the discs are rotated in opposite directions and the charge produced on the strips by induction is collected by metal combs or brushes. It was invented by J. Wimshurst (1836–1903).

window 1. A band of electromagnetic wavelengths that is able to pass through a particular medium with little reflection or absorption. For example, there is a *radio window* in the atmosphere allowing radio waves of wavelengths 5 mm to 30 m to pass through. This radio window enables *radio telescopes to be used on the surface of the earth. **2.** A period of time during which an event may occur in order to achieve a desired result. For example a *launch window* is the period during which a space vehicle must be launched to achieve a planned encounter.

wind power The use of winds in the earth's atmosphere to drive machinery, especially to drive an electrical generator. Practical land-based *wind generators* (*aerogenerators*) are probably capable of providing some 10^{20} J (10^{14} kW h) of energy per year throughout the world and interest in this form of renewable energy is increasing. The power, P, available to drive a wind generator is given by $P = kd^2v^3$, where k is the air density, d is the diameter of the blades, and v is the average wind speed.

wino *See* supersymmetry.

Wollaston prism A type of quartz prism for producing plane-polarized light. It deviates the ordinary and extraordinary rays in opposite directions by approximately the same amount. The Wollaston prism, like the *Rochon prism, can be used with ultraviolet radiation. It is named after the inventor W. H. Wollaston (1766–1828).

Wood's metal A low-melting (71°C) alloy of bismuth (50%), lead (25%),

tin (12.5%), and cadmium (12.5%). It is used for fusible links in automatic sprinkler systems. The melting point can be changed by varying the composition.

woofer A large loudspeaker designed to reproduce sounds of relatively low frequency, in conjunction with a *tweeter and often a mid-range speaker, in a high-fidelity sound reproducing system.

word A number of *bits, often 32, 48, or 64, processed by a computer as a single unit.

work The work done by a force acting on a body is the product of the force and the distance moved by its point of application in the direction of the force. If a force F acts in such a way that the displacement s is in a direction that makes an angle θ with the direction of the force, the work done is given by: $W = Fs\cos\theta$. Work is the scalar product of the force and displacement vectors. It is measured in joules.

work function A quantity that determines the extent to which *thermionic or *photoelectric emission will occur according to the Richardson equation or *Einstein's photoelectric equation. It is sometimes expressed as a potential difference (symbol ϕ) in volts and sometimes as the energy required to remove an electron (symbol W) in electronvolts or joules. The former has been called the *work function potential* and the latter the *work function energy*.

work hardening An increase in the hardness of metals as a result of working them cold. It causes a permanent distortion of the crystal structure and is particularly apparent with iron, copper, aluminium, etc., whereas with lead and zinc it does not occur as these metals are capable of recrystallizing at room temperature.

W particle *See* W boson.

wrought iron A highly refined form of iron containing 1–3% of slag (mostly iron silicate), which is evenly distributed throughout the material in threads and fibres so that the product has a fibrous structure quite dissimilar to that of crystalline cast iron. Wrought iron rusts less readily than other forms of metallic iron and it welds and works more easily. It is used for chains, hooks, tubes, etc.

WS model Weinberg–Salam model. *See* electroweak theory.

X

X-ray astronomy The study of *X-ray sources by rockets and balloons in the earth's atmosphere and by satellites beyond it. The first nonsolar X-ray source was detected during a rocket flight in 1962, and this observation heralded an entirely new branch of astronomy which developed rapidly with the availability of satellites in the 1970s.

X-ray crystallography The use of *X-ray diffraction to determine the structure of crystals or molecules. The technique involves directing a beam of X-rays at a crystalline sample and recording the diffracted X-rays on a photographic plate. The diffraction pattern consists of a pattern of spots on the plate, and the crystal structure can be worked out from the positions and intensities of the diffraction spots. X-rays are diffracted by the electrons in the molecules and if molecular crystals of a compound are used, the electron density distribution in the molecule can be determined. *See also* neutron diffraction.

X-ray diffraction The diffraction of X-rays by a crystal. The wavelengths of X-rays are comparable in size to the distances between atoms in most crystals, and the repeated pattern of

the crystal lattice acts like a diffraction grating for X-rays. Thus, a crystal of suitable type can be used to disperse X-rays in a spectrometer. X-ray diffraction is also the basis of X-ray crystallography. *See also* Bragg's law.

X-ray fluorescence The emission of *X-rays from excited atoms produced by the impact of high-energy electrons, other particles, or a primary beam of other X-rays. The wavelengths of the fluorescent X-rays can be measured by an X-ray spectrometer as a means of chemical analysis. X-ray fluorescence is used in such techniques as *electron-probe microanalysis.

X-rays Electromagnetic radiation of shorter wavelength than ultraviolet radiation produced by bombardment of atoms by high-quantum-energy particles. The range of wavelengths is 10^{-11} m to 10^{-9} m. Atoms of all the elements emit a characteristic *X-ray spectrum* when they are bombarded by electrons. The X-ray photons are emitted when the incident electrons knock an inner orbital electron out of an atom. When this happens an outer electron falls into the inner shell to replace it, losing potential energy (ΔE) in doing so. The wavelength λ of the emitted photon will then be given by $\lambda = ch/\Delta E$, where c is the speed of light and h is the Planck constant. *See also* Bremsstrahlung.

X-rays can pass through many forms of matter and they are therefore used medically and industrially to examine internal structures. X-rays are produced for these purposes by an *X-ray tube.

X-ray sources Sources of X-radiation from outside the solar system. Some 100 sources within the Galaxy have been observed as objects that emit most of their energy in the X-ray region of the electromagnetic spectrum and only a relatively small proportion of their energy in the vis-

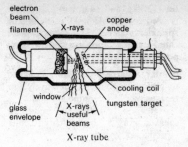

X-ray tube

ible spectrum. Many of these X-ray sources appear to be members of a binary system, consisting of one optically visible star and one very compact object; it is thought that the latter is either a *neutron star or (if very massive) a *black hole. Owing to the absorption of X-rays by the earth's atmosphere these X-ray sources are only visible by *X-ray telescopes* carried by space probes and satellites, although some high-energy X-rays can penetrate the upper atmosphere and are detectable by X-ray telescopes mounted on balloons.

X-ray spectrum *See* X-rays.

X-ray tube A device for generating *X-rays by accelerating electrons to a high energy by an electrostatic field and making them strike a metal target either in a tube containing a low-pressure gas or, as in modern tubes, in a high vacuum. The target is made from a heavy metal, usually tungsten, and is backed by a massive metal anode to conduct the heat away (see illustration showing a liquid-cooled copper anode). The electron beam is produced by heating the cathode by means of a white-hot tungsten filament. A transformer supplies the high voltage, often 100 kV, the tube acting as its own rectifier. On the half-cycles when the target is negative nothing happens. When the target becomes positive, the electrons bombarding it generate X-rays.

Y

Z

Yagi aerial A directional aerial array widely used for television and *radio telescopes. It consists of one or two dipoles, a parallel reflector, and a series of closely spaced directors (0.15–0.25 wavelength apart) in front of the dipole. When used for reception this arrangement focuses the incoming signal on the dipole. For transmission, the output of the dipole is reinforced by the directors. It is named after Hidetsuga Yagi (1886–1976).

Yang–Mills theory *See* gauge theory.

yard The former Imperial standard unit of length. In 1963 the yard was redefined as 0.9144 metre exactly.

year The measure of time on which the calendar is based. It is the time taken for the earth to complete one orbit of the sun. The *calendar year* consists of an average of 365.25 mean solar days – three successive years of 365 days followed by one (leap) year of 366 days. The *solar year* (or *astronomical year*) is the average interval between two successive returns of the sun to the first point of Aries; it is 365.242 mean solar days. The *sidereal year* is the average period of revolution of the earth with respect to the fixed stars; it is 365.256 mean solar days. The *anomalistic year* is the average interval between successive perihelions; it is 365.259 mean solar days. *See also* ephemeris time.

yield point *See* elasticity.

Young modulus of elasticity *See* elastic modulus.

Young's slits *See* interference.

Z boson An electrically neutral elementary particle, Z^0, which – like *W bosons – is thought to mediate the weak interactions in the *electroweak theory. The Z^0 boson was discovered at CERN in 1983 and has a mass of about 90 GeV as had been predicted from theory.

Zeeman effect The splitting of the lines in a spectrum when the source of the spectrum is exposed to a magnetic field. It was discovered in 1896 by P. Zeeman (1865–1943). In the *normal Zeeman effect* a single line is split into three if the field is perpendicular to the light path or two lines if the field is parallel to the light path. This effect can be explained by classical electromagnetic principles in terms of the speeding up and slowing down of orbital electrons in the source as a result of the applied field. The *anomalous Zeeman effect* is a complicated splitting of the lines into several closely spaced lines, so called because it does not agree with classical predictions. This effect is explained by quantum mechanics in terms of electron spin.

Zener diode A type of semiconductor diode, consisting of a *p-n* junction with high doping concentrations on either side of the junction. It acts as a rectifier until the applied reverse voltage reaches a certain value, the *Zener breakdown voltage*, when the device becomes conducting. This effect occurs as a result of electrons being excited directly from the valence band into the conduction band (*see* energy bands). Zener diodes are used in voltage-limiting circuits; they are named after C. M. Zener (1905–).

zenith The point on the *celestial sphere that lies directly above an observer. *Compare* nadir.

zero-point energy The energy remaining in a substance at the *absolute zero of temperature (0 K). This is in accordance with quantum theory, in which a particle oscillating with simple harmonic motion does not have a stationary state of zero kinetic energy. Moreover, the *uncertainty principle does not allow such a particle to be at rest at exactly the centrepoint of its oscillations.

zeroth law of thermodynamics *See* thermodynamics.

zino *See* supersymmetry.

zodiac A band that passes round the *celestial sphere, extending 9° on either side of the *ecliptic. It includes the apparent paths of the sun, moon, and planets (except Pluto). The band is divided into the twelve *signs of the zodiac*, each 30° wide. These signs indicate the sun's position each month in the year and were named by the ancient Greeks after the *zodiacal constellations* that occupied the signs some 2000 years ago. However, as a result of the *precession of the equinoxes the constellations have since moved eastwards by over 30° and no longer coincide with the signs.

zodiacal light A faint luminous glow in the sky that can be observed on a moonless night on the western horizon after sunset or on the eastern horizon before sunrise. It is caused by the scattering of sunlight by dust particles in interplanetary space.

zone refining A technique used to reduce the level of impurities in certain metals, alloys, semiconductors, and other materials. It is based on the observation that the solubility of an impurity may be different in the liquid and solid phases of a material. To take advantage of this observation, a narrow molten zone is moved along the length of a specimen of the material, with the result that the impurities are segregated at one end of the bar and the pure material at the other. In general, if the impurities lower the melting point of the material they are moved in the same direction as the molten zone moves, and vice versa.

zwitterion (ampholyte ion) An ion that has a positive and negative charge on the same group of atoms. Zwitterions can be formed from compounds that contain both acid groups and basic groups in their molecules. For example, aminoethanoic acid (the amino acid glycine) has the formula $H_2N.CH_2.COOH$. However, under neutral conditions, it exists in the different form of the zwitterion $^+H_3N.CH_2.COO^-$, which can be regarded as having been produced by an internal neutralization reaction (transfer of a proton from the carboxyl group to the amino group). Aminoethanoic acid, as a consequence, has some properties characteristic of ionic compounds; e.g. a high melting point and solubility in water. In acid solutions, the positive ion $^+H_3NCH_2COOH$ is formed. In basic solutions, the negative ion $H_2NCH_2COO^-$ predominates. The name comes from the German *zwei*, two.

Appendix 1 SI units

Table 1.1 Base and supplementary SI units

Physical quantity	Name	Symbol
length	metre	m
mass	kilogram	kg
time	second	s
electric current	ampere	A
thermodynamic temperature	kelvin	K
luminous intensity	candela	cd
amount of substance	mole	mol
*plane angle	radian	rad
*solid angle	steradian	sr

*supplementary units

Table 1.2 Derived SI units with special names

Physical quantity	Name of SI unit	Symbol of SI unit
frequency	hertz	Hz
energy	joule	J
force	newton	N
power	watt	W
pressure	pascal	Pa
electric charge	coulomb	C
electric potential difference	volt	V
electric resistance	ohm	Ω
electric conductance	siemens	S
electric capacitance	farad	F
magnetic flux	weber	Wb
inductance	henry	H
magnetic flux density (magnetic induction)	tesla	T
luminous flux	lumen	lm
illuminance	lux	lx
absorbed dose	gray	Gy
activity	becquerel	Bq
dose equivalent	sievert	Sv

Table 1.3 Decimal multiples and submultiples to be used with SI units

Submultiple	Prefix	Symbol	Multiple	Prefix	Symbol
10^{-1}	deci	d	10	deca	da
10^{-2}	centi	c	10^2	hecto	h
10^{-3}	milli	m	10^3	kilo	k
10^{-6}	micro	μ	10^6	mega	M
10^{-9}	nano	n	10^9	giga	G
10^{-12}	pico	p	10^{12}	tera	T
10^{-15}	femto	f	10^{15}	peta	P
10^{-18}	atto	a	10^{18}	exa	E

Table 1.4 Conversion of units to SI units

From	To	Multiply by
in	m	2.54×10^{-2}
ft	m	0.3048
sq. in	m^2	6.4516×10^{-4}
sq. ft	m^2	9.2903×10^{-2}
cu. in	m^3	1.63871×10^{-5}
cu. ft	m^3	2.83168×10^{-2}
l(itre)	m^3	10^{-3}
gal(lon)	m^3	$4.546\ 09 \times 10^{-3}$
gal(lon)	l(itre)	4.546 09
miles/hr	$m\ s^{-1}$	0.477 04
km/hr	$m\ s^{-1}$	0.277 78
lb	kg	0.453 592
$g\ cm^{-3}$	$kg\ m^{-3}$	10^3
lb/in^3	$kg\ m^{-3}$	$2.767\ 99 \times 10^4$
dyne	N	10^{-5}
kgf	N	9.806 65
poundal	N	0.138 255
lbf	N	4.448 22
mmHg	Pa	133.322
atmosphere	Pa	$1.013\ 25 \times 10^5$
hp	W	745.7
erg	J	10^{-7}
eV	J	$1.602\ 10 \times 10^{-19}$
kW h	J	3.6×10^6
cal	J	4.1868

Appendix 2 Fundamental constants

Constant	Symbol	Value in SI units
acceleration of free fall	g	$9.806\,65$ m s^{-2}
Avogadro constant	L, N_A	$6.022\,1367(36) \times 10^{23}$ mol^{-1}
Boltzmann constant	$k = R/N_A$	$1.380\,658(12) \times 10^{-23}$ J K^{-1}
electric constant	ε_0	$8.854\,187\,817 \times 10^{-12}$ F m^{-1}
electronic charge	e	$1.602\,177\,33(49) \times 10^{-19}$ C
electronic rest mass	m_e	$9.109\,3897(54) \times 10^{-31}$ kg
Faraday constant	F	$9.648\,5309(29) \times$ 10^4 C mol^{-1}
gas constant	R	$8.314\,510(70)$ J K^{-1} mol^{-1}
gravitational constant	G	$6.672\,59(85) \times$ 10^{-11} m^3 kg^{-1} s^{-2}
Loschmidt's constant	N_L	$2.686\,763(23) \times 10^{25}$ m^{-3}
magnetic constant	μ_0	$4\pi \times 10^{-7}$ H m^{-1}
neutron rest mass	m_n	$1.674\,9286(10) \times 10^{-27}$ kg
Planck constant	h	$6.626\,0755(40) \times 10^{-34}$ J s
proton rest mass	m_p	$1.672\,6231(10) \times 10^{-27}$ kg
speed of light	c	$2.997\,924\,58 \times 10^8$ m s^{-1}
Stefan–Boltzmann constant	σ	$5.670\,51(19) \times$ 10^{-8} W m^{-2} K^{-4}

Appendix 3   The solar system

Planet	Equatorial diameter (km)	Mean distance from sun (10^6 km)	Sidereal period	
Mercury	4878	57.91	87.969	days
Venus	12 100	108	224.7	days
Earth	12 756	149.60	365.256	days
Mars	6762	227.94	686.980	days
Jupiter	142 700	778	11.86	years
Saturn	120 800	1430	29.46	years
Uranus	51 800	2869.6	84.01	years
Neptune	49 400	4496	164.8	years
Pluto	3500	5900	248.4	years

OXFORD LIVES

Biography at its best—this popular series offers authoritative accounts of the lives of famous men and women from the arts and sciences, politics and exploration.

'SUBTLE IS THE LORD'
The Science and the Life of Albert Einstein
Abraham Pais

Abraham Pais, an award-winning physicist who knew Einstein personally during the last nine years of his life, presents a guide to the life and the thought of the most famous scientist of our century. Using previously unpublished papers and personal recollections from their years of acquaintance, the narrative illuminates the man through his work with both liveliness and precision, making this *the* authoritative scientific biography of Einstein.

'The definitive life of Einstein.'
Brian Pippard, *Times Literary Supplement*

'By far the most important study of both the man and the scientist.' Paul Davies, *New Scientist*

'An outstanding biography of Albert Einstein that one finds oneself reading with sheer pleasure.' *Physics Today*

Also in the Oxford Lives series:

Peter Fleming: A Biography Duff Hart-Davies
Gustav Holst: A Biography Imogen Holst
T. H. White Sylvia Townsend Warner
Joyce Cary: Gentleman Rider Alan Bishop

LYRA SELENE was born under a full moon and has never quite managed to wipe the moonlight out of her eyes. When she isn't dreaming up fantastical cities and brooding landscapes, Lyra enjoys hiking, rainstorms, autumn, and pretending she's any good at art.

She lives in New England with her husband, in an antique farmhouse that's probably not haunted. *Amber & Dusk* is her debut novel.

for holding my hand since the beginning—thank dog for Craigslist, amirite? To Spellbound Scribes past and future, but especially Shauna Granger, Nicole Evelina, and Liv Rancourt—your experience, humor, sophistication, and scholarship cannot be overstated, and I feel lucky to count myself among you. To the Table of Trust, otherwise known as PitchWars 2014, for being an unparalleled wealth of information and advice, as well as an excellent place to vent.

To Tammy Meyers, Ann Dunn, Dr. Ewert, Dr. Harpold, Kevin Hyde, Dragan Kujundzic, Professor O'Neill, and all the other educators who attempted to mentor me despite myself.

To Jess, for bone crushing, Darcy-ing, and infinite snuffa loving—arf arf arf! To the Marshall "frat," for mead halls, horsey dances, and late-night games of Fishbowl. To Michelle, for never reading all the words. And to Hannah, Lauren, and Sonia, my F4: for a decade and a half of weird fan fiction, inappropriate Dracos, dollar-store prank gifts, black licorice in my shoes, too much Frontera, *Bachelorette* fantasy leagues, and unconditional love.

To my parents, Monica and Michael, for teaching me the value of a library card from such a young age, always reading to me at bedtime, and listening to all my wacky dreams. To my siblings, Sarée, Erik, Siobhán, and Shane, for never not giving me a hard time. You keep me sane and grounded. Our expanding family makes me feel so wealthy in music, laughter, and limitless love.

And finally, to Steve: for castle Christmases and woodland wanderings, for black-and-white music and midnight musings, for anticipating plot twists and always sympathizing with my villains. I love you to Olympus Mons and back.